ORGANOMETALLIC REACTIONS

Volume 4

ADVISORY BOARD

ORGANOMETALLIC REACTIONS

Volume 4

EDITED BY

Ernest I. Becker

Department of Chemistry
University of Massachusetts
Boston, Massachusetts

Minoru Tsutsui

Department of Chemistry
Texas A & M University
College Station, Texas

Wiley-Interscience

a division of John Wiley & Sons, Inc.

NEW YORK · LONDON · SYDNEY · TORONTO

Library of Congress Catalog Card Number: 74 92108

ISBN 0 471 06137–9

Printed in the United States of America.

10 9 8 7 6 5 4 3 2 1

Preface

The primary literature on organometallic chemistry has undergone phenomenal growth. The number of papers published from 1955 to 1970 is about equal to all prior literature. Together with this intense activity there has developed a complexity in the literature. Thus specialized texts and teaching texts, a review journal, an advances series, and a research journal have all appeared during this period. The present series also reflects this growth and recognizes that many categories of organometallic compounds now have numerous representatives in the literature.

The purpose of *Organometallic Reactions* is to provide complete chapters on selected categories of organometallic compounds, describing the methods by which they have been synthesized, and the reactions they undergo. The emphasis is on the preparative aspects, although structures of compounds and mechanisms of reactions are briefly discussed and referenced. Tables of all of the compounds prepared in the category under consideration and detailed directions for specific types make these chapters particularly helpful to the preparative chemist. While the specific directions have not been refereed in the same way as are those in *Organic Syntheses* and *Inorganic Syntheses*, the personal experiences of the authors often lend special merit to the procedures and enables the reader to avoid many of the pitfalls frequently encountered in selecting an experimental procedure from the literature.

We acknowledge a debt of gratitude to the contributing authors whose dedication and skill in preparing the manuscripts cannot adequately be rewarded. It has been gratifying to note that virtually all invitations to contribute have been accepted at once. We also owe thanks to the publisher for encouragement and even the "gentle prod" when necessary to see these volumes to their completion.

Ernest I. Becker
Minoru Tsutsui
Editors

September 1970

Contents

Contents for Volume 1

Contents for Volume 2

Contents for Volume 3

ORGANOMETALLIC REACTIONS

Volume 4

σ–π Rearrangements of Organotransition Metals

M. Hancock, M. N. Levy, and M. Tsutsui

Chemistry Department, Texas A & M University, College Station, Texas

I. SCOPE AND LIMITATION

Not until 1957 was it recognized that the polyaromatic chromium complexes isolated by Hein in 1921 were in fact the same π-arene complexes[1] that were obtained from the reaction of phenyl Grignard with chromium(III) chloride via an isolable intermediate, tri-σ-phenylchromium.[2] From this beginning has grown the field known as σ–π rearrangements,[3] in which an organic group σ-bonded to a transition metal rearranges to a π-bonded moiety. The σ–π rearrangements have been observed for almost all of the transition metals with a variety of ligands, including groups bonded through an atom other than carbon. These rearrangements are not only of interest in the field of organometallic chemistry but also involved in such industrially important processes using transition-metal catalysts as the Ziegler–Natta polymerization of olefins, the oxo process (hydroformylation of olefins), and in fact homogeneous catalysis in general. The rearrangement is also proposed in such organic reactions as the Cope reaction, which is induced by stoichiometric or catalytic amounts of metallic compounds, and in the Kharasch coupling reaction, again with the organometallic compound in stoichiometric or catalytic amounts.

This chapter attempts to give a general survey of the field, including both the sparse mechanistic data available and experimental details.

The rearrangements are divided into two broad classifications. (No doubt as the field expands, more distinctly different mechanisms may be elucidated.) The first classification involves addition or abstraction of ligands on the metal atom; the second involves rearrangements induced by reactions on the organic moiety. A special case of the second type, *cis*-ligand insertion, is considered separately.[4] The few examples that are known to not correspond to such dovetailing are dealt with separately.

II. REACTIONS ON THE METAL

A. Arene π-Complexes

The one reaction that has been studied in detail is that which leads to Hein's complexes, i.e., π-arenechromium complexes.[1] The reaction of 3 equivalents of phenylmagnesium bromide with 1 equivalent of chromium(III) chloride tristetrahydrofuranate gives bright-red, crystalline tri-σ-phenyl-chromium tristetrahydrofuranate (1), which either by washing with ether or by heating above the boiling point of tetrahydrofuran, or under reduced pressure loses 3 moles of tetrahydrofuran to give a black, pyrophoric solid. This solid, on treatment with deoxygenated water, gives bis(biphenyl) chromium(0) (2) and benzenebiphenylchromium(0) (3) Hein's complexes.

The black solid is paramagnetic and very sensitive to air and water.[2,5] Solvolysis with deuterium oxide leads to the incorporation of one deuterium atom into each benzene group but none into the biphenyl moiety.[6] Thermal decomposition gives biphenyl and a complete loss of any π-character. Zeiss proposed the formation of radical intermediates (the black, pyrophoric solid) to explain these results with reaction scheme (1).[5] The existence of a transition state involving π-radical hybridization has been postulated, the metal–carbon σ-bonds cleaving homolytically, with a corresponding three-electron reduction of the chromium to its zero valent state.[7] Investigations with electron-paramagnetic-resonance (EPR) spectroscopy show the homolytic fission of the chromium–carbon bond and the possible formation of radical π-complexes.[8] A π-radical hybrid transition state, and proximity of the organic groups to the metal, is supported by the fact that the yield of π-arenechromium complexes decreases drastically in going from phenyl to benzyl to phenylethyl moieties.[9] From hydrolysis and deuterolysis reactions between phenyl and benzyl Grignards and chromium(III) chloride tristetrahydrofuranate it was concluded that π-radical formation, hydrogen abstraction, and hydrogen transfer occur within the confines of the intermediate organochromium complexes.[10]

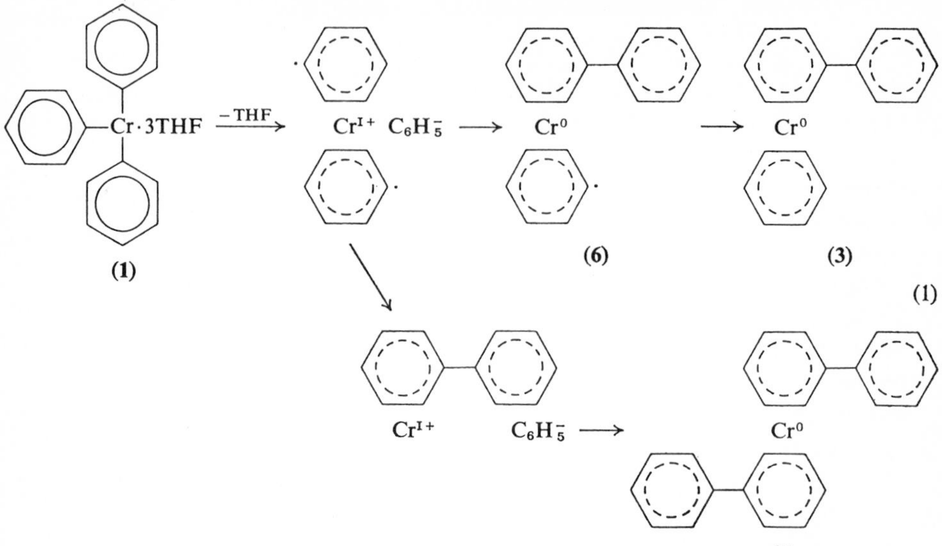

In these examples the σ-state is stabilized by the fairly good coordinating ability of the tetrahydrofuran ligand and the synergic stabilizing effect of the π-orbitals on the phenyl group. With cyclopentadienyl groups little stabilization is obtained in the σ-form: di-σ-cyclopentadienyliron(III) chloride tetrahydrofuranate rearranges to the π-ferricinium complex on losing the tetrahydrofuran above $-50°$, on treatment with an organic solvent at $-60°$, or under vacuum at $-60°$.[11]

B. Addition and Elimination of Carbon Monoxide

Many rearrangements involve the addition or elimination of carbon monoxide from the organometallic compound. The elimination, being accompanied by a σ–π rearrangement, is achieved by irradiation with ultraviolet light or by heating, whereas the reverse reaction is achieved under pressure of carbon monoxide. The question of timing in this reaction—i.e., whether elimination or rearrangement occurs first or whether they occur concurrently—has not been reported.

Thus on irradiation with ultraviolet light σ-alkyl π-cyclopentadienyl-molybdenum tricarbonyl (4)[12] and σ-alkyl π-cyclopentadienyltungsten tricarbonyl (5)[13] compounds give the corresponding π-allene complexes (6) and (7) with the loss of one molecule of carbon monoxide. Irradiation of σ-benzyl π-cyclopentadienylmolybdenum tricarbonyl in hexane gives, with

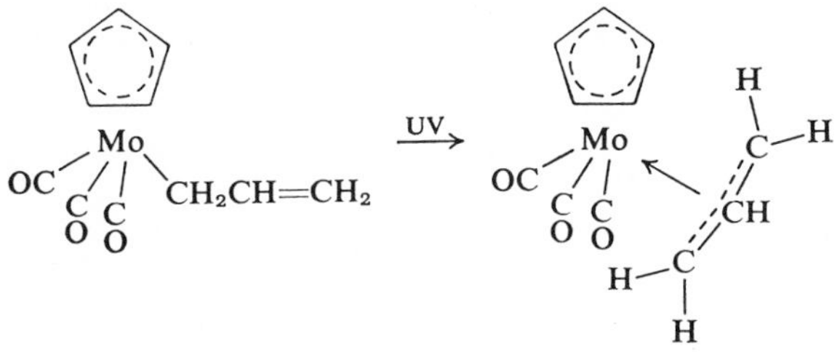

(4)   (5)

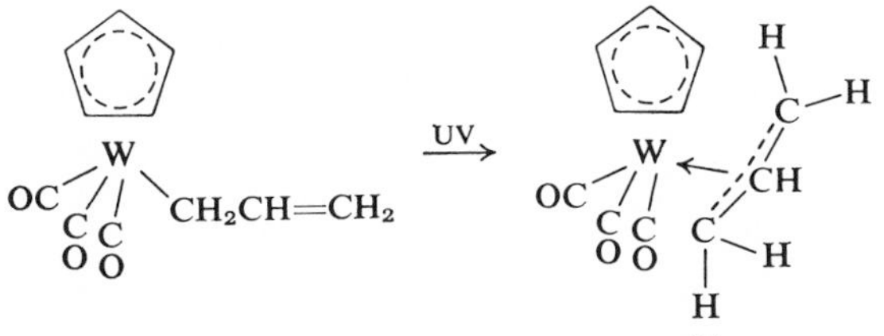

(6)   (7)

loss of carbon monoxide, a low yield of π-benzyl π-cyclopentadienyl-molybdenum dicarbonyl. The benzyl group is bonded through an allylic system involving three of the carbon atoms. From variable-temperature nuclear-magnetic-resonance (NMR) measurements it is found that the π-benzyl group is sterochemically dynamic.[14] Heating or irradiating with ultraviolet light causes rearrangement of σ-bonded methylthiomethyl π-cyclopentadienylmolybdenum tricarbonyl with loss of carbon monoxide. The structure of the π-complex obtained in this reaction could not be determined unambiguously.[15] Heating σ-allylmanganese pentacarbonyl to 100° causes evolution of one molecule of carbon monoxide, leaving π-allyl-manganese tetracarbonyl.[16,17]

The reaction of carbon monoxide on π-allylic rhodium complexes of the type $L_2Rh(\pi\text{-}C_3H_4R)Cl_2$ (where $L = Ph_3P$, Ph_3As, or Ph_3Sb; $R = H$ or CH_3) gives $L_2Rh(CO)Cl$, with a methallyl chloride being eliminated. The reaction proceeds via a number of intermediates (π- and σ-bonded allylic trivalent rhodium complexes and insertion products). With sulfur dioxide the π-allylic rhodium complexes give rise to σ-allylrhodium sulfur dioxide compounds. Ethylene also causes the π-methallyl group to rearrange to a σ-bonded moiety.[18]

C. Addition and Elimination of the Cyanide Ion

Because of the formal similarity of RNC, CN^-, and NO^+ to CO, similar rearrangements might be expected, but only rearrangements involving addition and abstraction of CN^- are reported. Isomerization is found between σ- and π-allylcobalt cyanides: σ-bonded compounds (8) lose a cyanide ion to give the π-bonded complexes (9), the rearrangement being reversed on addition of the cyanide ion. Rearrangement of the phenacyl

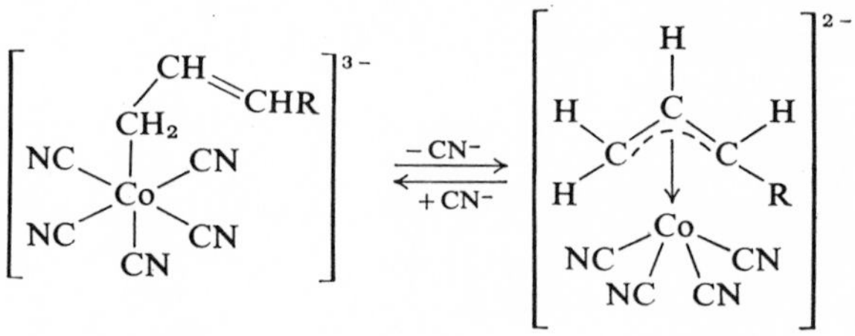

(8)   (9)

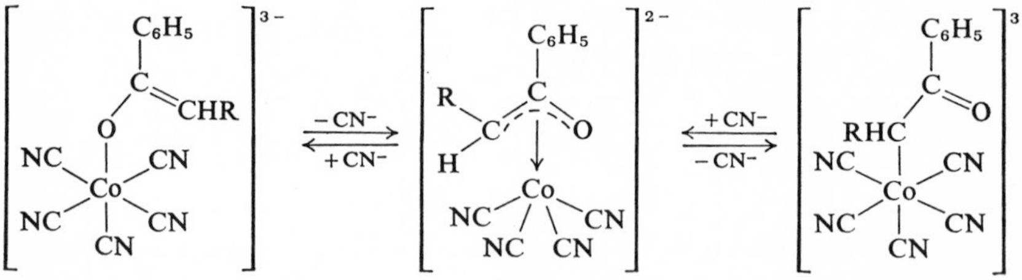

(10)   (11)

group is also noted, although complexes (10) and (11) were not obtained in a pure state.[19]

Analogous σ–π structures have been proposed as determining the stereo-selectivity of the butene products obtained by the hydrogenation of buta-diene, catalyzed by the pentacyanocobaltate(II) ion. With excess ion, 1-butene is the major product formed exclusively from a σ-butenyl intermediate. In the absence of excess cyanide ion *trans*-2-butene is the major product and may derive from either a π-butenyl complex or an isomeric σ-butenyl compound in equilibrium with the π-structures.[20]

D. Temperature- and Solvent-Dependent Equilibrium and Nonrigidity

Recently considerable discussion has arisen on the nature of the stereochemically nonrigid metal allyl compounds. Variable-temperature NMR measurements have been used extensively in attempts to understand their nature. On sufficient cooling a spectrum of a static, rigidly bound π-allyl is often observed. On warming, however, the static π-allyl resonances coalesce to the more simple spectrum of a dynamic allylic group. Internal rotation[21,22] and σ-π rearrangements have been proposed as explanations of the phenomenon.

Allylpalladium chloride (12) is dimeric in the solid state,[23] but in benzene and dioxane solutions a dimer–monomer (75:25%) equilibrium has been suggested from cryoscopic and dipole-moment measurements.[24] The NMR spectrum of compound (12) in dimethyl sulfoxide (DMSO) shows only one proton-resonance peak, explained by the following rapid equilibrium (coordinated DMSO not being shown):[25]

$$CH_2=CX-\overset{*}{C}H_2-Pd-Cl \rightleftarrows \overset{*}{C}H_2=CX-CH_2-Pd-Cl \qquad (2)$$

It has been suggested, however, that the variable-temperature (from 25 to 65°) NMR spectrum can be explained by a π-bonded structure for the allylpalladium chloride with hindered rotation of the CH_2-group about the C—C bonds.[21] The temperature dependence of the NMR spectra of a number of allylic palladium complexes with various strongly bonding ligands has been studied, and the results have been explained by ligand exchange, followed by a head-over-tail equilibration.[26]

Ligand exchange:

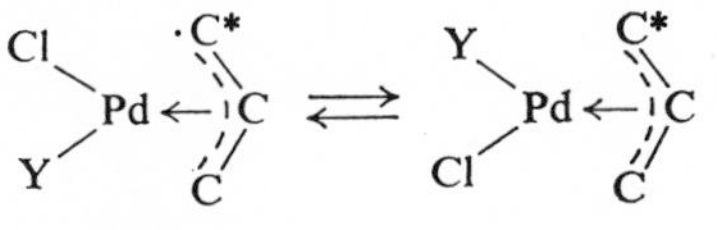

(3)

(12)

π–σ Equilibration:

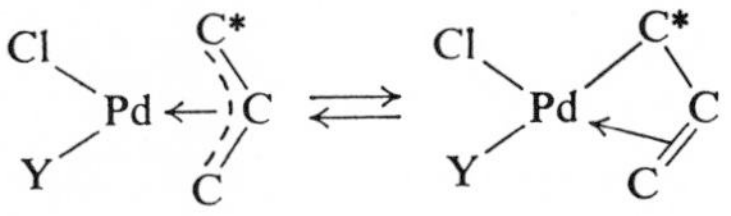

(4)

Head-over-tail equilibration:

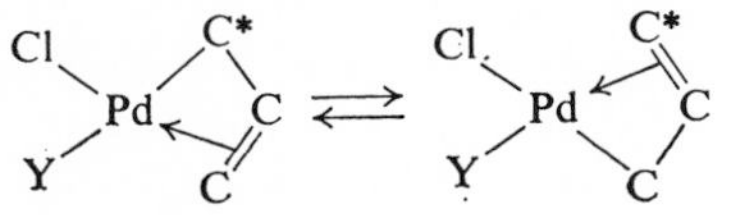

(5)

Addition of triphenylphosphine to π-methallylpalladium chloride (up to 2 moles of phosphine being added) has been observed by study of the NMR spectra and their changes, which indicate that a σ-compound is formed and then undergoes a rapid head-to-tail exchange of the allylic group. Methallyl-palladium chloride triphenylphosphine is isolated from the reaction mixture, and its NMR spectrum indicates that its structure might be (13), with two carbon atoms weakly bonded to the palladium.[27] X-Ray analysis of (13)

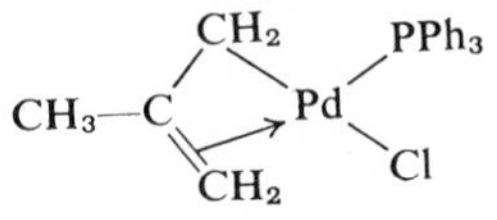

(13)

supports this structure.[28] Further work casts doubt on the structure of the intermediate proposed by Shaw et al.[27]

The reactions of π-allylpalladium chloride with the ligands PPh_3, $P(n-C_4H_9)_3$, $P(OCH_2)_3CCH_3$, $AsPh_3$, and $SbPh_3$ have been studied by variable-temperature NMR measurements. It appears that at least three different conformational rearrangements may occur. In the phosphine systems a change occurs, giving rise at a low temperature to an interchange of protons (3) and 4) in compound (14). The fact that protons (1) and (2) maintain their positions is explainable by an intermediate with structure

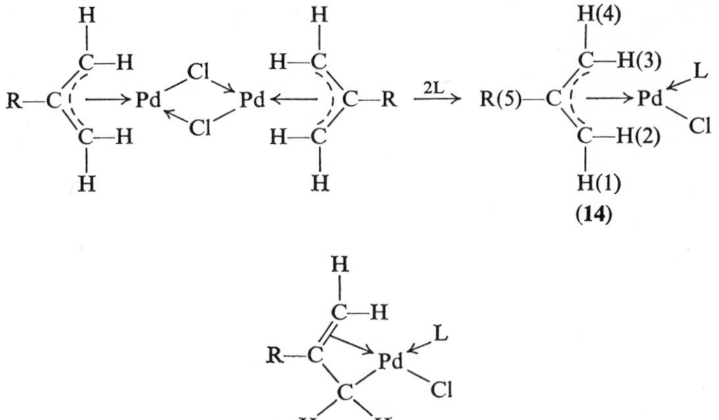

(14)

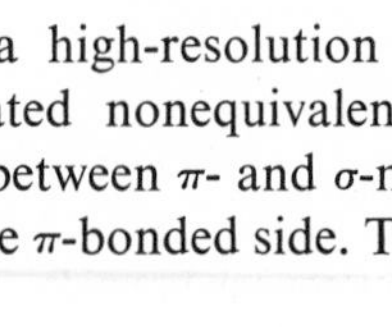

(15)

(15). However, study with a high-resolution spectrometer and very low temperatures has demonstrated nonequivalence for all protons. This is explained by an equilibrium between π- and σ-moieties, with the equilibrium lying almost completely on the π-bonded side. The second observable process depends on the ratio of the ligand to π-allylpalladium and is attributed to a rotating allyl group. Finally, complete coalescence may be a combination of rotation of the allyl group and rapid formation of a σ-allylic compound.[29]

The reaction between π-methallylpalladium chloride and triphenylarsine has also been studied by variable-temperature NMR. Three equilibria are occurring [reactions (6)–(8)]. In reaction (8) two mechanisms are involved: between -70 and $-40°$ triphenylarsine exchange occurs along with the formation of a σ-allylic compound or an activated state involving the σ-bonded compound.[30]

$$\pi\text{-}C_4H_7PdCl(Ph_3As) \rightleftharpoons \pi\text{-}C_4H_7PdCl + Ph_3As \qquad (6)$$

$$[\pi\text{-}C_4H_7PdCl]_2 + 2Ph_3As \rightleftharpoons 2\pi\text{-}C_4H_7PdCl(Ph_3As) \qquad (7)$$

$$\pi\text{-}C_4H_7PdCl(Ph_3As) + Ph_3^*As \rightleftharpoons \pi\text{-}C_4H_7PdCl(Ph_3^*As) + Ph_3As \qquad (8)$$

Variable-temperature NMR studies of the reactions between π-allylpalladium complexes and triphenylphosphine, DMSO, and dimethyl sulfide (DMS) shows that σ–π rearrangements occur as in reactions (9) and (10). The

$$\frac{1}{2}\left[\langle\text{\textemdash}(Pd\text{—}Cl)_2 \right] + B: \underset{k_{-1}}{\overset{k_1}{\rightleftharpoons}} \langle\text{\textemdash}Pd\overset{Cl}{\underset{B}{\diagup}} \qquad (9)$$

$$\langle\text{\textemdash}Pd\overset{Cl}{\underset{B}{\diagup}} + B: \rightleftharpoons \diagup\diagup\diagdown PdCl\ B_2 \qquad (10)$$

disappearance of coordinated allyl and the appearance of uncoordinated olefin absorptions in the infrared spectra demonstrate the formation of σ-bonded allyl groups. Equilibrium lies far to the right with triphenylphosphine, but with DMSO and DMS it lies far to the left.[31]

An NMR study at 34° of a series of allylic palladium complexes with phosphine, arsine, and stibine ligands shows that, as the ligand-to-palladium ratio is varied up to 2, several fast processes occur. These include π-allylic to σ-allylic rearrangements, during which rotations about the C—C bond and Pd—C bond and exchange of the coordinated ligand with the free ligand occur. Carbon monoxide also acts like the phosphine and arsine ligands, and the NMR spectrum of the reaction product from carbon monoxide and $Pd_2Cl_2[\pi\text{-}2\text{-methallyl}]_2$ in deuterated chloroform corresponds to that of a dynamic σ-2-methallylic system.[32]

A diastereoisomeric mixture is prepared in ethyl acetate by cleaving the chlorine bridge of chloro-(1-acetyl-2-methallyl)palladium dimer with S-α-phenethylamine. Resolution is achieved by crystallizing the crude diastereoisomeric mixture from carbon tetrachloride. Optical activity measurements performed on acetone solutions at very low and higher temperatures indicate that (a) only one of the two diastereoisomers is quantitatively obtained in the carbon tetrachloride crystallization through a "second-order asymmetrical transformation" and (b) epimerization of the pure (−) diastereomer takes place very rapidly at temperatures above −20°. The epimerization can occur only through rotation around the carbon (2)–carbon (3) bond and thus occurs through a σ-bonded intermediate.[33]

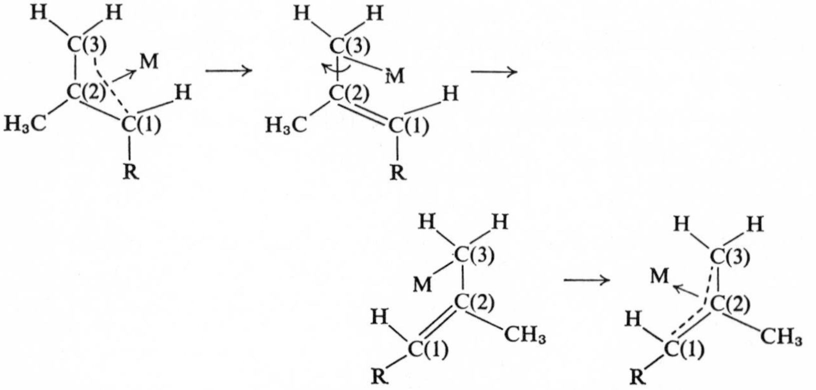

$$(11)$$

Most of the work on the dynamic allylic rearrangements has been carried out on organopalladium systems, but considerable data have been published on other metals. In the presence of Lewis acids π-allylnickel halides catalyze the dimerization of propylene. The structure of the dimer can be varied by adding phosphine to the catalyst. From NMR studies it has been shown that 1:1 and 1:2 derivatives of triphenylphosphine and triphenylphosphite contain a π-allyl group. However, the 1:2 complex with triethylphosphine exists in a dynamic σ-bonded equilibrium, although the 1:1 complex is π-bonded.[34] A variable temperature study of the NMR spectrum of allylic platinum complexes on addition of triphenylphosphine indicates that σ–π equilibria occur.[35] Other studies on π-methallylrhodium(II) chloride bistriphenylphosphine or triphenylarsine show that allyl interchange occurs via a short-lived σ-allyl intermediate.[36]

Allylirontricarbonyliodine, isolated from the reaction between allyl iodide and iron pentacarbonyl, has been assigned a π-allylic structure because no olefin-stretching frequencies were observed in the infrared. However, the NMR spectra obtained in cyclohexane could not be interpreted on the basis of the π-bonded structure, and considerable dimerization was found. Four carbonyl-stretching frequencies, instead of the expected three were observed in the infrared, and it was suggested that a π–σ equilibrium occurs.[37] In view of this proposed equilibrium it is somewhat surprising that DMSO completely displaces the allyl group from allyliron tricarbonyl complexes and no π–σ rearrangement is observed.[38] A di-π-allyliron can be prepared from the reaction of allyl bromide with allyliron tricarbonylsodium (obtained from the reaction of allyliron tricarbonyliodine with sodium amalgam). A σ-bonded allyl compound is possibly formed, losing carbon monoxide[39] to give the more stable $(\pi\text{-}C_3H_5)_2Fe(CO)_2$.

A survey of compounds in which σ–π rearrangements involve the addition or abstraction of ligands on the metal atom is presented in Table I.

III. REARRANGEMENTS INDUCED BY REACTIONS ON THE LIGAND

Rearrangements induced by reactions on the ligand differ from those discussed in Section II in that the metal remains coordinately saturated and the basic stereochemistry of the metal remains unchanged. Thus the π-group formed will only be a two-electron donor, and delocalized systems, as found in rearrangements induced by reactions on the metal, are not observed.

A. Protonation of σ-Bonded Allyl and Acetylene Compounds

σ-Bonded metal allyl compounds are readily protonated by hydrogen chloride or by mineral acids to give π-allene complexes.[52-54] In the case of σ-allyliron compounds a bimolecular reaction is proposed, and, by using deuterium chloride, attack is shown[54] to occur at carbon (3) [see reaction (12)].

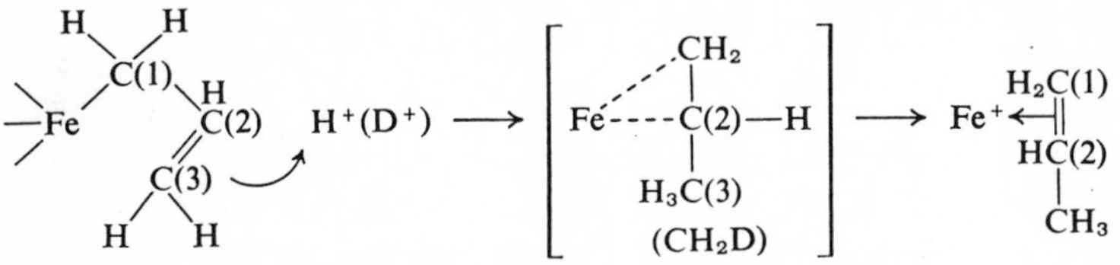

In the case of σ-allylmanganese pentacarbonyl, however, it has been found that the π-allyl complex is obtained only when perchloric acid is employed. Otherwise cleavage of the manganese–carbon bond occurs[55] to give $(CO)_5MnA$, where A is Cl^-, NO_3^-, CF_3COO^-, or SO_4H^-.

Protonation of other unsaturated groups has been reported. The σ-compound $\pi\text{-}C_5H_5Fe(CO)_2\text{-}\sigma\text{-}CH_2\text{---}C\equiv CH$ (16) gives a hexachloroantimonate (17) in concentrated hydrochloric acid. When hydrolyzed, this compound gives acetone, indicating that a π-allene system is present in the cation.[56]

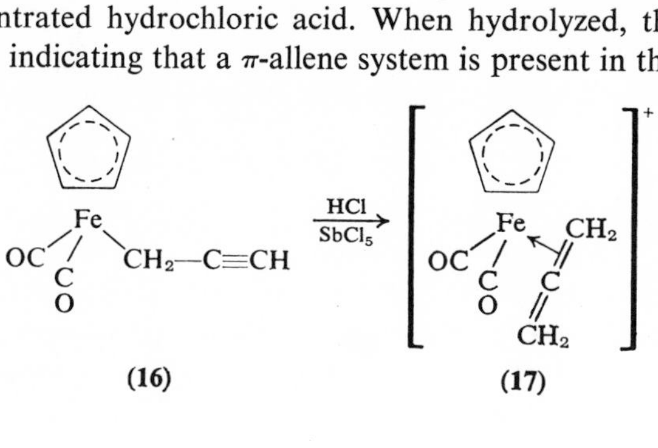

(16)   (17)

TABLE I
σ–π Rearrangements Induced by Reactions on the Metal

Initial compound	Final compound	Reaction conditions	How followed[a]	Ref.
Group VIA				
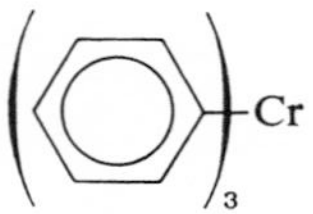 $(C_6H_5)_3Cr$	Hein's π-complexes	Reaction between C_6H_5MgBr and $CrCl_3$, at room temperature in ether	A	1
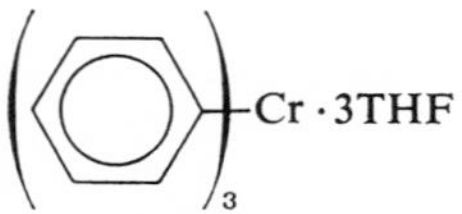 $(C_6H_5)_3Cr \cdot 3THF$	Hein's π-complexes	On heating, under vacuum, washing with ether	B	2
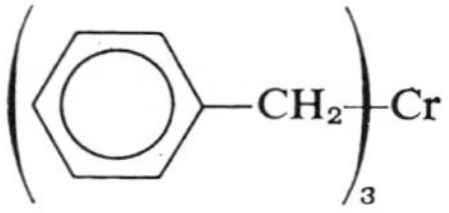 $(C_6H_5CH_2)_3Cr$	π-Bibenzyl π-bitoluene-chromium	Hydrolysis of reaction mixture of $C_6H_5CH_2MgBr + CrCl_3 \cdot 3THF$	A	9, 10
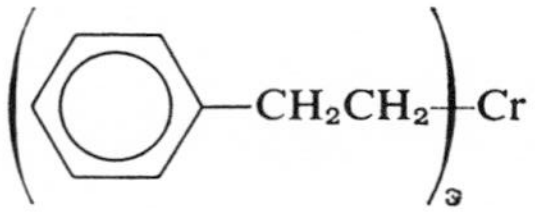 $(C_6H_5CH_2CH_2)_3Cr$	Uncharacterized π-complexes	Hydrolysis of reaction mixture of $C_6H_5CH_2CH_2MgBr + CrCl_3 \cdot 3THF$	A	9
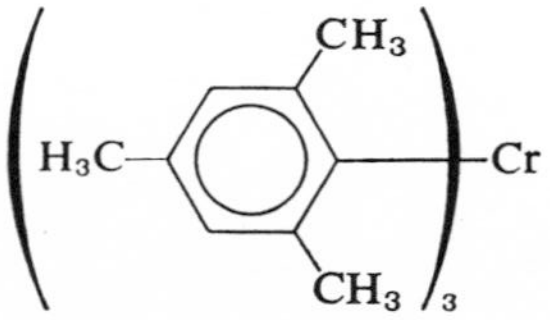 Mesityl–Cr	π-Dimesitylene chromium tetraborate	Hydrolysis of reaction mixture of $C_6H_2(CH_3)_3$—$MgBr + CrCl_3 \cdot 3THF$	A	9

12

Na$_2$[Cr(C$_6$H$_5$)$_5$Et$_2$O]·2Et$_2$O	Hein's π-complexes	Treatment of starting material with CrCl$_3$·3THF in ether	B	40
Li$_3$Cr(C$_6$H$_5$)$_6$·2.5Et$_2$O	Hein's π-complexes	Treatment of starting material with CrCl$_3$·3THF in ether	B	40
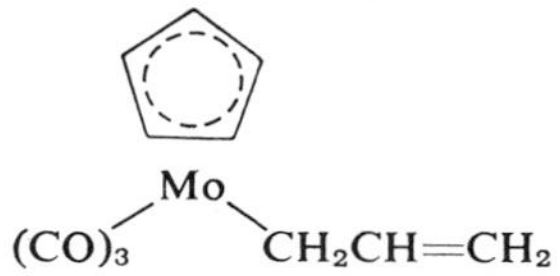 (CO)$_3$Mo—CH$_2$CH=CH$_2$	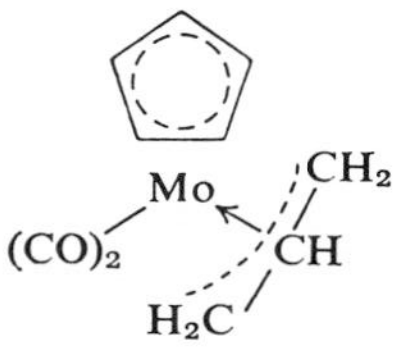 (CO)$_2$Mo（CH$_2$—CH—CH$_2$)	Loss of CO on irradiation with ultraviolet light	B	12
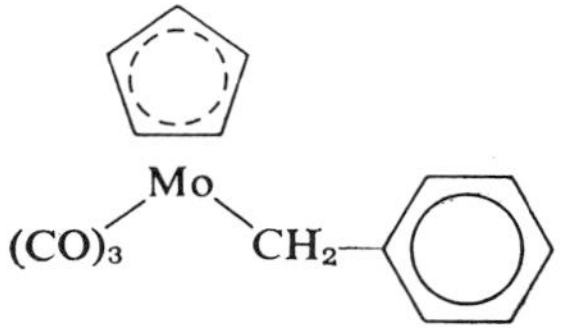 (CO)$_3$Mo—CH$_2$—C$_6$H$_5$	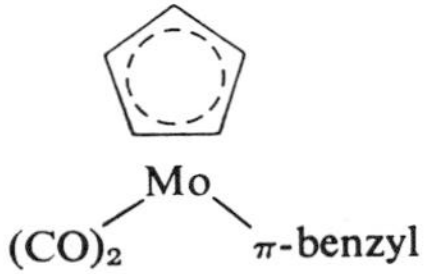 (CO)$_2$Mo—π-benzyl	Loss of CO on irradiation with ultraviolet light	B	14
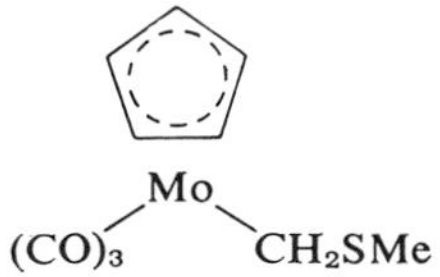 (CO)$_3$Mo—CH$_2$SMe	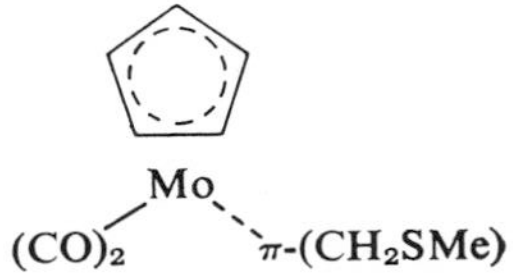 (CO)$_2$Mo—π-(CH$_2$SMe)	Loss of CO on irradiation with ultraviolet light or on heating	B	15
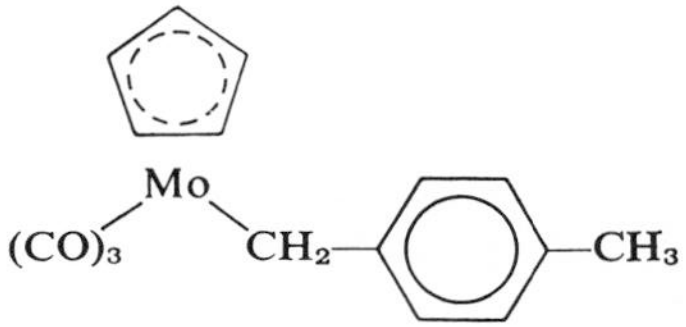 (CO)$_3$Mo—CH$_2$—C$_6$H$_4$—CH$_3$	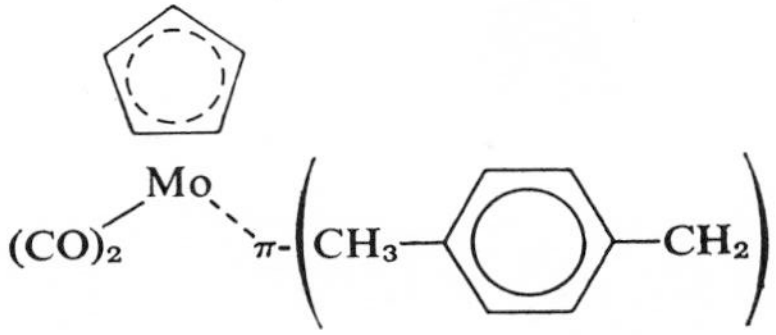 (CO)$_2$Mo—π-(CH$_3$—C$_6$H$_4$—CH$_2$)	Heating at 105° under vacuum for 1.3 hr	B	41

13

(continued)

TABLE I (continued)

Initial compound	Final compound	Reaction conditions	How followed[a]	Ref.
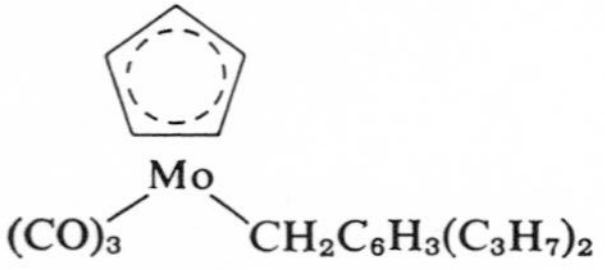 (C₅H₅)Mo(CO)₃—CH₂C₆H₃(C₃H₇)₂	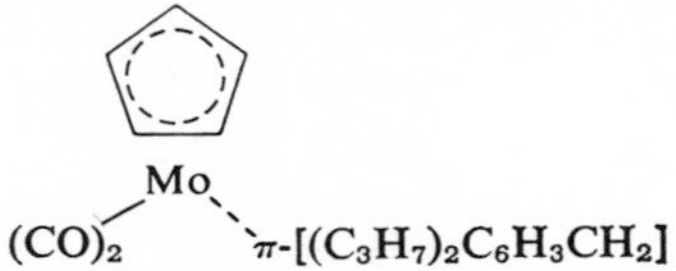 (C₅H₅)Mo(CO)₂⋯π-[(C₃H₇)₂C₆H₃CH₂]	Heating at 110° under vacuum for 2.2 hr	B	31
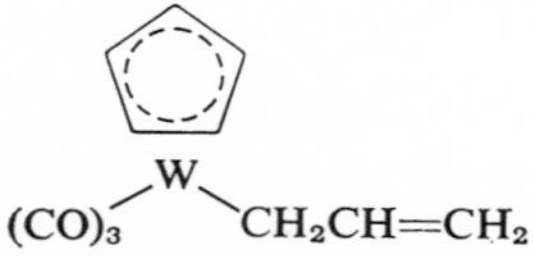 (C₅H₅)W(CO)₃—CH₂CH=CH₂	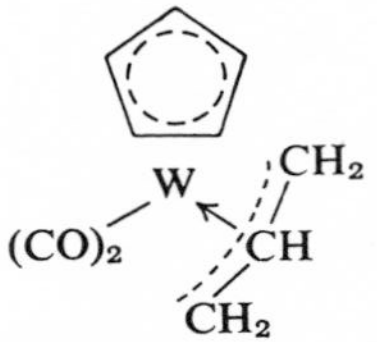 (C₅H₅)W(CO)₂⋯π-(CH₂–CH–CH₂)	Loss of CO on irradiation with ultraviolet light		
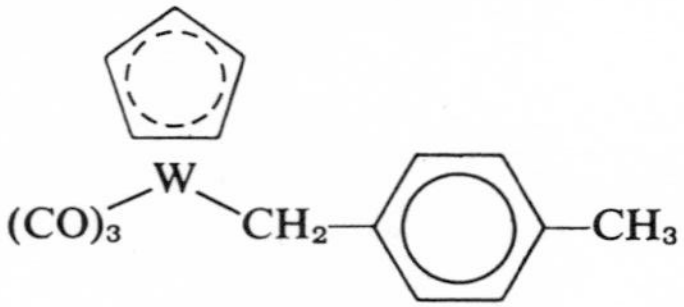 (C₅H₅)W(CO)₃—CH₂—C₆H₄—CH₃	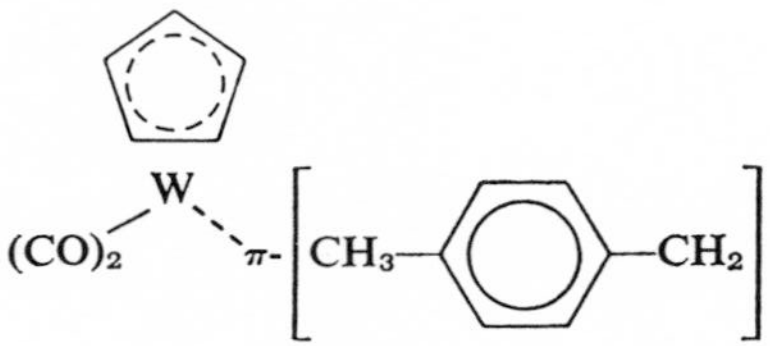 (C₅H₅)W(CO)₂⋯π-[CH₃—C₆H₄—CH₂]	Irradiation with ultraviolet light for 24 hr under N₂	B	41
Group VIIA				
(CO)₅MnCH₂CH=CH₂	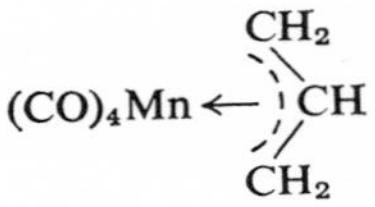 (CO)₄Mn←(CH₂–CH–CH₂)	Loss of CO on heating	B	16, 17
(CO)₅MnCH₂CH=CHCl	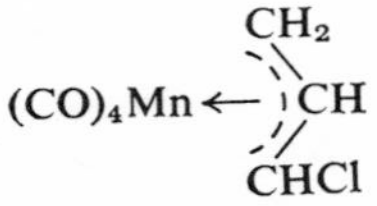 (CO)₄Mn←(CH₂–CH–CHCl)	Loss of CO at 85° for 3 hr	B	16

14

(CO)$_5$MnCH$_2$CH=CHCH$_3$ (structure: CH$_2$···CH–CHCH$_3$ → (CO)$_4$Mn)	Loss of CO on refluxing in THF	B	16
(CO)$_5$MnCH$_2$CH=C(CH$_3$)$_2$ (structure: CH$_2$···CH–C(CH$_3$)$_2$ → (CO)$_4$Mn)	Loss of CO at 95°	B	16
Me$_3$SnCF$_2$CF$_2$Mn(CO)$_5$ (structure: (CO)$_4$Mn with CF$_2$–CF$_2$ and F$_2$C=CF–Mn(CO)$_4$)	Heating Me$_3$SnMn(CO)$_5\cdot$4C$_2$F$_4$ at 50° for 6 hr under ultraviolet irradiation	A	42
Group VIII			
[FeCl·THF]$_2$ (cyclopentadienyl structure)	Ferricinium cation	B	11
Fe (ferrocene structure)$_3$	Ferrocene	A	11
σ-CH$_2$=CHCH$_2$Fe(CO)$_3$I (structure: CH$_2$···CH···CH$_2$ → Fe(CO)$_3$–I)	σ-CH$_2$=CHCH$_2$Fe(CO)$_3$I	C, D	37
π-(C$_3$H$_5$)$_2$Fe(CO)$_2$ (structure: CH$_2$···CH···CH$_2$ → Fe(CO)$_3$ with CH$_2$CH=CH$_2$)	Addition of allyl bromide to π-allyliron tricarbonyl sodium	A	39

(continued)

TABLE I (continued)

Initial compound	Final compound	Reaction conditions	How followed[a]	Ref.
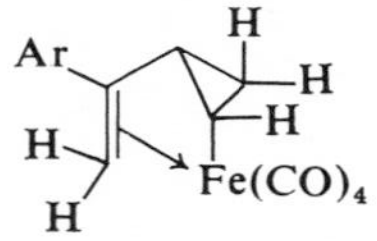 Ar, H, H, H, Fe(CO)$_4$ (cyclic structure with Ar substituent)	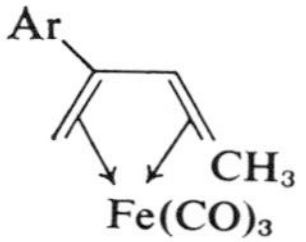 Ar–CH=CH–C(CH$_3$)=, Fe(CO)$_3$	Refluxing in di-n-butyl ether for 10 hr	E	43
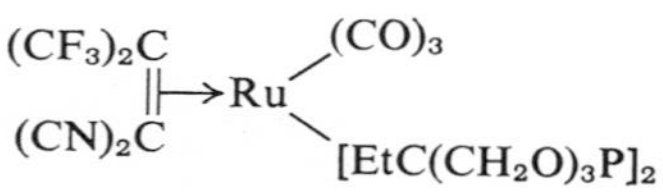 (CF$_3$)$_2$C=Ru(CO)$_3$ [EtC(CH$_2$O)$_3$P]$_2$ with (CN)$_2$C	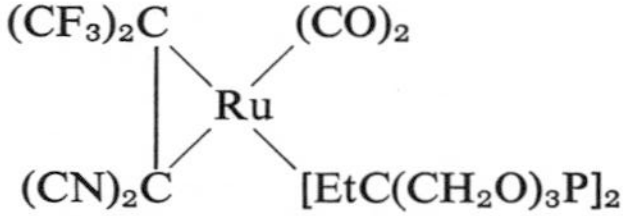 (CF$_3$)$_2$C, (CN)$_2$C, Ru, (CO)$_2$, [EtC(CH$_2$O)$_3$P]$_2$	Addition of the olefin to Ru(CO)$_3$[EtC(CH$_2$O)$_3$P]$_2$; reaction complete after 2–3 hr	A	44
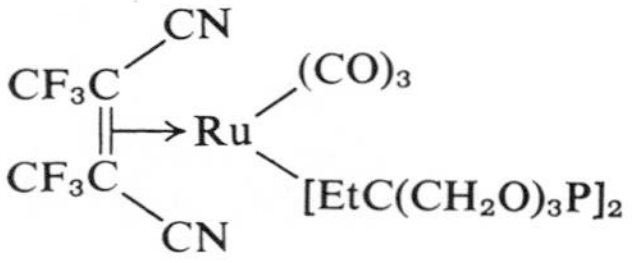 CF$_3$C(CN)=C(CN)CF$_3$ →Ru(CO)$_3$ [EtC(CH$_2$O)$_3$P]$_2$	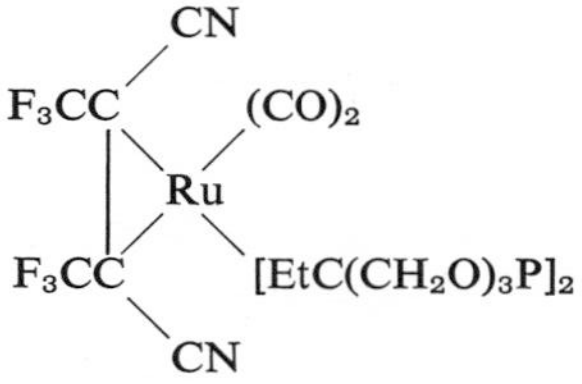 F$_3$CC(CN), F$_3$CC(CN), Ru, (CO)$_2$, [EtC(CH$_2$O)$_3$P]$_2$	Reaction of CH$_2$Cl$_2$–hexane at room temperature for 30 min	A	44
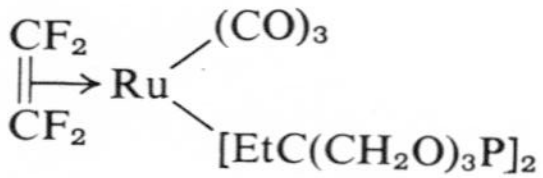 CF$_2$=CF$_2$ →Ru(CO)$_3$ [EtC(CH$_2$O)$_3$P]$_2$	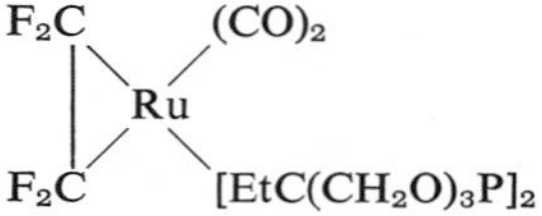 F$_2$C, F$_2$C, Ru, (CO)$_2$, [EtC(CH$_2$O)$_3$P]$_2$	Reaction between olefin and Ru(CO)$_3$[EtC(CH$_2$O)$_3$P]$_2$ at 80° for 10 days	C	44
σ-CH$_2$=CHCH$_2$Co(CN)$_5$	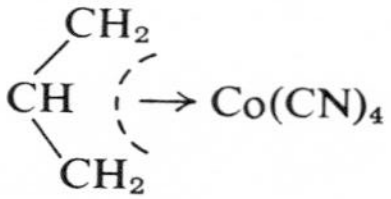 CH$_2$, CH, CH$_2$ → Co(CN)$_4$	Equilibrium loss of CN$^-$ in D$_2$O	C	19

16

σ-Phenacyl Co(CN)$_5$	Equilibrium loss of CN$^-$ in D$_2$O	π-Phenacyl Co(CN)$_4$	C, D	19
σ-Butenyl Co(CN)$_5$	Catalytic hydrogenation of butadiene	π-Butenyl Co(CN)$_4$	C, D	20
CH$_3$CH=CHCH$_2$Co(CO)$_4$	Loss of CO at room temperature	π-C$_4$H$_7$Co(CO)$_3$	—	20, 45
CH$_2$=CHCH$_2$Co(CO)$_4$	Loss of CO at room temperature	π-C$_3$H$_5$Co(CO)$_3$	D	45
$\begin{array}{c}\text{CH}_2\\ \text{CH}\;\; {\rightarrow}\text{Rh}{<}^{(\text{Ph}_3\text{P})_2}_{\text{Cl}_2}\\ \text{CH}_2\end{array}$	Under CO pressure	Intermediate; σ-CH$_2$=CHCH$_2$Rh	A	18
$\begin{array}{c}\text{CH}_2\\ \text{CH}\;\; {\rightarrow}\text{Rh}{<}^{(\text{Ph}_3\text{As})_2}_{\text{Cl}_2}\\ \text{CH}_2\end{array}$	Under CO pressure	Intermediate; σ-CH$_2$=CHCH$_2$Rh	A	18
$\begin{array}{c}\text{CH}_2\\ \text{CH}\;\; {\rightarrow}\text{Rh}{<}^{(\text{Ph}_3\text{Sb})_2}_{\text{Cl}_2}\\ \text{CH}_2\end{array}$	Under CO pressure	Intermediate; σ-CH$_2$=CHCH$_2$Rh	A	18
$\begin{array}{c}\text{CH}_2\\ \text{CH}_3\text{C}\;\; {\rightarrow}\text{Rh}{<}^{(\text{Ph}_3\text{P})_2}_{\text{Cl}_2}\\ \text{CH}_2\end{array}$	Under CO pressure	Intermediate; σ-CH$_2$=C(CH$_3$)CH$_2$Rh	A	18
$\begin{array}{c}\text{CH}_2\\ \text{CH}_3\text{C}\;\; {\rightarrow}\text{Rh}{<}^{(\text{Ph}_3\text{As})_2}_{\text{Cl}_2}\\ \text{CH}_2\end{array}$	Under CO pressure	Intermediate; σ-CH$_2$=C(CH$_3$)CH$_2$Rh	A	18

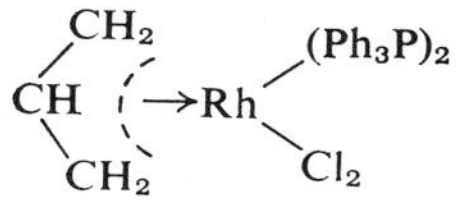

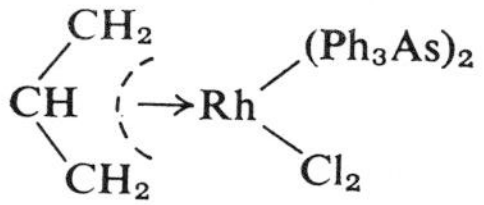

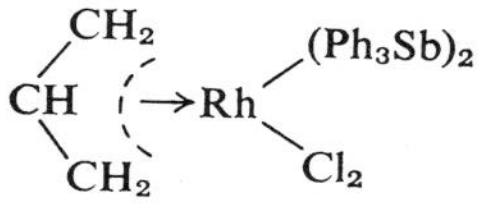

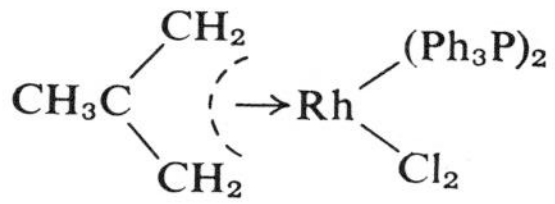

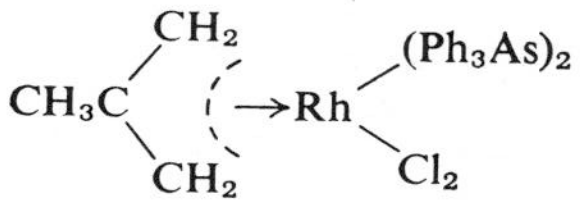

(continued)

17

TABLE I (continued)

Initial compound	Final compound	Reaction conditions	How followed[a]	Ref.
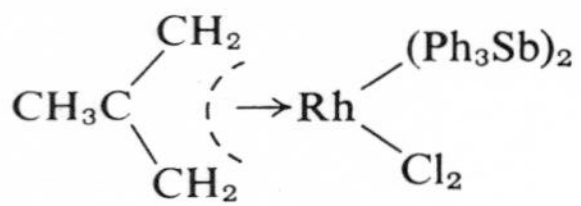	Intermediate; σ-CH₂=C(CH₃)CH₂Rh(Ph₃Sb)₂	Under CO pressure	A	18
	σ-CH₂=CHCH₂Rh(SO₂)Cl₂	Reaction with liquid SO₂ at 20° for 40 hr	B	18
	σ-CH₂=CHCH₂Rh—π—C₂H₄	Reaction with ethylene	A	18
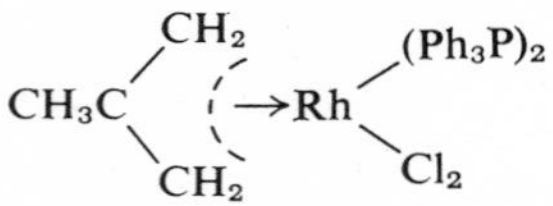	Intermediate; σ-CH₂=C(CH₃)CH₂Rh	Allylic interchange in solution with increase in temperature	C	35, 36
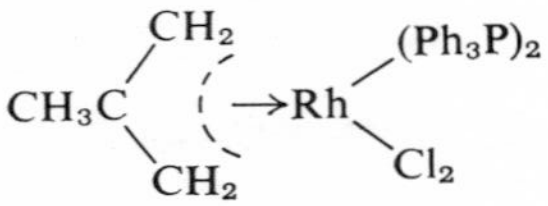	Intermediate; σ-CH₂=C(CH₃)CH₂Rh	Allylic interchange in solution with increase in temperature	C	35, 36
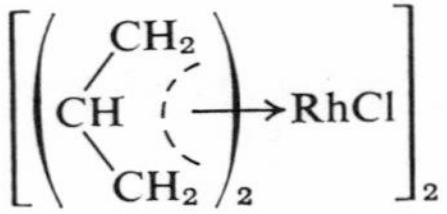	Dynamic σ-CH₂=CHCH₂Rh	140° in o-dichlorobenzene	C	

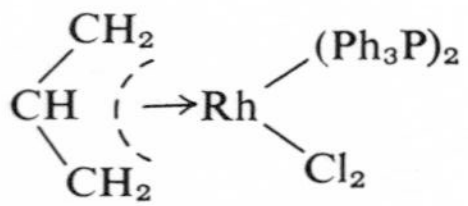

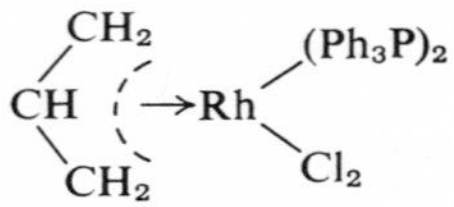

18

Compound	Observations	Conditions	Type	Ref.
$[(CH_2=CH-CH_2/_2) \rightarrow RhCl]_2$	$\sigma\text{-}CH_2=CHCH_2Rh$ involved in exchange processes	34° in $CDCl_3$	C	46
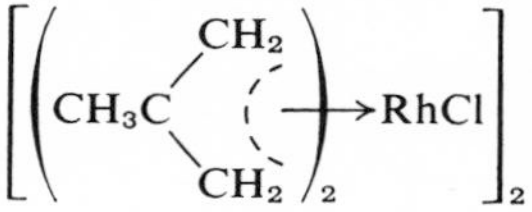 $[(CH_3C(CH_2)(CH_2)/_2) \rightarrow RhCl]_2$	$\sigma\text{-}CH_2=C(CH_3)CH_2Rh$ involved in exchange processes	34° in $CDCl_3$	C	46
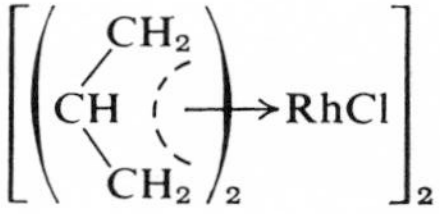 $[(CH_2=CH-CH_2/_2) \rightarrow RhCl]_2$	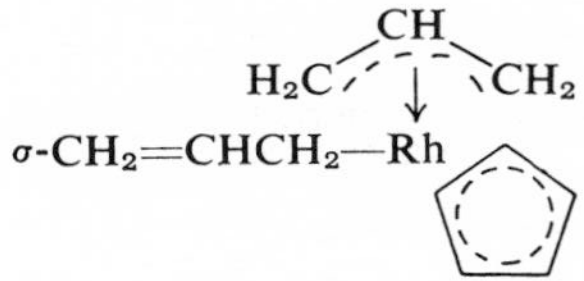 $H_2C=C(CH)=CH_2 \rightarrow CHCH_2\text{—}Rh$; $\sigma\text{-}CH_2=CHCH_2\text{—}Rh$	Shaking with Tl—[cyclopentadienyl] in CH_2Cl_2 for 4 hr 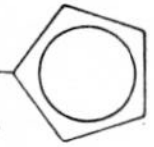	B	46, 47
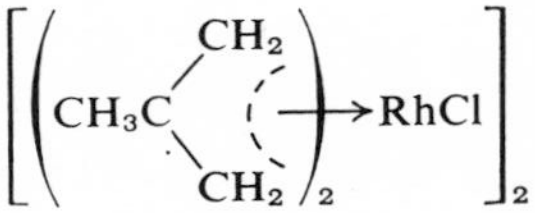 $[(CH_3C(CH_2)(CH_2)/_2) \rightarrow RhCl]_2$	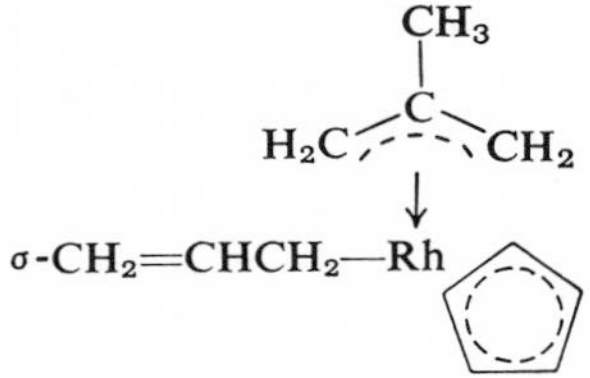 $H_2C=C(CH_3)C=CH_2 \rightarrow Rh$; $\sigma\text{-}CH_2=CHCH_2\text{—}Rh$	Shaken with Tl—[cyclopentadienyl] in CH_2Cl_2 for 5 min 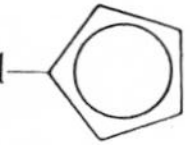	B	46
$Rh(\pi\text{-}CH_2CHCH_3)_3$	Intermediates; $\sigma\text{-}CH_2=CHCH_2Rh$	Variable temperature in solution	C	46
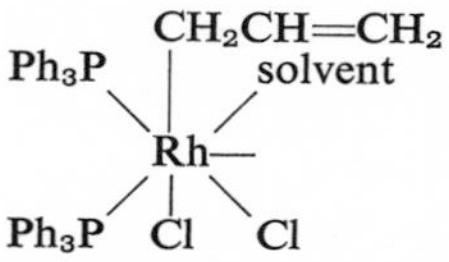 $CH_2CH=CH_2$, solvent, Ph_3P Rh Cl Cl (with Ph_3P, $CH_2=CH$/CH_2 Rh Cl/Cl)	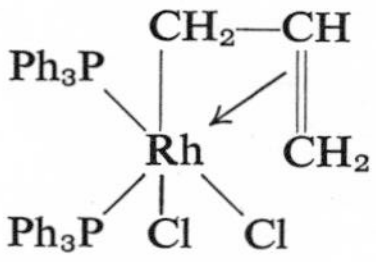	σ-Bonded in solution, π-bonded in solid state	C, D	48

(continued)

19

TABLE I (continued)

Initial compound	Final compound	Reaction conditions	How followed[a]	Ref.
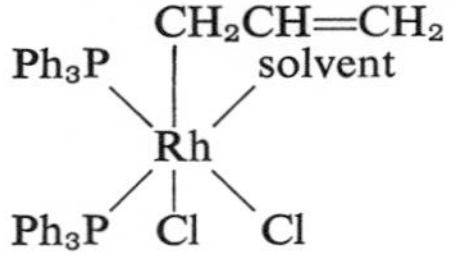 Ph₃P—Rh(Cl)(Cl)(Cl), $CH_2CH=CH_2$ solvent	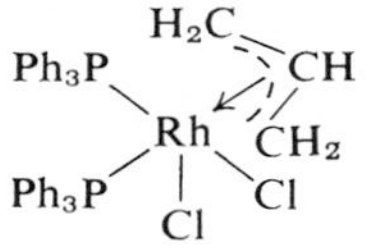 Ph₃P, Ph₃P—Rh with H₂C—CH, CH₂, Cl, Cl	On refluxing in solution	C, D	48
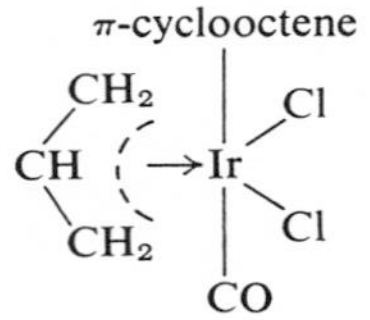 π-cyclooctene; CH₂ CH CH₂ → Ir(Cl)(Cl)(CO)	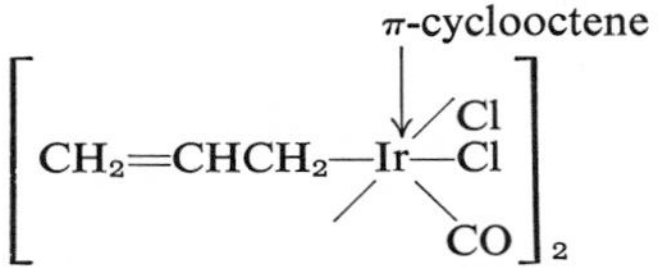 π-cyclooctene; $[CH_2=CHCH_2\text{—Ir—Cl (Cl)(Cl)(CO)}]_2$	Dimer formation on dissolving in MeOH–CHCl₃	C, D	49
IrCl₂(σ-allyl)(PMe₂Ph)₃	IrCl₂(π-allyl)(PMe₂Ph)₂	Refluxed in MeOH with KOH for 10 min	B	50
IrCl₂(π-methallyl)-(PMe₂Ph)₂	IrCl₂CO(σ-methallyl)-(PMe₂Ph)₂	CO passed into a refluxing solution in MeOH for 45 min	B	50
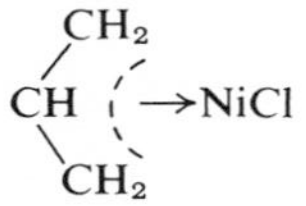 CH₂ CH CH₂ → NiCl	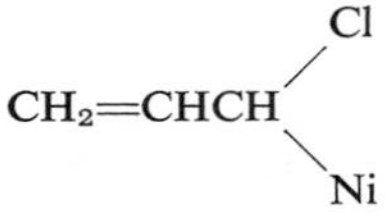 CH₂=CHCH with Cl—Ni	Addition of 2 equivalents of triethylphosphine	C	34
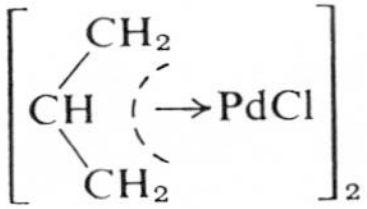 [CH₂ CH CH₂ → PdCl]₂	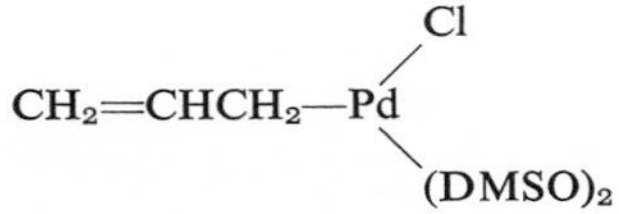 CH₂=CHCH₂—Pd with Cl, (DMSO)₂	50% solution in DMSO	C	25

20

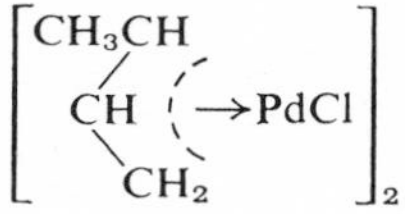 $\left[\begin{array}{c} CH_3CH \\ CH \cdots CH_2 \end{array} \rightarrow PdCl \right]_2$	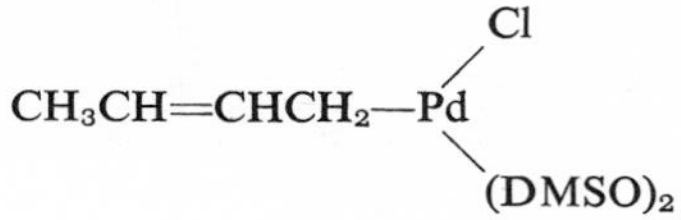 $\underset{\displaystyle CH_3CH=CHCH_2-\overset{\displaystyle Cl}{\underset{\displaystyle }{Pd}}(DMSO)_2}{}$	25% solution in DMSO	C	25
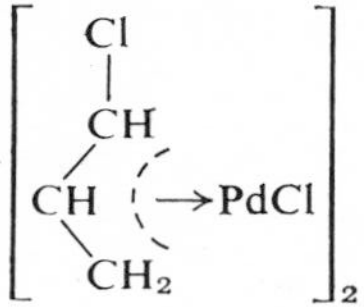 $\left[\begin{array}{c} Cl \\ CH \\ CH \cdots CH_2 \end{array} \rightarrow PdCl \right]_2$	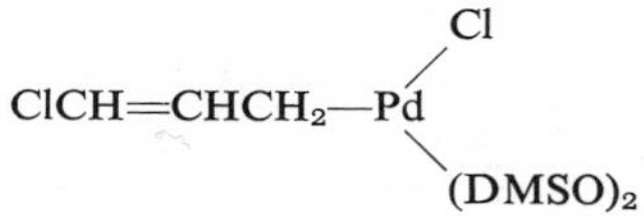 $ClCH=CHCH_2-\overset{Cl}{Pd}(DMSO)_2$	50% solution in DMSO	C	25
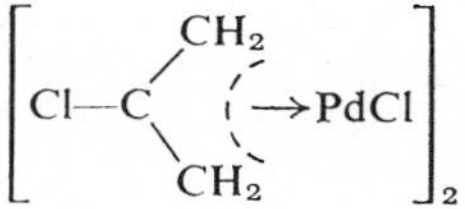 $\left[\begin{array}{c} CH_2 \\ Cl-C \\ CH_2 \end{array} \rightarrow PdCl \right]_2$	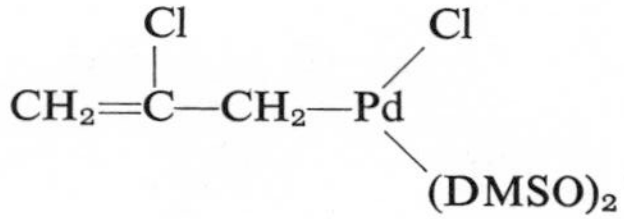 $CH_2=\overset{Cl}{C}-CH_2-\overset{Cl}{Pd}(DMSO)_2$	20% solution in DMSO	C	25
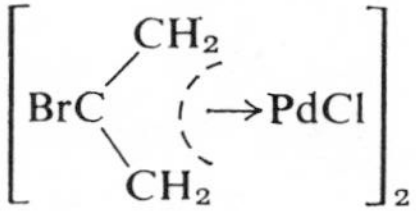 $\left[\begin{array}{c} CH_2 \\ BrC \\ CH_2 \end{array} \rightarrow PdCl \right]_2$	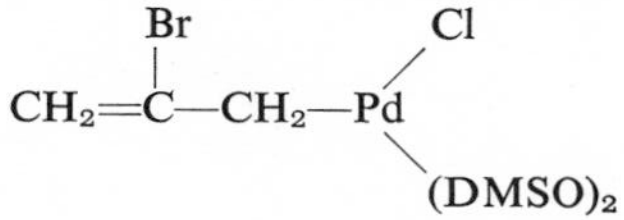 $CH_2=\overset{Br}{C}-CH_2-\overset{Cl}{Pd}(DMSO)_2$	25% solution in DMSO	C	25
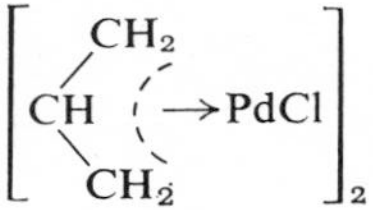 $\left[\begin{array}{c} CH_2 \\ CH \cdots CH_2 \end{array} \rightarrow PdCl \right]_2$	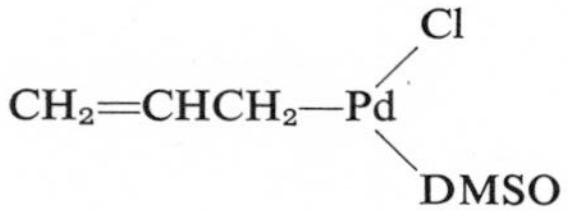 $CH_2=CHCH_2-\overset{Cl}{Pd}DMSO$	Addition of 1 mole of DMSO to a solution in CDCl$_3$	C	26
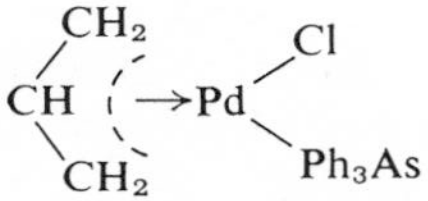 $\begin{array}{c} CH_2 \\ CH \cdots CH_2 \end{array} \rightarrow \overset{Cl}{Pd}Ph_3As$	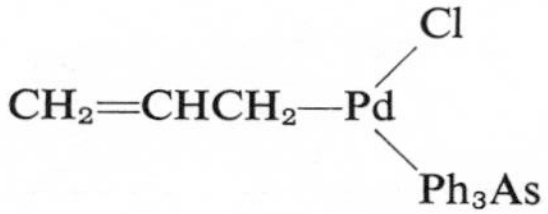 $CH_2=CHCH_2-\overset{Cl}{Pd}Ph_3As$	Variable temperature in CDCl$_3$	C	26
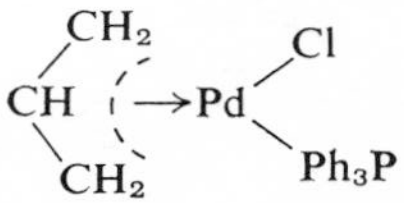 $\begin{array}{c} CH_2 \\ CH \cdots CH_2 \end{array} \rightarrow \overset{Cl}{Pd}Ph_3P$	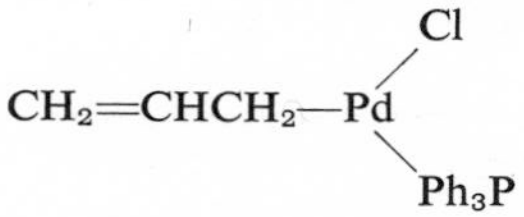 $CH_2=CHCH_2-\overset{Cl}{Pd}Ph_3P$	140° in o-dichlorobenzene	C	26

21

(continued)

TABLE I (*continued*)

Initial compound	Final compound	Reaction conditions	How followed[a]	Ref.
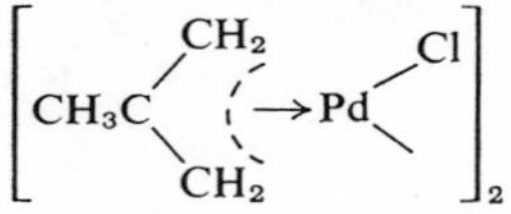 $\left[\begin{array}{c} CH_3C\overset{CH_2}{\underset{CH_2}{<}} {\to} Pd\overset{Cl}{<} \end{array} \right]_2$	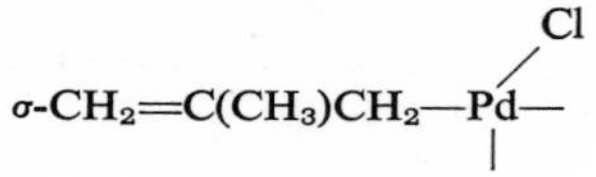 $\sigma\text{-}CH_2{=}C(CH_3)CH_2{-}Pd\overset{Cl}{<}$	Addition of up to 2 moles of Ph_3P	C	27
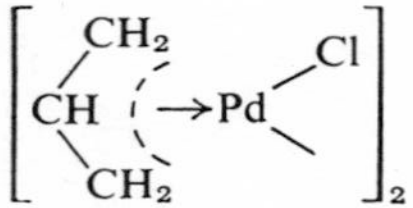 $\left[\begin{array}{c} CH\overset{CH_2}{\underset{CH_2}{<}} {\to} Pd\overset{Cl}{<} \end{array} \right]_2$	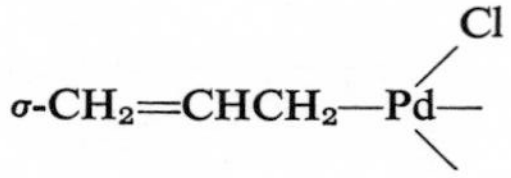 $\sigma\text{-}CH_2{=}CHCH_2{-}Pd\overset{Cl}{<}$	Reaction with Ph_3P at variable temperature	C	29
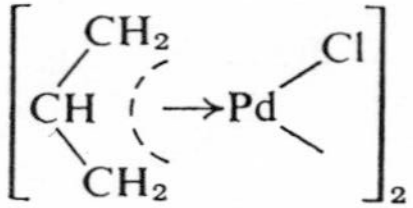 $\left[\begin{array}{c} CH\overset{CH_2}{\underset{CH_2}{<}} {\to} Pd\overset{Cl}{<} \end{array} \right]_2$	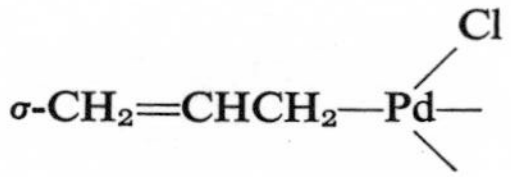 $\sigma\text{-}CH_2{=}CHCH_2{-}Pd\overset{Cl}{<}$	Reaction with $(n\text{-}C_4H_9)_3P$ at variable temperature	C	29
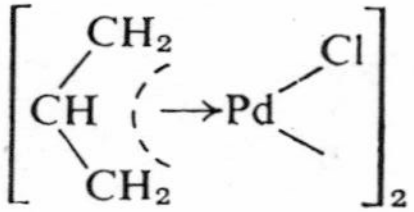 $\left[\begin{array}{c} CH\overset{CH_2}{\underset{CH_2}{<}} {\to} Pd\overset{Cl}{<} \end{array} \right]_2$	 $\sigma\text{-}CH_2{=}CHCH_2{-}Pd\overset{Cl}{<}$	$CH_3C(CH_2O)_3P$ at variable temperature	C	29
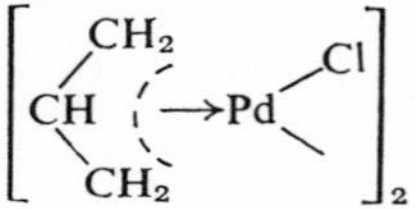 $\left[\begin{array}{c} CH\overset{CH_2}{\underset{CH_2}{<}} {\to} Pd\overset{Cl}{<} \end{array} \right]_2$	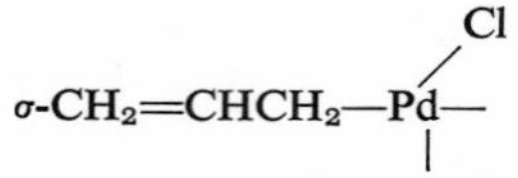 $\sigma\text{-}CH_2{=}CHCH_2{-}Pd\overset{Cl}{<}$	Ph_3As at variable temperature	C	29
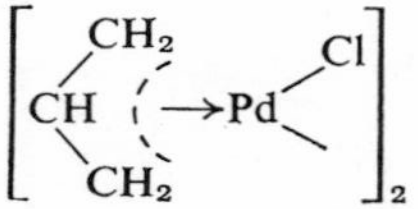 $\left[\begin{array}{c} CH\overset{CH_2}{\underset{CH_2}{<}} {\to} Pd\overset{Cl}{<} \end{array} \right]_2$	 $\sigma\text{-}CH_2{=}CHCH_2{-}Pd\overset{Cl}{<}$	Ph_3Sb at variable temperature	C	29

22

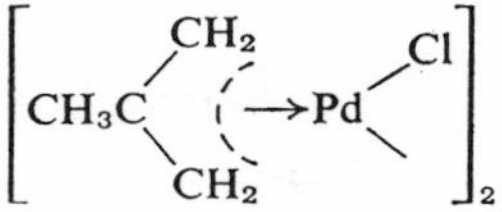 $\left[\begin{array}{c}\text{CH}_2 \\ \text{CH}_3\text{C} \quad \rightarrow\text{Pd—Cl} \\ \text{CH}_2\end{array}\right]_2$	$\sigma\text{-CH}_2\text{=CHCH}_2\text{—Pd}$	Ph$_3$As at variable temperature	C	30
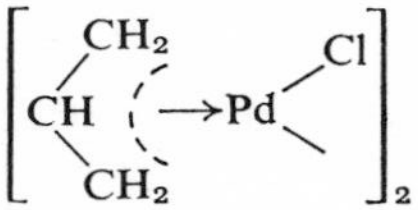 $\left[\begin{array}{c}\text{CH}_2 \\ \text{CH} \quad \rightarrow\text{Pd—Cl} \\ \text{CH}_2\end{array}\right]_2$	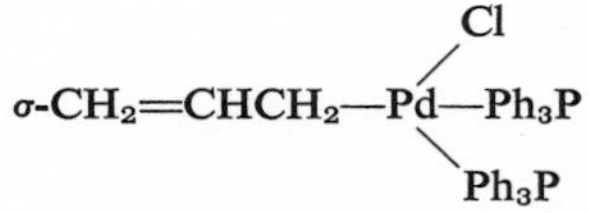 $\sigma\text{-CH}_2\text{=CHCH}_2\text{—Pd—Ph}_3\text{P}$ (Cl, Ph$_3$P)	Addition of 2 equivalents of Ph$_3$P to a CHCl$_3$ solution	C, D	31
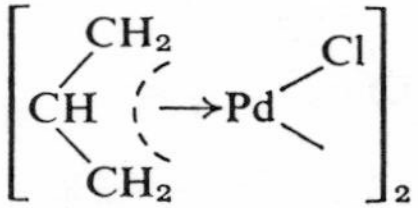 $\left[\begin{array}{c}\text{CH}_2 \\ \text{CH} \quad \rightarrow\text{Pd—Cl} \\ \text{CH}_2\end{array}\right]_2$	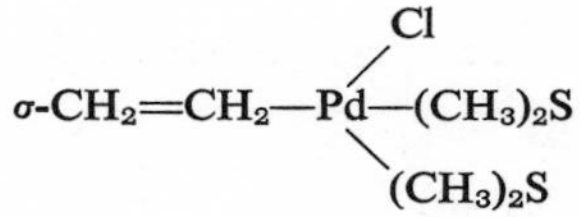 $\sigma\text{-CH}_2\text{=CH}_2\text{—Pd—(CH}_3)_2\text{S}$ (Cl, (CH$_3$)$_2$S)	Addition of 3 equivalents of (CH$_3$)$_2$S; equilibrium lying well to π-complex	C, D	31
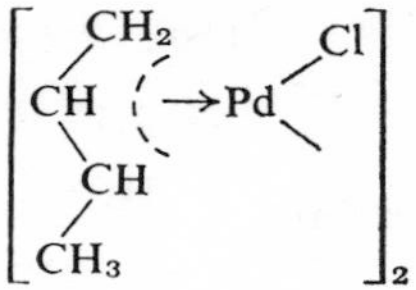 $\left[\begin{array}{c}\text{CH}_2 \\ \text{CH} \quad \rightarrow\text{Pd—Cl} \\ \text{CH—CH}_3\end{array}\right]_2$	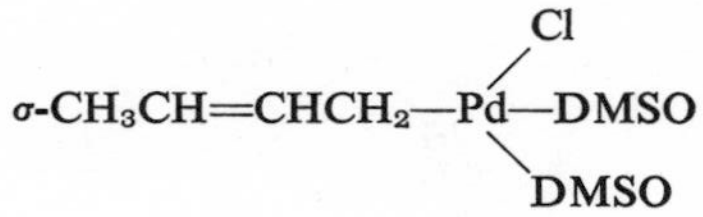 $\sigma\text{-CH}_3\text{CH=CHCH}_2\text{—Pd—DMSO}$ (Cl, DMSO)	Addition of more than 20 equivalents of DMSO; equilibrium lying well to π-complex	C, D	31
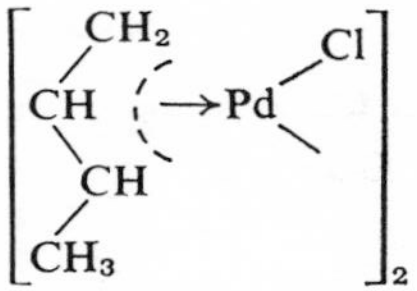 $\left[\begin{array}{c}\text{CH}_2 \\ \text{CH} \quad \rightarrow\text{Pd—Cl} \\ \text{CH—CH}_3\end{array}\right]_2$	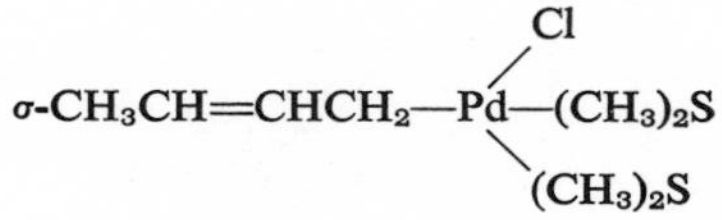 $\sigma\text{-CH}_3\text{CH=CHCH}_2\text{—Pd—(CH}_3)_2\text{S}$ (Cl, (CH$_3$)$_2$S)	Addition of more than 20 equivalents of (CH$_3$)$_2$S; equilibrium lying well to π-complex	C, D	31
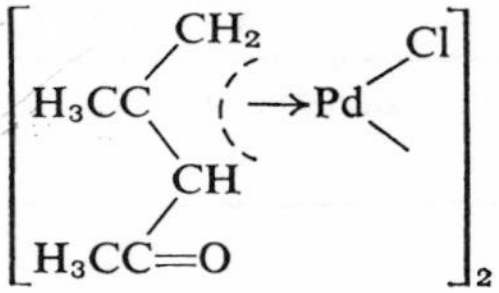 $\left[\begin{array}{c}\text{CH}_2 \\ \text{H}_3\text{CC} \quad \rightarrow\text{Pd—Cl} \\ \text{CH} \\ \text{H}_3\text{CC=O}\end{array}\right]_2$	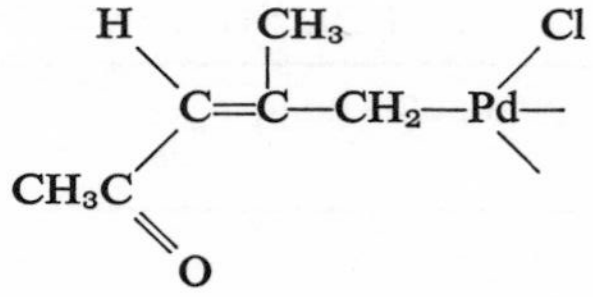 (structure: H, CH$_3$, C=C, C—CH$_2$—Pd—Cl, CH$_3$C=O)	Addition of S-α-phenethylamine	F	33

23

(continued)

TABLE I (*continued*)

Initial compound	Final compound	Reaction conditions	How followed[a]	Ref.
$(\pi\text{-}C_{12}H_{17})_2Pd_2Br_2$	$BrPd\sigma\text{-}C_{12}H_{17}P(CH_3)_2Ph$	Addition of 2 equivalents of $(CH_3)_2PhP$	C	45
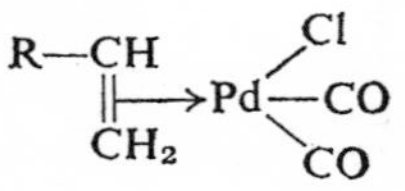 (see structure below)	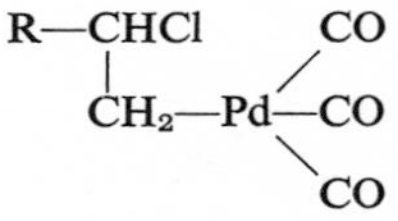 (see structure below)	Reaction of π-olefin palladium complexes with CO	B	51
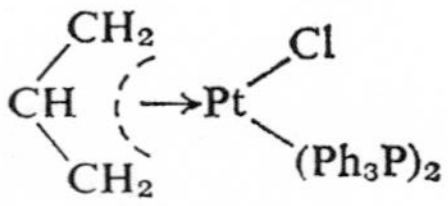 (see structure below)	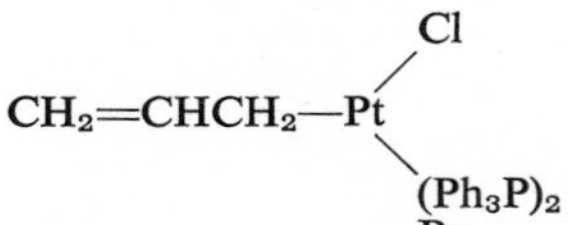 (see structure below)	Room-temperature solution in $CDCl_3$	C	35
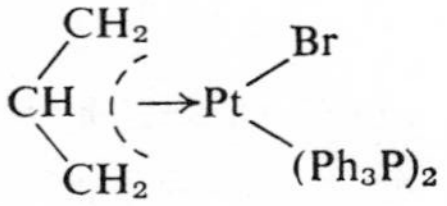 (see structure below)	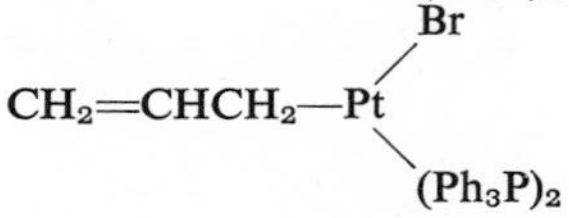 (see structure below)	Room-temperature solution in $CDCl_3$	C	35
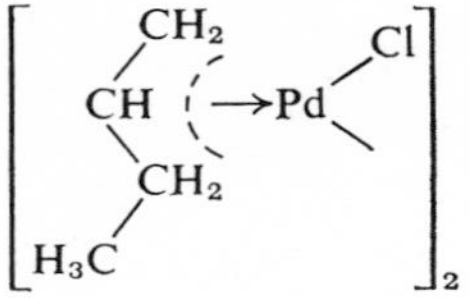 (see structure below)	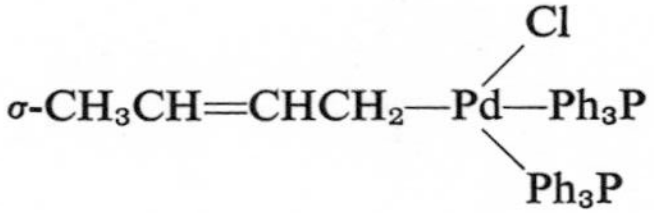 (see structure below)	Addition of 2 equivalents of Ph_3P; equilibrium lying well to π-complex	C, D	31
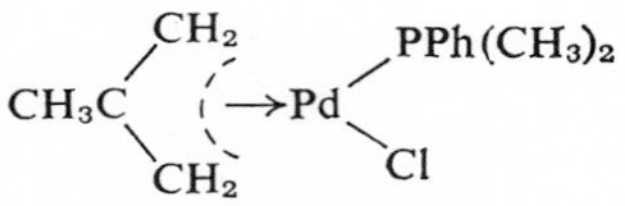 (see structure below)	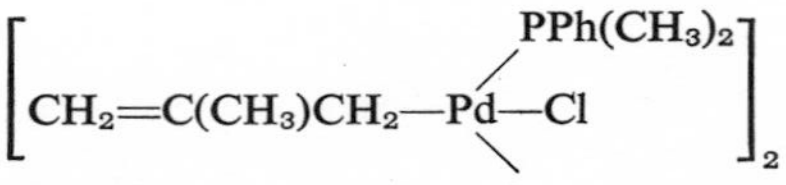 (see structure below)	Reaction of $[PdCl(2\text{-methallyl})]$ $Ph(CH_3)_2P$ with $[PdCl(2\text{-methallyl})]_2$	C	32

Initial compound structures:

Row 2:
$$R—CH \xrightarrow{} Pd \quad (Cl,\ CH_2,\ CO,\ CO)$$

Row 3:
$$\begin{array}{c} CH_2 \\ CH \rightarrow Pt \\ CH_2 \end{array} \quad (Cl,\ (Ph_3P)_2)$$

Row 4:
$$\begin{array}{c} CH_2 \\ CH \rightarrow Pt \\ CH_2 \end{array} \quad (Br,\ (Ph_3P)_2)$$

Row 5:
$$\left[\begin{array}{c} CH_2 \\ CH \rightarrow Pd \\ CH_2 \\ H_3C \end{array} \quad (Cl) \right]_2$$

Row 6:
$$\begin{array}{c} CH_2 \\ CH_3C \rightarrow Pd \\ CH_2 \end{array} \quad (Cl,\ PPh(CH_3)_2)$$

Final compound structures:

Row 2:
$$R—CHCl,\ CH_2—Pd—CO \quad (CO)$$

Row 3:
$$CH_2=CHCH_2—Pt \quad (Cl,\ (Ph_3P)_2)$$

Row 4:
$$CH_2=CHCH_2—Pt \quad (Br,\ (Ph_3P)_2)$$

Row 5:
$$\sigma\text{-}CH_3CH=CHCH_2—Pd—Ph_3P \quad (Cl,\ Ph_3P)$$

Row 6:
$$\left[CH_2=C(CH_3)CH_2—Pd—Cl \quad (PPh(CH_3)_2) \right]_2$$

σ-compound structure	π-compound structure	Method		Ref.

Structure (π)	Structure (σ)	Preparation	Studies	Ref.
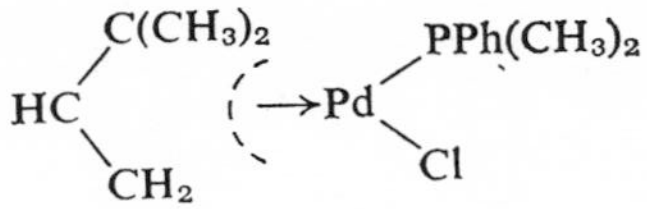 (Pd with C(CH$_3$)$_2$, HC, CH$_2$ chelate; PPh(CH$_3$)$_2$ and Cl)	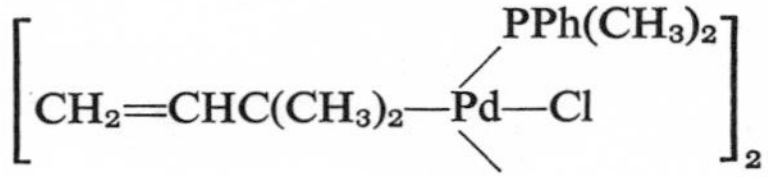 $\left[\text{CH}_2=\text{CHC(CH}_3)_2-\text{Pd}-\text{Cl, PPh(CH}_3)_2\right]_2$	Reaction of [PdCl(1,1'-dimethallyl)] PhMe$_2$P with [PdCl(1,1'-dimethallyl)]$_2$	C	32
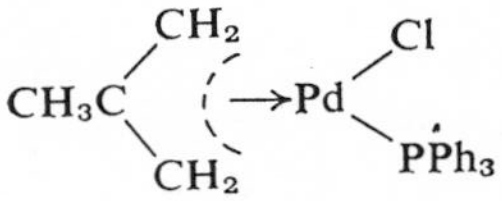 (Pd with CH$_2$, CH$_3$C, CH$_2$ chelate; Cl and PPh$_3$)	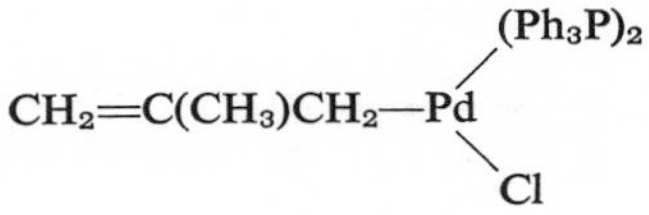 $\text{CH}_2=\text{C(CH}_3)\text{CH}_2-\text{Pd, (Ph}_3\text{P)}_2, \text{Cl}$	Reaction of [PdCl(2-methallyl)]$_2$ with 1 equivalent of PPh$_3$	C	32
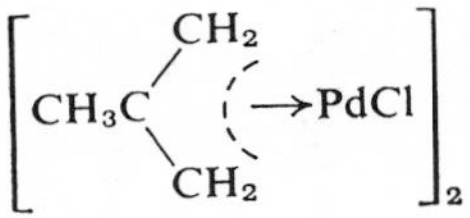 $\left[\text{CH}_3\text{C}(\text{CH}_2)(\text{CH}_2)\rightarrow\text{PdCl}\right]_2$	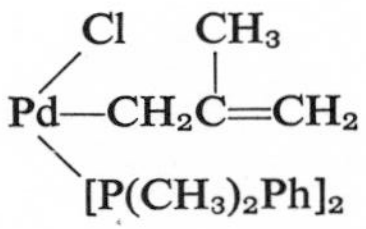 $\left[\text{Pd}-\text{CH}_2\text{C(CH}_3)=\text{CH}_2, \text{Cl}, \text{CH}_3, \text{P(CH}_3)_2\text{Ph}\right]_2$	Addition of PMe$_2$Ph to a solution in CDCl$_3$	C	32
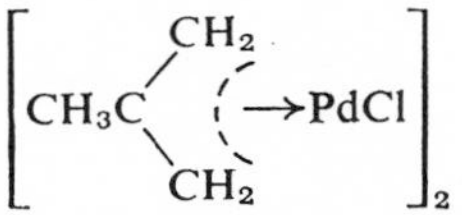 $\left[\text{CH}_3\text{C}(\text{CH}_2)(\text{CH}_2)\rightarrow\text{PdCl}\right]_2$	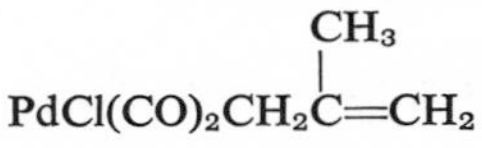 $\text{PdCl(CO)}_2\text{CH}_2\text{C(CH}_3)=\text{CH}_2$	Saturating a CHCl$_3$ solution with CO	C, D	32

 Key: A = reduced from reaction products; B = isolation and characterization of σ- and π-compounds; C = NMR studies; D = infrared studies; E = degeneration and kinetic studies; F = changes in optical activity.

25

This would be expected if the course of the protonation were similar to that of the isoelectronic iron σ-1-cyanoalkyl compound (**18**), which undergoes a reversible rearrangement to a π-keteneimine complex (**19**).[57]

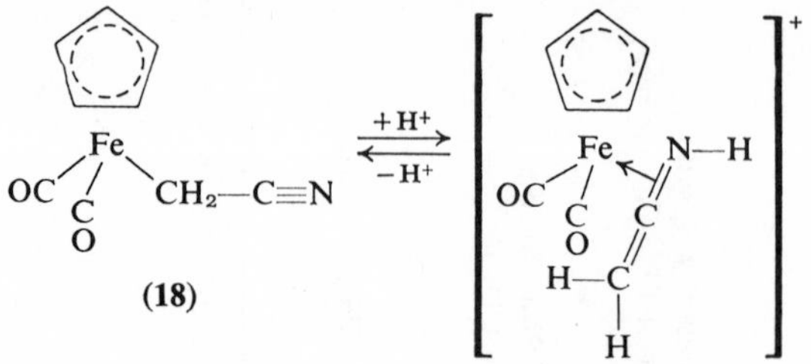

(**18**) (**19**)

Protonation of a σ-bonded α-ketone iron compound (**20**) traps "vinyl alcohol" in the rearranged product (**21**),[58] and protonation of σ-cyclopentadienyl π-cyclopentadienyliron dicarbonyl (**22**) gives a π-olefin (**23**);[59] i.e., both σ-compounds show the same behavior as the σ-bonded allyl compounds.

(**20**) (**21**)

(**22**) (**23**)

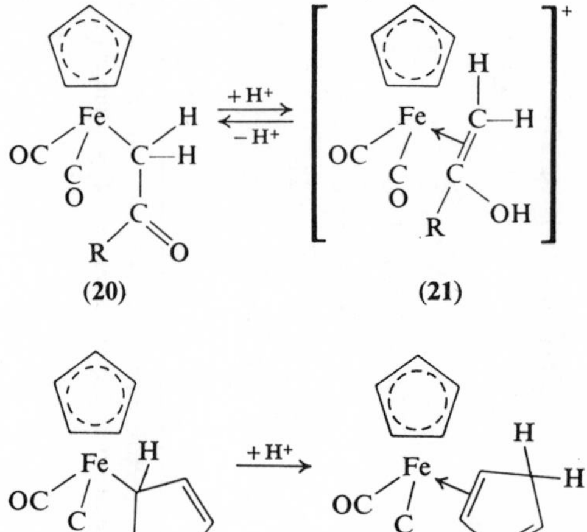

B. Elimination of the Hydride Ion

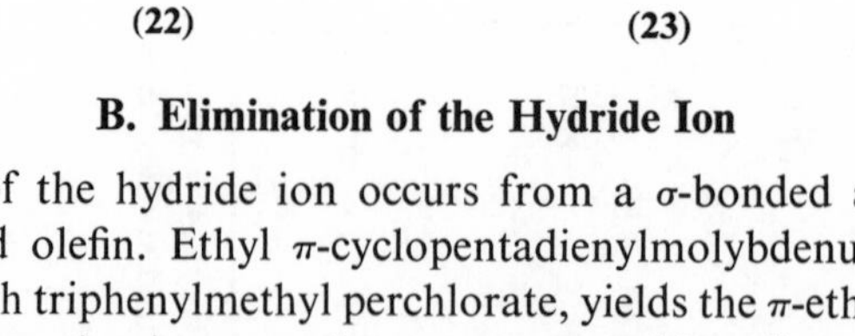

Elimination of the hydride ion occurs from a σ-bonded alkyl group to give a π-bonded olefin. Ethyl π-cyclopentadienylmolybdenum tricarbonyl, on treatment with triphenylmethyl perchlorate, yields the π-ethylene complex, whereas the abstraction is reversed on treatment with sodium borohydride.[60] Small amounts of π-ethylenemanganese pentacarbonyl tetrafluoborate are obtained on treating ethylmanganese pentacarbonyl with triphenylmethyl tetrafluoborate; the reaction is reversed on addition of sodium borohydride.[61] It was also found that when σ-alkyliron π-cyclopentadienyl dicarbonyl compounds (alkyl being ethyl or *n*-propyl) are treated with a stoichiometric amount of triphenylmethyl perchlorate, a fast reaction occurs, giving a good yield of the corresponding π-complex.[62] When the alkyl group is primary, the reaction is found to be reversible on addition of sodium borohydride.[63]

C. Dimeric and Monomeric Complexes

In 1908 Hofmann and Von Narbutt[64] described three compounds obtained by the reaction of dicyclopentadiene with potassium chloroplatinite in aqueous alcohol at 35°. The reaction required 10–14 days and yielded, from aqueous methanol and ethanol, compounds of the composition $C_{10}H_{12}Pt(OMe)Cl$ and $C_{10}H_{12}Pt(OEt)Cl$, respectively, but from aqueous propanol the dichloride was isolated. These were formulated as addition products (**24**) and (**25**), respectively.

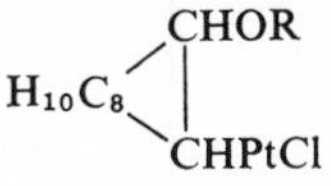

$$
\begin{array}{cc}
\underset{H_{10}C_8}{\diagup}\overset{CHOR}{\underset{CHPtCl}{\diagdown\big|}} & \underset{H_{10}C_8}{\diagup}\overset{CHCl}{\underset{CHPtCl}{\diagdown\big|}} \\
\textbf{(24)} & \textbf{(25)}
\end{array}
$$

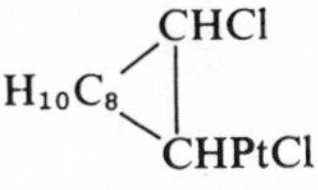

Chatt, Vallarino, and Venanzi[65] have demonstrated the formation of a π-diolefin monomeric complex (**26**), which then undergoes an addition reaction with the alcohol, in the presence of anhydrous sodium carbonate, giving a σ-bonded dimeric complex (**27**), with the alkoxy groups *trans* to each other. The results were confirmed by X-ray analysis.[66] The reaction is reversed in boiling hydrochloric acid. A π–σ–π rearrangement was also found with 1,5-cyclooctadiene and dipentene. With methanol adding to a dicyclopentadiene complex similar results were obtained.[67]

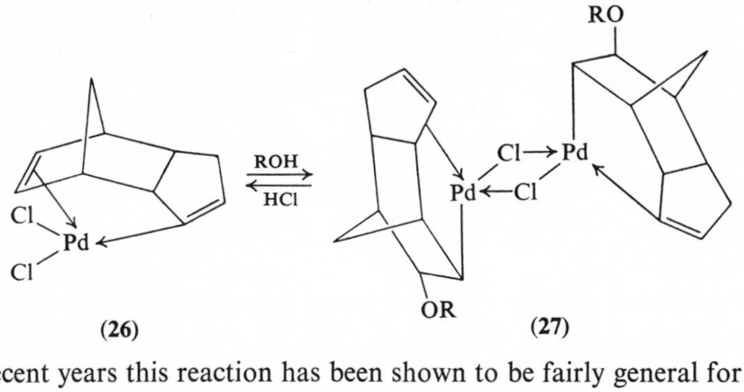

(**26**)   (**27**)

In recent years this reaction has been shown to be fairly general for large-ring diolefins chelated to palladium and platinum. The reaction of palladium(II) chloride with *endo*-dicyclopentadiene gives a monomeric π-complex that reacts with methanol to give a dimeric σ-bonded compound. The reverse (elimination) reaction is brought about by treatment with hydrochloric acid.[68] 1,5-Cyclooctadiene reacts with sodium tetrachloropalladite(II) in methanol to give a π-complex that reacts with methanol in the presence of sodium bicarbonate to give a σ-bonded compound.[69] The rearrangement has been reported for the dienes, 1,5-cyclooctadiene, norbornadiene, 4-vinylcyclohexene, 1,5-hexadiene, dicyclopentadiene, and dipentene, the adding groups being ethyl malonate,[70] β-diketones,[71] and primary amines.[72] The reaction of the methoxide ion with bicyclo[2.2.1]heptadienepalladium(II) chloride gives addition, as in all the above examples, forming (28), with the methoxy group having the *exo* configuration. Thus *trans* addition to the olefin has occurred.[73]

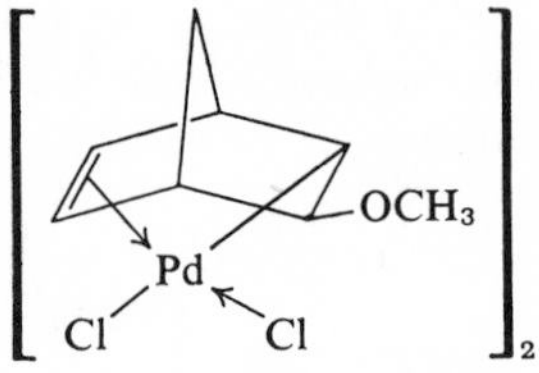

(28)

Malatesta's historic synthesis[74] of a cyclobutadiene complex can be considered with these reactions. Diphenylacetylene reacts with alcoholic palladium(II) chloride to give a σ-bonded compound (29), which on treatment with halogen acids gives the π-cyclobutadienepalladium complex (30). It has also been reported that the above reaction gives as one product a compound assigned structure (31), which on refluxing in ethanol–hydrochloric acid also gives (30).[75]

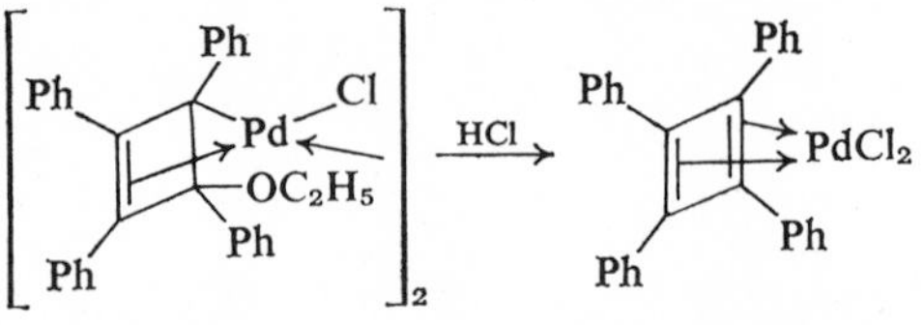

(29)   (30)

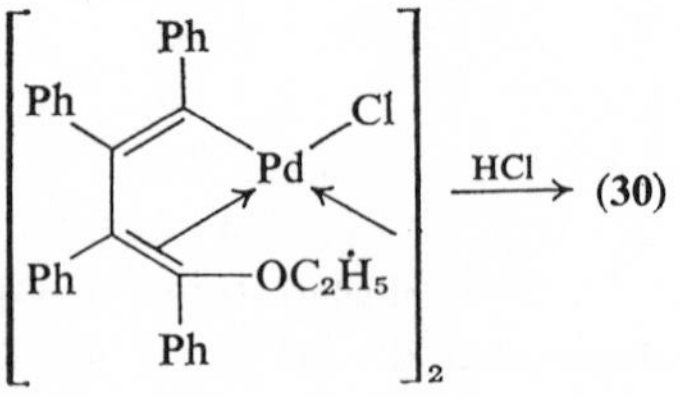

(31)

π-Cyclopentadienyl rings appear to be resistant to rearrangement, although two reactions are reported to give σ-bonded compounds. On treating di-π-cyclopentadienylrhenium hydride (32) with lithium, the dilithium compound (33) is formed and on methylation gives (34).[76] A similar reaction is produced with the di-π-cyclopentadienylrhodium cation (35).[77] Phenyllithium

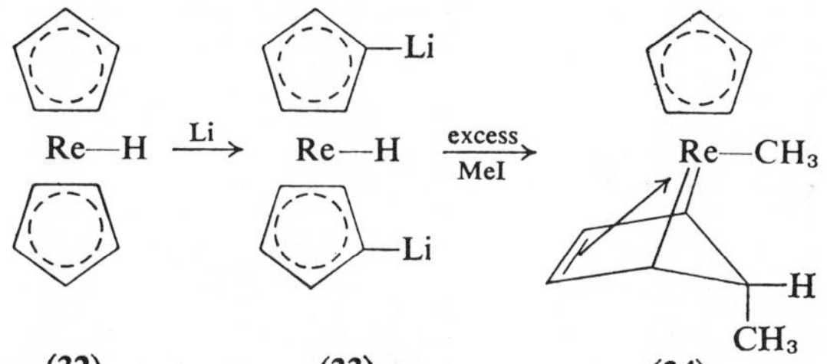

(32)   (33)   (34)

reacts with (35) to give a compound with the formula C_5H_5Rh-1-exo-$C_6H_5C_5H_5$, to which the structure (36) was assigned on the basis of its NMR spectrum and its X-ray powder diffraction pattern. The data show that it is isomorphous with the corresponding cobalt compound. The latter structure has been elucidated by detailed X-ray analysis.[78]

A survey of compounds in which σ–π rearrangements are induced by reactions on the ligand is presented in Table II.

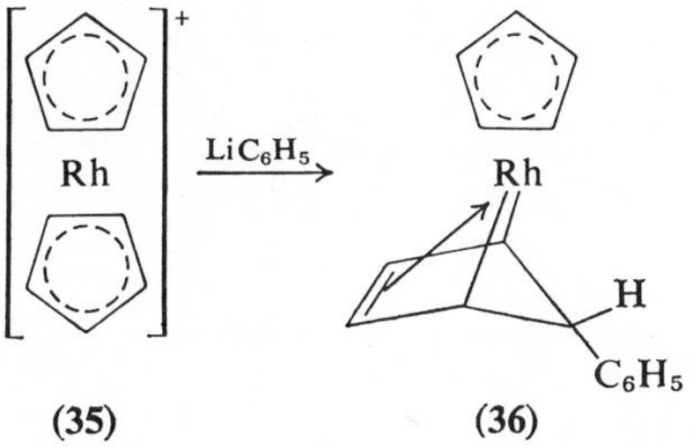

(35)   (36)

IV. MIGRATION OR INSERTION REACTIONS

A general reaction of the type

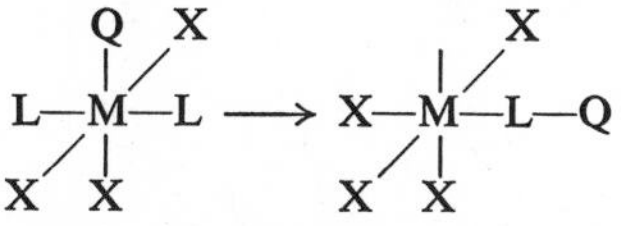

involves either the insertion of the group L into the metal—Q bond or the migration of Q. In a number of instances there is no unambiguous evidence as to which mechanism is operating. In any case it is evident that this rearrangement involves a π–σ rearrangement.

TABLE II

σ–π Rearrangements Induced by Reactions on the Ligand

Initial compound	Final compound	Reaction conditions	How followed[a]	Ref.
Group VIA				
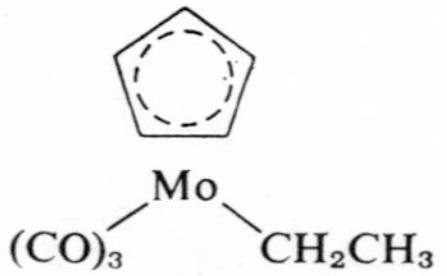	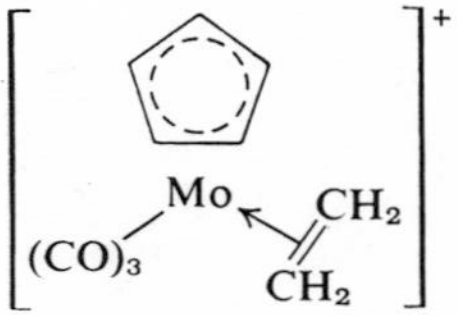	Treatment with triphenylmethyl perchlorate; reversed on treatment with NaBH₄		60
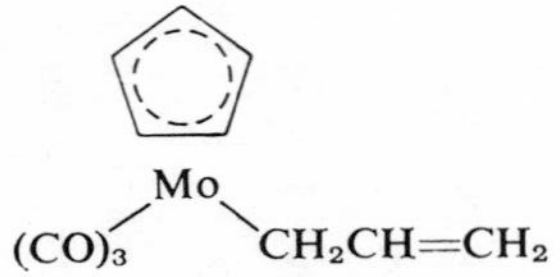	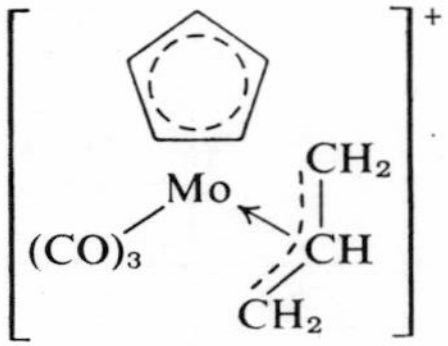	Treatment with gaseous HCl, isolated as fluoborate		60
Group VIIA				
σ-CH₂=CH—CH₂—Mn(CO)₅	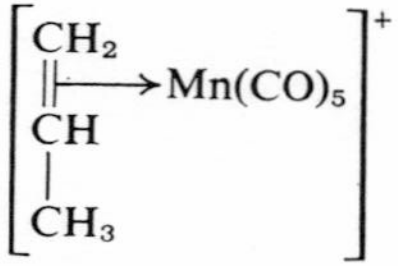	Treatment with perchloric acid		55

30

55   Treatment with lithium, followed by methylation with MeI

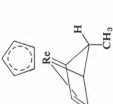

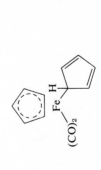

Group VIII

56   Treatment with concentrated HCl; isolated as hexachloroantimonate

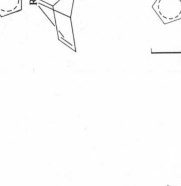

59   Gaseous HCl or dilute HCl

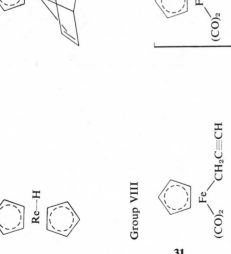

TABLE II (*continued*)

Initial compound	Final compound	Reaction conditions	How followed[a] / Ref.
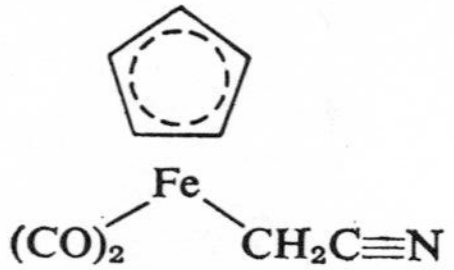 (C₅H₅)(CO)₂Fe—CH₂C≡N	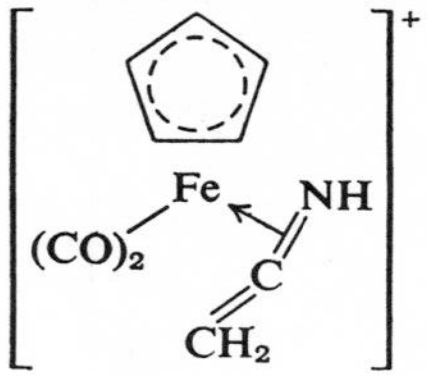 [(C₅H₅)(CO)₂Fe←C(=NH)CH₂]⁺	Gaseous HCl or dilute HCl	57
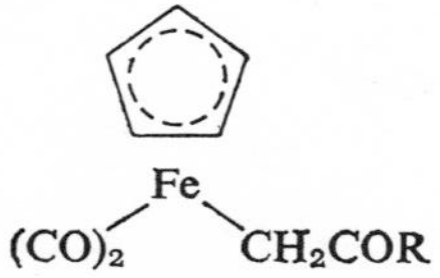 (C₅H₅)(CO)₂Fe—CH₂COR	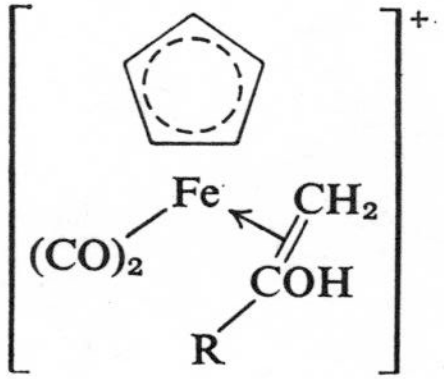 [(C₅H₅)(CO)₂Fe(CH₂=C(OH)R)]⁺	Gaseous HCl or dilute HCl	58
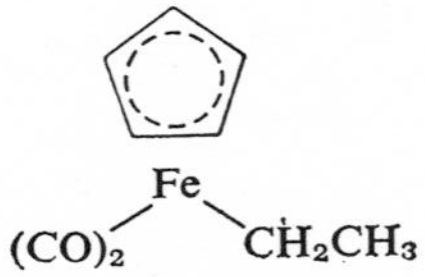 (C₅H₅)(CO)₂Fe—CH₂CH₃	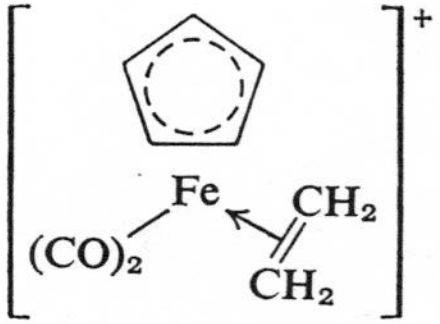 [(C₅H₅)(CO)₂Fe←(CH₂=CH₂)]⁺	Treatment with triphenylmethyl perchlorate; reversed on treatment with NaBH₄	61, 62
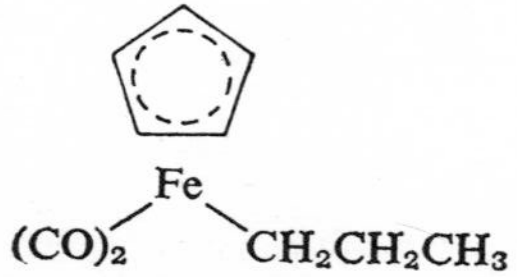 (C₅H₅)(CO)₂Fe—CH₂CH₂CH₃	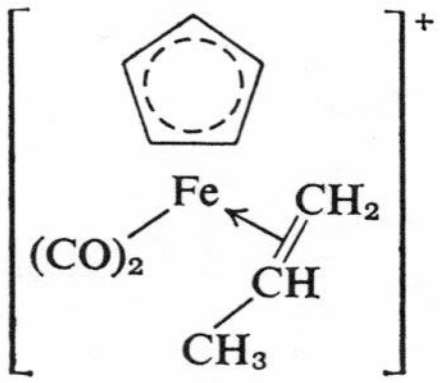 [(C₅H₅)(CO)₂Fe←(CH₂=CHCH₃)]⁺	Treatment with triphenylmethyl perchlorate	61, 62

32

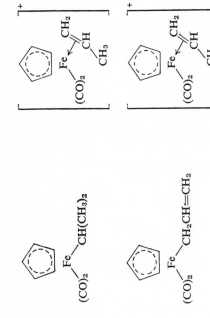

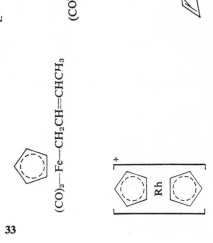

Treatment with triphenylmethyl perchlorate; reversed with NaBH$_4$ — 62

Gaseous HCl or dilute HCl — 79

Gaseous HCl or dilute HCl — 79

Treatment with phenyllithium — 77

33

TABLE II (continued)

Initial compound	Final compound	Reaction conditions	How followed[a]	Ref.
$[(\pi\text{-}C_2H_4)_2RhCl]_2$	$C_2H_5(\pi\text{-}C_2H_4)RhCl_2$	Gaseous HCl in CH_3OD[b]		80
$\pi\text{-}C_5H_5(\pi\text{-}C_2H_4)_2Rh$[1]	$\pi\text{-}C_5H_5Rh^{III}(\pi\text{-}C_2H_4)Cl$ C_2H_5	Gaseous HCl at $-60°$ in chloroform[b]		80
$[\pi\text{-}C_2H_4)_2RhCl]_2$	$Cs[C_2H_5RhCl_3H_2O]$	Loss of C_2H_4 in 1 M methanolic HCl		80
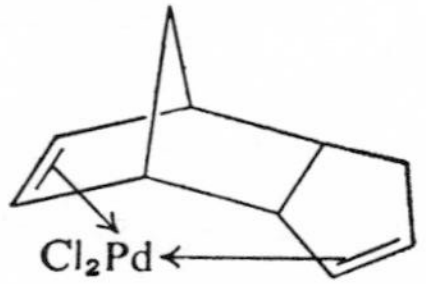	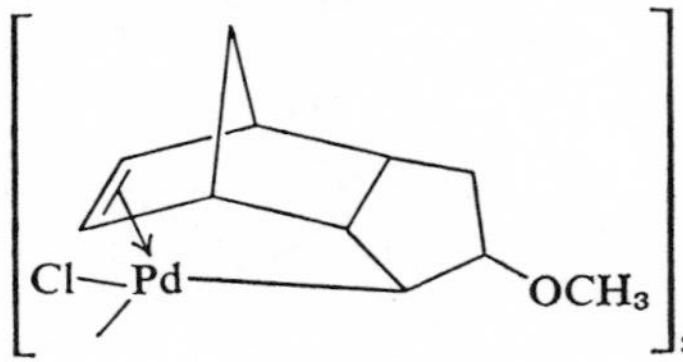	MeOH–Na_2CO_3 treatment; reversible on addition of concentrated HCl		68
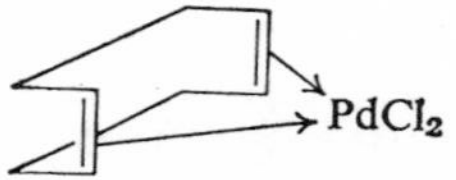	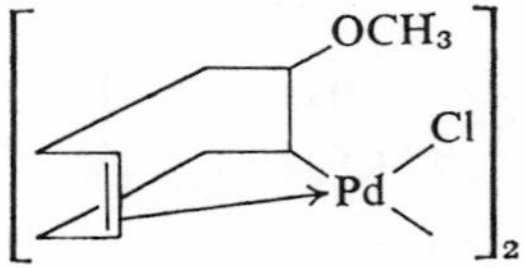	MeOH–Na_2CO_3 treatment; reversible on addition of concentrated HCl		69
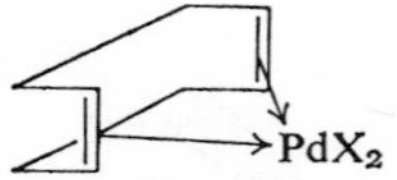 $(X = Cl, Br, I)$	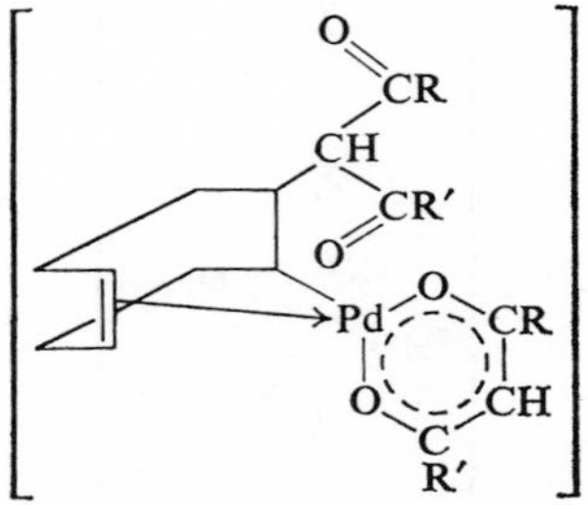 $(R = CH_3, C_6H_5; R' = CH_3, C_6H_5)$	Treatment with Tl^+ [RCOCHCOR']$^-$		71, 81

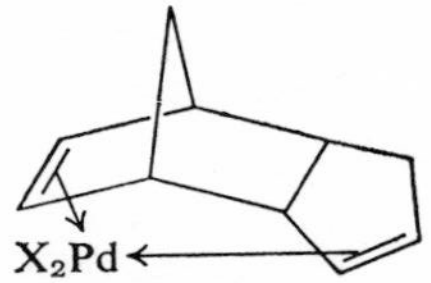

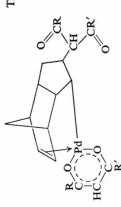

X₂Pd → X_2Pd

$(X = Cl, Br, I)$

Treatment with Tl⁺ [RCOCHOR']⁻   71, 81

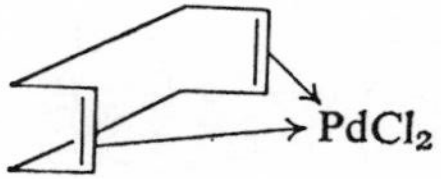

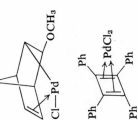

$(R = CH_3, C_6H_5; R' = CH_3, C_6H_5)$

Treatment with $CH_2(COOEt)_2$ and Na_2CO_3 70

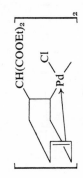

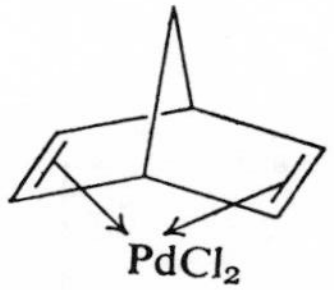

Treatment with NaOMe   73

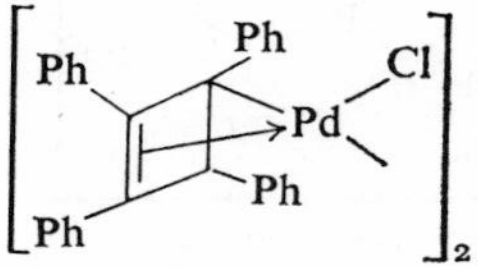

Treatment with HCl   74

TABLE II (continued)

Initial compound	Final compound	Reaction conditions	How followed[a]	Ref.
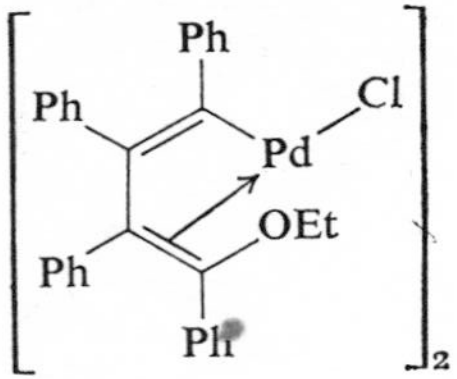 [structure: Ph₄-cyclobutadiene Pd–Cl with OEt]₂	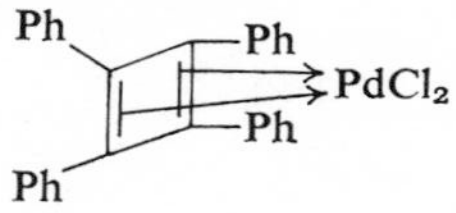 [structure: Ph₄-cyclobutadiene → PdCl₂]	Treatment with HCl		75
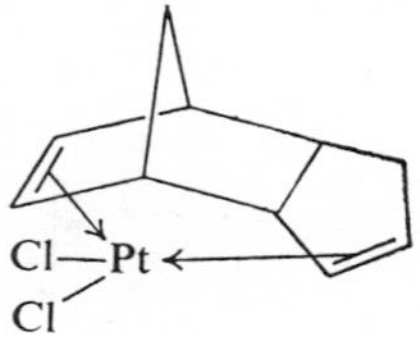 [Pt complex structure with Cl, Cl]	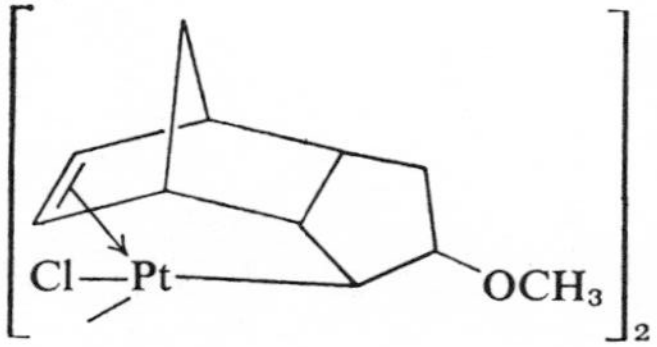 [Pt complex structure with OCH₃]₂	Treatment with MeOH–NaOAc; reversible in boiling aqueous HCl		65, 67, 68
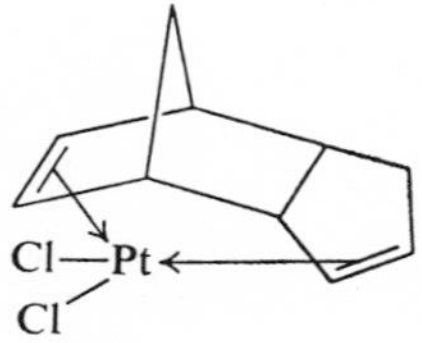 [Pt complex structure with Cl, Cl]	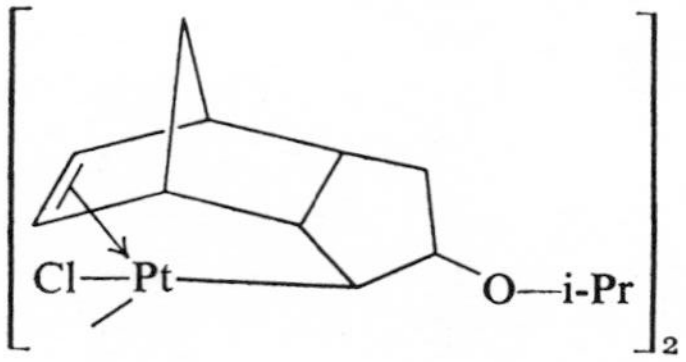 [Pt complex structure with O—i-Pr]₂	Treatment with 2-propanol		65
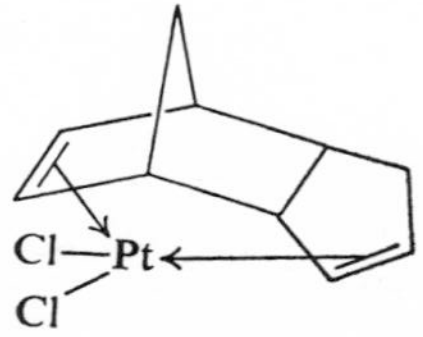 [Pt complex structure with Cl, Cl]	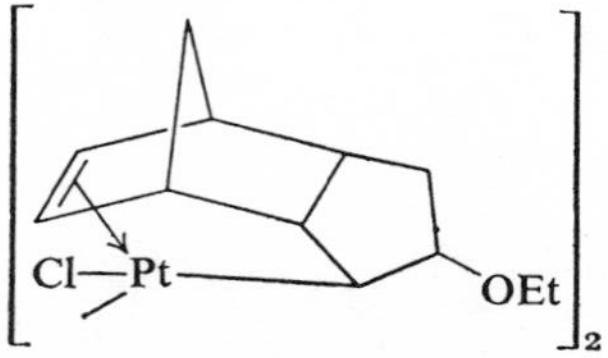 [Pt complex structure with OEt]₂	Boiling ethanol		68

36

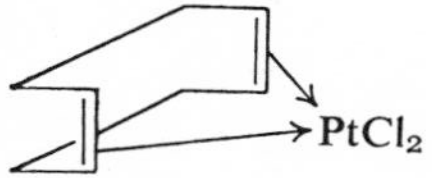	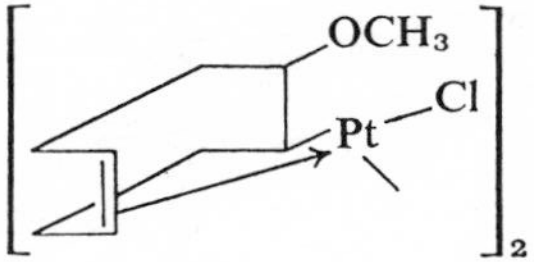	Boiling methanol in presence of anhydrous Na_2CO_3	65, 68
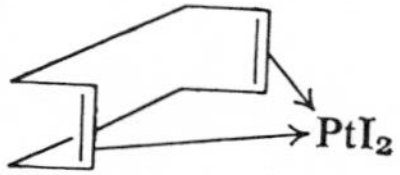	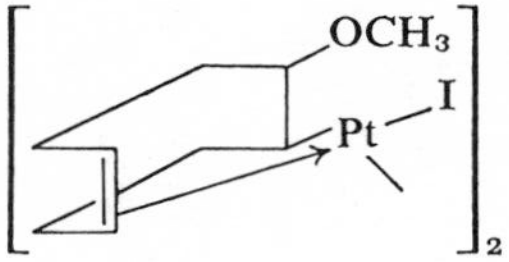	Boiling methanol	65
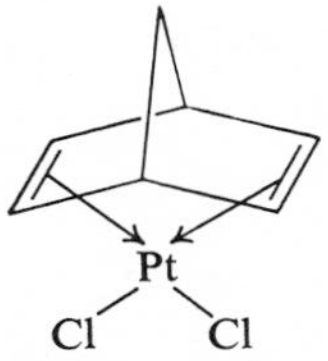	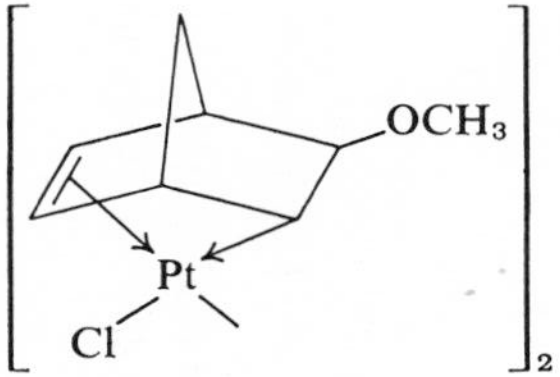	In boiling $MeOH-Na_2CO_3$	65, 68
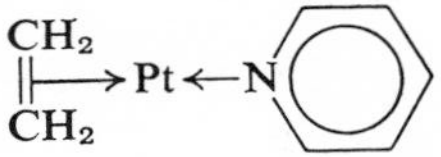	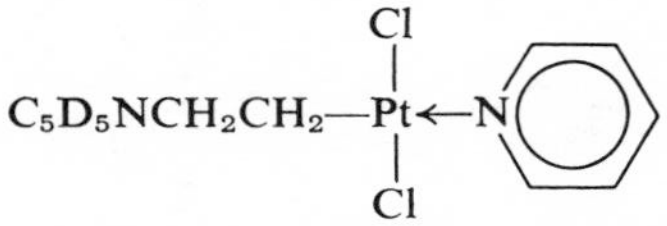	Addition of deuteropyridine to chloroform solution at $-50°$[b]	82

[a] Unless otherwise indicated, the reaction was followed by isolation and characterization of σ- and π-compounds.
[b] Reaction was followed by NMR studies.

37

A. Ziegler–Natta Polymerization

In 1963 Ziegler and Natta were awarded the Nobel Prize in Chemistry for their contribution to olefin polymerization.[83,84] A catalyst consisting of a transition-metal halide (e.g., $TiCl_4$) and a nontransition-metal alkyl [e.g., $Al(C_2H_5)_3$][85,86] readily polymerizes olefins. Initially alkylation of the transition-metal halide occurs to give (37). Formation of a π-complex (38) between the olefin and the organotransition-metal compound occurs and is followed by insertion of the olefin into the metal alkyl σ-bond in (39). Repetition of this process leads to a growing polymer unit (40).

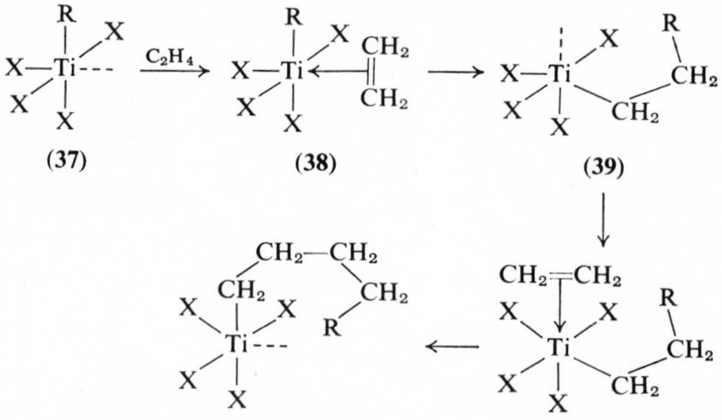

B. The Wacker Process

The oxidation of olefins to aldehydes by using a palladium chloride–copper(II) chloride catalyst (the Wacker process) is given by the general mechanism in reaction (13).

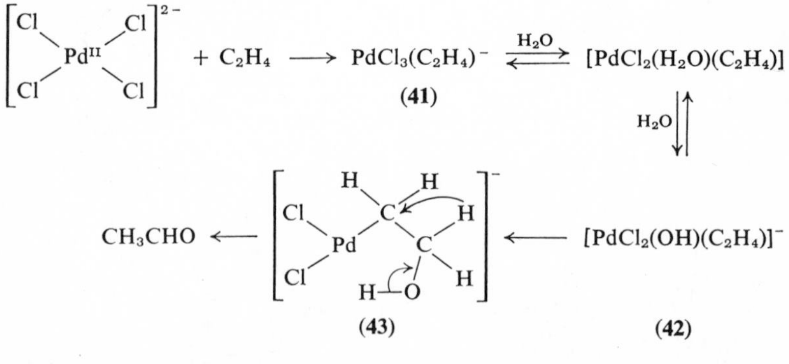

$$\text{(13)}$$

Initially a π-olefin complex (41) is probably formed. Substitution of a water molecule for a chloride ion occurs and is followed by elimination of

H^+ to give the π-olefin hydroxy complex (42). Subsequent migration of the coordinated OH^- group gives a σ-bonded β-hydroxy compound (43), which undergoes a hydride shift with rearrangement and elimination of acetaldehyde.[87-90]

C. The Oxo Reaction

The catalytic addition of hydrogen and carbon monoxide to olefins to give higher alcohols (usually C_6–C_9) via the aldehyde constitutes the commercially important hydroformylation, or oxo, reaction:

$$RCH{=}CH_2 + CO + H_2 \longrightarrow RCH_2CH_2CHO \qquad (14)$$

It is usually carried out at high pressures and temperatures with a cobalt catalyst.

On the basis of spectroscopic data, the first step in the reaction has been postulated as involving the addition of cobalt hydridotetracarbonyl to olefins.[91] Late work, however, by Karapinka and Orchin[92] and by Heck and Breslow[93] led the latter authors to conclude[93] that the addition to the olefin involves cobalt hydridotricarbonyl (44), which forms a π-complex by an essentially S_N1 type of reaction. The π-complex then rearranges to an alkylcobalt tricarbonyl (45). Compound (45) then reacts with carbon monoxide to give an alkylcobalt tetracarbonyl (46), which is in equilibrium with the acylcobalt tricarbonyl (47). Compound (47) is then reduced by cobalt hydridocarbonyl or molecular hydrogen to the aldehyde.

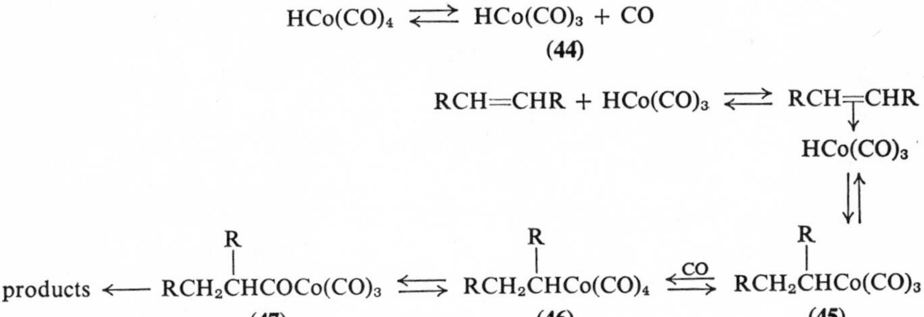

$$HCo(CO)_4 \rightleftarrows HCo(CO)_3 + CO$$
$$(44)$$

$$RCH{=}CHR + HCo(CO)_3 \rightleftarrows \underset{\underset{HCo(CO)_3}{|}}{RCH{-}CHR}$$

$$\text{products} \longleftarrow \underset{(47)}{\overset{R}{\underset{|}{RCH_2CHCOCo(CO)_3}}} \rightleftarrows \underset{(46)}{\overset{R}{\underset{|}{RCH_2CHCo(CO)_4}}} \overset{CO}{\underset{}{\rightleftarrows}} \underset{(45)}{\overset{R}{\underset{|}{RCH_2CHCo(CO)_3}}}$$

D. Carbonylation of Acetylene

Closely allied to the hydroformylation reaction are the carbonylation of acetylenes[94] and the rearrangements of alkenoylcobalt carbonyls.[95]

The reaction of acetylene with acylcobalt involves the formation of a π-complex (48), followed by addition across the triple bond by a cobalt carbonyl bond to the σ-complex (49). Reaction with, (50), and then insertion

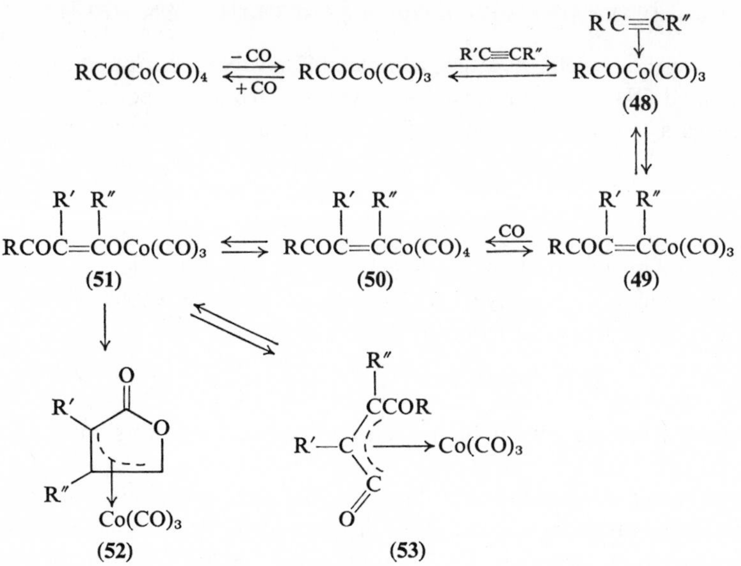

(48) (49) (50) (51) (52) (53)

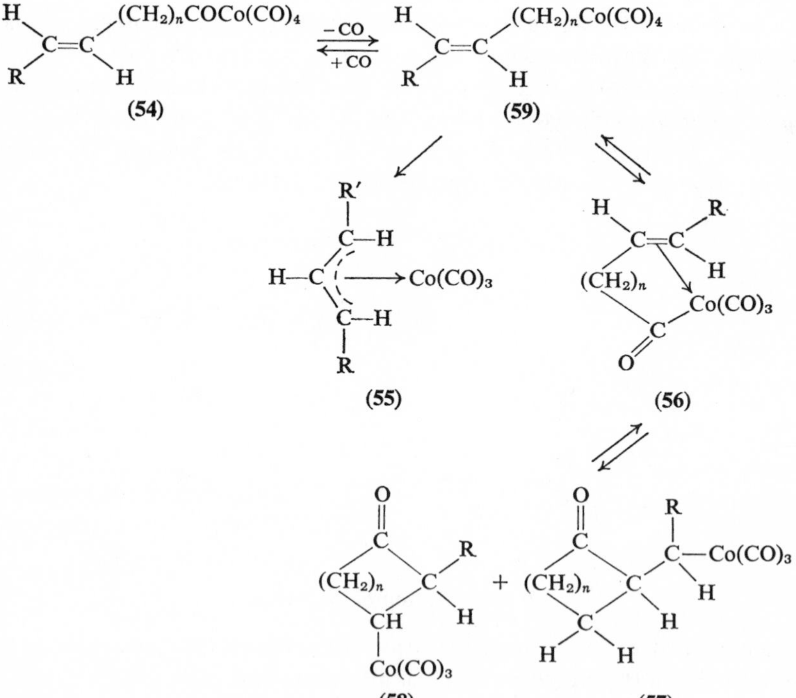

(54) (59) (55) (56) (58) (57)

by, (51), carbon monoxide occurs, and finally rearrangement gives the π-allyl type of system in (52) and (53).[94] A similar rearrangement is postulated for the thermal decomposition of alkenoylcobalt tetracarbonyl (54). In dilute ethereal solution (54) decomposes to several products, including π-allylcobalt tricarbonyl (55), π-alkylenylcobalt tricarbonyl (56), and the σ-bonded complexes (57) and (58). The formation of a σ-bonded tetracarbonyl (59) is postulated as occurring initially.[95]

E. Catalytic Hydrogenation

The catalytic hydrogenation of unsaturated compounds has attracted extensive interest in recent years.[96] Numerous complexes have been found to activate molecular hydrogen in solution and under homogeneous conditions to catalyze the hydrogenation of olefins. Complex mechanisms are involved, and each metal has its eccentricities, but a σ–π rearrangement has clearly been shown to operate in some cases. One such case is the homogeneous catalysis of activated olefins, such as maleic, fumaric, and acrylic acids, by ruthenium(II) chloride. The reaction proceeds via the formation of the π-olefin ruthenium hydride complex (60), with subsequent insertion of the olefin into the metal hydride bond to produce a σ-alkyl compound (61). The hydrogenation is completed by an electrophilic attack on the metal-bonded carbon atom by a proton.[96]

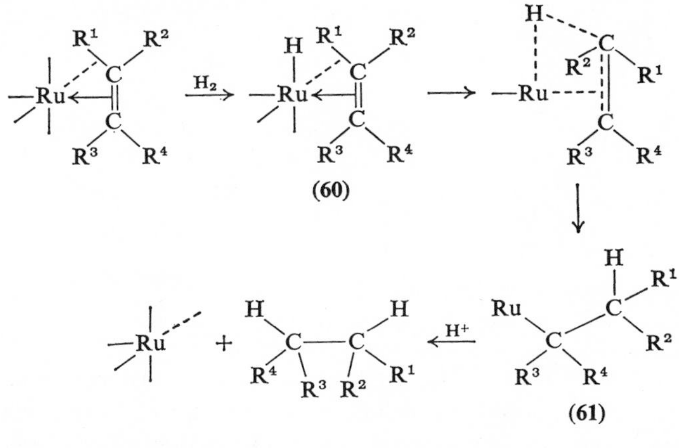

A similar mechanism has been proposed for the catalytic hydration of unsaturated compounds. The catalytic hydration of acetylenic compounds by ruthenium(III) chloride involves the formation of a π-intermediate (62), followed by insertion of the acetylene across the metal–oxygen bond to give the σ-bonded compound (63), which then rearranges to ruthenium chloride and a ketone.[97]

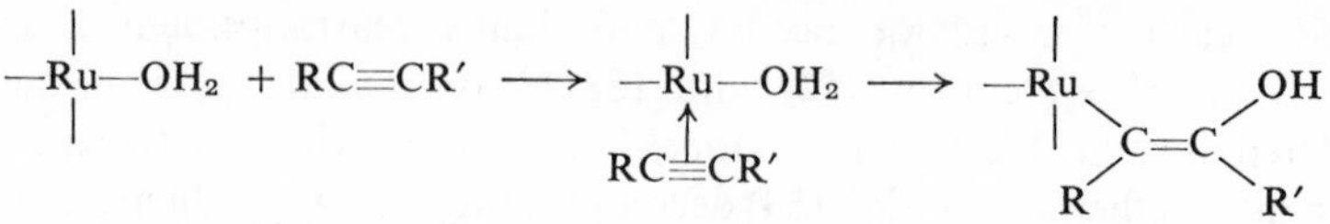

$$(62) \qquad\qquad (63)$$

F. Oligomerization

Related to the polymerization and hydrogenation of olefins is the oligo-merization of unsaturated compounds catalyzed by transition-metal com-plexes. A four-step cyclic mechanism is proposed for the rhodium chloride–catalyzed dimerization of ethylene to linear butenes. Initially protonation of a bis(ethylene)rhodium(I) complex occurs to give an ethylrhodium(III) com-pound, which then rearranges in the rate-determining step to a butylrho-dium(III) compound. The latter collapses to butene and rhodium(I), which then undergoes ethylene coordination to give the starting π-ethylenerhodium complex.[80] Allene is dimerized by bubbling it into a methanolic solution of sodium chloropalladite(II), giving di-μ-chloro-di-[β-(3-chloroprop-1-en-2-yl) allyl]dipalladium (64). This undergoes a π–σ rearrangement, which is followed by allene insertion into the palladium–carbon σ-bond.[98]

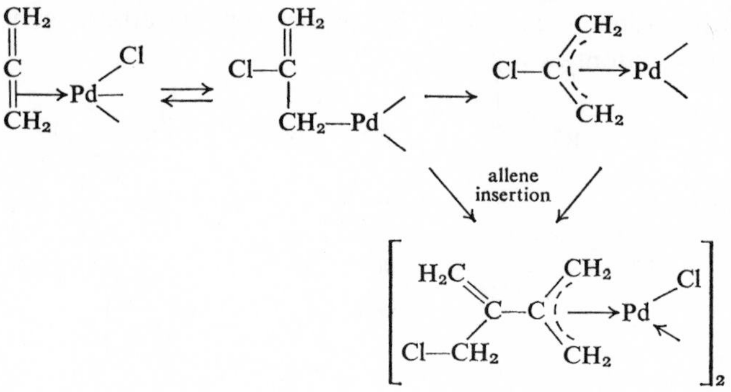

$$(64)$$

G. Double-Bond Migration

Another general field of homogeneous catalysis is that involving double-bond migration in long-chain olefins. As in the case of hydrogenation, the mechanism varies with the metal, but several reaction schemes involving a σ–π mechanism have been proposed. These involve the initial metal–olefin complex formation of a metal-hydride intermediate. Addition of the olefin to the metal-hydride bond gives a σ-bonded alkylmetal compound, which finally rearranges to an isomeric olefin and the metal hydride. With normal olefins the isomerization is catalyzed, for example, by hydrated rhodium(III) chloride and bisbenzonitrilepalladium(II) chloride.[99]

A survey of migration and insertion reactions is presented in Table III.

V. OTHER σ-π REARRANGEMENTS

A. Oligomerization of Acetylenes

Nickel complexes can cause the oligomerization of acetylenes; these reactions differ from the oligomerizations discussed in the preceding sections in that an initial π–σ rearrangement is proposed to proceed without either reaction occurring on the coordinated acetylene or attack on the metal. Initial formation of a π-complex (**65**) is postulated, and this undergoes an oxidative addition to the nickel, giving a σ-compound (**66**). The oligomers, cyclic or linear, are then formed by the π-complexation of further acetylene and subsequent ligand migration.[111,112]

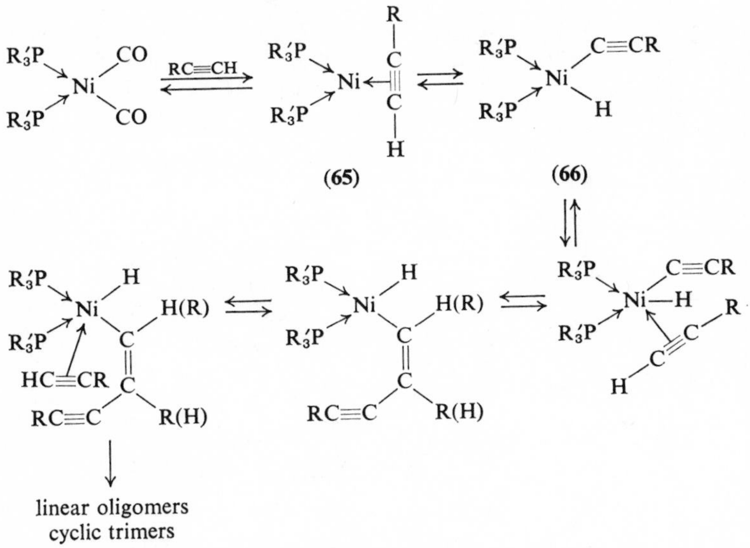

linear oligomers
cyclic trimers

B. Coupling Reactions

In 1914 Bennett and Turner obtained biphenyl from the reaction of phenylmagnesium halide and chromium(III) chloride.[113] This was the first recognized instance of a coupling reaction, the very general reaction occurring between Grignard reagents and organic halides, induced by a polyvalent transition-metal complex either in catalytic or stoichiometric amounts (compared with the organic compound). Mechanistically the coupling reactions have been a source of considerable debate.[114,115]

In 1921 Hein isolated phenylchromium complexes from the reaction used by Bennett and Turner but under milder conditions.[116] With the elucidation

TABLE III
Migration or Insertion Reactions

Initial compound	Final compound	Reaction conditions	How followed[a]	Ref.
Group IVA				
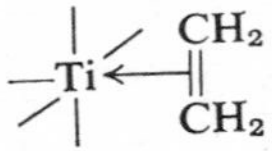 $-Ti\overset{CH_2}{\underset{CH_2}{\cdots}}$	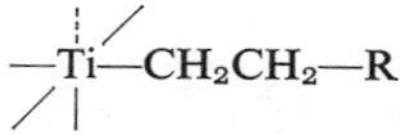 $-Ti-CH_2CH_2-R$	Ziegler–Natta polymerization of olefins	A–D	71, 83, 84, 86
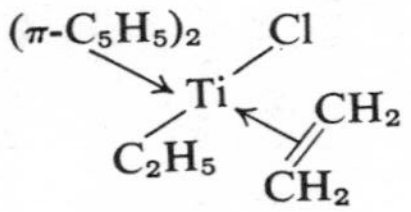 $(\pi-C_5H_5)_2\underset{C_2H_5}{\overset{Cl}{Ti}}\overset{CH_2}{\underset{CH_2}{\parallel}}$	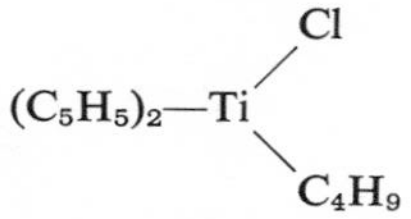 $(C_5H_5)_2-\underset{C_4H_9}{\overset{Cl}{Ti}}$	Treatment of Cp_2TiCl_2- $EtAlCl_2$ with ethylene under pressure	C	100
Group VIII				
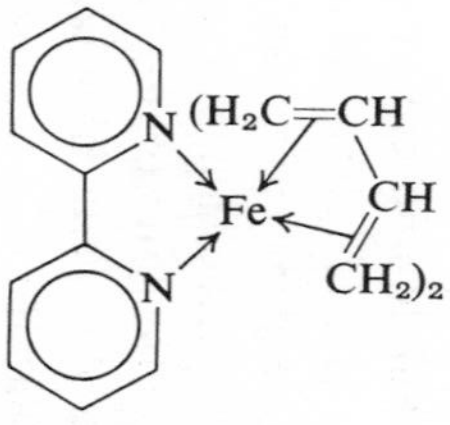 $(H_2C=CH-CH \cdots CH_2)_2 \to Fe$ with dipyridyl N,N	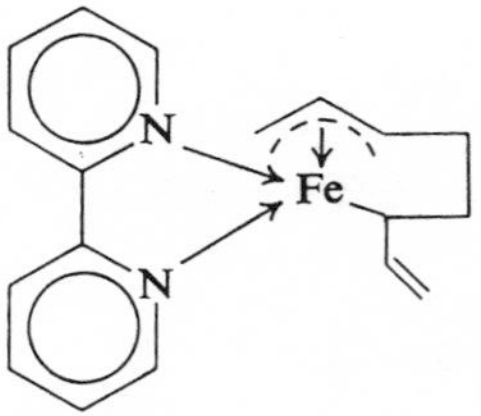 Fe with vinyl and $(CH_2)_n$ coordination, dipyridyl	Butadiene cyclodimerization by $Et_2Fe(dipyridyl)_2$, $Fe(dipyridyl)_2$, $Fe(dipyridyl)_3$	C, D	101
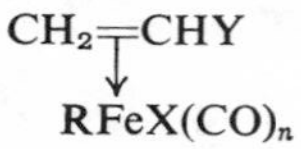 $CH_2=CHY \to RFeX(CO)_n$	$RCH_2CHY-FeX(CO)_n$	$Fe_2(CO)_9$ or $Fe_3(CO)_{12}$ in the presence of alkyl halides	C	102
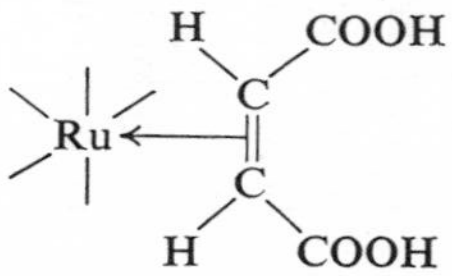 $\underset{H}{\overset{H}{C}}\text{COOH} = \underset{H}{\overset{H}{C}}\text{COOH} \to Ru$	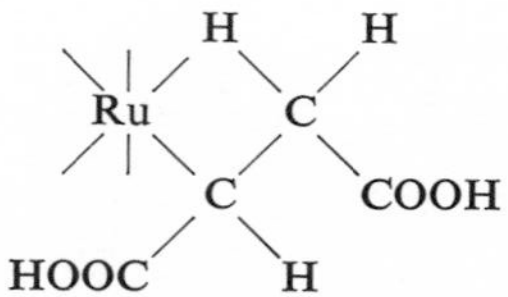 $\underset{H}{\overset{H}{C}}\text{COOH}, \underset{HOOC}{\overset{C}{H}}\to Ru$	Hydrogenation of maleic acid, catalyzed by ruthenium(II)	D	96

44

Reactant	Product	Conditions	Method	Ref.
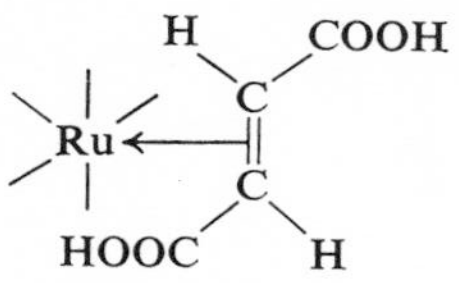 Ru complex: C=C with H, COOH / HOOC, H, arrow to Ru	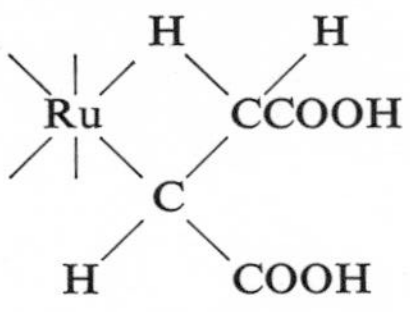 Ru complex: C with H, H, CCOOH, H, COOH	Hydrogenation of fumaric acid, catalyzed by ruthenium(II)	D	96
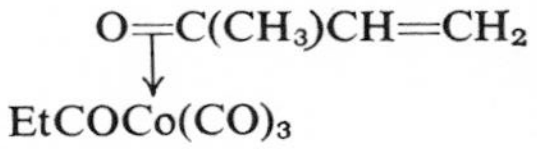 $O{=}C(CH_3)CH{=}CH_2$ $EtCOCo(CO)_3$	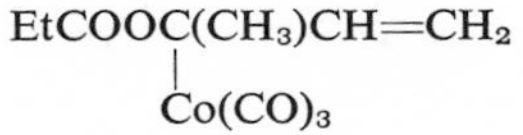 $EtOOC(CH_3)CH{=}CH_2$ $Co(CO)_3$	Reversible reaction between $NaCo(CO)_4$, methyl vinyl ketone, and ethyl iodide	C	79
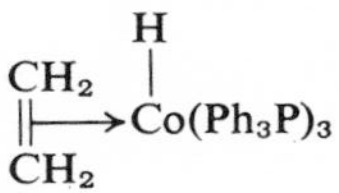 H, $CH_2{=}Co(Ph_3P)_3$, CH_2	$C_2H_5Co(Ph_3P)_3$	Reaction of ethylene with $N_2CoH(Ph_3P)_3$ at room temperature for 32 hr	C	103
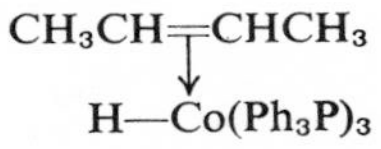 $CH_3CH{=}CHCH_3$ $Co(Ph_3P)_3$	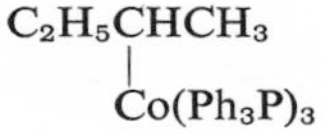 $CH_3CH{-}CHCH_3$ $H{-}Co(Ph_3P)_3$	Reaction of ethylene with $N_2CoH(Ph_3P)_3$ at room temperature for 32 hr	C	103
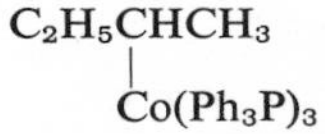 $C_2H_5CHCH_3$ $Co(Ph_3P)_3$	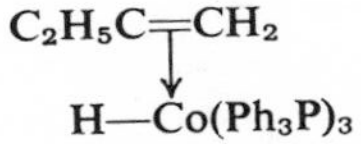 $C_2H_5C{=}CH_2$ $H{-}Co(Ph_3P)_3$	Reaction of ethylene with $N_2CoH(Ph_3P)_3$ at room temperature for 32 hr	C	103
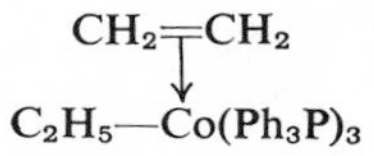 $CH_2{=}CH_2$ $Co(Ph_3P)_3$ C_2H_5	$C_2H_5CH_2CH_2Co(Ph_3P)_3$	Reaction of ethylene with $N_2CoH(Ph_3P)_3$ at room temperature for 32 hr	C	103
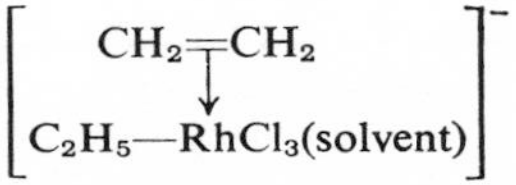 $\left[\begin{array}{c} CH_2{=}CH_2 \\ C_2H_5{-}RhCl_3(solvent) \end{array} \right]^{-}$	$[\sigma{-}C_4H_9RhCl_3(solvent)]$	Above $-10°$ in solution in presence of halide ion	A, D	80

TABLE III (continued)

Initial compound	Final compound	Reaction conditions	How followed[a]	Ref.
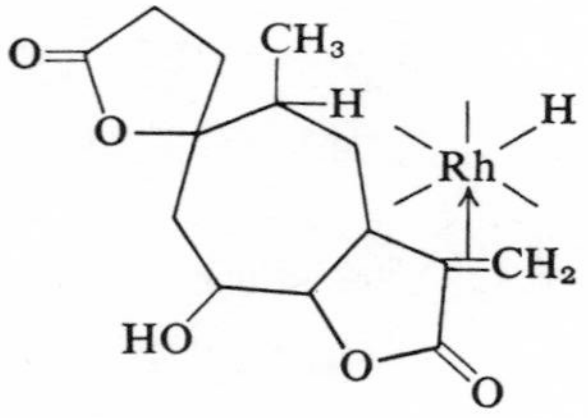 (CH₃, H) Rh←CH₂ tricyclic lactone structure with HO	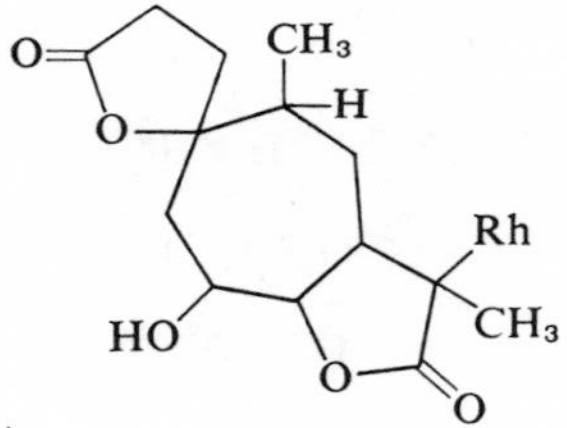 (CH₃, H) Rh, CH₃ tricyclic lactone structure with HO, O	Catalytic hydrogenation of psilostachyine by RhH₂Cl(PPh₃)₂	C	104
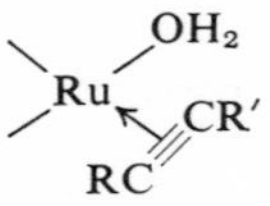 Ru structure with OH₂, RC≡CR'	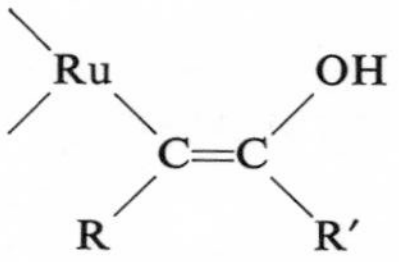 Ru structure with OH, C=C (R, R')	Catalytic hydration of acetylenic compounds by ruthenium(III) compounds	C	97
π-1-Pentene HCo(CO)₃	σ-Pentyl Co(CO)₃	Reaction of 1-pentene with HCo(CO)₄ under N₂	C	93
Et Et CH₃COC=C—Co(CO)₃	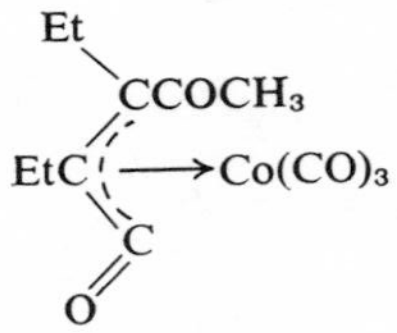 Et—CCOCH₃ , EtC→Co(CO)₃ bridged structure with C=O	Addition of 3-hexene to acetylcobalt tetracarbonyl (prepared "in situ")	C	94
EtC≡CEt → CH₃COCo(CO)₃	Et Et CH₃COC=CCo(CO)₃	Addition of 3-hexyne to acetylcobalt tetracarbonyl (prepared "in situ")	C	94

46

Structure		Method	Ref.
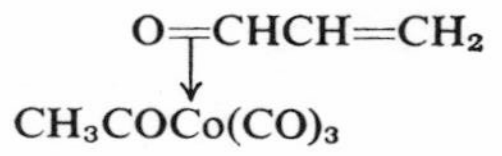 $O=CHCH=CH_2 \xrightarrow{} CH_3COCo(CO)_3$	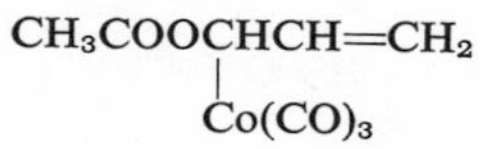 $\begin{array}{c} CH_3COOCHCH=CH_2 \\ \vert \\ Co(CO)_3 \end{array}$	Reversible reaction between $NaCo(CO)_4$, acrolein, and methyl iodide	*C*	79
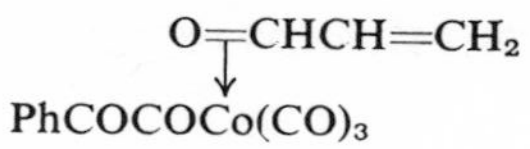 $O=CHCH=CH_2 \xrightarrow{} PhCOCoCo(CO)_3$	 $\begin{array}{c} PhCOOCHCH=CH_2 \\ \vert \\ Co(CO)_3 \end{array}$	Reversible reaction between $NaCo(CO)_4$, acrolein, and methyl iodide	*C*	79
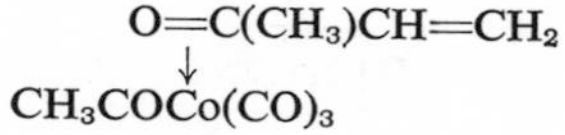 $O=C(CH_3)CH=CH_2 \xrightarrow{} CH_3COCo(CO)_3$	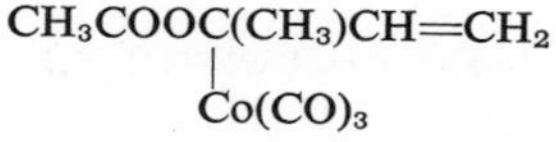 $\begin{array}{c} CH_3COOC(CH_3)CH=CH_2 \\ \vert \\ Co(CO)_3 \end{array}$	Reversible reaction between $NaCo(CO)_4$, methyl vinyl ketone, and methyl iodide	*C*	79

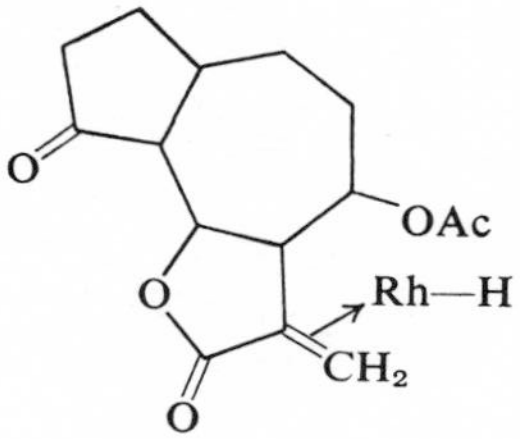

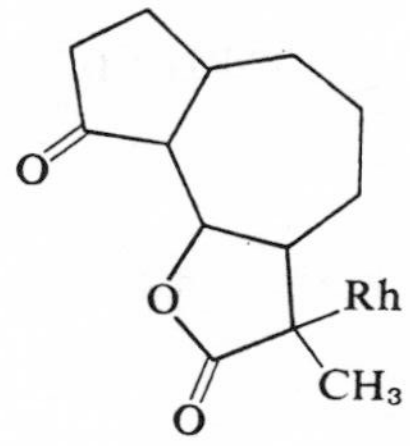

Catalytic hydrogenation of confetiflorin by $RhH_2Cl(PPh_3)_2$ — *C* — 104

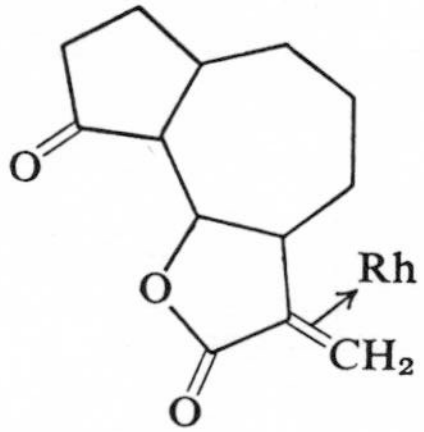

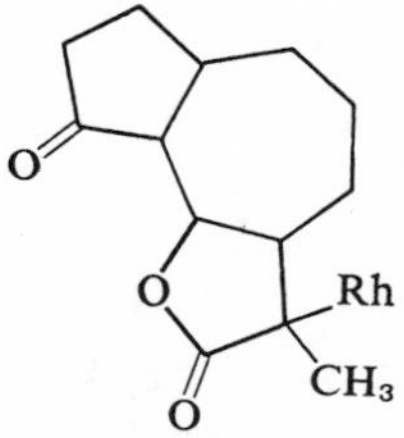

Isomerization of damsin to isodamsin by $RhH_2Cl(PPh_3)_2$ — *C* — 104

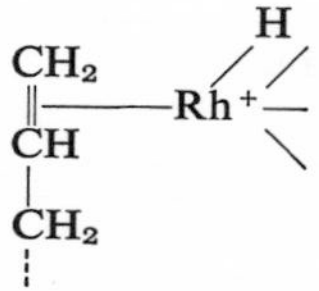

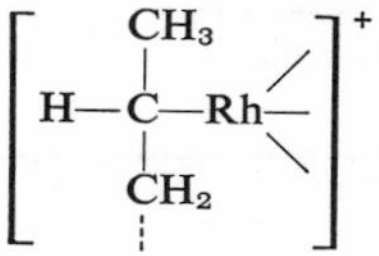

Reversible isomerization of normal olefins by hydrated rhodium(III) chloride or rhodium heptanoate — *C, D* — 99

TABLE III (continued)

Initial compound	Final compound	Reaction conditions	How followed[a]	Ref.
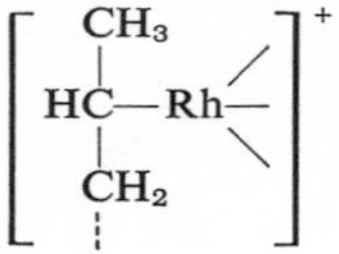 $\left[\begin{array}{c}CH_3\\HC-Rh-CH_2\cdots\end{array}\right]^+$	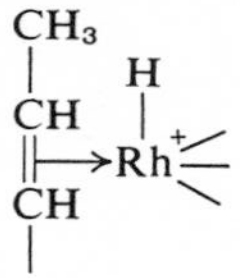 $\begin{array}{c}CH_3\\CH-H\\CH{\Rightarrow}Rh^+\end{array}$	Reversible isomerization of normal olefins by hydrated rhodium(III) chloride or rhodium heptanoate	C, D	99
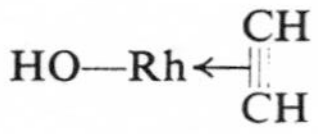 $HO-Rh\leftarrow\overset{CH}{\underset{CH}{\parallel}}$	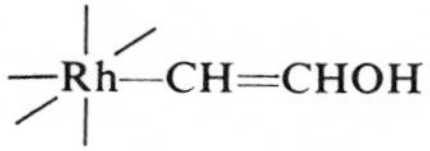 $Rh-CH{=}CHOH$	Hydration of acetylene catalyzed by $RhCl_3\cdot3H_2O$ in 3 M HCl at 50–65°	B, D	105
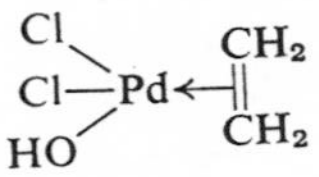 $\begin{array}{c}Cl\\Cl-Pd\leftarrow\overset{CH_2}{\underset{CH_2}{\parallel}}\\HO\end{array}$	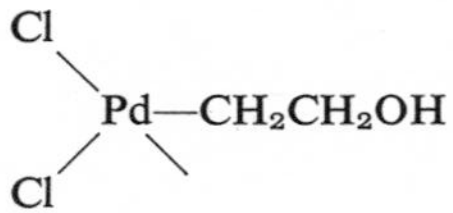 $\begin{array}{c}Cl\\Pd-CH_2CH_2OH\\Cl\end{array}$	Wacker oxidation of olefins	A–D	87–89
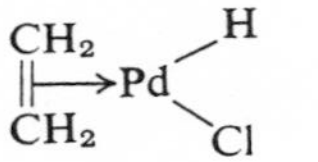 $\begin{array}{c}H\\CH_2{\Rightarrow}Pd\\CH_2\quad Cl\end{array}$	CH_3CH_2PdCl	Heating ethylene and SO_2 in the presence of a benzene suspension of $PdCl_2$	C	106
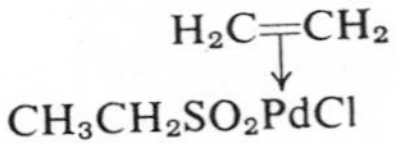 $\begin{array}{c}H_2C{=}CH_2\\CH_3CH_2SO_2PdCl\end{array}$	$CH_3CH_2SO_2CH_2CH_2PdCl$	Heating ethylene and SO_2 in the presence of a benzene suspension of $PdCl_2$	C	106
$CH_3CH_2SO_2CH_2CH_2PdCl$	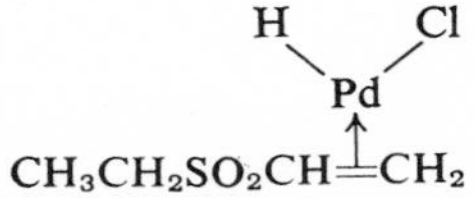 $\begin{array}{c}H\quad Cl\\Pd\\{\leftarrow}CH_2{=}CH_2\\CH_3CH_2SO_2CH{=}CH_2\end{array}$	Heating ethylene and SO_2 in the presence of a benzene suspension of $PdCl_2$	C	106

48

Structure	Conditions		Ref.
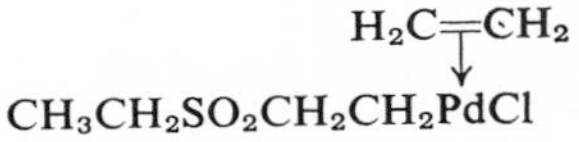 $\underset{\downarrow}{H_2C=CH_2}$ $CH_3CH_2SO_2CH_2CH_2PdCl$ $CH_3CH_2SO_2CH_2CH_2CH_2CH_2PdCl$	Heating ethylene and SO_2 in the presence of a benzene suspension of $PdCl_2$	C	106
$CH_3CH_2SO_2(CH_2)_4PdCl$ $\overset{H—Pd—Cl}{\underset{\downarrow}{CH_3CH_2SO_2CH_2CH_2CH=CH_2}}$	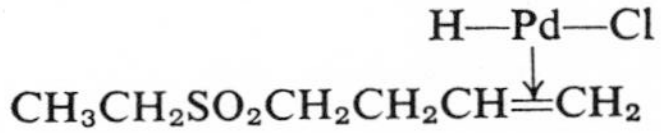 Heating ethylene and SO_2 in the presence of a benzene suspension of $PdCl_2$	C	106
$\overset{Pd—Cl}{\underset{\mid}{CH_3CH_2SO_2CH_2CH_2CHCH_3}}$ $CH_3—CH_2SO_2CH_2CH_2CH\overset{H—Pd—Cl}{=}CH_2$	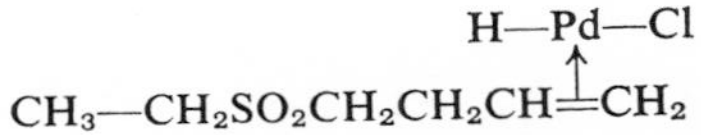 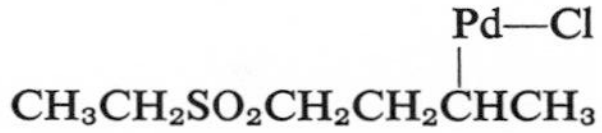 Heating ethylene and SO_2 in the presence of a benzene suspension of $PdCl_2$	C	106
$\begin{array}{l} CH_2Cl \\ \mid \\ CH \\ \parallel \\ CH \quad Cl \\ \mid \quad \mid \\ CH_2CO—Pd(CO)_x \end{array}$ $\left[\begin{array}{c} CH_2Cl \\ \mid \\ CH \\ \mid \\ CH \end{array} \;\; Pd—Cl \;\; CH_2 \right]_2$	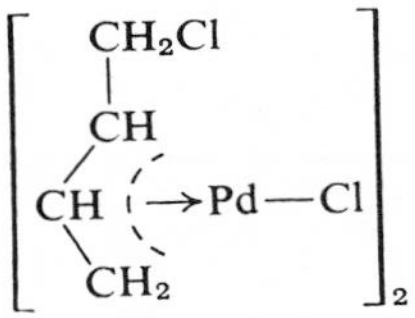 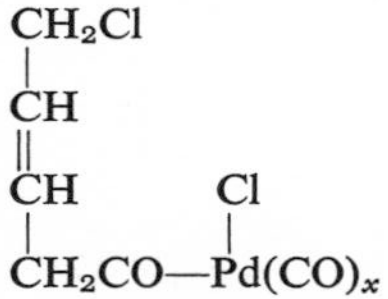 Treatment of Pd complex in benzene with CO at room temperature	C	107
$\begin{array}{c} CH_2 \\ \parallel \\ Cl—C \qquad CH_2—Pd— \end{array}$ $\begin{array}{c} CH_2 \\ \parallel \quad Cl \\ CH_2 \; Pd \\ \parallel \quad \mid \\ C \\ \parallel \\ CH_2 \end{array}$	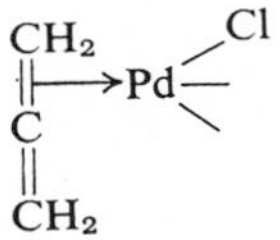 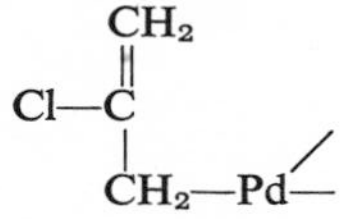 Reaction of allene with Na_2PdCl_4 in MeOH or $PdCl_2$ (benzonitrile)$_2$ in benzene	C	97
$\begin{array}{c} CH_2 \\ \mid \\ Cl—C \overset{\cdots}{\underset{\cdots}{}} Pd \\ \mid \\ CH_2 \end{array}$ $\begin{array}{c} CH_2 \\ \parallel \\ Cl—C \qquad CH_2—Pd \end{array}$	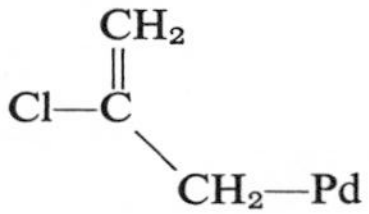 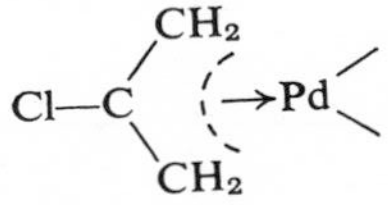 Reaction of allene with Na_2PdCl_4 in MeOH or $PdCl_2$ (benzonitrile)$_2$ in benzene	C	97
$\left[\begin{array}{c} CH_2 \\ \mid \\ H_2C=C—C \overset{\cdots}{\underset{\cdots}{}} Pd \\ \mid \quad\quad \mid \\ Cl—CH_2 \;\; CH_2 \end{array}\right]_2$ $\begin{array}{c} CH_2 \\ \parallel \\ H_2C=C \\ \mid \\ Cl—CH_2—Pd— \end{array}$	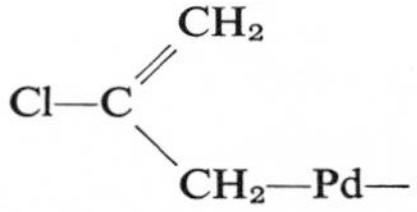 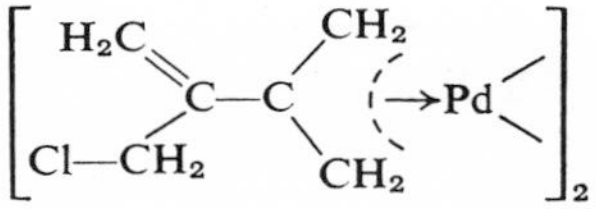 Reaction of allene with Na_2PdCl_4 in MeOH or $PdCl_2$ (benzonitrile)$_2$ in benzene	C	97

49

TABLE III (continued)

Initial compound	Final compound	Reaction conditions	How followed[a]	Ref.
$\left[\begin{array}{c} CH_2 \\ \| \\ CH_2 \end{array} \!\!\longrightarrow\! Rh \begin{array}{c} {-}CO \\ \\ Cl \end{array} \right]_2$	$[RhCl_2Et(CO)]_x$	Saturation with HCl	E	108
$RuCl_2(\pi\text{-}CH_2{=}CHCN)_3$	$RuCl_2(\sigma\text{-}CH_2{=}CHCN)$	In presence of amines $RuEt_2(CH_2{=}CHCN)_3$ catalyzes dimerization of acrylonitrile	C	109
π-Polyaromatic Pt complex	Pt-σ-Aromatic	Homogeneous exchange of isotopic hydrogen, catalyzed by Pt compounds	D	110

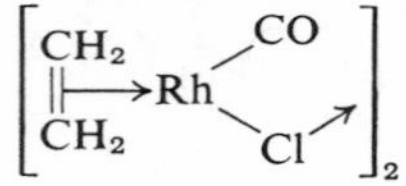

[a] Key: A = NMR studies; B = infrared studies; C = reduced from reaction products; D = degradation and kinetic studies; E = isolation and characterization of σ- and π-compounds.

of the structures of Hein's complexes,[1] and the isolation of a σ-bonded intermediate,[2] came the realization that the coupling reaction probably involves a σ–π rearrangement. Initially the σ-bonded compound is formed. The σ-bond cleaves homolytically to give a π-radical complex, which, under the vigorous conditions used, couples to give biphenyl and chromium. Under the milder conditions used by Hein the radical complex gives diarene complexes.[117]

The stoichiometric reaction of *cis-* or *trans*-stilbenemagnesium bromide and chromium(III) or cobalt(II) chloride in tetrahydrofuran at −30° gives *cis,cis*-1,2,3,4-tetraphenylbutadiene. However, the corresponding reaction with nickel or palladium chloride gives *trans,trans*-1,2,3,4-tetraphenylbutadiene. That is, metals that usually have octahedral coordination give *cis* coupling, whereas those that take a square planar form give *trans* coupling.[118] This can be explained by the formation of π-radical intermediates.

Vinyl Grignard reagents react with titanium(IV) halides to produce four compounds: 4-vinyl-1-cyclohexene, 2,6-octadiene, 3-methyl-1,5-heptadiene, and 3-methyl-1,4,6-heptatriene. Tetra-σ-vinyltitanium (**67**), is probably formed, and the vinyl groups then couple to give 1,3-butadiene π-radical (**68**) complexes. Final coupling of the butadiene complexes then occurs to give the organic products.[119]

$$TiCl_4 + 4CH_2{=}CHMgCl \longrightarrow (CH_2{=}CH)_4{-}Ti$$

(67)

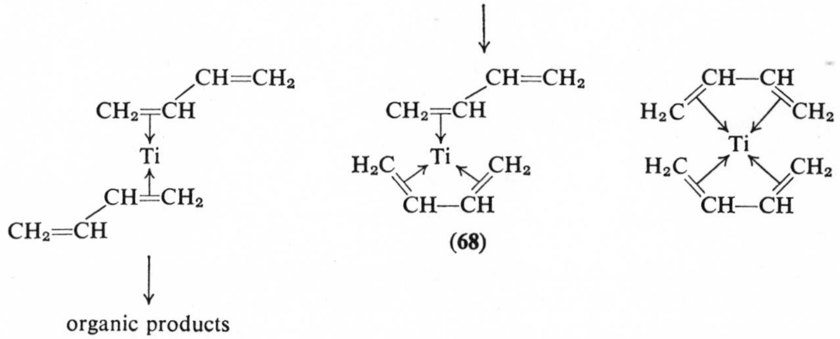

(68)

organic products

Corresponding to this stoichiometric coupling reaction of vinyl groups on titanium is the catalytic coupling of vinylmagnesium chloride by titanium(IV) chloride in the presence of ethyl bromide. The reaction products are 3-methyl-1,5-heptadiene and 3-methyl-1,4,6-heptatriene. The coupling probably involves the initial formation of tetra-σ-vinyltitanium, which undergoes radical hybridization and coupling. The ethyl bromide is required to react with activated titanium formed to give titanium bromide in a cycle.[119]

C. Cope Rearrangements

Cope rearrangements cover all processes of the following type, irrespective of mechanism:

$$A{=}B{-}C{-}C'{-}B{=}A' \longrightarrow C{=}B{-}A{-}A'{-}B'{=}C' \quad \text{or} \quad A{=}B{-}C{-}A'{-}B'{=}C'$$

(15)

These rearrangements can occur on thermal excitation, photolysis, acid catalysis, and by reaction with metal compounds in stoichiometric amounts.

The reaction of bisbenzonitrilepalladium(II) chloride with cis,trans-1,5-cyclodecadiene gives a palladium complex of 1,2-divinylcyclohexane (71). Initially a π-allylic complex (69) is postulated, followed by ring opening to give complex (70) or (72). Rearrangement of (70) then occurs, giving the σ-compound (73), which rearranges to (71).[120] A Cope rearrangement of cis-1,2-divinylcyclobutane catalyzed by nickel–phosphine complexes is reported to go via σ–π rearrangements.[121]

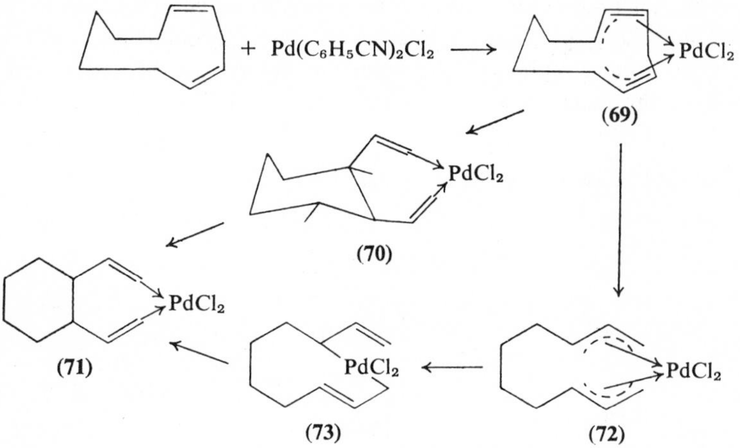

The mass spectra of unsaturated σ-bonded ligands show that rearrangement ions are produced and can best be rationalized by unique σ–π rearrangements.[122] Another type of rearrangement that has been reported involves a redistribution type of reaction between allylic metal complexes and metal complexes. Sodium tetracarbonylcobaltate (74) reacts with chloro-π-allyl-palladium (75) and with tricarbonyl-π-allylcobalt compounds to form π-allylpalladium dimers.[123] A possible mechanism for the formation of the π-allylcobalt derivative (79) involves the formation of a palladium–cobalt π-complexed intermediate (76), which then undergoes a 1,2 shift of the allyl group, probably via the σ-bonded intermediates (77) and (78). Evidence for the formation of the intermediate (76) comes from the isolation of π-1,1,2-

trimethyl-π-allylpalladium triphenylphosphinecobalt tetracarbonyl (81), from the reaction between chloro-1,1,2-trimethyl-π-allylpalladium dimer (80) and (74).

$$
\text{NaCo(CO)}_4 \;+\;
\begin{bmatrix}
\text{CH}_2 \\
\text{CH} \rightarrow \text{Pd} \diagdown \text{Cl} \\
\text{CH}_2
\end{bmatrix}_2
\;\longrightarrow\;
\begin{bmatrix}
\text{CH}_2 \\
\text{CH} \rightarrow \text{Pd} \diagup \text{Cl} \diagdown \text{Co(CO)}_4 \\
\text{CH}_2
\end{bmatrix}^-
$$

(74)   (75)   (76)

$$
\begin{bmatrix}
\text{CH}_2 \\
\text{CH} \rightarrow \text{Co(CO)}_3 \\
\text{CH}_2
\end{bmatrix}
\;\longleftarrow\;
\begin{bmatrix}
\text{Pd} \diagup \text{Cl} \diagdown \text{Co(CO)}_4 \\
\text{CH}_2 \\
\text{CH}-\text{CH}_2
\end{bmatrix}
\;\rightleftharpoons\;
\begin{bmatrix}
\text{CH}_2 \\
\text{CH} \diagdown \text{Pd} \diagup \text{Cl} \diagdown \text{Co(CO)}_4 \\
\text{CH}_2
\end{bmatrix}^-
$$

(79)   (78)   (77)

$$
\begin{bmatrix}
\text{H}_3\text{C}\diagdown \text{C} \diagup \text{CH}_3 \\
\text{CH}_3\text{C} \rightarrow \text{Pd} \diagdown \text{Cl} \\
\text{CH}_2
\end{bmatrix}_2
\;+\;(74)\;\xrightarrow{\;\text{P(C}_6\text{H}_5)_3\;}\;
\begin{array}{c}
\text{H}_3\text{C}\diagdown \text{C} \diagup \text{CH}_3 \\
\text{CH}_3\text{C} \rightarrow \text{Pd} \diagup \text{P(C}_6\text{H}_5)_3 \diagdown \text{Co(CO)}_4 \\
\text{CH}_2
\end{array}
$$

(80)   (81)

π-Allylic palladium and platinum halide complexes react with metallic mercury to give allylmercury halides. A reaction mechanism for π-allylpalladium chloride, for example, was suggested to involve the cleavage of the halide bridges in the dimeric molecule and a π–σ rearrangement of the π-allyl ligand, causing migration of the σ-bonded allyl group from palladium to the mercury atom.[124]

A survey of the reactions covered in this section is presented in Table IV.

As can be seen from the reactions outlined here, there remains a vast quantity of work to be done on the mechanisms involved in rearrangements, particularly with respect to the mode of cleavage of the σ- or π-bonds and with respect to the nature of any intermediates. There is also the possibility of further new mechanisms being discovered, as in the σ–π rearrangements observed during mass-spectral analysis of σ-bonded compounds.

TABLE IV

Coupling Reactions, Cope Rearrangements, and Other σ–π Rearrangements

Initial compound	Final compound	Reaction conditions	How followed[a]	Ref.
Group IV $(CH_2=CH)_2Ti$	$\left(\underset{Ti}{\overset{\rightarrow}{H_2C=CHCH=CH_2}} \right)_2$	Coupling of vinyl groups induced by titanium(IV) compounds either in stoichiometric or catalytic amounts	*A*	119
Group VI (Cr^{III} triphenyl)	(Cr with three phenyl radicals)	Coupling of phenyl groups induced by chromium(III) compounds	*A*	117
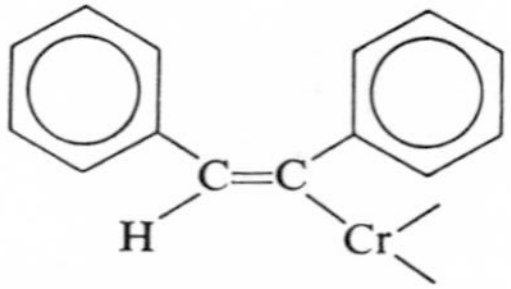 (diphenyl-vinylidene Cr)	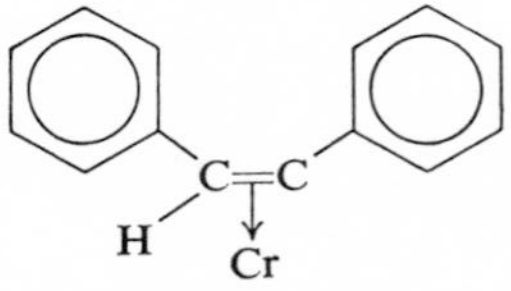 (phenyl–C=C(H)–Cr)	Stereospecific *cis* coupling of *cis*- or *trans*- stilbene by chromium(III) chloride	*A, B*	118
Group VIII (Fe(CO)₂ cyclopentadiene complex)	(ferrocene and diiron carbonyl dimer)	On heating	*C*	125

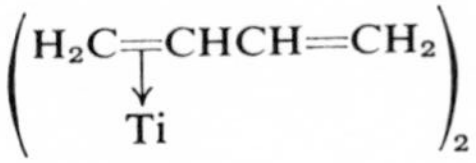

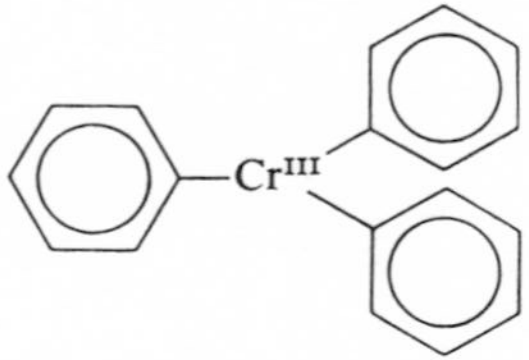

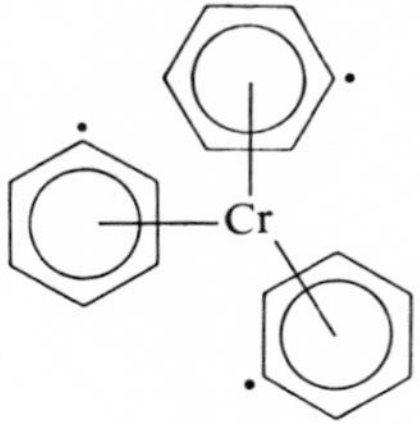

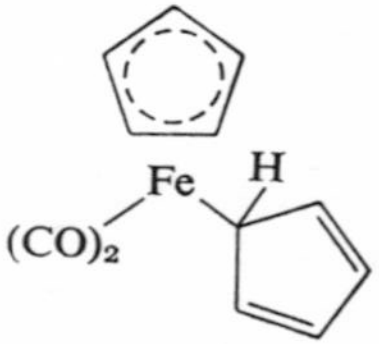

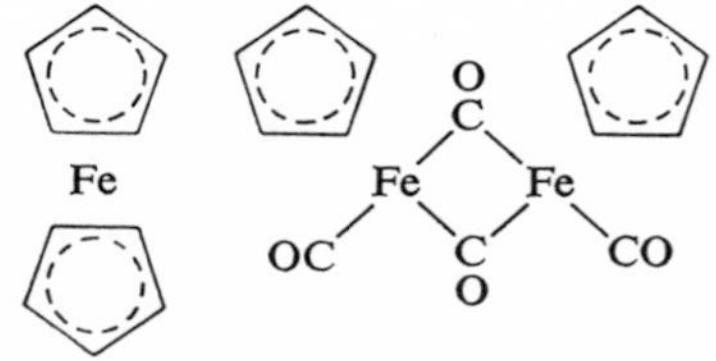

54

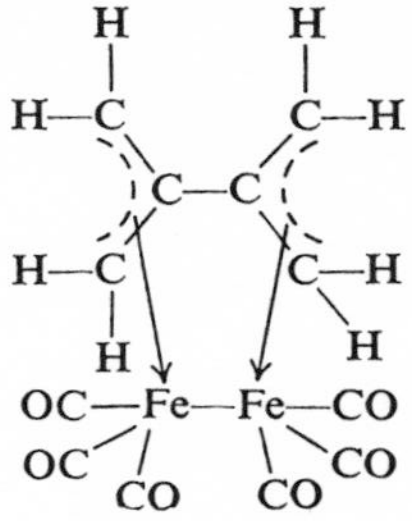

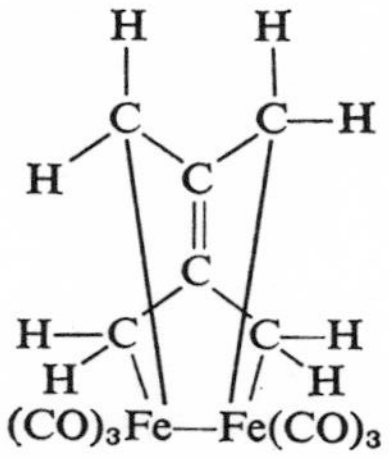

A σ–π equilibrium occurs in solution at $-10°$

D

126

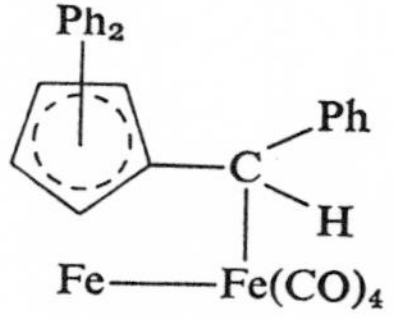

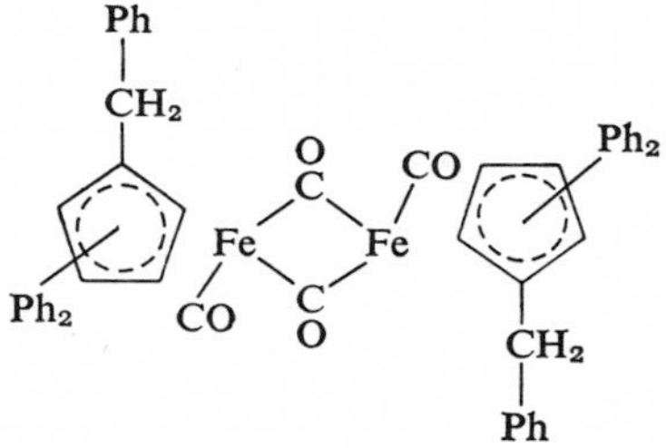

Disproportionation on heating

C

127

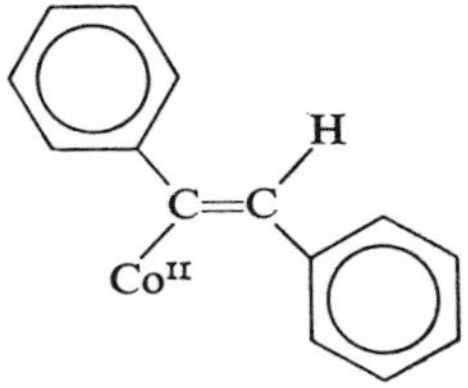

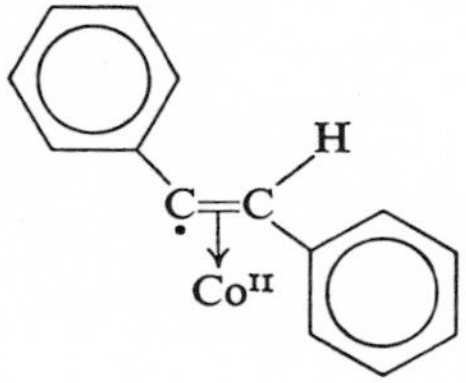

The stereospecific *cis* coupling of *cis* or *trans*-stilbene by cobalt(II) chloride

A, B

118

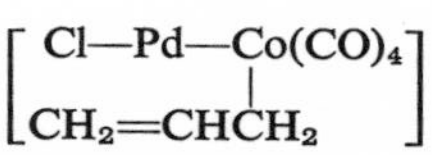

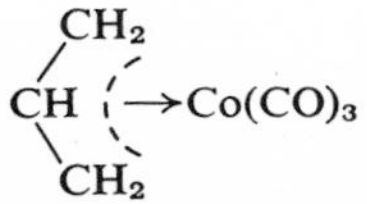

Reaction of $NaCo(CO)_4$ and π-allyl PdCl

A

123

55

TABLE IV (continued)

Initial compound	Final compound	Reaction conditions	How followed[a]	Ref.
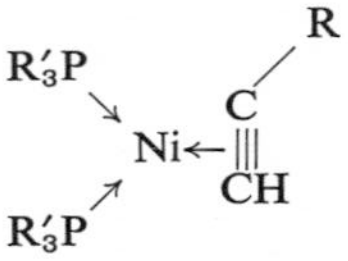 $R'_3P \rightarrow Ni \leftarrow$ (with $C \equiv CH$, R)	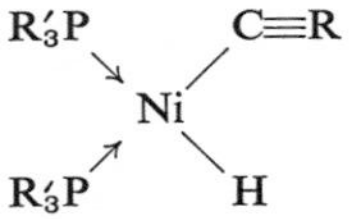 $R'_3P \rightarrow Ni \leftarrow C\equiv R$, H	Catalytic trimerization of acetylenes by $(R'_3P)_2Ni(CO)_2$ at 60–70°	A	111, 112
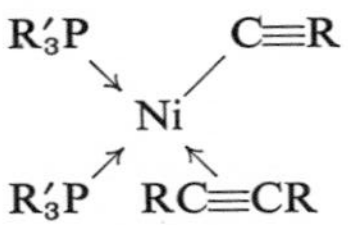 $R'_3P \rightarrow Ni \leftarrow C\equiv R$, $RC\equiv CR$	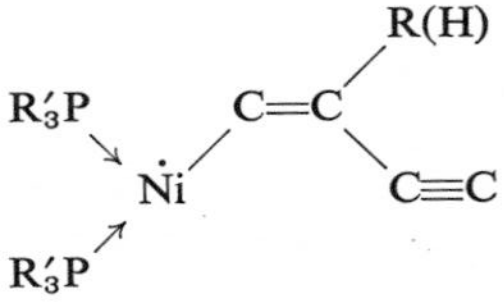 $R'_3P \rightarrow Ni \leftarrow C=C$, $R(H)$, $C\equiv C$	Catalytic trimerization of acetylenes by $(R'_3P)_2Ni(CO)_2$ at 60–70°	A	111, 112
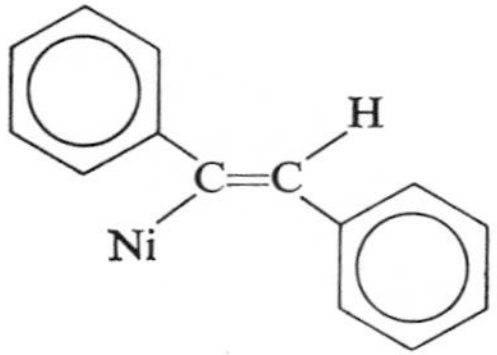 (diphenyl vinylidene–Ni complex)	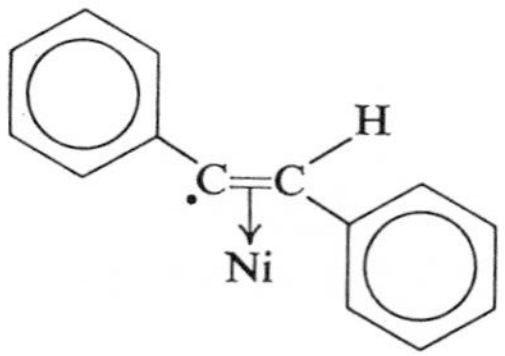 (diphenyl carbene–Ni complex)	Stereospecific *trans* coupling of *cis* or *trans*-stilbene by nickel(II) compounds	A, B	118
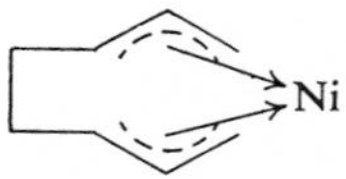 (divinylcyclobutane–Ni complex)	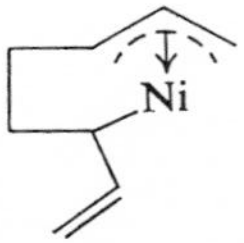 (vinyl cyclohexene–Ni complex)	Cope rearrangement of *cis*-1,2-divinylcyclobutane catalyzed by nickel tris(2-biphenylyl) phosphite, nickel triphenylphosphine, and nickel tricyclohexylphosphine complexes	A	121

56

		Cope rearrangement of *cis*-1,2-divinylcyclobutane catalyzed by nickel tris(2-biphenylyl) phosphite, nickel triphenylphosphine, and nickel tricyclohexylphosphine complexes	*A*	121
		Stereospecific *trans* coupling of *cis*- or *trans*-stilbene by palladium(II) compounds	*A, B*	118
		Cope rearrangement of *cis, trans*-cyclodecadi-1,5-ene induced by PdCl₂bis (benzonitrile)	*A*	120
	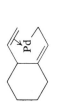	Cope rearrangement of *cis, trans*-cyclodecadi-1,5-ene induced by PdCl₂bis (benzonitrile)	*A*	120
		Reaction of NaCo(CO)₄ and [π-allyl PdCl]₂	*A*	123
		Reaction of [π-allyl PdCl]₂ and mercury	*A*	124

ᵃ Key: *A* = reduced from reaction products; *B* = degradation and kinetic studies; *C* = isolation and characterization of σ- and π-compounds; *D* = NMR studies.

VI. EXPERIMENTAL PROCEDURES

A. σ–π Rearrangements of Aryl Groups

1. *Preparation of Triphenylchromium Tristetrahydrofuranate*

A mixture of anhydrous chromium(III) chloride (12.21 g, 77.2 millimoles) and a trace amount of zinc powder is extracted into 140 ml of tetrahydrofuran. This tetrahydrofuranate is diluted with 310 ml of tetrahydrofuran and cooled in a three-necked flask under argon to $-30°$. To this solution is added 220 ml (0.235 mole) of phenylmagnesium bromide (1.07 M in tetrahydrofuran) over a 45-min period with vigorous stirring. The violet color of the solution changes immediately to red brown, accompanied by the precipitation of a dark-red solid. After dilution with 200 ml of tetrahydrofuran, the mixture is stirred for 4 hr at room temperature under argon. The result is a completely clear, dark, red-brown solution of triphenylchromium(III) tetrahydrofuranate (approximately 600 ml of a 0.25 N solution). However, if the reaction mixture is finally diluted to a total volume of 750 ml with tetrahydrofuran and then stirred, 1.2 g of blood-red needles of triphenylchromium(III) tristetrahydrofuranate, m.p. 85° (decomposition), can be isolated by filtration under argon. Purification by fractional crystallization is very difficult due to the very similar solubilities of the chromium compound and magnesium halides in tetrahydrofuran.

2. *Rearrangement of Triphenylchromium(III)*[5]

a. Under Reduced Pressure. Triphenylchromium tristetrahydrofuranate at 0.05 mm, kept between 20 and 40° for 2–4 hr, rearranges completely to a black, pyrophoric solid that is soluble in tetrahydrofuran and insoluble in diethyl ether. Then 4.79 g of this solid is hydrolyzed with oxygen-free water under nitrogen and extracted into benzene as a mixture of bisarenechromium (0) complexes. The mixture is transferred quantitatively into an aqueous layer, in the presence of air, [converted to chromium(I) complexes] and precipitated with sodium tetraphenylboron, giving 0.90 g (23%) of a mixture of dibenzenechromium(I) and benzene biphenylchromium(I) tetraphenylborates in the ratio of 60:40. The benzene biphenylchromium fraction always contains traces of bisphenylchromium(I).

b. With Diethyl Ether. The addition of triphenylchromium(III) as its magnesium halide salt to diethyl ether immediately produces rearrangement and formation of a black powder. After ether arrangement, hydrolysis, and tetraphenylborate precipitation, 2.78 g of the σ-compound gives 0.32 g (23%) of the mixed π-arenechromium tetraphenylborate salts in the same 60:40 ratio.

c. By Heating. A sample of triphenylchromium(III) tristetrahydrofura-nate is warmed in a narrow tube under nitrogen and at atmospheric pressure. At 85° the sample decomposes with foaming to a black solid, which on hydrolysis in air dissolves to a yellow solution. Precipitation of the bisarene-chromium salts is carried out as before.

3. Reaction of Benzyl, Mesityl, β-Phenethyl, β-Styryl, and β-Phenylethynylmagnesium Halides with Chromium(III) Chloride[9] *

Freshly distilled diethyl ether (100 ml) is added to 4.71 g (0.03 mole) of flame-dried, nitrogen-flushed chromium(III) chloride. The suspension is chilled to a Dry Ice–acetone bath temperature, and 0.09 mole of freshly prepared benzylmagnesium chloride is added under nitrogen, with stirring. The reaction mixture is allowed to come slowly to room temperature. The brown-black mixture is cooled below 0°, hydrolyzed cautiously with ice-water, and extracted in air with 250 ml of water. The hydrolyzed mixture is filtered, and concentrated aqueous potassium iodide solution is added. After standing for several days, orange-yellow crystals of π-bibenzyl-π-toluene chromium(I) iodide form (1.2 g; 8.8% based on $CrCl_3$).

Mesitylmagnesium bromide (0.12 mole) is added dropwise to dried chromium(III) chloride (6.32 g, 0.04 mole) in ether (430 ml) at −70°. After warming to room temperature, the mixture is stirred for 36 hr. The ether is removed under vacuum, and the dried solids are hydrolyzed below 0°. On treatment with sodium tetraphenylborate, the water extracts give π-dimesitylenechromium tetraphenylborate (∼3% yield).

β-Phenethylmagnesium chloride (0.16 mole) is reacted with chromium(III) chloride (8.0 g, 0.05 mole) in 150 ml of ether. Trace amounts of a golden-orange material, probably a π-complex, are isolated, but the main product is the coupled 1,4-diphenylbutane.

β-Styrylmagnesium bromide (0.1 mole) and chromium(III) chloride (4.71 g, 0.03 mole) are stirred in 150 ml of ether. The main product is 1,4-diphenyl-1,3-butadiene. An orange-colored water-insoluble and benzene-soluble material containing only trace amounts of chromium is also isolated.

β-Phenylethynylmagnesium bromide (0.1 mole) and chromium(III) chloride (4.71 g, 0.03 mole) are reacted as above. (The coupled product 1,4-diphenyl-1,3-butadiyne was isolated, but no π-complex was detected.)

4. Preparation and Rearrangement of σ-Benzyl π-Cyclopentadienylmolybdenum Tricarbonyl[14]

A mixture of 0.1 mole of $NaMo(CO)_3$-π-C_5H_5 and 0.12 mole of benzyl chloride in 300 ml of tetrahydrofuran is stirred for approximately 16 hr at room temperature. After removal of the tetrahydrofuran at 25° (30 mm), the

* σ-Intermediates not isolated.

residue is extracted with three 100-ml portions of dichloromethane. Removal of the solvent from the filtered dichloromethane solution leaves yellow crystals of crude σ-$C_6H_5CH_2Mo(CO)_3$-π-C_5H_5, which are extracted with approximately 300 ml of boiling diethyl ether in three portions. The filtered, yellow-orange diethyl ether solutions at $-78°$ give, after 16 hr, yellow crystals of σ-$C_6H_5CH_2(CO)_3$-π-C_5H_5 (22.38 g, 67%), m.p. 87–88°. (Elemental analysis as well as infrared and NMR spectra were in accordance with a σ-bonded compound.)

A mixture of 10.0 g (29.7 millimoles) of the σ-benzyl compound, σ-C_6H_5 $CH_2Mo(CO)_3$-π-C_5H_5, and 200 ml of n-hexane is exposed in a quartz tube to a 450-W ultraviolet lamp for 5 days. The yellow solid dissolves, and a red-violet precipitate forms. After the reaction period, this precipitate of $[C_5H_5Mo(CO)_3]_2$ (2.36 g, 31%) is removed by filtration, washed with hexane (250 ml), and dried.

The hexane filtrate (~ 250 ml) is cooled for about 16 hr at $-78°$. The resulting red mixture of π-$C_6H_5CH_2Mo(CO)_3$-σ-C_5H_5 and organic material is filtered and dried. It is then extracted with four 15-ml portions of benzene. The filtered red benzene solutions are chromatographed on a 5 × 50-cm alumina column. Benzene elutes a yellow zone of unchanged σ-$C_6H_5CH_2$ $Mo(CO)_3$-π-C_5H_5, followed by an incompletely separated red zone of π-$C_6H_5CH_2Mo(CO)_3$-σ-C_5H_5. The eluent from the portions of overlap between the yellow and red zones is discarded. Evaporation (at 25° and 30 mm) of the filtered eluate from the yellow zone leaves yellow crystals. After one crystallization from a mixture of pentane and diethyl ether, 1.4 g (14% recovery) of σ-$C_6H_5CH_2Mo(CO)_3$-π-C_5H_5 is obtained.

The red eluate from the red zone leaves dark crystals on evaporation at about 25° and 30 mm. These are washed with three 15-ml portions of pentane and dried. Sublimation at 80° (0.1 mm) for 6 hr gives 0.5 g of dark-red crystalline π-$C_6H_5CH_2Mo(CO)_3$-σ-C_5H_5, m.p. 83–85°. The red crystals gradually become black on storage at room temperature in closed vials. Solutions in organic solvents oxidize noticeably after exposure to air for several minutes.

B. σ–π Rearrangements of σ-Allyl Groups

1. Preparation and Rearrangement of σ-Allylmanganese Pentacarbonyl[16]

Allyl chloride (5.7 g, 0.074 mole) is added under nitrogen to a stirred solution (100 ml, 0.65 M) of lithium manganese pentacarbonyl. After stirring for 18 hr, the precipitated lithium chloride is removed by filtration, and the tetrahydrofuran is removed by distillation under reduced pressure. Distillation of the yellow residue gives 10.8 g (71%) of σ-allylmanganese penta-carbonyl, b.p. 45° (15 mm).

When 12.5 g (0.053 mole) of allylmanganese pentacarbonyl is heated at 86°, 1160 ml of carbon monoxide (theoretical 1200 ml) is evolved over a 3-hr period. The yellow residue is distilled to give 9.5 g (88%) of π-allylmanganese tetracarbonyl, b.p. 66° (16 mm), m.p. 55–56°.

2. Rearrangement of π-Methallylrhodium Bis(triphenylphosphine) Chloride by Reaction with Sulfur Dioxide[18]

A solution of π-methallylrhodium bis(triphenylphosphine) chloride (0.5 g) in 15 ml of liquid sulfur dioxide is kept at 20° for 40 hr. Addition of 200 ml of pentane to the reaction mixture yields, after evaporation of the excess sulfur dioxide, 0.46 g of σ-methallylrhodium bis(triphenylphosphine) sulfur dioxide dichloride.

The structure is based on infrared spectra and analytical data; insertion products are precluded by mass-spectral analysis. Studies with NMR spectroscopy are difficult because of the compound's low solubility.

3. Rearrangement of σ-Allylcobalt Cyanide Compounds[19]

Allyl bromide (0.03 mole) is injected into a freshly prepared solution of $K_3[Co(CN)_5]^{20}$ (200 ml, 0.25 M cobalt, 0.075 M KOH, CN:Co = 5.1) under nitrogen. The reaction mixture changes from dark green to orange within 2 min. The mixture of complexes so formed is isolated by addition to 800 ml of acetone, and the aqueous layer is decanted from the brown oil that settled out. Addition of ethanol to the oil yields a tan powder, which is collected on a sintered-glass filter, washed with several portions of ethanol followed by ether, and dried briefly *in vacuo*.

The NMR spectrum in D_2O reveals the presence of the σ-allyl compound together with minor quantities of the π-complex. After 2.5 hr the spectrum shows the presence of the π-allylic complex. It is formed through loss of a cyanide ion, and the σ-structure is immediately reformed on addition of the cyanide ion.

4. Rearrangement of π-Allylpalladium(II) Chloride with Dimethyl Sulfoxide[26]

π-Allylpalladium(III) chloride is synthesized from Na_2PdCl_4 and allyl alcohol. The variable-temperature NMR spectra indicating rearrangement from π to σ are obtained with solutions in deuteriochloroform to which has been added 1 mole of dimethyl sulfoxide-d_6 per mole of palladium complex.

C. π–σ Rearrangement of π-Allylpalladium Chloride with Substituted Phosphines[29]

This rearrangement was observed by a study of NMR characteristics at various temperatures. The NMR spectrum of the monomer (with π = H) consisted of a triplet at 4.60, a quartet at 3.53, and two doublets at 3.44 and

2.63 ppm from tetramethylsilane. The triplet arises from the accidental coincidence of the central lines of two doublets, one originating from coupling between proton (1) and the ^{31}P nucleus ($J_{P-1} = 7.0$ Hz), the other from a coupling with the *cis*-proton (5) ($J_{1-5} = 7.0$ Hz). The quartet is caused by analogous couplings of proton (2) with the phosphorus nucleus and the *trans*-proton (5) ($J_{P-2} = 9.5$ Hz, $J_{2-5} = 14.1$ Hz).

When the temperature of the reaction mixture of tri-*n*-butylphosphine and π-allylpalladium chloride dimer was raised, the triplet and quartet were not affected. However, the doublets due to protons (3) (2.63 ppm) and (4) (3.44 ppm) collapsed to form one broad band. The interchange of protons (3) and (4) is explainable by the formation of a short-lived σ-complex. At higher temperatures and excess ligand concentrations, however, protons (1) and (4) and protons (2) and (3) become equivalent.

D. Rearrangement of σ-Allyl and σ-Ethyl π-Cyclopentadienylmolybdenum Tricarbonyl[60]

The starting materials are prepared by treating sodium tricyclopentadienyl-molybdenum tricarbonyl in dry tetrahydrofuran with the appropriate halide in tetrahydrofuran.

σ-Allyl π-cyclopentadienylmolybdenum tricarbonyl (2 g) in petroleum ether (25 ml) is treated with dry hydrogen chloride. A bright-yellow precipitate is formed and is readily extracted into water. The solution is treated immediately with a concentrated solution of potassium hexafluorophosphate, The yellow precipitate of hexafluorophosphate is separated by filtration, washed with ether and water, dried under vacuum, and finally crystallized from a liquid sulfur dioxide–ether mixture. If the σ-allyl compound is treated with excess hydrogen chloride, π-cyclopentadienylmolybdenum tricarbonyl chloride is formed.

Ethyl π-cyclopentadienylmolybdenum tricarbonyl (0.8 g) in chloroform is treated with a solution of triphenylmethyl fluoroborate (1 g) in chloroform. The mixture changes from orange to dark red, and deep-orange crystals are formed. After 10 min the precipitated π-ethylene tetrafluoroborate complex is filtered off, washed with chloroform, and recrystallized from acetone as golden crystals ($\sim 30\%$ yield).

E. σ–π and π–σ Rearrangements of Olefin- and Acetylene-Type Groups

1. Hydride Addition to $[\pi\text{-}C_2H_4C_5H_5Mo(CO)_3]^+$ BF_4^-

A suspension of the π-ethylene complex (0.2 g in 25 ml of tetrahydrofuran) is treated with a 10% excess of sodium hydride. The mixture is stirred in a stream of nitrogen for 10 min and then extracted with ether and water. The ether layer is separated, washed with water, and dried. The solvent is removed, and the product is sublimed under vacuum to give yellow crystals (30%). (It was identified as the ethyl compound by infrared and NMR spectroscopy).

2. Reaction of the Methoxide Ion with Bicyclo[2.2.1]heptadienepalladium Chloride[73]

A solution of sodium methoxide (0.513 M, 10 ml) in methanol is added dropwise to a stirred solution of bicylo[2.2.1]heptadienepalladium chloride (1.40 g, 4.2 millimoles) in methanol at −78°. After 1 hr the cream-colored precipitate is filtered off, and the crude product is crystallized from dichloromethane and petroleum ether to give di-μ-chloro-bis(6-methoxybicyclo-[2.2.1]hepta-2-endo)palladium (0.08 g, 1.83 millimoles, 20%).

3. Addition of Acylcobalt Carbonyls to Acetylenes[94]

In a 100-ml reaction flask, which has been filled with ether-saturated carbon monoxide at 0° and attached to a gas buret, are placed 30 ml of 0.07 M sodium cobalt tetracarbonyl in ether solution and 3.0 ml of 1.2 M acetyl chloride in ether solution. After 1.5 hr of stirring at 0°, the infrared spectrum of a sample of the reaction solution shows that acetylcobalt tetracarbonyl has been formed. To this solution is added 2.9 ml of 3-hexyne. The solution gradually changes color from yellow to orange, and gas is evolved. (After 10 ml of gas evolved in 2 hr, the evolution stopped.) The infrared spectrum of the reaction mixture had carbonyl bands at 4.78 (w), 4.85 (s), 4.90 (m), 5.00 (vs), and 5.70 (m) μ. These bands and their intensities are identical with those of 3-hexynedicobalt hexacarbonyl. Elution with ether–pentane on an alumina column gives several colored fractions, each containing 5.7 μ carbonyl bands. (Since several new absorptions bands appeared in these eluates, decomposition was apparently taking place on the alumina column.)

The triphenylphosphine derivative of the π-lactone complex is prepared by adding 4.0 ml of 1.0 M triphenylphosphine in ether solution at 0° to a solution of the complex in ether at 0° prepared from 30 ml of 0.07 M sodium cobalt carbonyl complex as described above. The solution gradually becomes a darker red, and gas is evolved. (In 2.5 hr 36 ml, or 1.56 millimoles, of gas was evolved. The rate of gas evolution was $6.22 \pm 0.25 \times 10^{-4}$ sec^{-1}.) Evaporation of the reaction mixture at 0° under vacuum, followed by extraction with tetrahydrofuran (4 ml) and centrifuging, separates the inorganic salts. Addition of 5 ml of pentane to the clear orange tetrahydrofuran extract causes the product to crystallize out as fine orange needles. After cooling to −80°, the solid is separated by centrifuging and recrystallized three more times from tetrahydrofuran–pentane at −80°. The product has no definite melting point, but it becomes dark at about 85° and gradually decomposes on further heating.

4. Reaction of Acetylenes with Ni(CO)$_2$(R$_3$P)$_2$[112]

The acetylene (1.9 g), the ethyl propiolate of 1-heptyne, is added under nitrogen to 15 ml of the solvent contained in a 50-ml three-necked flask provided with a thermometer, reflux condenser, and a self-sealing vaccine cap for taking aliquots. An initial 0.5-ml aliquot is taken. The solid Ni(CO)$_2$ (Ph$_3$P)$_2$ catalyst (50 mg) is then added, and the solution is either heated rapidly to reflux with an oil bath or brought to 75–80° if the solvent boils above 100°. After 5 min at this temperature, a second aliquot is taken. A final aliquot is taken after 6 hr, and the reaction is terminated. The aliquots (which were stored at 0°) are analyzed in the infrared for disappearance of the triple-bond-stretching band, whose position varies in the different solvents from 2120 to 2139 cm^{-1}. The concentration of acetylene is found to be proportional to the optical density after correcting for the solvent absorption at that frequency. The percentage of reaction can then be calculated by assuming no reaction in the initial aliquot. The acetylenes are stable in the pure refluxing solvents.

5. Rearrangement of σ-Cyanomethyl π-Cyclopentadienyliron Dicarbonyl[57]

Cyanomethyl π-cyclopentadienyliron dicarbonyl (0.5 g) in petroleum ether (150 ml) is treated with dry hydrogen chloride. The bright-yellow precipitate formed is washed three times with petroleum ether by decantation. After drying under vacuum, the product is recrystallized from liquid sulfur dioxide–ether. The π-ketimine complex is isolated as the chloride in about 90% yield.

F. σ–π and π–σ Rearrangements Involving Monomers, Dimers and Coupling Reactions

1. Reaction of Alkoxide Ions with π-Dicyclopentadieneplatinum Chloride[65]

Dicyclopentadiene (4 ml) is added to a solution of sodium chloroplatinite tetrahydrate (4 g) in 1-propanol (80–100 ml) and kept at room temperature for 2 days. The crystals that separate are filtered off, washed first with ether and then water, and dried. The product is purified by dissolving it in hot chloroform, treating the solution with a small amount of charcoal, filtering, and diluting the filtrate with ether. White needles (3.2 g), m.p. 200–220° (decomposition), are obtained. Dicyclopentadieneplatinum dichloride (0.4 g), suspended in methanol (25 ml), is heated to boiling, and sodium acetate (~0.2 g) is added. The solid dissolves, and on continued heating a white solid is precipitated. After cooling, the solid is filtered off, washed with methanol, and dried. Recrystallization is effected by diluting a chloroform solution with ether (0.3-g yield).

2. Preparation of Triphenylphosphinecobalt Tetracarbonyl 1,1,2-trimethyl-π-allylpalladium

A mixture of 0.63 g (1.5 millimoles) of chloro-1,1,2-trimethyl-π-allyl-palladium dimer and 45 ml of 0.07 N $NaCo(CO)_4$ in ether is stirred under nitrogen at room temperature for 2 hr. Then 3.5 ml of 1.0 M triphenylphosphine in ether is added, and stirring is continued for another hour. The solvent is removed under reduced pressure, and the product is extracted from the residue with dichloromethane. The dichloromethane extracts are concentrated to a few milliliters and diluted with several volumes of pentane. Cooling in Dry Ice produces red-brown crystals of the product. An additional recrystallization in the same manner gives 0.12 g (6.5%) of the product, m.p. 117–20° (decomposition).

3. Chloro-π-Allylpalladium Dimer from π-Allylcobalt Tricarbonyl

Allyl chloride (4.5 ml of 1.0 M) in ether is added under nitrogen to a solution of 60 ml of 0.07 M $NaCo(CO)_4$ in ether. The solution is stirred at room temperature overnight. The solvent is then removed under reduced pressure at 0°, and the remaining π-allylcobalt tricarbonyl is redissolved in 20 ml of acrylonitrile at 0°. Thirty milliliters of 0.1 M $LiPdCl_3$ in acrylonitrile is added, and the mixture is stirred at room temperature overnight. The entire solution is poured onto an alumina column and chromatographed. The yellow product is eluted with 1% methanol in dichloromethane. Evaporation of the solvent under reduced pressure and recrystallization from dichloromethane gives 0.166 g (22%) of π-allylpalladium chloride, m.p. 152–155°.

4. Ethylene Dimerization Catalyzed by Rhodium(II)[80]

a. Induction Period with $RhCl_3 3H_2O$. A solution of 0.1 g $RhCl_3 3H_2O$ in 5 ml of ethanol and 1 ml of aqueous hydrochloric acid is placed in a flask connected with a gas buret, a manometer, and a cylinder of ethylene. The flask is cooled to −80°, evacuated, and purged with ethylene; it is then heated to 50.0 ± 0.1° and pressured with ethylene to 5 atm. The rate of ethylene absorption varies with the hydrogen chloride concentration.

b. Formation of an Ethylrhodium Compound. An NMR tube cooled in liquid nitrogen is charged with 0.08 g of $[(C_2H_4)_2RhCl]_2$, 0.4 ml of CD_3OD, 0.01 ml of tetramethylsilane, 25 ml of HCl gas, and 15 ml of ethylene, evacuated, and sealed. After several hours at −33°, the complex dissolves and the spectrum is recorded at −30°.*

---

* In a second experiment a cooled, evacuated tube containing 0.04 g of π-C_5H_5Rh $(C_2H_4)_2$, 0.4 ml of $CHCl_3$, 0.01 ml of tetramethylsilane, and 10 ml of HCl gas was warmed to −60°, and the spectrum was recorded at that temperature. The spectrum did not change in 2 hr at −20°, but showed marked differences at −10°.

The ethylene dimerization is followed by the change in the pressure accompanying the reaction in a Warburg apparatus, a standard manometric device. Flasks with three compartments are used, and standardized ethanol solutions of H^+ (as HCl or H_2SO_4), Cl^- (as HCl or LiCl), and Rh^{2+} (as $acacRh(C_2H_4)_2$) are pipetted into separate compartments. The flasks are then attached to their manometers and cooled to $-80°$ while the manometers are immobilized by freezing the bottoms at $-80°$. The reactors are purged by alternately evacuating and pressurizing with ethylene, finally leaving them filled with ethylene. They are then warmed to room temperature; the pressure that develops is relieved from time to time by "cracking" a stopcock to allow excess ethylene to escape. After a group of reactors containing mixtures differing only in the concentration of one of the reactants has been charged in this manner, they are positioned in the thermostatted bath for 5 min to allow the unmixed reagents to come to $30 \pm 0.1°$. Then the reactants are mixed, and the reaction is followed by the change in pressure as 10–20% of the ethylene dimerizes.

5. Stereospecific Coupling Reaction of 1,2-Disubstituted Vinyl Groups[118]

Stilbenylmagnesium bromide (0.026 mole), prepared from magnesium turnings and 2-bromostilbene, is added dropwise, with stirring, to a solution of 1.53 g (0.013 mole) of chromium(II) chloride in 75 ml of tetrahydrofuran, keeping the temperature at $-30°$. The temperature of the solution is gradually raised to room temperature, and the solution is stirred overnight. The solvent is removed under reduced pressure, and 100 ml of ether is added to the residue. After digesting the residue in ether, 20 ml of water is added to hydrolyze it. After hydrolysis, 300 ml of water is added, and the water solution is extracted with ether three times. After drying the combined ether extract over sodium sulfate, the ether is distilled off, leaving a resinous material, which is fractionally recrystallized from ethyl acetate into two products, trans-stilbene, m.p. 116–120° (1 g), and cis,cis-1,2,3,4-tetraphenylbutadiene, m.p. 180–184° (0.05 g).

Stilbenylmagnesium bromide (0.02 mole) is added dropwise with rapid stirring to a suspension of 2.17 g (0.01 mole) nickel(II) bromide in 75 ml of tetrahydrofuran at $-40°$. The reaction is carried out as above, yielding trans,trans-1,2,3,4-tetraphenylbutadiene, m.p. 146°.

G. π-Allylic Ligand-Transfer Reactions between Cobalt and Palladium Complexes: Triphenylphosphine-π-allylcobalt Dicarbonyl from Chloro-π-allylpalladium dimer[123]

A mixture of 0.182 g (0.5 millimole) of $[\pi\text{-}C_3H_5PdCl]_2$ and 15 ml of 0.07 M $NaCo(CO)_4$ in ether is stirred at room temperature under nitrogen for 1 hr. Gas is evolved, and a black precipitate appears during the reaction.

(An infrared spectrum of the solution showed absorptions at 2000 and 2070 cm^{-1}. The bands are characteristic of π-allylcobalt tricarbonyl). Then 1.5 ml of 1.0 M triphenylphosphine in ether is added. After stirring at room temperature for about 1 hr, the mixture is centrifuged, and the clear-yellow solution that is obtained is concentrated under reduced pressure to about 5 ml. On cooling in Dry Ice, yellow crystals of triphenylphosphine-π-allylcobalt dicarbonyl are obtained. The crystals are separated by centrifuging and dried under reduced pressure. The product is obtained as yellow-orange prisms (0.21 g, 50%), m.p. 119° (decomposition).

VII. RELATED REARRANGEMENTS

Allied reactions include *cis*-ligand insertions, olefin isomerizations, and stereochemically dynamic organometallic compounds that do not involve σ-π rearrangements.

A. Isomerization

The mechanism of isomerization of olefins catalyzed by transition-metal complexes appears to be dependent on, among other factors, the metal. Thus for normal olefins the isomerization involving a π-σ-π rearrangement mechanism is catalyzed by rhodium(III) chloride, but when the catalyst is bisbenzonitrilepalladium(II) chloride, the mechanism involves a π-olefin to π-allylic rearrangement.[99] The isomerization of tetramethylbutadiene catalyzed by iron pentacarbonyl is postulated to go via a di-π-olefin complex through a π-allylic system to products.[128] Isomerization has been shown to occur in metal–olefin complexes by the isolation of two isomers (**82**) and (**83**), which are interconverted at 120° but are normally stable.[129]

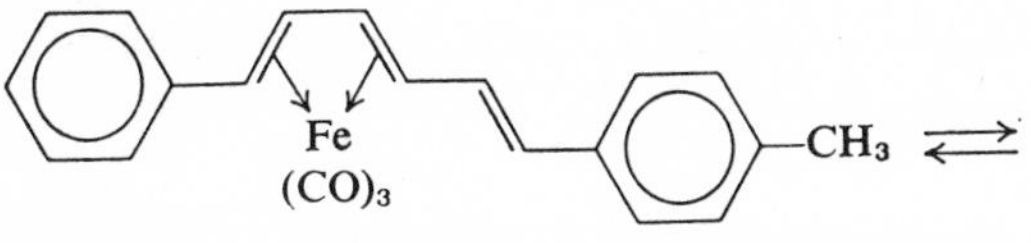

(**82**)

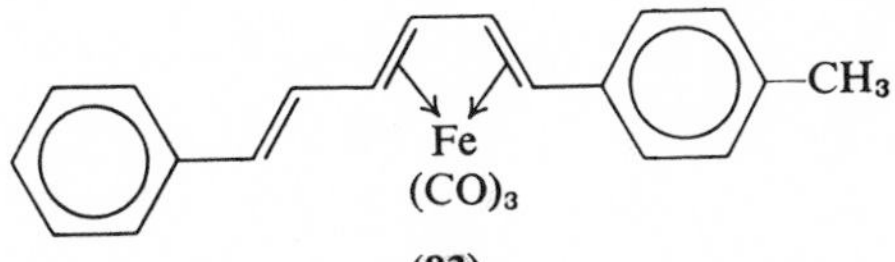

(**83**)

Olefin reorientation has been detected in a series of platinum acetylacetonate π-olefin chloride complexes. The observed NMR spectra and calculated energy barriers are consistent with an intramolecular rotation of the olefin about the platinum–olefin axis.[130]

B. Stereochemically Dynamic Compounds ("Ring Whizzing")

Stereochemically dynamic behavior has been observed to be fairly common in organometallic chemistry, and only a few random examples are presented here. In π-cyclopentadienyliron σ-cyclopentadienyl dicarbonyl the protons on the σ-bonded ring were found to be magnetically equivalent at room temperature.[131] By the use of variable-temperature NMR measurements, the molecule has been shown to be stereochemically nonrigid, the σ-bonded ring undergoing a 1,2 shift ("ring whizzing").[132] This behavior is also observable in other σ-bonded cyclopentadienyl metal compounds, such as $Hg(C_5H_5)_2$.

Another type of stereochemically dynamic compound involves a rapid shift of π-orbital to metal interaction. In the crystalline state $C_8H_8Fe(CO)_3$ has an asymmetrical structure, but its protons are all equivalent magnetically.[133] From variable-temperature NMR and from infrared it and the corresponding chromium and molybdenum complexes were shown to be fluxional molecules that rearrange via 1,2 shifts but have 1,3-diene bonding in the frozen state.[134] Similar behavior is observed in the corresponding ruthenium complex and in polynuclear ruthenium carbonyl complexes.[135]

Stereochemically dynamic behavior has also been used to explain the spectral behavior of allylic metal complexes. As we have already pointed out, rotation about the C—C bonds explains the NMR spectra of $Zr(allyl)_4$ in solution.[21] Ramey and co-workers report that the NMR spectra at variable temperatures for the compound $[(allyl)_2RhCl]_2$ support neither a σ–π mechanism nor a rotation about the C—C bond.[135]

C. Carbon Monoxide Insertion

Closely related to the oxo reaction are carbon monoxide insertion reactions observed for several metal complexes and typified by the insertion of carbon monoxide into the manganese–methyl bond:

$$CH_3Mn(CO)_5 + CO \longrightarrow CH_3COMn(CO)_5 \qquad (16)$$

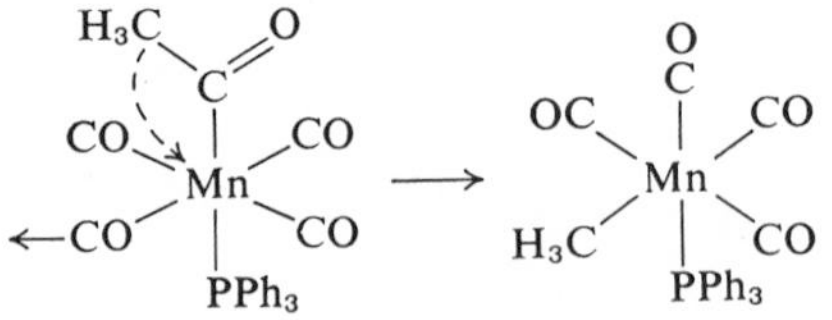

$$\qquad (17)$$

Tracer studies have shown that the insertion is intramolecular, and from study of the decarbonylation it appears that the reaction goes via methyl migration rather than carbon monoxide insertion.[136,137]

ACKNOWLEDGMENT

We are grateful for the support given by the Robert A. Welch Foundation (A-420) for the preparation of this manuscript.

REFERENCES

1. H. H. Zeiss and M. Tsutsui, *J. Amer. Chem. Soc.*, **79**, 3062 (1957).
2. W. Herwig and H. H. Zeiss, *J. Amer. Chem. Soc.*, **79**, 6561 (1957).
3. M. Tsutsui, M. Hancock, J. Aryoshi, and M. N. Levy, *Angew. Chem. Intern. Ed.*, **8**, 410 (1969).
4. See, for example, P. Cossee, *Rec. Trav. Chim.*, **85**, 1151 (1966).
5. H. H. Zeiss and W. Herwig, *J. Amer. Chem. Soc.*, **81**, 4798 (1959).
6. H. H. Zeiss and W. Herwig, *Ann.*, **606**, 209 (1957).
7. M. Tsutsui, *Ann. N.Y. Acad. Sci.*, **93**, 33 (1961).
8. P. Kasai, M. Tsutsui, and J. Ariyoshi, unpublished results.
9. M. Tsutsui and M. N. Levy, *Z. Naturforsch.*, **21b**, 823 (1966).
10. R. P. Sneeden, F. Clockling, and H. H. Zeiss, *J. Organometal. Chem.*, **6**, 149 (1966).
11. M. Tsutsui, M. Hancock, J. Aryoshi, and M. N. Levy, *J. Amer. Chem. Soc.*, **91**, 5233 (1969).
12. M. L. H. Green and P. L. I. Nagy, *J. Chem. Soc.*, **1963**, 189.
13. M. L. H. Green and A. N. Stear, *J. Organometal. Chem.*, **1**, 230 (1964).
14. R. B. King and A. Fronzaglia, *J. Amer. Chem. Soc.*, **88**, 709 (1966).
15. R. B. King and M. B. Bisnette, *Inorg. Chem.*, **4**, 486 (1965).
16. W. R. McClellan, H. H. Hoeln, H. N. Crips, E. L. Muetterties, and B. W. Houk, *J. Amer. Chem. Soc.*, **83**, 1601 (1961).
17. H. D. Kaesz, R. B. King, and F. G. A. Stone, *Z. Naturforsch.*, **15B**, 682 (1960).
18. H. C. Volger and K. Vrieze, *J. Orgamometal. Chem.*, **13**, 479 (1968).
19. J. Kwiatek and J. K. Seyler, *J. Organometal. Chem.*, **3**, 421 (1965).
20. J. Kwiatek, I. L. Mador, and J. K. Seyler, *Advances in Chemistry Series*, **37**, 201 (1963).
21. J. K. Becconsall and S. O'Brien, *Chem. Commun.*, **1966**, 302.
22. G. Wilke, B. Bogdonovic, P. Hardt, P. Heinbeck, W. Kein, M. Kroener, W. Oberkirch, K. Tanaka, and D. Walter, *Angew. Chem., Intern. Ed.*, **5**, 151 (1966).
23. A. E. Smith, *Acta Cryst.*, **18**, 331 (1965); W. E. Oberhansli and L. F. Dahl, *J. Organometal. Chem.*, **3**, 43 (1965).
24. I. I. Moiseev, E. A. Fedorovskaya, and Ya. K. Syrkin, *Zh. Neorg. Khim.*, **4**, 2641 (1959). Quoted in Ref. 25.
25. J. C. W. Chien and H. C. Diem, *Chem. Ind. (London)*, **1961**, 745.
26. K. C. Ramey and G. L. Statton, *J. Amer. Chem. Soc.*, **88**, 1327, 4387 (1966).
27. J. Powell, S. D. Robinson, and B. L. Shaw, *Chem. Commun.*, **1965**, 78.
28. R. Mason and D. R. Russell, *Chem. Commun.*, **1966**, 26.
29. K. Vrieze, C. Maclean, P. Cossee, and C. W. Hilbers, *Rec. Trav. Chim.*, **85**, 1077 (1966).
30. K. Vrieze, P. Cossee, C. W. Hilbers, and A. P. Praat, *Rec. Trav. Chim.*, **86**, 769 (1967).
31. F. A. Cotton, J. W. Faller, and A. Musco, *Inorg. Chem.*, **6**, 179 (1967).
32. J. Powell and B. L. Shaw, *J. Chem. Soc.*, **1967A**, 1839.
33. P. Corradini, G. Maglio, A. Musco, and G. Paiaro, *Chem. Commun.*, **1966**, 618.

34. D. Walter and G. Wilke, *Angew. Chem., Intern. Ed.*, **5**, 897 (1966).
35. H. C. Volger and K. Vrieze, *J. Organometal. Chem.*, **6**, 297 (1966).
36. H. C. Volger and K. Vrieze, *J. Organometal. Chem.*, **9**, 537 (1967).
37. R. A. Plowman and F. G. A. Stone, *Z. Naturforsch.*, **17b**, 575 (1962).
38. A. N. Nesmeyanov and I. I. Kritskaya, *J. Organometal. Chem.*, **14**, 387 (1968).
39. A. N. Nesmeyanov, I. I. Kritskaya, Yu. A. Ustynyuk, and E. I. Fedn, *Dokl. Akad. Nauk SSSR*, **176**, 341 (1967); *Chem. Abstr.*, **68**, 29845u (1968).
40. F. Hein and K. Schmiedeknecht, *J. Organometal. Chem.*, **6**, 45 (1966).
41. F. A. Cotton and T. J. Marks, *J. Amer. Chem. Soc.*, **91**, 1339 (1969).
42. H. C. Clark and J. H. Tsai, *Chem. Commun.*, **1965**, 111.
43. S. Savel, R. Ben-Shoshan, and B. Kioson, *J. Amer. Chem. Soc.*, **87**, 2517 (1965).
44. M. Cooke, M. Green, and D. C. Wood, *Chem. Commun.*, **1968**, 773.
45. B. L. Shaw and G. Shaw, *J. Chem. Soc.*, **1969A**, 602.
46. J. Powell and B. L. Shaw, *J. Chem. Soc.*, **1968A**, 583.
47. J. Powell and B. L. Shaw, *Chem. Commun.*, **1966**, 236.
48. D. N. Lawson, J. A. Gibson, and G. Wilkinson, *J. Chem. Soc.*, **1966A**, 1733.
49. B. L. Shaw and E. Singleton, *J. Chem. Soc.*, **1967A**, 1683.
50. J. Powell and B. L. Shaw, *J. Chem. Soc.*, **1968A**, 780.
51. J. Tsuji, M. Morkawa, and J. Kiju, *J. Amer. Chem. Soc.*, **86**, 785 (1964).
52. M. L. H. Green, in *Proc. 7th Intern. Conf. Coordination Chemistry, Stockholm, 1962*, p. 301.
53. M. L. H. Green and P. L. I. Nagy, *Proc. Chem. Soc.*, **1961**, 378.
54. J. K. P. Ariyartine, M. L. H. Green, and P. L. I. Nagy, *Proc. Chem. Soc.*, **1963**, 107.
55. M. L. H. Green, A. G. Massey, J. T. Moelwyn-Hughes, and P. L. I. Nagy, *J. Organometal. Chem.*, **8**, 511 (1967).
56. J. K. P. Ariyartine and M. L. H. Green, *J. Organometal. Chem.*, **1**, 90 (1963).
57. J. K. P. Ariyartine and M. L. H. Green, *J. Chem. Soc.*, **1963**, 2976.
58. J. K. P. Ariyartine and M. L. H. Green, *J. Chem. Soc.*, **1964**, 1.
59. M. L. H. Green and P. L. I. Nagy, *Z. Naturforsch.* **18b**, 162 (1963).
60. M. L. H. Green and M. Cousins, *J. Chem. Soc.*, **1963**, 889.
61. M. L. H. Green and P. L. I. Nagy, *J. Organometal. Chem.*, **1**, 58 (1963).
62. M. L. H. Green and P. L. I. Nagy, *Proc. Chem. Soc.*, **1962**, 74.
63. M. L. H. Green and P. L. I. Nagy, *J. Amer. Chem. Soc.*, **84**, 1310 (1962).
64. K. A. Hofmann and J. von Narbutt, *Chem. Ber.*, **41**, 1625 (1908).
65. J. Chatt, L. M. Vallarino, and L. M. Venanzi, *J. Chem. Soc.*, 2496 (1957).
66. W. A. Whitla, H. M. Powell, and L. M. Venanzi, *Chem. Commun.*, **1966**, 310.
67. F. Paiaro, A. Paninzi, and A. De Renzi, *Tetrahedron Letters*, **1966**, 3905.
68. J. K. Stille and R. A. Morgan, *J. Amer. Chem. Soc.*, **88**, 5135 (1966).
69. R. A. Schultz, *J. Organometal. Chem.*, **6**, 435 (1966).
70. J. Tsuji and H. Takahashi, *J. Amer. Chem. Soc.*, **87**, 3275 (1965).
71. B. F. T. Johnson, J. Lewis, and M. S. Subramanian, *Chem. Commun.*, **1966**, 117.
72. G. Paiaro, A. De Renzi, and R. Palumbo, *Chem. Commun.*, **1967**, 1150.
73. M. L. H. Green and R. I. Hancock, *J. Chem. Soc.*, **1967A**, 2064.
74. L. Malatesta, A. Santarella, L. Vallarino, and F. Zingales, *Angew. Chem.*, **73**, 34 (1960).
75. L. M. Vallarino and A. Santarella, *Gazz. Chim. Ital.*, **94**, 252 (1964).
76. R. L. Cooper, M. L. H. Green, and J. T. Moelwyn-Hughes, *J. Organometal. Chem.*, **3**, 261 (1965).
77. R. J. Angelici and E. O. Fischer, *J. Amer. Chem. Soc.*, **85**, 3233 (1963).
78. M. R. Churchill and R. Mason, *Proc. Chem. Soc.*, **1963**, 112.

79. M. L. H. Green and P. L. I. Nagy, *J. Chem. Soc.*, **1963**, 189.
80. R. Cramer, *J. Amer. Chem. Soc.*, **87**, 4717 (1965).
81. B. F. G. Johnson, J. Lewis, and M. S. Subramanian, *J. Chem. Soc.*, **1968A**, 1993.
82. P. D. Kaplan, P. Schmidt, and M. Orchin, *J. Amer. Chem. Soc.*, **90**, 4175 (1968).
83. K. Ziegler, E. Holzkamp, H. Brill, and H. Martin, *Angew. Chem.*, **67**, 541 (1955).
84. G. Natta and I. Pasquio, *Adv. in Catalysis*, **11**, 1 (1959).
85. E. O. Fischer, paper presented at the International Congress of Coordination Chemistry, London, 1959; *Chem. Soc. Spec. Publ.* **13**, 73 (1959).
86. J. C. W. Chien, *J. Amer. Chem. Soc.*, **81**, 86 (1959).
87. J. Schmidt, *Chem. Ind. (London)*, **1962**, 54.
88. I. I. Moiseev, M. N. Worshaftig, and J. H. Sirkin, *Dokl. Akad. Nauk SSSR*, **130**, 820 (1960); *ibid.*, **133**, 377 (1960).
89. R. M. Henry, *J. Amer. Chem. Soc.*, **86**, 3246 (1964).
90. J. Halpern, in *Proc. 3rd. Intern. Congress on Catalysis*, North-Holland, Amsterdam, 1965, p. 146.
91. R. F. Heck and D. S. Breslow, *Chem. Ind. (London)*, **1960**, 467.
92. G. Karapinka and M. Orchin, *Abstracts of Papers Presented at the 167th Meeting of the American Chemical Society, Cleveland, Ohio, April 5–14, 1960*, p. 92.
93. R. F. Heck and D. S. Breslow, *J. Amer. Chem. Soc.*, **83**, 4023 (1961).
94. R. F. Heck, *J. Amer. Chem. Soc.*, **86**, 2819 (1964).
95. R. F. Heck, *J. Amer. Chem. Soc.*, **85**, 3116 (1963).
96. J. Halpern, J. F. Harrod, and B. R. James, *J. Amer. Chem. Soc.*, **88**, 5150 (1966).
97. J. Halpern, B. R. James, and A. L. Kemp, *J. Amer. Chem. Soc.*, **83**, 4097 (1961).
98. M. S. Lupin, J. Powell, and B. L. Shaw, *J. Chem. Soc.*, **1966A**, 1687.
99. J. F. Harrod and A. J. Chalk, *J. Amer. Chem. Soc.*, **86**, 1776 (1964).
100. D. S. Breslow and N. R. Newburg, *J. Amer. Chem. Soc.*, **81**, 81 (1959).
101. A. Yamamoto, K. Morifuji, S. Ikeda, T. Saito, Y. Uchida, and A. Misona, *J. Amer. Chem. Soc.*, **90**, 1878 (1968).
102. J. Rhee, M. Ryang, and S. Tsutsumi, *J. Organometal. Chem.*, **9**, 361 (1967).
103. L. S. Pu, A. Yamamoto, and S. Ikeda, *J. Amer. Chem. Soc.*, **90**, 7170 (1968).
104. J. F. Biellmann and M. J. Jung, *J. Amer. Chem. Soc.*, **90**, 1673 (1968).
105. B. R. James and G. L. Rempel, *J. Amer. Chem. Soc.*, **91**, 863 (1969).
106. H. S. Klein, *Chem. Commun.*, **1968**, 377.
107. J. Tsuji and S. Hosaka, *J. Amer. Chem. Soc.*, **87**, 4075 (1965).
108. J. Powell and B. L. Shaw, *J. Chem. Soc.*, **1968A**, 211.
109. J. D. McClure, R. Owyang, and L. H. Slaugh, *J. Organometal. Chem.*, **12**, 9 (1968).
110. J. L. Garnett and R. J. Hedges, *Chem. Commun.*, **1967**, 1220.
111. W. Reppe and W. J. Schweckendick, *Ann.*, **560**, 104 (1948).
112. M. S. Meriwether, M. F. Leto, E. C. Colthup, and G. W. Kennerly, *J. Org. Chem.* **27**, 3930 (1962).
113. G. M. Bennett and E. E. Turner, *J. Chem. Soc.*, **1914**, 1054.
114. M. S. Kharasch and E. K. Fields, *J. Amer. Chem. Soc.*, **63**, 2316 (1941).
115. A. L. Wilds and M. B. McCormack, *J. Org. Chem.*, **14**, 215 (1949).
116. F. Hein, *Chem. Ber.*, **54**, 1905, 2708, 2727 (1921).
117. M. Tsutsui, *Ann. N.Y. Acad. Sci.*, **93**, 133 (1961).
118. M. Tsutsui, *Trans. N.Y. Acad. Sci.*, **26**, 423 (1964).
119. M. Tsutsui and J. Ariyoshi, *Trans. N.Y. Acad. Sci.*, **26**, 431 (1964).
120. J. C. Trebellas, J. R. Oleckowskii, and H. B. Jonassen, *J. Organometal. Chem.*, **6**, 412 (1966).

121. P. Heinback and W. Brenner, *Angew. Chem., Intern. Ed.*, **6**, 800 (1967).
122. J. D. Hawthorne, M. J. Mays, and R. N. F. Simpson, *J. Organometal. Chem.*, **12**, 407 (1968).
123. R. F. Heck, *J. Amer. Chem. Soc.*, **90**, 317 (1968).
124. A. N. Nesmeyanov, A. Z. Rubezhov, L. A. Leites, and S. P. Gubin, *J. Organometal. Chem.*, **12**, 187 (1968).
125. B. F. Hallam and P. L. Pauson, *J. Chem. Soc.*, **1956**, 3030.
126. A. Nakamura and N. Hagihara, *J. Organometal. Chem.*, **3**, 480 (1965).
127. E. H. Braye and W. Hückel, *J. Organometal. Chem.*, **3**, 25 (1965).
128. R. Pettit and G. F. Emerson, *Adv. Organometal. Chem.*, **1**, 16 (1964).
129. H. W. Whitlock, Jr., and Y. N. Chuah, *J. Amer. Chem. Soc.*, **87**, 3605 (1965); *Inorg. Chem.*, **7**, 425 (1965).
130. C. E. Holloway, G. Hulley, B. F. G. Johnson, and J. Lewis, *J. Chem. Soc.*, **1969A**, 53.
131. T. S. Piper and G. Wilkinson, *J. Inorg. Nucl. Chem.*, **3**, 104 (1956).
132. M. J. Bennett, Jr., F. A. Cotton, A. Davison, J. W. Faller, S. J. Lippard, and S. M. Morehouse, *J. Amer. Chem. Soc.*, **88**, 4371 (1966).
133. T. A. Manuel and F. G. A. Stone, *J. Amer. Chem. Soc.*, **82**, 366 (1960).
134. C. G. Kreiter, A. Maasbol, F. A. L. Anet, H. D. Kaesz, and S. Winstein, *J. Amer. Chem. Soc.*, **88**, 3444 (1966).
135. K. C. Ramey, D. C. Lini, and W. B. Wise, *J. Amer. Chem. Soc.*, **90**, 4275 (1968).
136. F. Calderazzo and F. A. Cotton, *Inorg. Chem.*, **1**, 30 (1962).
137. R. J. Mawby, F. Basolo, and R. G. Pearson, *J. Amer. Chem. Soc.*, **86**, 5043 (1964).

Onium Compounds in the Synthesis of Organometallic Compounds

O. A. REUTOV AND O. A. PTITSYNA

Department of Chemistry, Moscow State University, Moscow, U.S.S.R.

I. INTRODUCTION

At present aromatic onium compounds represent one of the most interesting classes of organic substances. They all can be described by the general formula $Ar_nE^+X^-$, where E is the onium-generating element of groups V (P, As, Sb, Bi), VI(0, S, Se, Te), or VII of the periodic table, n is 4, 3, or 2, and X^- is the anion of an inorganic or organic acid. Aryldiazonium salts $ArN_2^+X^-$ also belong to the aromatic onium compounds.

Of all the various arylonium salts, only aryldiazonium and diarylhalogenonium ($Ar_2Hal^+X^-$) salts are employed in the synthesis of organoelement compounds.

It should be noted that syntheses of organoelement compounds via onium salts have an important function. The diazo method, first discovered by A. N. Nesmeyanov in 1929, is of great importance for the preparation of organomercury compounds. It involves the decomposition of double salts of aryldiazonium and heavy-metal chlorides by metallic powders in an organic medium:

$$(ArN_2Cl)_m \cdot MCl_n + \frac{2m}{p} M' \longrightarrow Ar_mMCl_{n-m} + \frac{2m}{p} M'Cl_p + mN_2$$

where M is the n-valent metal undergoing arylation and M' is the p-valent reducing metal.

In this review we do not assign to the diazo method (as is sometimes reported in the literature) the syntheses of organometallic compounds via other diazonium salts (e.g., fluoborates).

Reutov et al. have found that syntheses of organometallics via double diaryliodonium salts are reminiscent of the diazo method.

Organometallic syntheses via aryldiazonium salts and their mechanisms (unlike diarylhalogenonium salts) are discussed in a number of reviews.[1-8] It is profitable to review again this subject and to extend it to include the diarylhalogenonium salts. Such a material choice was demanded by the following reasons. First, most of the above cited reviews are devoted mainly to the syntheses and mechanisms of organoelement derivatives of group V of the periodic table.[3,4,6-8] Second, recent data permit application of modern viewpoints to the mechanisms of the preparation of organometallics from diazo compounds. Third, syntheses of organometallic compounds via diarylhalogenonium and aryldiazonium salts are quite similar. Thus to depict this similarity a comparison is made of both methods in this review.

Sections II–VI cover the syntheses of organoelement compounds via diazonium and halogenonium salts. The most important syntheses of the respective organoelement compounds are first discussed, then mention is also made of other methods that are of purely theoretical interest. Section VII is concerned with the mechanism of formation of organoelement compounds via onium compounds, and Section VIII is devoted to the organoelement compounds synthesized by the preparatively most important methods. When the same procedure is employed for several compounds, the reaction is usually described in a general way.

Organoelement compounds prepared via aryldiazonium and diaryl-halogenonium salts are listed in various tables throughout this review. Arylarsinic and arylstibonic acids prepared by the Bart–Schmidt–Scheller methods are deliberately not included in the tables because their yields depend so much on the reaction conditions. In most cases no detailed description of synthetic procedures is provided, and the yields of acids are not always presented. Moreover syntheses of arylarsinic acids via Bart's method have been previously reviewed.[9]

II. SYNTHESIS OF ORGANOMETALLIC DERIVATIVES OF MERCURY AND MAGNESIUM

A. Organomercury Compounds

As outlined in the introduction, the possibility of applying the Nesmeyanov diazo method to the preparation of organometallic compounds was first established for the mercury derivatives.[10,11] At present it is the most universal and well-studied approach leading to a variety of organometallics of the benzene,[10–19] naphthalene,[10,11] anthraquinone,[20] and pyridine series.[21]

$$ArN_2X \cdot HgX_2 + M \longrightarrow ArHgX + MX_2 + N_2 \qquad (1)$$

The reaction is best carried out in acetone, ethyl acetate,[1,10,14] or, as shown recently, in water,[22,23] using copper powder as the reducing metal.[1,10] The yield of the organomercury compound usually increases at low temperatures. When the aromatic ring in a diazonium salt has electron-attracting substituents, the temperature should be much lower (from -10 to $-12°$).[14–16,21] The diazo method usually provides high yields of organomercury compounds (50–80%), whereas lower yields are attained for the derivatives with electron-attracting substituents (30–60%).[14,15]

Double salts of mercury halides and diarylhalogenonium compounds[24,25] can be employed instead of double diazonium salts for the preparation of organomercury compounds:

$$Ar_2HalX \cdot HgX_2 + M \longrightarrow ArHgX + ArHal + MX_2 \qquad (2)$$

In contrast to the diazo method, however, in the decomposition of the double salt of diphenyliodonium and mercury(II) chlorides metallic mercury (not copper) was shown to be the best reducing metal (Table I). Iron as a reducing agent gives diphenylmercury as the main product instead of the phenylmercury chloride that results from the decomposition of $(C_6H_5)_2$ $ICl \cdot HgCl_2$ by other metals (Table I).

TABLE I

Yields of Phenylmercury Chloride Obtained in the Decomposition
of $(C_6H_5)_2ICl \cdot HgCl_2$ under Various Conditions

Solvent	Yield of phenylmercury chloride, %				
	Reducing metal				
	Hg	Fe	Zn	Cu	Ag
Water	70	—	—	—	—
Acetone	34	3 (39)[a]	30	16	Not isolated
Ethanol	—	5 (21)[a]	Trace	9	—

[a] Yield of diphenylmercury is shown in parentheses.

In contrast to reaction (1), reaction (2) has been studied for only a few examples and is of purely theoretical interest. It may indicate only that the double diazonium and diarylhalogenonium salts behave analogously in the syntheses of organomercury compounds.

For synthetic purposes, instead of double salts of the type $Ar_2ICl \cdot HgCl_2$, it is more convenient to use diaryliodonium chlorides that decompose in the presence of mercury in acetone to arylmercury chlorides:

$$Ar_2ICl + Hg \longrightarrow ArHgCl + ArI \qquad (3)$$

The arylmercury chlorides were obtained in about the same (or sometimes higher) yields as in the reaction of copper with the double diazonium salts (Tables II and III). Taking into account the simplicity of the synthetic procedures and the availability of diaryliodonium salts, it can be concluded that both methods [reactions (1) and (3)] are convenient approaches to the preparation of organomercury compounds.

Aryldiazonium chlorides react with metallic mercury in an aqueous acidic medium[26] or acetone[27] in a manner similar to that of diaryliodonium chlorides

$$ArN_2Cl + Hg \longrightarrow ArHgCl + N_2 \qquad (4)$$

as also do diphenylchloronium and diphenylbromonium halides:[28]

$$(C_6H_5)_2Hal{-}X + Hg \longrightarrow C_6H_5Hal + C_6H_5Hg{-}X \qquad (5)$$
$$(Hal = Cl, Br; X = Cl, Br, I)$$

Yields of phenylmercury halides produced in the decomposition of phenyldiazonium chlorides and diarylhalogenonium halides with mercury are shown in Table II. As seen from this table, reactions (4) and (5) provide comparatively high yields of organomercury compounds (except the decomposition of diphenylchloronium chloride and iodide), about the same as the yields obtained from reactions (1) and (3). Reactions (4) and (5), however, are interesting only theoretically but not preparatively since diazonium salts are thermally unstable, and decompose sometimes explosively. On the other hand, the chloronium and bromonium salts are less available.[40]

Unlike halides, onium fluoborates reacting with mercury give no organomercury derivatives.[28,30,33] The latter, however, can be isolated if the reaction is conducted in the presence of substantially strong reducing agents. For example, the phenyldiazonium fluoborate–mercury(II) chloride mixture in acetone reacts with vigorously stirred $SnCl_2 \cdot 2H_2O \cdot HgCl_2$ suspended in aqueous acetone at room temperature, giving rise to phenylmercury chloride (60%).[33] Other organomercury compounds have been prepared analogously.[31,33] The authors[31,33] suggest that it is the very active, finely dispersed mercury produced in the reduction of mercury(II) chloride with tin(II) chloride that reacts with aryldiazonium fluoborate under the conditions described:

$$HgCl_2 + SnCl_2 \longrightarrow Hg + SnCl_4 \qquad (6)$$

In our opinion, however, such an explanation has no firm basis. It does not account for the possible exchange rections

$$2ArN_2BF_4 + HgCl_2 \longrightarrow 2ArN_2Cl + Hg(BF_4)_2 \qquad (7)$$

or

$$2ArN_2BF_4 + SnCl_2 \longrightarrow 2ArN_2Cl + Sn(BF_4)_2 \qquad (8)$$

and the subsequent decomposition of aryldiazonium chloride with mercury produced according to reaction (6):

$$ArN_2Cl + Hg \longrightarrow ArHgCl + N_2$$

Thus in this case one cannot ascertain unequivocally whether aryldiazonium chloride or its fluoborate is the reaction participant. This concept is also applicable to the reaction among diphenyliodonium fluoborate, tin(II) chloride, and mercury(II) chloride in acetone,[41] which also gives phenylmercury chloride.

TABLE II

Yields of Arylmercury Halides Obtained in the Decomposition of Aryldiazonium and Diaryliodonium Halides by Mercury

Starting material	Reaction Conditions	Product	Yield, %	Ref.
$p\text{-}(ClC_6H_4)_2ICl$	Acetone	$p\text{-}ClC_6H_4HgCl$	77	24
$p\text{-}(BrC_6H_4)_2ICl$	Acetone	$p\text{-}BrC_6H_4HgCl$	75	24
$m\text{-}(O_2NC_6H_4)_2ICl$	Acetone	$m\text{-}O_2NC_6H_4HgCl$	40	24
$C_6H_5N_2Cl$	Aqueous solution, $< 5°$	C_6H_5HgCl	45	26
	Acetone	C_6H_5HgCl	28	27
	Aqueous isopropanol	C_6H_5HgCl	15	28
$(C_6H_5)_2ClICl$	Isopropanol	C_6H_5HgCl	47	28
$(C_6H_5)_2BrCl$	Propanol	C_6H_5HgCl	40, 50	29, 30
$(C_6H_5)_2ICl$	Acetone	C_6H_5HgCl	76	24
$(C_6H_5)_2ClBr$	Aqueous isopropanol	C_6H_5HgBr	66	28
$(C_6H_5)_2BrBr$	Isopropanol	C_6H_5HgBr	41	28
$(C_6H_5)_2ClI$	Aqueous isopropanol	C_6H_5HgI	26	28
$(C_6H_5)_2BrI$	Isopropanol	C_6H_5HgI	45	28
$o\text{-}CH_3C_6H_4N_2Cl$	Aqueous solution, $< 5°$	$o\text{-}CH_3C_6H_4HgCl$	72	26
$p\text{-}CH_3C_6H_4N_2Cl$	Aqueous solution, $< 5°$	$p\text{-}CH_3C_6H_4HgCl$	52	26
$p\text{-}(CH_3C_6H_4)_2ICl$	Acetone	$p\text{-}CH_3C_6H_4HgCl$	55	24
$p\text{-}(CH_3OC_6H_4)_2ICl$	Acetone	$p\text{-}CH_3OC_6H_4HgCl$	53	24
$2,5\text{-}(CH_3)_2C_6H_3N_2Cl$	Aqueous solution, $< 5°$	$2,5\text{-}(CH_3)_2C_6H_3HgCl$	64	26
$m\text{-}(C_2H_5OCOC_6H_4)_2ICl$	Acetone	$m\text{-}C_2H_5OCOC_6H_4HgCl$	47	24
$\alpha\text{-}C_{10}H_7N_2Cl$	Aqueous solution, $< 5°$	$\alpha\text{-}C_{10}H_7HgCl$	20	26

TABLE III
Yields of Arylmercury Halides Obtained from Aryldiazonium and Diaryliodonium Double Salts

Starting material	Reaction conditions	Product	Yield, %	Ref.
2,5-Cl$_2$C$_6$H$_3$N$_2$Cl·HgCl$_2$	Cu, acetone	2,5-Cl$_2$C$_6$H$_3$HgCl	15	10, 11
o-FC$_6$H$_4$N$_2$BF$_4$	HgCl$_2$, SnCl$_2$, acetone + water	o-FC$_6$H$_4$HgCl	24	31
m-FC$_6$H$_4$N$_2$BF$_4$	HgCl$_2$, SnCl$_2$, acetone + water	m-FC$_6$H$_4$HgCl	28	31
p-FC$_6$H$_4$N$_2$BF$_4$	HgCl$_2$, SnCl$_2$, acetone + water	p-FC$_6$H$_4$HgCl	24	31
o-ClC$_6$H$_4$N$_2$Cl·HgCl$_2$	Cu, acetone, $-10°$	o-ClC$_6$H$_4$HgCl	56	10, 11
	Cu, water, 0°	o-ClC$_6$H$_4$HgCl	39	23
p-ClC$_6$H$_4$N$_2$Cl·HgCl$_2$	Cu, acetone, $-10°$	p-ClC$_6$H$_4$HgCl	25–46	10, 11
	Cu, water, 0°	p-ClC$_6$H$_4$HgCl	43	23
p-(ClC$_6$H$_4$)$_2$ICl·HgCl$_2$	Hg, water, 20°	p-ClC$_6$H$_4$HgCl	45	24
m-BrC$_6$H$_4$N$_2$Cl·HgCl$_2$	Cu, water, 0°	m-BrC$_6$H$_4$HgCl	43	23
p-BrC$_6$H$_4$N$_2$Cl·HgCl$_2$	Cu, acetone	p-BrC$_6$H$_4$HgCl	28	10, 11, 32
	Hg, acetone	p-BrC$_6$H$_4$HgCl	55	32
m-IC$_6$H$_4$N$_2$Cl·HgCl$_2$	Cu, water, 0°	m-IC$_6$H$_4$HgCl	53	23
p-IC$_6$H$_4$N$_2$Cl·HgCl$_2$	Cu, acetone	p-IC$_6$H$_4$HgCl	45	10, 11
o-O$_2$NC$_6$H$_4$N$_2$Cl·HgCl$_2$	Cu, ethyl acetate, $-10°$	o-O$_2$NC$_6$H$_4$HgCl	46	14
m-O$_2$NC$_6$H$_4$N$_2$Cl·HgCl$_2$	Cu, acetone, $-15°$	m-O$_2$NC$_6$H$_4$HgCl	59	14
	Cu, water, 0°	m-O$_2$NC$_6$H$_4$HgCl	27	23
p-O$_2$NC$_6$H$_4$N$_2$Cl·HgCl$_2$	Cu, ethyl acetate, $-10°$	p-O$_2$NC$_6$H$_4$HgCl	55	14, 19
m-HOC$_6$H$_4$N$_2$Cl·HgCl$_2$	Cu, ethanol	m-HOC$_6$H$_4$HgCl	43	13

$p\text{-}HOC_6H_4N_2Cl \cdot HgCl_2$	$p\text{-}HOC_6H_4HgCl$	Cu, ethanol, $-10°$	56	10, 11
$p\text{-}HO_3SC_6H_4N_2BF_4$	$p\text{-}HO_3SC_6H_4HgCl$	$HgCl_2$, $SnCl_2$, acetone + water	46	33
$p\text{-}HO_3SC_6H_4N_2Cl$	$p\text{-}HO_3SC_6H_4HgOSO_3H$	$HgCl_2$, Cu, acetone, $-20°$	30	14
$p\text{-}H_2NO_2SC_6H_4N_2Cl$	$p\text{-}H_2NO_2SC_6H_4HgCl$	$HgCl_2$, Cu_2Cl_2, water, HCl	33	34
$C_6H_5N_2Cl \cdot HgCl_2$	C_6H_5HgCl	Cu, acetone	46–86	1, 10, 35
	C_6H_5HgCl	Hg, acetone	18	32
	C_6H_5HgCl	Cu, water, $0°$	53	23
$C_6H_5N_2BF_4$	C_6H_5HgCl	$HgCl_2$, $SnCl_2$, acetone + water	60	33
$C_6H_5N_2I \cdot HgI_2$	C_6H_5HgI	Cu, ethanol	40	10, 11
$(C_6H_5)_2ClI \cdot HgI_2$	C_6H_5HgI	Cu, acetone, $20°$	22	25
$(C_6H_5)_2BrI \cdot HgI_2$	C_6H_5HgI	Cu, acetone, $20°$	39	25
$m\text{-}CF_3C_6H_4N_2Cl \cdot HgCl_2$	$m\text{-}CF_3C_6H_4HgCl$	Hg, acetone	20	32
$o\text{-}HOCOC_6H_4N_2Cl$	$o\text{-}HO_2CC_6H_4HgCl$	$HgCl_2$, Cu, acetone, $-70°$	39	14
$o\text{-}HOCOC_6H_4N_2BF_4$	$o\text{-}HO_2CC_6H_4HgCl$	$HgCl_2$, $SnCl_2$, water + acetone	34	33
$3\text{-}HO_2C\text{-}4\text{-}HOC_6H_3N_2BF_4$	$3\text{-}HO_2C\text{-}4\text{-}HOC_6H_3HgCl$	$HgCl_2$, $SnCl_2$, water + acetone	26	33
$o\text{-}CH_3C_6H_4N_2Cl \cdot HgCl_2$	$o\text{-}CH_3C_6H_4HgCl$	Cu, ethanol, $-5°$	66	10, 11
$o\text{-}CH_3C_6H_4N_2Cl \cdot HgCl_2$	$o\text{-}CH_3C_6H_4HgCl$	Cu, water, $0°$	58	23
$m\text{-}CH_3C_6H_4N_2Cl \cdot HgCl_2$	$m\text{-}CH_3C_6H_4HgCl$	Cu, acetone	57	12
$p\text{-}CH_3C_6H_4N_2Cl \cdot HgCl_2$	$p\text{-}CH_3C_6H_4HgCl$	Cu, acetone, $-5°$	66	10
$p\text{-}CH_3C_6H_4N_2Cl \cdot HgCl_2$	$p\text{-}CH_3C_6H_4HgCl$	Cu, water, $0°$	68	23
$o\text{-}CH_3OC_6H_4N_2Cl \cdot HgCl_2$	$o\text{-}CH_3OC_6H_4HgCl$	Cu, ethanol	72	10, 11
$o\text{-}CH_3OC_6H_4N_2Cl \cdot HgCl_2$	$o\text{-}CH_3OC_6H_4HgCl$	Cu, acetone	14	36
$p\text{-}CH_3OC_6H_4N_2Cl \cdot HgCl_2$	$p\text{-}CH_3OC_6H_4HgCl$	Cu, acetone	16	36
$(p\text{-}CH_3OC_6H_4)_2ICl \cdot HgCl_2$	$p\text{-}CH_3OC_6H_4HgCl$	Hg, water	28	24

(continued)

TABLE III (continued)

Starting material	Reaction conditions	Product	Yield, %	Ref.
o-CH$_3$SC$_6$H$_4$N$_2$Cl·HgCl$_2$	Cu, acetone, cool	o-CH$_3$SC$_6$H$_4$HgCl	53	18
p-(CH$_3$SC$_6$H$_4$N$_2$Cl)$_2$·HgCl$_2$	Cu, acetone, cool	p-CH$_3$SC$_6$H$_4$HgCl	75	18
o-CH$_3$OCOC$_6$H$_4$N$_2$Cl·HgCl$_2$	Cu, acetone	o-CH$_3$OCOC$_6$H$_4$HgCl	56	12
m-CH$_3$OCOC$_6$H$_4$N$_2$Cl·HgCl$_2$	Cu, acetone, −10°	m-CH$_3$OCOC$_6$H$_4$HgCl	31	12
p-CH$_3$OCOC$_6$H$_4$N$_2$Cl·HgCl$_2$	Cu, acetone, −15°	p-CH$_3$OCOC$_6$H$_4$HgCl	37	12
o-C$_2$H$_5$OC$_6$H$_4$N$_2$Cl·HgCl$_2$	Cu, acetone, −15°	o-C$_2$H$_5$OC$_6$H$_4$HgCl	19	36
p-C$_2$H$_5$OC$_6$H$_4$N$_2$Cl·HgCl$_2$	Cu, ethanol	p-C$_2$H$_5$OC$_6$H$_4$HgCl	77	10, 11
	Cu, water, 0°	p-C$_2$H$_5$OC$_6$H$_4$HgCl	69	23
	Cu, acetone, −15°	p-C$_2$H$_5$OC$_6$H$_4$HgCl	19	36
o-C$_2$H$_5$OCOC$_6$H$_4$N$_2$Cl·HgCl$_2$	Cu, acetone, −10°	o-C$_2$H$_5$OCOC$_6$H$_4$HgCl	29	12
m-C$_2$H$_5$OCOC$_6$H$_4$N$_2$Cl·HgCl$_2$	Cu, acetone, −10°	m-C$_2$H$_5$OCOC$_6$H$_4$HgCl	33	12
p-C$_2$H$_5$OCOC$_6$H$_4$N$_2$Cl·HgCl$_2$	Cu, acetone, −10°	p-C$_2$H$_5$OCOC$_6$H$_4$HgCl	45	12
	Cu, water, 0°	p-C$_2$H$_5$OCOC$_6$H$_4$HgCl	46–56	23
p-C$_2$H$_5$OCOC$_6$H$_4$N$_2$Cl	HgCl$_2$, Cu$_2$Cl$_2$, water, HCl	p-C$_2$H$_5$OCOC$_6$H$_4$HgCl	40	34
α-C$_{10}$H$_7$N$_2$Cl·HgCl$_2$	Cu, acetone	α-C$_{10}$H$_7$HgCl	20–58	10, 11, 37
	Cu, water, 0°	α-C$_{10}$H$_7$HgCl	67	23
β-C$_{10}$H$_7$N$_2$Cl·HgCl$_2$	Cu, acetone	β-C$_{10}$H$_7$HgCl	47	10, 11, 37
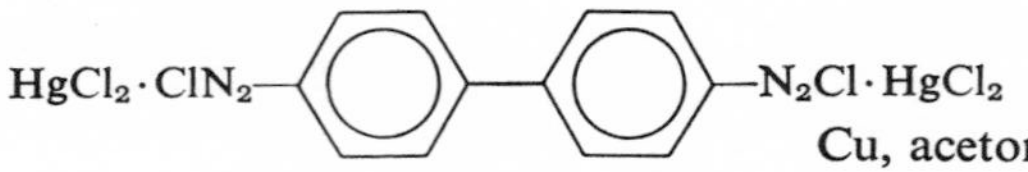 HgCl$_2$·ClN$_2$—C$_6$H$_4$—C$_6$H$_4$—N$_2$Cl·HgCl$_2$	Cu, acetone	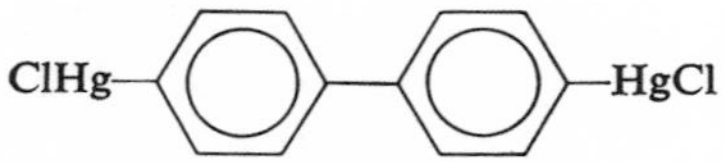 ClHg—C$_6$H$_4$—C$_6$H$_4$—HgCl	32	38
o-C$_6$H$_5$C$_6$H$_4$N$_2$Cl·HgCl$_2$	Cu, acetone	o-C$_6$H$_5$C$_6$H$_4$HgCl	—	38
p-C$_6$H$_5$C$_6$H$_4$N$_2$Cl·HgCl$_2$	Cu, acetone	p-C$_6$H$_5$C$_6$H$_4$HgCl	35	38

82

Starting material	Conditions	Product	Yield	Ref.
$p\text{-}C_6H_5C_6H_4N_2BF_4$	$HgCl_2$, $SnCl_2$, acetone + CH_3CO_2H	$p\text{-}C_6H_5C_6H_4HgCl$	Low	33
$o\text{-}C_6H_5OC_6H_4N_2Cl\cdot HgCl_2$	Cu, acetone	$o\text{-}C_6H_5OC_6H_4HgCl$	64	36
$m\text{-}C_6H_5OC_6H_4N_2Cl\cdot HgCl_2$	Cu, acetone	$m\text{-}C_6H_5OC_6H_4HgCl$	Low	36
$p\text{-}C_6H_5OC_6H_4N_2Cl\cdot HgCl_2$	Cu, acetone	$p\text{-}C_6H_5OC_6H_4HgCl$	59	36
$m\text{-}C_6H_5COC_6H_4N_2Cl\cdot HgCl_2$	Cu, acetone, $-10°$	$m\text{-}C_6H_5COC_6H_4HgCl$	46	15
$p\text{-}C_6H_5COC_6H_4N_2Cl\cdot HgCl_2$	Cu, acetone, $-10°$	$p\text{-}C_6H_5COC_6H_4HgCl$	40	15
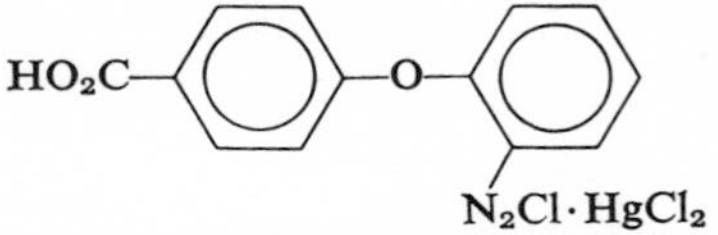 HO_2C-(diphenyl ether)-$N_2Cl\cdot HgCl_2$	Cu, acetone, $-60°$	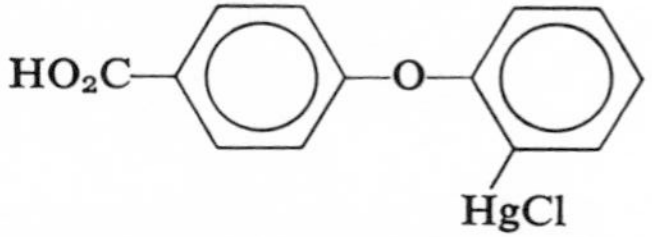 HO_2C-(diphenyl ether)-$HgCl$	—	39
$o\text{-}(m\text{-}CH_3C_6H_4O)C_6H_4N_2Cl\cdot HgCl_2$	Cu, acetone, $-60°$	$o\text{-}(m\text{-}CH_3C_6H_4O)C_6H_4HgCl$	57	39
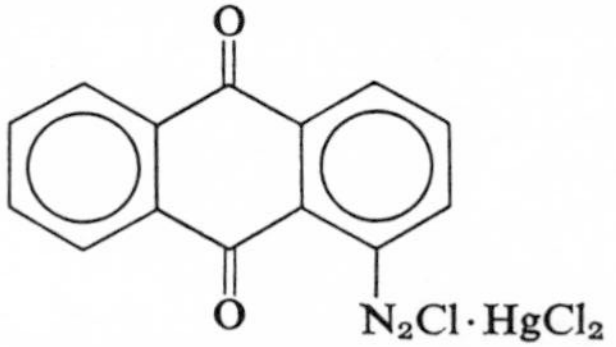 (anthraquinon-1-yl)$N_2Cl\cdot HgCl_2$	Cu, acetone, 20–$25°$	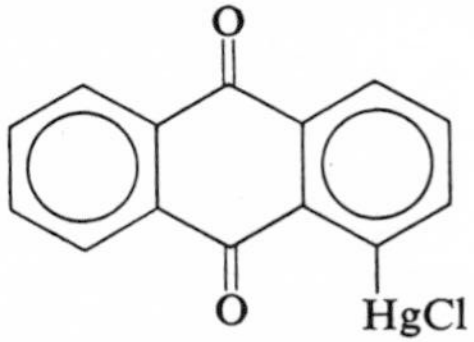 (anthraquinon-1-yl)$HgCl$	43	20
$p\text{-}CH_3C_6H_4COC_6H_4N_2Cl\cdot HgCl_2$	Cu, acetone, $-10°$	$p\text{-}(p\text{-}C_7H_7CO)C_6H_4HgCl$	45	15
$o\text{-}(C_6H_5)_2CHC_6H_4N_2Cl\cdot HgCl_2$	Cu, acetone, $-10°$	$o\text{-}(C_6H_5)_2CHC_6H_4HgCl$	12	16
$m\text{-}(C_6H_5)_2CHC_6H_4N_2Cl\cdot HgCl_2$	Cu, acetone, $-10°$	$m\text{-}(C_6H_5)_2CHC_6H_4HgCl$	31	16
$p\text{-}[(C_6H_5)_2CHC_6H_4N_2Cl]_2\cdot HgCl_2$	Cu, acetone, $-10°$	$p\text{-}(C_6H_5)_2CHC_6H_4HgCl$	41	16
$o\text{-}(C_6H_5)_2C(OH)C_6H_4N_2Cl\cdot HgCl_2$	Cu, acetone, $-10°$	$o\text{-}(C_6H_5)_2C(OH)C_6H_4HgCl$	12	16
$p\text{-}[(C_6H_5)_2C(OH)C_6H_4N_2Cl]_2\cdot HgCl_2$	$HgCl_2$, Cu, ethyl acetate, cooling	$p\text{-}(C_6H_5)_2C(OH)C_6H_4HgCl$	46	16
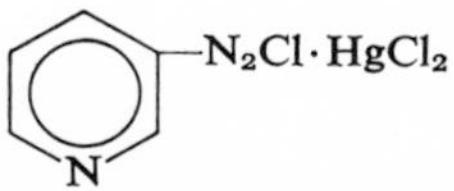 (pyridin-3-yl)$N_2Cl\cdot HgCl_2$	Cu, acetone, $-12°$	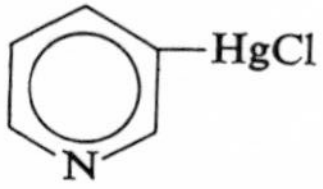 (pyridin-3-yl)$HgCl$	30	21

Diaryliodonium fluoborate decomposes with iron or copper in the presence of mercury.[42] It is an example in which organomercury derivatives are prepared from onium fluoborates under conditions excluding exchange reactions (7) and (8). It leads to diarylmercury compounds (Table IV):

$$2Ar_2IBF_4 + M + Hg \longrightarrow Ar_2Hg + 2ArI + M(BF_4)_2 \qquad (9)$$

As seen from Table IV, the yields of organomercury compounds obtained when iron is used as the reducing agent are satisfactory and can be compared with those attained by the Nesmeyanov diazo method, although the reaction proceeds rather slowly. The reaction rate increases sharply when copper is used instead of iron, but the yield of diarylmercury decreases comparably.

Thus in the Nesmeyanov diazo method copper is the best reducing agent for the preparation of both symmetrical (Ar_2Hg) and asymmetrical ($ArHgX$) organomercury derivatives. However, in the synthesis of these compounds from diaryliodonium salts copper is one of the least suitable reducing agents.

It should be pointed out that reaction (9) proceeds readily only in alcohol and does not take place in acetone. Factors that may be responsible for this phenomenon are discussed in Section VII.

It has been shown[47] that diazo compounds of another type—arylazocarboxylic salts—can in principle also be employed for the preparation of organomercury compounds. They react immediately with mercury(II) chloride in acetone. Gas evolution and formation of arylmercury halide are observed:

$$ArN{=}NCOOK + HgCl_2 \longrightarrow ArHgCl + N_2 + CO_2 + KCl \qquad (10)$$

Yields of ArHgCl range from 30 to 50% (Table V), being somewhat lower than those obtained by the Nesmeyanov diazo method. Large quantities of by-products were isolated: mercury(I) chloride and the products of replacement of the diazo group with H—ArH. When phenylmercury chloride is used instead of mercury(II) chloride, diphenylmercury is the reaction product:

$$C_6H_5N{=}N{-}COOK + C_6H_5HgCl \longrightarrow (C_6H_5)_2Hg + N_2 + CO_2 + KCl \quad (11)$$

B. Reactions with Magnesium, Zinc, and Cadmium

In contrast to the case of mercury reactions, information on the reactions of onium compounds with magnesium, zinc, and cadmium is rather scant and very approximate.

Of all these metals, only magnesium leads to organometallic compounds via onium salts. As the onium salts, aryldiazonium fluoborates are used. It may be noted that aryldiazonium fluoborates react very slowly with magnesium. For example, at room temperature the reaction terminates in 5 months in

TABLE IV

Yields of Symmetrical Organomercury Compounds Obtained from Onium Salts

Starting material	Reaction conditions[a]	Product	Yield, %	Ref.
$2,5\text{-}Cl_2C_6H_3N_2Cl\cdot HgCl_2$	NH_3, $-15°$	$(2,5\text{-}Cl_2C_6H_3)_2Hg$	20	43
$p\text{-}(ClC_6H_4)_2IBF_4$	$20°$, 22 hr[b]	$(p\text{-}ClC_6H_4)_2Hg$	26	42
$p\text{-}BrC_6H_4N_2Cl\cdot HgCl_2$	NH_3, $-15°$	$(p\text{-}BrC_6H_4)_2Hg$	57	43, 44
$p\text{-}IC_6H_4N_2Cl\cdot HgCl_2$	NH_3, $-15°$	$(p\text{-}IC_6H_4)_2Hg$	70	43
$p\text{-}O_2NC_6H_4N_2Cl\cdot HgCl_2$	NH_3, $-15°$	$(p\text{-}O_2NC_6H_4)_2Hg$	10	43
$C_6H_5N_2Cl\cdot HgCl_2$	NH_3, $-15°$	$(C_6H_5)_2Hg$	65	43, 44
$(C_6H_5)_2ICl\cdot HgCl_2$	$20°$, 30 hr[b]	$(C_6H_5)_2Hg$	53	42
$(C_6H_5)_2IBF_4$	$20°$, 1 hr	$(C_6H_5)_2Hg$	14	42
$m\text{-}CH_3C_6H_4N_2Cl\cdot HgCl_2$	NH_3	$(m\text{-}CH_3C_6H_4)_2Hg$	55, 79	12, 45
$p\text{-}CH_3C_6H_4N_2Cl\cdot HgCl_2$	NH_3	$(p\text{-}CH_3C_6H_4)_2Hg$	76	43, 44
$p\text{-}(CH_3C_6H_4)_2IBF_4$	$20°$, 25 hr[b]	$(p\text{-}CH_3C_6H_4)_2Hg$	66	42
$o\text{-}CH_3OC_6H_4N_2Cl\cdot HgCl_2$	NH_3	$(o\text{-}CH_3OC_6H_4)_2Hg$	23–60	36, 44
$p\text{-}CH_3OC_6H_4N_2Cl\cdot HgCl_2$	NH_3	$(p\text{-}CH_3OC_6H_4)_2Hg$	58	36, 45
$(p\text{-}CH_3OC_6H_4)_2IBF_4$	$20°$, 50 hr[b]	$(p\text{-}CH_3OC_6H_4)_2Hg$	43	42
$p\text{-}CH_3SC_6H_4N_2Cl\cdot HgCl_2$	Cool[c]	$(p\text{-}CH_3SC_6H_4)_2Hg$	89	18
$o\text{-}CH_3O_2C\text{—}C_6H_4N_2Cl\cdot HgCl_2$	$-10°$[c]	$(o\text{-}CH_3O_2C\text{—}C_6H_4)_2Hg$	23	12
$m\text{-}CH_3O_2C\text{—}C_6H_4N_2Cl\cdot HgCl_2$	$-10°$[c]	$(m\text{-}CH_3O_2C\text{—}C_6H_4)_2Hg$	28	12
$p\text{-}CH_3O_2C\text{—}C_6H_4N_2Cl\cdot HgCl_2$	NH_3	$(p\text{-}CH_3O_2C\text{—}C_6H_4)_2Hg$	68	12
$o\text{-}C_2H_5OC_6H_4N_2Cl\cdot HgCl_2$	NH_3	$(o\text{-}C_2H_5OC_6H_4)_2Hg$	60	36, 45
$p\text{-}C_2H_5OC_6H_4N_2Cl\cdot HgCl_2$	NH_3	$(p\text{-}C_2H_5OC_6H_4)_2Hg$	59	45
$2,4,5\text{-}(CH_3)_3C_6H_2N_2Cl\cdot HgCl_2$	NH_3	$[2,4,5\text{-}(CH_3)_3C_6H_2]_2Hg$	72	45
$o\text{-}C_2H_5O_2CC_6H_4N_2Cl\cdot HgCl_2$	NH_3	$(o\text{-}C_2H_5O_2C\text{—}C_6H_4)_2Hg$	60	12

(continued)

85

TABLE IV (continued)

Starting Material	Reaction Conditions[a]	Product	Yield, %	Ref.
m-$C_2H_5O_2C$—$C_6H_4N_2Cl \cdot HgCl_2$	NH_3	(m-$C_2H_5O_2C$—$C_6H_4)_2Hg$	60	12
p-$C_2H_5O_2C$—$C_6H_4N_2Cl \cdot HgCl_2$	NH_3	(p-$C_2H_5O_2C$—$C_6H_4)_2Hg$	89	12
α-$C_{10}H_7N_2Cl \cdot HgCl_2$	NH_3	(α-$C_{10}H_7)_2Hg$	53	43
β-$C_{10}H_7N_2Cl \cdot HgCl_2$	NH_3	(β-$C_{10}H_7)_2Hg$	40–48	37, 46
o-$C_6H_5OC_6H_4N_2Cl \cdot HgCl_2$	NH_3	(o-$C_6H_5OC_6H_4)_2Hg$	—	36
p-$C_6H_5OC_6H_4N_2Cl \cdot HgCl_2$	NH_3	(p-$C_6H_5OC_6H_4)_2Hg$	81	36
p-$C_6H_5COC_6H_4N_2Cl \cdot HgCl_2$	$-10°$	(p-$C_6H_5COC_6H_4)_2Hg$	—	46
[anthraquinone bearing $N_2Cl \cdot HgCl_2$]	NH_3, $0°$		98	20
[4-bromopyridine bearing $N_2Cl \cdot HgCl_2$]				

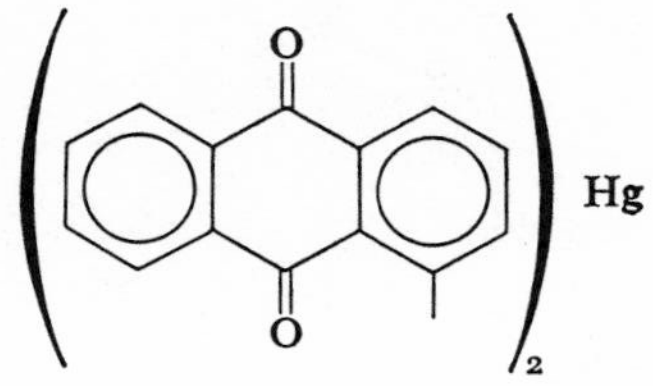

−12°, KI, NaOH

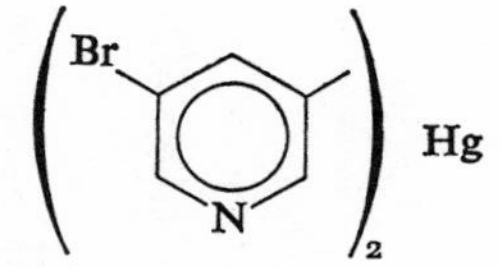

13   21

[a] Unless otherwise indicated, all reactions conducted with copper powder in acetone in the presence of mercury.
[b] Reaction with iron.
[c] Reaction in aqueous acetone.

anisole and in 6 months in diethyl or in dibutyl ether. In tetrahydrofuran the reaction is somewhat faster, but it again requires no less than 3–6 days.[48] The yields of organomagnesium compounds are negligible. Hence the reaction is of purely theoretical interest.

TABLE V

Yields of Organomercury Compounds Obtained from
Arylazocarboxylic Salts[47]

Ar in ArN_2COOK	Catalyst[a]	Product	Yield, %
p-BrC_6H_4—	$HgCl_2$	p-BrC_6H_4HgCl	33
p-$O_2NC_6H_4$—	$HgCl_2$	p-$O_2NC_6H_4HgCl$	42
p-$HO_3SC_6H_4$—	$HgCl_2$, Cu	p-$HO_3SC_6H_4HgOSO_3H$	31
C_6H_5—	$HgBr_2$	C_6H_5HgBr	40
C_6H_5—	$HgCl_2$	C_6H_5HgCl	54
p-$CH_3C_6H_4$—	$HgCl_2$	p-$CH_3C_6H_4HgCl$	33
β-$C_{10}H_7$—	$HgCl_2$	β-$C_{10}H_7HgCl$	41

[a] All reactions conducted in acetone at room temperature.

Reaction of the above-mentioned metals with phenyldiazonium salts was also investigated.[49] Magnesium and cadmium react very slowly when cooled. Only traces of the corresponding salts ($MgCl_2$, $CdCl_2$) were isolated, along with benzene and diphenyl.[49] Zinc reacts very rapidly at 0°, giving rise to zinc chloride and benzene. In aryldiazonium fluoborates the diazo group exchanges with hydrogen in reaction with zinc in ethanol. The yields of the corresponding ArH are usually 70–80%.[50]

III. SYNTHESIS OF THALLIUM ORGANIC COMPOUNDS

The preparation of organothallium compounds is best performed by using onium fluoborates as the starting materials. The decomposition of ArN_2BF_4 in acetone with thallium powder or thallium–sodium alloy results in diarylthallium derivatives Ar_2TlX:[51]

$$2ArN_2BF_4 + 2Tl \longrightarrow Ar_2TlBF_4 + 2N_2 + TlBF_4 \tag{12}$$

or

$$2ArN_2BF_4 + NaTl \longrightarrow Ar_2TlBF_4 + 2N_2 + NaBF_4 \tag{13}$$

In the case of the phenyl group the yield is 20%; for other aryls it is as high as 10%.[51]

TABLE VI
Yields of Organothallium Compounds Obtained from Onium Salts

Starting salt	Reaction conditions[a]	Product	Yield, %	Ref.
m-$ClC_6H_4N_2BF_4$	Tl/Na, −8°	(m-ClC_6H_4)$_2$TlCl	<10	51
p-$ClC_6H_4N_2BF_4$	Tl, −4°	(p-ClC_6H_4)$_2$TlCl	<10	51
$C_6H_5N_2BF_4$	Tl, −14°	(C_6H_5)$_2$TlCl	20	51
	Tl/Na, −15°	(C_6H_5)$_2$TlCl	18	51
(C_6H_5)$_2$ClBF$_4$	Tl, 20°	(C_6H_5)$_2$TlCl	19	28
(C_6H_5)$_2$BrBF$_4$	Tl, 20°	(C_6H_5)$_2$TlCl	11.5	28
(C_6H_5)$_2$IBF$_4$	Tl, 20°	(C_6H_5)$_2$TlCl	12	28
$C_6H_5N_2Cl·TlCl_3$	Fe, Tl, or Zn[b]	(C_6H_5)$_2$TlCl	<10	51
(C_6H_5)$_2$BrI	Tl, 20°		0	28
o-$CH_3C_6H_4N_2BF_4$	Tl/Na, −18°	(o-$CH_3C_6H_4$)$_2$TlCl	<10	51
p-$CH_3C_6H_4N_2BF_4$	Tl/Na, −18°	(p-$CH_3C_6H_4$)$_2$TlCl	<10	51
p-$CH_3C_6H_4N_2Cl·TlCl_3$	Tl/Na, −8°	(p-$CH_3C_6H_4$)$_2$TlCl	<10	51
o-$CH_3OC_6H_4N_2BF_4$	Tl/Na, −17°	(o-$CH_3OC_6H_4$)$_2$TlCl	10	51
p-$CH_3OC_6H_4N_2BF_4$	Tl/Na, −15°	(p-$CH_3OC_6H_6$)$_2$TlCl	10	51
p-$C_2H_5OC_6H_4N_2BF_4$	Tl/Na, −16°	(p-$C_2H_5OC_6H_4$)$_2$TlCl	<10	51
p-$C_2H_5OCOC_6H_4N_2BF_4$	Tl/Na, 0°	(p-$C_2H_5OCOC_6H_4$)$_2$TlCl	<10	51

[a] All reactions conducted in acetone.
[b] Zinc first treated with CuSo$_4$.

Diphenylchloronium, diphenylbromonium, and diphenyliodonium fluoborates[28] react analogously to phenyldiazonium fluoborate:

$$(C_6H_5)_2HalBF_4 + 2Tl \longrightarrow (C_6H_5)_2TlBF_4 + 2C_6H_5Hal + TlBF_4 \qquad (14)$$

The method employing double diazonium salts for the preparation of organothallium compounds is practically unacceptable. The double salts of thallium chloride and phenyldiazonium or p-tolyldiazonium chloride are decomposed by thallium, iron, and zinc powders (zinc is first treated with copper sulfate solution). The yields of organothallium compounds Ar_2TlX are negligible.[51]

The reaction of phenyldiazonium chloride[49] or diphenylbromonium iodide[28] with metallic thallium in acetone gave no thallium derivatives.

The yields of thallium organic derivatives from various onium compounds are listed in Table VI.

IV. PREPARATION OF ORGANOMETALLIC COMPOUNDS OF GERMANIUM, TIN, AND LEAD

A. Organogermanium Compounds

Organogermanium compounds have been obtained only by the decomposition of aryldiazonium fluoborates with metallic powders in the presence of germanium(IV) chloride. Zinc is the best reducer and acetone the best solvent. These conditions lead to monoarylgermanium derivatives isolated in the form of acids. The yield is maximal in the case of the phenyl compound (28%). Other arylgermanium acids are obtained in negligible quantities.[52] (see Table VII).

TABLE VII

Yields of Organogermanium Compounds Obtained from Onium Salts[52]

Starting salt	T, °C[a]	Product	Yield, %
p-ClC$_6$H$_4$N$_2$BF$_4$	-7.5 to -0.5	$(p$-ClC$_6$H$_4$GeO)$_2$O	~ 2
p-BrC$_6$H$_4$N$_2$BF$_4$	-11 to -5	$(p$-BrC$_6$H$_4$GeO)$_2$O	~ 3
C$_6$H$_5$N$_2$BF$_4$	-7 to $+6$	$(C_6H_5GeO)_2O$	27
p-CH$_3$OC$_6$H$_4$N$_2$BF$_4$	-7 to $+6$	$(p$-CH$_3$OC$_6$H$_4$GeO)$_2$O	~ 2
p-C$_2$H$_5$OC$_6$H$_4$N$_2$BF$_4$	-4 to $+5$	$(p$-C$_2$H$_5$OC$_6$H$_4$GeO)$_2$O	~ 2

[a] All reactions conducted in acetone with zinc powder in the presence of GeCl$_4$.

Preparation of the germanium organic derivatives by the diazo method is again unacceptable since, unlike tin(IV) and lead(IV) chlorides, germanium (IV) chloride forms no double salts with diazonium salts.[52]

Phenyldiazonium chloride does not react with germanium in acetone.[49]

B. Organotin Compounds

Organotin compounds (unlike the germanium ones) can be obtained by decomposing either onium fluoborates[28,41,53] or the double salts $(ArN_2Cl)_2 \cdot SnCl_4$[54,55] and $[(C_6H_5)_2HalCl]_2 \cdot SnCl_4$ (Hal = Cl, Br, or I),[25] as can be seen from Table VIII. The use of the double salts of diarylhalogenonium and

TABLE VIII
Preparation of Diphenyl and Triphenyl Tin Compounds
via Onium Salts

Starting material	T, °C[a]	Yield, %			Ref.
		Ar_2SnX_2	Ar_3SnX	Total	
$(C_6H_5N_2Cl)_2 \cdot SnCl_4$	78[b]	23	—	23	54, 55
$[(C_6H_5)_2ClCl]_2 \cdot SnCl_4$	20	57	—	57	25
$[(C_6H_5)_2BrCl]_2 \cdot SnCl_4$	20	55	—	55	25
$[(C_6H_5)_2ICl]_2 \cdot SnCl_2$	20	76	—	76	56
$C_6H_5N_2BF_4$	3–18[c]	41	2	43	53
$(C_6H_5)_2BrBF_4$	56			51	28
$(C_6H_5)_2IBF_4$	40–60[d]	—	37	37	41
$C_6H_5N_2Cl$	< 20	~2		2	57
$(C_6H_5)_2ICl$		No reaction			56
$(C_6H_5)_2BrI$	20	Trace	15	15	28

[a] Unless otherwise indicated, all reactions conducted in acetone with tin powder.
[b] Ethyl acetate was used as solvent.
[c] $SnCl_2/Zn$ was used as catalyst.
[d] Ethanol was used as solvent.

tin(IV) chlorides provides good yields of tin organic derivatives. These reactions, however, have been studied only for the phenyl radical and are of purely theoretical interest. In contrast, the decomposition of the double salts of aryldiazonium and tin(IV) chlorides has been investigated in more detail[54,55] By employing a variety of reducing metals and solvents, the authors have found that maximal yield of diphenylstannanic acid can be attained by refluxing $(ArN_2Cl)_2 \cdot SnCl_4$ with tin powder in ethyl acetate. Other organotin derivatives are obtained in much lower yields under the conditions described (Table IX), which essentially precludes the method.

TABLE IX
Yields of Organotin Compounds Obtained from Onium Salts

	Total yield, %, of organotin compounds obtained from		Ar$_2$ICl + SnCl$_2$	
Ar	ArN$_2$BF$_4$ + SnCl$_2$ + Zn[a]	(ArN$_2$Cl)$_2$·SnCl$_4$[b]	A[c]	B[d]
p-ClC$_6$H$_4$—	21	4.7	82	67
p-BrC$_6$H$_4$—	29.4	6	47	62
p-IC$_6$H$_4$—			39	
p-O$_2$NC$_6$H$_4$—	2.5			
C$_6$H$_5$—	43	23	76	62
o-CH$_3$C$_6$H$_4$—	40.3	20		
p-CH$_3$C$_6$H$_4$—	38.4		67	42
o-CH$_3$OC$_6$H$_4$—		7.5		
p-CH$_3$OC$_6$H$_4$—			50	
o-CH$_3$OCOC$_6$H$_4$—	7.3	10		
m-C$_2$H$_5$OCOC$_6$H$_4$—			42	51
β-C$_{10}$H$_7$—	11			

[a] Data from Ref. 53.
[b] Data from Refs. 54 and 55.
[c] Reaction conducted with tin powder in acetone. Data from Ref. 56.
[d] Reaction conducted in methanol. Data from Ref. 58.

The use of aryldiazonium fluoborates instead of double salts of the type $(ArN_2Cl)_2·SnCl_4$ substantially improves the yields of organotin derivatives but leads to a mixture of monoaryl, diaryl, and triaryl tin compounds.[53] Decomposition of the mixture of diaryliodonium and tin(II) chlorides with tin in acetone[56] is most convenient preparatively:

$$2Ar_2ICl + Sn \xrightarrow{\text{SnCl}_2} Ar_2SnCl_2 + SnCl_2 + 2ArI \qquad (15)$$

We have since found[58] that diaryliodonium salts may also decompose with tin(II) chloride alone. This reaction is much slower than reaction (15), and, depending on conditions, can lead to aryl or diaryl tin derivatives. When methanol, for example, is used as solvent, diaryl compounds of the type Ar_2SnCl_2 result in good yields at relatively high reagent concentrations (about 0.5 M and higher). Yields of the organotin derivatives obtained are listed in Table IX, which also shows the yields of organotin compounds produced in the decomposition of the mixture of Ar$_2$ICl and SnCl$_2$ with tin powder.

As seen from Table IX, both methods provide good yields of organotin compounds. Taking into account the availability of diaryliodonium salts and the simplicity of their preparation, these methods can be recommended as convenient preparative procedures for diaryl tin compounds.

The tin(II) chloride is very important in the preparation of organotin compounds by the decomposition of a mixture of Ar_2ICl with tin, since diazonium and halogenonium halides are known to exhibit absolutely no interaction with tin[56] or to give very small quantities of tin derivatives[28,49] (Table VIII).

C. Lead Organic Derivatives

Diazonium,[59] iodonium,[41] and bromonium[28] fluoborates are most favorable for the preparation of lead organic derivatives. They decompose with lead powder in acetone. Diazonium fluoborate also decomposes with lead–sodium alloy.

$$ArN_2BF_4 + Pb \longrightarrow Ar_4Pb + N_2 + Pb(BF_4)_2 \qquad (16)$$

or

$$Ar_2HalBF_4 + Pb \longrightarrow Ar_4Pb + ArHal + Pb(BF_4)_2 \qquad (17)$$
$$(Ar = phenyl\ and\ p\text{-}tolyl)$$

However, as may be seen from Table X, the yields of organolead compounds are rather low. The preparation of the organolead compounds via onium

TABLE X

Yields of Organolead Compounds Obtained from Onium Salts

Starting material	Reaction conditions[a]	Total yield of product, %	Ref.
$C_6H_5N_2BF_4$	Pb, 15–17°	15	59
	Pb/Na, 15–17°	30	59
$C_6H_5N_2Cl + PbCl_2$	Cu, 56°	Low	60
$(C_6H_5N_2Cl)_2PbCl_4$	Zn or Cu[b]	Low	60
$(C_6H_5)_2BrBF_4$	Pb, 20°	19	28
$(C_6H_5)_2IBF_4$	Pb, 20°[c]	25	41
	Pb, 20°[d]	28	41
$p\text{-}FC_6H_4N_2BF_4$	Pb	[e]	59
$p\text{-}CH_3C_6H_4N_2BF_4$	Pb/Na	15	59

[a] Unless otherwise indicated, all reactions conducted in acetone.
[b] Reaction conducted in ether.
[c] Reaction conducted in absolute ethanol.
[d] Reaction conducted in water.
[e] Not isolated.

TABLE XI

Yields of Phosphonic and Phosphinic Acids Obtained from Diazonium Salts

Starting salt	Reaction conditions[a]	Yield, %			Ref.
		$ArPO_3H_2$	Ar_2PO_2H	Total	
2-Br-5-$O_2NC_6H_3N_2BF_4$	PBr$_3$, isopropyl acetate	15	12	27	63
2-Cl-4-$O_2NC_6H_3N_2BF_4$	PBr$_3$, ethyl acetate	20	2	22	63
2,5-$Cl_2C_6H_3N_2BF_4$	PBr$_3$, ethyl acetate	32	13	45	63
o-BrC$_6$H$_4$N$_2$BF$_4$	PCl$_3$, ethyl acetate	37	13	50	62
	PCl$_3$, isopropyl acetate	31	13	44	
	PBr$_3$, ethyl acetate	35	14	49	62
	PBr$_3$, isopropyl acetate	17	17	34	
m-BrC$_6$H$_4$N$_2$BF$_4$	PCl$_3$, ethyl acetate	47	6	53	62
	PCl$_3$, isopropyl acetate	34	20	54	
	PBr$_3$, ethyl acetate	39	15	54	62
	PBr$_3$, isopropyl acetate	21	19	40	
p-BrC$_6$H$_4$N$_2$BF$_4$	PCl$_3$, ethyl acetate	61	1	62	62
	PCl$_3$, isopropyl acetate	49	15	54	
	PBr$_3$, ethyl acetate	45	8	53	62
	PBr$_3$, isopropyl acetate	21	11	33	
(p-BrC$_6$H$_4$N$_2$Cl)$_2$·ZnCl$_2$	PCl$_3$	18	0	18	64
o-ClC$_6$H$_4$N$_2$BF$_4$	PCl$_3$, ethyl acetate	44	10	54	66
m-ClC$_6$H$_4$N$_2$BF$_4$	PCl$_3$, ethyl acetate	43	7	50	64, 66
(m-ClC$_6$H$_4$N$_2$)$_2$SiF$_6$	PCl$_3$, ethyl acetate	35	9	44	64
p-ClC$_6$H$_4$N$_2$BF$_4$	PCl$_3$, ethyl acetate	50	7	57	66
o-FC$_6$H$_4$N$_2$BF$_4$	PCl$_3$, ethyl acetate	41	11	52	63
o-IC$_6$H$_4$N$_2$BF$_4$	PBr$_3$, ethyl acetate	22	28	50	63

94

					References
m-$O_2NC_6H_4N_2BF_4$	PCl_3, ethyl acetate	37	6	43	64, 66
	PCl_3, isopropyl acetate	27	26	53	64, 66
$(m$-$O_2NC_6H_4N_2)_2SiF_6$	PCl_3, isopropyl acetate	48	3	51	64
p-$O_2NC_6H_4N_2BF_4$	PCl_3, isopropyl acetate	47	6	53	64, 65
$(p$-$O_2NC_6H_4N_2)_2SiF_6$	PCl_3, isopropyl acetate	50	3	53	64, 65
$(p$-$O_2NC_6H_4N_2Cl)_2 \cdot ZnCl_2$	PCl_3, isopropyl acetate	Trace	1		64
p-$H_2NO_2SC_6H_4N_2BF_4$	PCl_3, ethyl acetate	50	0	50	66
$C_6H_5N_2BF_4$	PCl_3, ethyl acetate	17	4	21	64, 66
$(C_6H_5N_2)_2SiF_6$	PCl_3, ethyl acetate	19	10	29	64, 66
o-$HO_2CC_6H_4N_2BF_4$	PBr_3, ethyl acetate	37	0	37	63
p-$HO_2CC_6H_4N_2BF_4$	PBr_3, ethyl acetate	39	0	39	66
2-Br-5-$CH_3C_6H_3N_2BF_4$	PBr_3, ethyl acetate	27	12	39	63
2-CH_3O-4-$O_2NC_6H_3N_2BF_4$	PBr_3, ethyl acetate	20	2	22	63
p-$CH_3C_6H_4N_2BF_4$	PBr_3, ethyl acetate	42		42	66
o-$CH_3OC_6H_4N_2BF_4$	PBr_3, ethyl acetate	20	10	30	63

ᵃ All reactions conducted with Cu_2Br_2.

fluoborates cannot be accepted as a common procedure since reaction (16) was carried out for only two examples. No organolead compounds were obtained from p-$FC_6H_4N_2BF_4$. We were also unable to prepare an organolead derivative by treating Ar_2IBF_4 ($Ar = p$-$CH_3C_6H_4$— and p-$CH_3OC_6H_4$—) with lead in acetone. Synthesis of organolead compounds from double diazonium salts is of purely theoretical interest[60] (Table X). It is noteworthy that the double salt $(C_6H_5N_2Cl)_2 \cdot PbCl_4$ reacts faster in ether with zinc powder as the reducing agent. A mixture of the double salt $C_6H_5N_2Cl \cdot PbCl_2$ and $PbCl_2$ is converted to the organolead derivative only in the presence of copper in acetone.

V. ORGANOELEMENT COMPOUNDS OF PHOSPHORUS, ARSENIC, ANTIMONY, AND BISMUTH

A. Organophosphorus Compounds

Of all possible onium compounds, only diazonium salts have been employed for the direct synthesis of organophosphorus compounds. Addition of PCl_3 (or PBr_3) and Cu_2Br_2 to a suspension of ArN_2BF_4 or $(ArN_2)_2SiF_6$ in ethyl acetate gives a mixture of phosphonic and phosphinic acids[61-66] in overall yields of 20–60% (Table XI). The ratio between them is defined by the substituent in the aromatic group and the anion of the diazonium salt, although phosphonic acid is always produced in larger quantity than phosphinic acid. Their overall yield depends little on the anion[64] and is practically unchanged for various phenyl-substituted isomers (see Table XI).

The use of phenylphosphine dichloride instead of phosphorus(III) chloride leads to asymmetrical phosphinic acids $Ar(C_6H_5)POOH$ (Table XII).[64,67]

TABLE XII

Yields of Phosphinic Acids Obtained by the Interaction of Diazonium Salts with $C_6H_5PCl_2$ in the Presence of Cu_2Br_2

	Yield, % from	
Product	ArN_2BF_4[a]	$(ArN_2)_2SiF_6$[b]
$(C_6H_5)_2PO_2H$	40–42	33
o-$BrC_6H_4(C_6H_5)PO_2H$	15–31	29
m-$ClC_6H_4(C_6H_5)PO_2H$	27–68	41
m-$O_2NC_6H_4(C_6H_5)PO_2H$	36–47	41
p-$O_2NC_6H_4(C_6H_5)PO_2H$	30	32

[a] Data from Refs. 64 and 67.
[b] Data from Ref. 64.

Double diazonium salts $(ArN_2Cl)_2 \cdot ZnCl_2$ can be used instead of ArN_2BF_4 or $(ArN_2)_2SiF_6$, but the yields of the phosphorus organic acids are somewhat lower.[64]

Waters[49] has shown that phenyldiazonium chloride does not react with red phosphorus in acetone.

B. Organoarsenic Compounds

According to published data, organoarsenic compounds, like phosphorus compounds, are obtained only from the diazonium salts. Waters[49,68] discovered that the double salt $(ArN_2Cl)_2 \cdot ZnCl_2$ decomposes with zinc in acetone below 5° in the presence of an equimolar amount of $AsCl_3$, giving a good yield of triphenylarsine.[68]

Reutov and Bundel[69-71] showed in detail that double diazonium salts of zinc and iron(III) chlorides are decomposed by metallic powders in the presence of arsenic(III) chloride in acetone. They found that by varying the reaction conditions (the starting double diazonium salt, its ratio with arsenic(III) chloride, and the amount of reducing metal) a variety of the organo-arsenic compounds can be obtained: $ArAsX_2$, Ar_2AsX, Ar_3As, Ar_3AsX_2.

Reaction between arylated [arsenic(III) chloride] and arylating (double diazonium salt) reagents defines greatly the structures of the products (Table XIII). In general the larger the amount of the double salt, the higher the yields of Ar_3As and Ar_3AsX_2, and thus the lower the yields of monosubstituted and disubstituted trivalent arsenic derivatives. The total yield of arsenic organic compounds is 3–66% (Table XIII).

Thus by varying the conditions, one may arrive at predominantly the aryl, diaryl, or triaryl derivative of arsenic. The reactions proceed as follows:

$$ArN_2Cl \cdot FeCl_3 + AsCl_3 + Fe \longrightarrow ArAsCl_2 + N_2 + FeCl_3 + FeCl_2 \qquad (18)$$

$$2ArN_2Cl \cdot FeCl_3 + AsCl_3 + 2Fe \longrightarrow Ar_2AsCl + 2N_2 + 2FeCl_3 + 2FeCl_2 \qquad (19)$$

$$3ArN_2Cl \cdot FeCl_3 + AsCl_3 + 3Fe \longrightarrow Ar_3As + 3N_2 + 3FeCl_3 + 3FeCl_2 \qquad (20)$$

$$3ArN_2Cl \cdot FeCl_3 + AsCl_3 + 2Fe \longrightarrow Ar_3AsCl_2 + 3N_2 + 3FeCl_3 + 2FeCl_2 \qquad (21)$$

In fact, however, arsenic compounds are probably produced from double diazonium salts and arsenic(III) chloride resulting from exchange reactions:

$$ArN_2Cl \cdot FeCl_3 + AsCl_3 \rightleftharpoons ArN_2Cl \cdot AsCl_3 + FeCl_3 \qquad (22)$$

$$ArN_2Cl \cdot AsCl_3 + Fe \longrightarrow ArAsCl_2 + N_2 + FeCl_2 \qquad (23)$$

$$(ArN_2Cl)_2 \cdot ZnCl_2 + 2AsCl_3 \rightleftharpoons 2ArN_2Cl \cdot AsCl_3 + ZnCl_2 \qquad (24)$$

$$ArN_2Cl \cdot AsCl_3 + Fe \longrightarrow ArAsCl_2 + N_2 + FeCl_2 \qquad (25)$$

Such a reaction course is favored by the fact that yields of organoarsenic compounds are much lower when iron(III) and zinc chlorides are taken in excess.[69]

TABLE XIII
Yields of Organoarsenic Compounds Obtained from Double Diazonium Salts in Acetone[69]

Starting diazonium salt (D)	Molar ratio		Products	Yield, %, based on	
	$D:AsCl_3$	Metal:D		$AsCl_3$	D
$C_6H_5N_2Cl \cdot FeCl_3$	1	5.7 Fe	$[(C_6H_5)_2As]_2O$	19	38
$C_6H_5N_2Cl \cdot FeCl_3$	1.4	4 Fe	$[(C_6H_5)_2As]O$	15	20
$C_6H_5N_2Cl \cdot FeCl_3$	2	3 Fe	$[(C_6H_5)_2As]_2O$;	31	3
			$(C_6H_5)_3AsO$	10	14
$(C_6H_5N_2Cl)_2 \cdot ZnCl_2$	1	4 Fe	$(C_6H_5)_3As$;	29	43
			$(C_6H_5)_3AsCl_2$	4	6
$(C_6H_5N_2Cl)_2 \cdot ZnCl_2{}^a$	2	5.3 Fe	$(C_6H_5)_3AsO$	23	17
$(C_6H_5N_2Cl)_2 \cdot ZnCl_2$	1	6 Fe	$[(C_6H_5)_2As]_2O$;	20	20
			$(C_6H_5)_3AsO$	7	7
$(C_6H_5N_2Cl)_2 \cdot ZnCl_2{}^b$	1	6 Fe	$[(C_6H_5)_2As]_2O$;	12	12
			$(C_6H_5)_3As(OH)_2$	16	24
$(C_6H_5N_2Cl)_2 \cdot ZnCl_2$	0.66	2 Fe	C_6H_5AsO;	11	8
			$[(C_6H_5)_2As]_2O$	23	35
$(C_6H_5N_2Cl)_2 \cdot ZnCl_2$	0.66	3 Zn	C_6H_5AsO;	5	4
			$[(C_6H_5)_2As]_2O$	12	18
$(p\text{-}ClC_6H_4N_2Cl)_2 \cdot ZnCl_2$	0.66	3 Fe	ClC_6H_4AsO;	17	13
			$[(ClC_6H_4)_2As]_2O$	24	36
$(p\text{-}ClC_6H_4N_2Cl)_2 \cdot ZnCl_2{}^a$	1.3	3 Fe	$[(ClC_6H_4)_2As]_2O$;	9	6
			$(ClC_6H_4)_3AsO$	13	14
$(p\text{-}CH_3C_6H_4N_2Cl)_2 \cdot ZnCl_2$	1	3 Fe	$CH_3C_6H_4AsO$;	9	4
			$(CH_3C_6H_4)_3As$;	29	13
			$(CH_3C_6H_4)_2AsO_2H$	13	13

(p-BrC$_6$H$_4$N$_2$Cl)$_2$·ZnCl$_2$	1	2 Fe	BrC$_6$H$_4$AsO;	13	7
			(BrC$_6$H$_4$)$_3$AsO	19	29
			(BrC$_6$H$_4$)$_3$As(OH)$_2$	4	6
(2,4,6-Br$_3$C$_6$H$_2$N$_2$Cl)$_2$·ZnCl$_2$	0.5	4 Fe	[(Br$_3$C$_6$H$_2$)$_2$As]$_2$O	33	66
(2,4,6-Br$_3$C$_6$H$_4$N$_2$Cl)$_2$·ZnCl$_2$[a]	1	4 Fe	[(Br$_3$C$_6$H$_2$)$_2$As]$_2$O;	11	11
			(Br$_3$C$_6$H$_2$)$_3$AsO	27	40

[a] Reaction was first conducted with half the amount of double salt. Then inorganic material was filtered and another half of the double salt was added to the mixture, reacting without metallic reducing agent.
[b] Solvent was taken in threefold excess.

TABLE XIV

Yields of Organoarsenic Compounds Obtained by the Arylation of Aryl and Diaryl Compounds of Trivalent Arsenic[71]

Arylated compound	Arylating compound	Product	Yield, %
$C_6H_5AsCl_2$	$p\text{-}(BrC_6H_4N_2Cl)_2 \cdot ZnCl_2$	$p\text{-}BrC_6H_4(C_6H_5)AsCl$	25
	$p\text{-}(ClC_6H_4N_2Cl)_2 \cdot ZnCl_2$	$p\text{-}ClC_6H_4(C_6H_5)AsCl$	39
	$o\text{-}O_2NC_6H_4N_2Cl \cdot FeCl_3$	$[o\text{-}O_2NC_6H_4(C_6H_5)As]_2O$	72
	$p\text{-}O_2NC_6H_4N_2Cl \cdot FeCl_3$	$p\text{-}O_2NC_6H_4(C_6H_5)AsCl$	40
	$(C_6H_5N_2Cl)_2 \cdot ZnCl_2$	$[(C_6H_5)_2As]_2O$	54
	$p\text{-}CH_3C_6H_4N_2Cl \cdot FeCl_3$	$p\text{-}CH_3C_6H_4(C_6H_5)AsCl$	37
	$o\text{-}CH_3OCOC_6H_4N_2Cl \cdot FeCl_3$	$o\text{-}CH_3OCOC_6H_4(C_6H_5)AsCl$	32
	$o\text{-}C_2H_5OC_6H_4N_2Cl \cdot FeCl_3$	$[o\text{-}C_2H_5OC_6H_4(C_6H_5)As]_2O$	64
	$\beta\text{-}C_{10}H_7N_2Cl \cdot FeCl_3$	$[\beta\text{-}C_{10}H_7(C_6H_5)As]_2O$	64
$(C_6H_5)_2AsCl$	$(p\text{-}BrC_6H_4N_2Cl)_2 \cdot ZnCl_2$	$p\text{-}BrC_6H_4(C_6H_5)_2As$	81
	$(p\text{-}ClC_6H_4N_2Cl)_2 \cdot ZnCl_2$	$p\text{-}ClC_6H_4(C_6H_5)_2As$	64
	$p\text{-}O_2NC_6H_4N_2Cl \cdot FeCl_3$	$p\text{-}O_2NC_6H_4(C_6H_5)_2As$	51
	$(p\text{-}CH_3C_6H_4N_2Cl)_2 \cdot ZnCl_2$	$p\text{-}CH_3C_6H_4(C_6H_5)_2As$	60
	$o\text{-}CH_3OCOC_6H_4N_2Cl \cdot FeCl_3$	$o\text{-}CH_3OCOC_6H_4(C_6H_5)_2As$	73
$p\text{-}BrC_6H_4$—AsCl—C_6H_5	$(CH_3C_6H_4N_2Cl)_2 \cdot ZnCl_2$	$p\text{-}BrC_6H_4$—As(C_6H_5)—$p\text{-}CH_3C_6H_4$	52
$p\text{-}ClC_6H_4$—AsCl—C_6H_5	$(CH_3C_6H_4N_2Cl)_2 \cdot ZnCl_2$	$p\text{-}ClC_6H_4$—As(C_6H_5)—$p\text{-}CH_3C_6H_4$	38

$p\text{-CH}_3\text{C}_6\text{H}_4$—AsCl
$\overset{|}{\text{C}_6\text{H}_5}$ + $p\text{-O}_2\text{NC}_6\text{H}_4\text{N}_2\text{Cl}\cdot\text{FeCl}_3$

$p\text{-O}_2\text{NC}_6\text{H}_4$
C_6H_5—As → 42
$p\text{-CH}_3\text{C}_6\text{H}_4$

$p\text{-BrC}_6\text{H}_4$—AsCl
$\overset{|}{\text{C}_6\text{H}_5}$ + $o\text{-CH}_3\text{OCOC}_6\text{H}_4\text{N}_2\text{Cl}\cdot\text{FeCl}_3$

$p\text{-BrC}_6\text{H}_4$
C_6H_5—As → 79
$o\text{-CH}_3\text{OCOC}_6\text{H}_4$

$p\text{-CH}_3\text{C}_6\text{H}_4$—AsCl
$\overset{|}{\text{C}_6\text{H}_5}$ + $o\text{-CH}_3\text{OCOC}_6\text{H}_4\text{N}_2\text{Cl}\cdot\text{FeCl}_3$

$o\text{-CH}_3\text{OCOC}_6\text{H}_4$
C_6H_5—As → 52
$p\text{-CH}_3\text{C}_6\text{H}_4$

101

The decomposition of the double diazonium salts of zinc[69-71] or iron(III)[71] chlorides with iron powder in the presence of $ArAsX_2$ or Ar_2AsX can serve as a convenient procedure for the preparation of the mixed organoarsenic compounds $ArAr'AsX$, $Ar_2Ar'As$, and $ArAr'Ar''As$, which are hardly available by other methods (see Table XIV). In particular, arylation of the trivalent arsenic derivatives with free aryldiazonium chloride[72] is preparatively inconvenient owing to their explosiveness.

TABLE XV

Yields of Organoarsenic Compounds Obtained by the
Reaction of ArN_2COOK with $AsCl_3$ (50% Excess)
in Acetone at 18–20°[73]

Ar in ArN_2COOK	Yield, %			
	ArAsO	$(Ar_2As)_2O$	$ArAs(OH)_2$	Total
C_6H_5—	42	21	—	63
p-$CH_3C_6H_4$—	32	20	—	52
p-BrC_6H_4—	47	34	—	81
p-$O_2NC_6H_4$—	—	—	64	64
β-$C_{10}H_7$—	—	—	30	30
2,4,6-$Br_3C_6H_2$—	36	—	—	36

Arylazocarboxylic salts afford good yields of the trivalent organoarsenic derivatives[73] (Table XV). Optimal reaction conditions are attained by the slow addition of arylazocarboxylic salt to a thoroughly mixed acetone solution of arsenic(III) chloride (50% excess) at room temperature.

These reactions can be described by the equation

$$ArN_2COOK + AsCl_3 \longrightarrow ArAsCl_2 + N_2 + CO_2 + KCl \qquad (26)$$

A mixture of arylarsinic and diarylarsinic acids (Table XVI) can be obtained from aryldiazonium fluoborates[61,64,74] or fluosilicates[64] decomposing in the presence of arsenic(III) chloride and various catalysts in organic media. Copper or its salts are often employed as catalysts of which cuprous bromide is the most effective one. Iron(II) chloride, potassium iodide, and hydroquinone are also used as catalysts, but they are less effective than copper or its salts.[74]

Arylarsonic acids are obtained according to the Bart–Schmidt–Scheller method,* which involves reaction of diazo derivatives with inorganic trivalent arsenic compounds [$As(OK)_3$, K_2HAsO_3, or $AsCl_3$] in aqueous

---

* This method is discussed in detail in Ref. 9.

TABLE XVI

Yields of $ArAsO_3H_2$ and Ar_2AsO_2H Obtained by the Interaction of $AsCl_3$ with Diazonium Salts in Ethanol

Starting salt	Catalyst and Solvent	Yield, %			Ref.
		$ArAsO_3H_2$	Ar_2AsO_2H	Total	
$(p\text{-}BrC_6H_4N_2Cl)_2 \cdot ZnCl_2$	Cu_2Br_2	35	3	38	64
$o\text{-}ClC_6H_4N_2BF_4$	Cu_2Br_2, ethanol	45	2	47	74
	Cu-bronze, 80% ethanol	19	13	32	74
$m\text{-}ClC_6H_4N_2BF_4$	Cu-bronze, 80% ethanol	39	18	57	74
$p\text{-}ClC_6H_4N_2BF_4$	Cu_2Cl_2, ethanol	62	Trace	62	74
	Cu_2Cl_2, ethanol	62	—	62	74
	Cu-bronze, 80% ethanol	23	14	37	74
$m\text{-}O_2NC_6H_4N_2BF_4$	Cu_2Cl_2, ethanol	42	0.8	42.8	74
	Cu-bronze, 80% ethanol	21	17	38	74
$p\text{-}O_2NC_6H_4N_2BF_4$	Cu_2Cl_2, ethanol	54	0.7	54.7	74
	Cu_2Cl_2, 80% ethanol	19	21	40	74
$p\text{-}O_2NC_6H_4N_2OSO_3H$	Cu_2Br_2, ethanol	45	7	52	64
	Cu_2Br_2, 80% ethanol	3	10	13	64
$(p\text{-}O_2NC_6H_4N_2)_2 \cdot ZnCl_4$	Cu_2Br_2, ethanol	21	3	24	64

TABLE XVII

Yields of Organoantimony Compounds of the Types $ArSbX_2$, Ar_2SbX, Ar_2SbX_3, Ar_3Sb, and Ar_3SbX_2 Obtained from Double Diazonium and Halogenonium Salts

Starting salt	Reaction conditions	Yield, %						Ref.
		$ArSbX_2$	Ar_2SbX	Ar_2SbX_3	Ar_3Sb	Ar_3SbX_2	Total	
$p\text{-}BrC_6H_4N_2Cl\cdot SbCl_3$	Zn, ethyl acetate	56	15			21	92	52
$(p\text{-}BrC_6H_4)_2ICl$	$SbCl_3$, Sb, acetone		42	1.7		18	61.7	85
$o\text{-}ClC_6H_4N_2Cl\cdot SbCl_3$	Zn, ethyl acetate	40	42		17	25	82	52
$m\text{-}ClC_6H_4N_2Cl\cdot SbCl_3$	Zn, ethyl acetate		77				77	52
$p\text{-}ClC_6H_4N_2Cl\cdot SbCl_3$	Zn, ethyl acetate	35	33			10	78	52
$(p\text{-}ClC_6H_4)_2ICl$	$SbCl_3$, acetone		15	11	43	69	69	85
$p\text{-}IC_6H_4N_2Cl\cdot SbCl_3$	Zn, ethyl acetate	40	9			23	72	52
$p\text{-}O_2NC_6H_4N_2Cl\cdot SbCl_3$	Zn, ethyl acetate	58					58	52
$C_6H_5N_2Cl\cdot SbCl_3$	Zn, ethyl acetate	46	16			18	80	52
$C_6H_5N_2Cl\cdot SbCl_3$	Sb, $CaCO_3$, acetone, 0°					11.5	11.5	83
$(C_6H_5)_2ClCl\cdot SbCl_3$	Sb, acetone	9	17				26	25
$(C_6H_5)_2BrCl\cdot SbCl_3$	Sb, acetone	18.5	24				42.5	25
$[(C_6H_5)_2ICl]_2\cdot SbCl_3$	Sb, acetone			31		32	63	85, 86
$(C_6H_5)_2ICl$	$SbCl_3$, Sb, acetone	20		41			61	85
$(C_6H_5N_2Cl)_2\cdot ZnCl_2$	Sb, $CaCO_3$, acetone					28	28	83
$(C_6H_5N_2Cl)_2\cdot SbCl_3$	Zn, ethyl acetate, 77°		46				46	87
$(C_6H_5N_2Cl)_2\cdot SbCl_3$	Zn, ethyl acetate, water				50		50	87
	Zn, $CaCl_2$, ethyl acetate, water					46	46	87

Diazonium compound	Reaction conditions							
$C_6H_5N_2Cl$	Sb, CaCO$_3$, acetone 20–56°					13	13	27
$(4\text{-}Cl\text{-}2\text{-}CH_3C_6H_3N_2Cl)_2 \cdot ZnCl_2$	Sb, CaCO$_3$, acetone, 56°			15	32	0.5	47.5	83
$5\text{-}Cl\text{-}2\text{-}CH_3OC_6H_4N_2Cl$	Sb, CaCO$_3$, acetone	Not indicated						83
$p\text{-}CH_3C_6H_4N_2Cl \cdot SbCl_3$	Zn, ethyl acetate	18	20			20	58	52
$(p\text{-}CH_3C_6H_4)_2ICl$	SbCl$_3$, Sb, acetone	22		29		8.5	59.5	85
$o\text{-}CH_3OC_6H_4N_2Cl \cdot SbCl_3$	Zn, ethyl acetate	24.5				20	44.5	52
$p\text{-}CH_3OC_6H_4N_2Cl \cdot SbCl_3$	Zn, ethyl acetate	17	8.8	9.5			35.3	52
$p\text{-}C_2H_5OC_6H_4N_2Cl \cdot SbCl_3$	Zn, ethyl acetate	40					40	52

alkaline,[9,75] neutral, [76] or acidic media.[77-81] In the last case the reaction is usually carried out in the presence of cuprous salts. The procedure affords satisfactory yields of arylarsonic acids. Its shortcomings are associated with considerable foaming and the necessity of employing large reaction volumes. Yields are also not constant. Even small changes in the pH of the medium, reagent concentrations, and order of reagent addition greatly influence the yields.

The reaction between phenyldiazonium chloride and arsenic in acetone is of a purely theoretical interest; the yield of the organoarsenic compound is very poor.[82]

C. Organoantimony Compounds

The decomposition of double diazonium or halogenonium salts is the most common procedure for the synthesis of organoantimony compounds.

Makin and Waters[83] were the first to demonstrate the possibility of preparing organoantimony compounds via double diazonium salts. In the presence of a suspension of antimony powder and chalk in acetone $(C_6H_5N_2 Cl)_2 \cdot ZnCl_2$ decomposes to $(C_6H_5)_3SbCl_2$. Nesmeyanov and Kocheshkov[84] have worked out a synthesis of organoantimony compounds via double diazonium salts. By decomposing the double salts $ArN_2Cl \cdot SbCl_3$ (May's salts) with zinc powder in ethyl acetate at 60–70° they obtained a mixture of the organoantimony derivatives Ar_2SbX, $ArSbX_2$, Ar_2SbX_3, Ar_3Sb, and Ar_3SbX_2 in high total yield (Table XVII).

The double salts of antimony(III) chloride and diphenyliodonium,[85,86] diphenylbromonium, or diphenylchloronium[25] chloride also decompose with antimony powder in acetone, resulting in a mixture of organoantimony derivatives. The latter gives about the same yield as the decomposition of May's salts (Table XVII). In the case of double iodonium salts, it is preferable to employ a mixture of Ar_2ICl and $SbCl_3$[85] instead of an authentic double salt. In such cases the yield of organoantimony compounds almost equals that from the decomposition of the authentic double iodonium salt with antimony(III) chloride (Table XVII).

The common shortcoming of the methods described is that mixtures are formed. In spite of the high total yield and good separation of the mixture, the yields of compounds of a particular type are usually small.

In later investigations this lack was successfully overcome and conditions were worked out making it possible to obtain only a certain type of antimony compound. Thus, depending on the reaction conditions, the double salt $(C_6H_5N_2Cl)_2 \cdot SbCl_3$ may decompose to $(C_6H_5)_2SbCl$ (major product, $\sim 50\%$), triphenylantimony, or triphenylantimony dichloride.[87] Good yields of diaryl-stibonic acids or compounds of the type Ar_3SbCl_2 are obtained from $ArN_2Cl \cdot SbCl_3$ when these are decomposed with iron powder in acetone at

TABLE XVIII

Yields of Organoantimony Compounds of the Type Ar_2SbX_3 and Ar_3SbX_2 Obtained from Onium Salts

Ar	Yield, %, of Ar_2SbX_3 from			Yield, %, of Ar_3SbX_2 from		
	$ArN_2Cl\cdot SbCl_3$[a]	$ArN_2Cl\cdot SbCl_5$[b]	$Ar_2ICl\cdot SbCl_5$[c]	$ArN_2Cl\cdot SbCl_3$[a]	$ArN_2Cl\cdot SbCl_5$[b]	$Ar_2ICl\cdot SbCl_5$[c]
$2,4\text{-}Cl_2C_6H_3-$	86	—		60		
$o\text{-}ClC_6H_4-$	85			73	10	—
$p\text{-}ClC_6H_4-$	90	59	65	30	9	—
$p\text{-}BrC_6H_4-$	85		46			
$p\text{-}IC_6H_4-$		81				
$m\text{-}O_2NC_6H_4-$	97	72				
$p\text{-}O_2NC_6H_4-$	85	88	—			
C_6H_5-	71	67	56[d]	29		
$p\text{-}CH_3C_6H_4-$	—	58	42			
$o\text{-}CH_3OC_6H_4-$					67	
$p\text{-}CH_3CONHC_6H_4-$	42			76		
$o\text{-}C_2H_5OC_6H_4-$				20	49	
$p\text{-}C_2H_5OCOC_6H_4-$				52		
$2,4\text{-}(CH_3)_2C_6H_3-$	96			79		
$\beta\text{-}C_{10}H_7-$						

[a] Data from Ref. 88.
[b] Data from Refs. 89 and 90.
[c] Data from Ref. 91.
[d] Besides this compound $(C_6H_5)_2SbOCOCH_3$ is isolated in 25% yield.

TABLE XIX

Yields of Arylstibonic Acids Obtained by the Decomposition of Aryldiazonium Salts in Organic Solvents

Starting salt	Reaction conditions	Ar in $ArSbO_3H_2$	Yield, %	Ref.
$o\text{-}BrC_6H_4N_2Cl \cdot SbCl_3$	Ethanol, acidic medium	$o\text{-}BrC_6H_4-$	1	99
$p\text{-}BrC_6H_4N_2Cl \cdot SbCl_3$	Ethanol, acidic medium	$p\text{-}BrC_6H_4-$	40	99
$p\text{-}BrC_6H_4N_2Cl \cdot SbCl_5$	Cu_2Cl_2, acetone, 25°	$p\text{-}BrC_6H_4-$	1	102
$o\text{-}ClC_6H_4N_2Cl \cdot SbCl_5$	Cu_2Cl_2, acetone, 25°	$o\text{-}ClC_6H_4-$	1	102
$p\text{-}ClC_6H_4N_2Cl \cdot SbCl_3$	Cu_2Cl_2, acetone, 25°	$p\text{-}ClC_6H_4-$	64–78	99, 103
$p\text{-}ClC_6H_4N_2Cl \cdot SbCl_5$	Cu_2Cl_2, acetone, 25°	$p\text{-}ClC_6H_4-$	5	102
$p\text{-}IC_6H_5N_2Cl \cdot SbCl_5$	Cu_2Cl_2, acetone, 25°	$p\text{-}IC_6H_4-$	9	102
$o\text{-}O_2NC_6H_4N_2Cl \cdot SbCl_3$	Cu_2Cl_2, acetone, 25°	$o\text{-}O_2NC_6H_4-$	16	99
$o\text{-}O_2NC_6H_4N_2Cl \cdot SbCl_5$	Cu_2Cl_2, acetone, 25°	$o\text{-}O_2NC_6H_4-$	1	102
$m\text{-}O_2NC_6H_4N_2Cl \cdot SbCl_3$	Cu_2,Cl_2 acetone, 25°	$m\text{-}O_2NC_6H_4-$	46	99
$m\text{-}O_2NC_6H_4N_2Cl \cdot SbCl_5$	Cu_2Cl_2, acetone, 25°	$m\text{-}O_2NC_6H_4-$	6	102
$p\text{-}O_2NC_6H_4N_2Cl \cdot SbCl_3$	Cu_2Cl_2, acetone, 25°	$p\text{-}O_2NC_6H_4-$	53	99
$p\text{-}O_2NC_6H_4N_2Cl \cdot SbCl_5$	Acetone, 56°	$p\text{-}O_2NC_6H_4-$	12	102
$p\text{-}O_2NC_6H_4N_2Cl$	$SbCl_3$, Cu_2Cl_2, acetone	$p\text{-}O_2NC_6H_4-$	55	92
$p\text{-}O_2NC_6H_4N_2Cl$	$SbCl_3$, Cu_2Cl_2, methanol	$p\text{-}O_2NC_6H_4-$	4	92
$p\text{-}O_2NC_6H_4N_2BF_4$	$SbCl_3$, Cu_2Cl_2, absolute ethanol	$p\text{-}O_2NC_6H_4-$	65	104
$C_6H_5N_2Cl \cdot SbCl_3$	Cu_2Br_2, ethanol, acidic medium	C_6H_5-	39	99
$C_6H_5N_2Cl \cdot SbCl_5$	Cu_2Cl_2, acetone, 25°	C_6H_5-	39	102
$C_6H_5N_2Cl$	$SbCl_3$, Cu_2Cl_2, acetone	C_6H_5-	60	92
$C_6H_5N_2BF_4$	$SbCl_3$, Cu_2Cl_2, methanol	C_6H_5-	10	92
	$SbCl_3$, Cu_2Cl_2, acetone	C_6H_5-	6	92

4-Cl-2-CH₃C₆H₃N₂Cl·SbCl₃	Cu₂Br₂, ethanol, acidic medium	4-Cl-2-CH₃C₆H₃—	73–84	103, 105
3-O₂N-4-CH₃C₆H₃N₂Cl·SbCl₃	Cu₂Br₂, ethanol, acidic medium	3-O₂N-4-CH₃C₆H₃—	27	99
6-O₂N-2-CH₃C₆H₃N₂Cl·SbCl₃	Cu₂Br₂, ethanol, acidic medium	6-O₂N-2-CH₃C₆H₃—	30	99
o-CH₃C₆H₄N₂Cl·SbCl₃	Cu₂Br₂, ethanol, acidic medium	o-CH₃C₆H₄—	2	99
m-CH₃C₆H₄N₂Cl·SbCl₃	Cu₂Br₂, ethanol, acidic medium	m-CH₃C₆H₄—	24	99
p-CH₃C₆H₄N₂Cl·SbCl₃	Cu₂Br₂, ethanol, acidic medium	p-CH₃C₆H₄—	47–68	99, 103 105
p-CH₃C₆H₄N₂Cl·SbCl₅	Cu₂Cl₂, acetone, 25°	p-CH₃C₆H₄—	30	102
p-CH₃C₆H₄N₂Cl	SbCl₃, Cu₂Cl₂, acetone	p-CH₃C₆H₄—	87	92
p-CH₃C₆H₄N₂BF₄	SbCl₃, Cu₂Cl₂, methanol	p-CH₃C₆H₄—	32	92
	SbCl₃, Cu₂Cl₂, acetone	p-CH₃C₆H₄—	25	92
p-CH₃OC₆H₄N₂Cl·SbCl₃	Cu₂Cl₂, acetone, 50°	p-CH₃OC₆H₄—	52	106
p-CH₃OC₆H₄N₂Cl·SbCl₅	Cu₂Cl₂, acetone, 25°	p-CH₃OC₆H₄—	4	102
2,4-(CH₃)₂C₆H₃N₂Cl·SbCl₅	Cu₂Cl₂, acetone, 25°	2,4-(CH₃)₂C₆H₃—	14	102
o-C₂H₅OC₆H₄N₂Cl·SbCl₅	Cu₂Cl₂, acetone, 25°	o-C₂H₅OC₆H₄—	4	102
p-C₂H₅OC₆H₄N₂Cl·SbCl₅	Cu₂Cl₂, acetone, 25°	p-C₂H₅OC₆H₄—	3	102
α-C₁₀H₇N₂Cl·SbCl₅	Cu₂Cl₂, acetone, 25°	α-C₁₀H₇—	4	102
β-C₁₀H₇N₂Cl·SbCl₅	Cu₂Cl₂, acetone, 25°	β-C₁₀H₇—	8	102

p-HO₂C—CHCH₂C₆H₄N₂Cl·SbCl₃
          |
      NHCOCH₃
	Cu₂Cl₂, ethanol, acidic medium	p-HOOC—CHCH₂C₆H₄—
		          |
		      NHCOCH₃
			38	107

$0°C.$[88] Decomposition of double diazonium ($ArN_2Cl \cdot SbCl_5$) or iodonium ($Ar_2ICl \cdot SbCl_5$) salts with iron[89,90] or antimony[91] powder, respectively, is a convenient route to such compounds as Ar_2SbCl_3 and Ar_3SbCl_2. The yields of these derivatives obtained by various methods are given in Table XVIII. As can be seen from this table, the yields of organoantimony compounds are rather high. However, the decomposition of the double salts $ArN_2Cl \cdot SbCl_3$ with iron powder in acetone is the best method for the preparation of compounds Ar_2SbX_3.[88]

The Bart–Schmidt reaction,[92–97] when carried out in aqueous alkaline or neutral media, can be employed for the preparation of arylstibonic acids:

$$ArN_2X + NaH_2SbO_3 \longrightarrow ArSbO(OH)_2 + N_2 + NaX \qquad (27)$$

However, along with such advantages as its selectivity for a particular type of organoantimony compound and the use of an aqueous medium, this method has several serious shortcomings. Among these are the large reaction volumes associated with intensive foaming and the need for diluted media; the formation of colored by-products in the "azocombination" reaction, which is sometimes predominant;[98] and poor yields of arylstibonic acids, usually about 20–30% and even lower.

Modifications of the Bart–Schmidt method only partially remove these shortcomings. For example, one can successfully employ Scheller's method[79,99,100] when the diazotized amine is unstable in an alkaline medium or the latter facilitates side reactions.[80,98,99] In such cases the reaction is usually conducted in an acidic medium in the presence of cuprous chloride:

$$ArN_2Cl + SbCl_3 \xrightarrow{\text{Cu}_2\text{Cl}_2} ArSbCl_4 + N_2 \qquad (28)$$

Hydrolysis of arylantimony tetrachloride gives arylstibonic acids. Foaming can be partially avoided when the double salts of aryldiazonium and antimony(III) chlorides are decomposed with some tertiary base—e.g., pyridine.[101]

Reaction temperature, the pH of the medium, and the extent of dilution considerably influence the yields of arylstibonic acids (Table XIX). However, in most papers neither Schmidt nor other authors provide detailed information on the synthetic routines, which makes it rather difficult to attain reproducible results.

Nesmeyanov, Reutov, and Knoll[102] worked out the preparation of arylstibonic acids via the double salts $ArN_2Cl \cdot SbCl_5$. The latter were prepared by an exchange reaction between the double salt $ArN_2Cl \cdot FeCl_3$ and antimony(V) chloride in acetone with subsequent precipitation of $ArN_2Cl \cdot SbCl_5$ by chloroform:[108]

$$ArN_2Cl \cdot FeCl_3 + SbCl_5 \rightleftharpoons ArN_2Cl \cdot SbCl_5 + FeCl_3 \qquad (29)$$

Decomposition of the double salt $ArN_2Cl \cdot SbCl_5$ with a twofold to threefold excess of cuprous chloride at 25–30° (4–5 hr) in acetone or methyl acetate

$$ArN_2Cl \cdot SbCl_5 \xrightarrow{Cu_2Cl_2} ArSbCl_4 + N_2 + 2CuCl_2 \qquad (30)$$

and subsequent hydrolysis of arylantimony tetrachloride

$$ArSbCl_4 \xrightarrow{H_2O} ArSbO(OH)_2 \qquad (31)$$

provide optimal conditions for the preparation of arylstibonic acids.

The method described has none of the disadvantages typical of the Bart–Schmidt reaction (large volumes, intensive foaming, poor reproducibility) and sometimes gives better yields of arylstibonic acids.*

Arylstibonic acids are also obtained along with negligible amounts of other organoantimony compounds (in particular diarylstibonic acids) when a mixture of ArN_2BF_4 and antimony(III) chloride is decomposed with cuprous chloride in organic media or when the double salts $ArN_2Cl \cdot SbCl_3$ decompose in absolute acetone at 0° with sodium iodide, copper, cuprous chloride, ferrous chloride, and other reducing agents.[109] It may be of interest that hydroquinone and formic acid[110] can also be employed as reducing agents, but they have no preparative significance.

Arylation of aryl and diaryl trivalent antimony compounds by diazo compounds[94,111–114] is also important for the preparation of asymmetrical compounds $ArAr'SbX_3$ and $Ar_2Ar'SbX_2$.

For the arylating reagents one may use aryl diazoacetates and the double salts of aryldiazonium and antimony(III) or zinc chlorides, where the double salts $ArN_2Cl \cdot SbCl_3$ are the most universal. Substituents in the arylating and arylated species determine the facility of arylation. Arylation is usually stimulated by electron-releasing substituents in the arylated compounds. Asymmetrical organoantimony compounds obtained by the arylation of $ArSbX_2$ or Ar_2SbX are shown in Table XX.

The double salts $ArSbCl_4 \cdot Ar'N_2Cl$ decompose with iron in acetone,[115] providing a convenient route to the asymmetrical organoantimony compound

$$ArSbCl_4 \cdot Ar'N_2Cl + Fe \longrightarrow ArAr'SbCl_3 + N_2 + FeCl_3 \qquad (32)$$

listed in Table XX.†

Note should be taken of such double salts as $C_6H_5SbCl_4 \cdot p\text{-}O_2NC_6H_4N_2Cl$ and $C_6H_5SbCl_4 \cdot p\text{-}C_2H_5OCOC_6H_4N_2Cl$, which decompose under common conditions and without arylation to the initial phenylantimony tetrachloride.[115]

---

* Yields are higher in the case of phenyl, p-tolyl, and β-naphthyl stibonic acids.

† Analogously to the diazonium double salts those of $ArSbCl_2$[116,117] $ArSbCl_4$,[108,118] and Ar_2SbCl_3[108,117] with antimony(III) and antimony(V) chlorides have also been obtained.

TABLE XX

Yields of Organoantimony Compounds Obtained by the Arylation of Organic Compounds of Antimony

Starting materials	Product	Yield, %	Ref.
$p\text{-}ClC_6H_4SbI_2 + ClC_6H_4N_2Cl\cdot SbCl_3$	$(p\text{-}ClC_6H_4)_2SbOOH$	86	113
$p\text{-}ClC_6H_4SbI_2 + p\text{-}O_2NC_6H_4N_2Cl\cdot SbCl_3$	$p\text{-}ClC_6H_4(p\text{-}O_2NC_6H_4)SbOOH$		113
$p\text{-}BrC_6H_4N_2Cl\cdot C_6H_5SbCl_4 + Fe$	$p\text{-}BrC_6H_4(C_6H_5)SbOOH$	86	115
$p\text{-}ClC_6H_4N_2Cl\cdot C_6H_5SbCl_4 + Fe$	$p\text{-}ClC_6H_4(C_6H_5)SbOOH$	76	115
$C_6H_5N_2Cl\cdot p\text{-}ClC_6H_4SbCl_4 + Fe$	$p\text{-}ClC_6H_4(C_6H_5)SbOOH$	80	115
$C_6H_5SbCl_2 + p\text{-}ClC_6H_4N_2Cl\cdot SbCl_3$	$p\text{-}ClC_6H_4(C_6H_5)SbOOH$	60	113
$p\text{-}ClC_6H_4SbI_2 + C_6H_5N_2Cl\cdot SbCl_3$	$p\text{-}ClC_6H_4(C_6H_5)SbOOH$	95	113
$p\text{-}IC_6H_4N_2Cl\cdot C_6H_5SbCl_4 + Fe$	$p\text{-}IC_6H_4(C_6H_5)SbOOH$	75	115
$C_6H_5N_2Cl\cdot p\text{-}O_2NC_6H_4SbCl_4 + Fe$	$p\text{-}O_2NC_6H_4(C_6H_5)SbOOH$	71	115
$C_6H_5N_2Cl\cdot C_6H_5SbCl_2$	$(C_6H_5)_2SbOOH$	26	116
$C_6H_5SbCl_2 + C_6H_5N_2Cl\cdot SbCl_3$	$(C_6H_5)_2SbOOH$	60	111
$p\text{-}CH_3C_6H_4SbCl_2 + ClC_6H_4N_2Cl\cdot SbCl_3$	$p\text{-}ClC_6H_4(p\text{-}CH_3C_6H_4)SbOOH$	45	113
$p\text{-}ClC_6H_4SbI_2 + p\text{-}CH_3C_6H_4N_2Cl\cdot SbCl_3$	$p\text{-}ClC_6H_4(p\text{-}CH_3C_6H_4)SbOOH$	85	113
$p\text{-}CH_3C_6H_4SbCl_2 + p\text{-}O_2NC_6H_4N_2Cl\cdot SbCl_3$	$p\text{-}CH_3C_6H_4(p\text{-}O_2NC_6H_4)SbOOH$	87	113
$p\text{-}ClC_6H_4SbI_2 + p\text{-}CH_3OC_6H_4N_2Cl\cdot SbCl_3$	$p\text{-}ClC_6H_4(p\text{-}CH_3OC_6H_4)SbOOH$	69	113
$p\text{-}CH_3C_6H_4SbCl_2 + C_6H_5N_2Cl\cdot SbCl_3$	$p\text{-}CH_3C_6H_4(C_6H_5)SbOOH$	45	113
$p\text{-}CH_3C_6H_4SbCl_2 + C_6H_5N_2OCOCH_3$	$p\text{-}CH_3C_6H_4(C_6H_5)SbOOH$	92	113
$C_6H_5N_2Cl\cdot p\text{-}CH_3C_6H_4SbCl_4 + Fe$	$p\text{-}CH_3C_6H_4(C_6H_5)SbOOH$	95	115
$p\text{-}CH_3C_6H_4N_2Cl\cdot C_6H_5SbCl_4 + Fe$	$p\text{-}CH_3C_6H_4(C_6H_5)SbOOH$	50	115
$p\text{-}O_2NC_6H_4N_2Cl\cdot p\text{-}C_2H_5OC_6H_4SbCl_4 + Fe$	$p\text{-}C_2H_5OC_6H_4(p\text{-}O_2NC_6H_4)SbOOH$	51	115
$p\text{-}C_2H_5OC_6H_4N_2Cl\cdot p\text{-}O_2NC_6H_4SbCl_4 + Fe$	$p\text{-}C_2H_5OC_6H_4(p\text{-}O_2NC_6H_4)SbOOH$		115
$p\text{-}CH_3C_6H_4SbI_2 + p\text{-}CH_3C_6H_4N_2Cl\cdot SbCl_3$	$(p\text{-}CH_3C_6H_4)_2SbOOH$	84	113
$p\text{-}CH_3C_6H_4SbCl_2 + p\text{-}CH_3C_6H_4N_2OCOCH_3$	$(p\text{-}CH_3C_6H_4)_2SbOOH$	20	113

	Product		
2,4-(CH₃)₂C₆H₃N₂Cl·C₆H₅SbCl₄ + Fe	[2,4-(CH₃)₂C₆H₃I]₂(C₆H₅)SbCl(OH)	56	115
p-CH₃C₆H₄SbI₂ + p-CH₃OC₆H₄N₂Cl·SbCl₃	p-CH₃OC₆H₄(p-CH₃C₆H₄)SbOOH	66	113
p-CH₃C₆H₄SbCl₂ + (p-CH₃OC₆H₄N₂Cl)₂·ZnCl₂	p-CH₃OC₆H₄(p-CH₃C₆H₄)SbOOH	32	113
p-C₂H₅OC₆H₄N₂Cl·C₆H₅SbCl₄ + Fe	p-C₂H₅OC₆H₄(C₆H₅)SbOOH	55	115
C₆H₅N₂Cl·p-C₂H₅OC₆H₄SbCl₄ + Fe	p-C₂H₅OC₆H₄(C₆H₅)SbOOH	85	115
(o-ClC₆H₄)₂SbCl + o-ClC₆H₄N₂Cl·SbCl₃	(o-ClC₆H₄)₃SbCl₂	73	113
(o-ClC₆H₄)₂SbCl + p-O₂NC₆H₄N₂Cl·SbCl₃	(o-ClC₆H₄)₂(p-O₂NC₆H₄)SbCl₂	45	113
(C₆H₅)₂SbOCOCH₃ + C₆H₅N₂OCOCH₃	(C₆H₅)₃Sb(OCOCH₃)₂	26	113
(p-CH₃C₆H₄)₂SbOCOCH₃ + p-CH₃C₆H₄N₂OCOCH₃	(p-CH₃C₆H₄)₃Sb(OH)OCOCH₃	59	113
(o-C₂H₅OC₆H₄)₂SbCl + (o-ClC₆H₄N₂Cl)₂·ZnCl₂	(o-C₂H₅OC₆H₄)₂(o-ClC₆H₄)SbCl₂	74	113
(o-C₂H₅OC₆H₄)₂SbCl + p-O₂NC₆H₄N₂Cl·SbCl₃	(o-C₂H₅OC₆H₄)₂(p-O₂NC₆H₄)SbCl₂	82	113
p-CH₃C₆H₄SbCl₂ + o-C₆H₅C₆H₄N₂Cl·SbCl₃	(o-C₆H₅C₆H₄)₂(p-CH₃C₆H₄)SbCl₂	12	114
p-C₂H₅OC₆H₄SbCl₂ + 4-Br(2-C₆H₅)C₆H₃N₂Cl·SbCl₃	(4-Br-2-C₆H₅-C₆H₃)₂	13	114

$$\begin{array}{c} \quad\quad\quad SbCl_2 \\ | \\ p\text{-}C_2H_5OC_6H_4 \end{array}$$

As seen from Table XX, the double salts $ArSbCl_4 \cdot Ar'N_2Cl$ lead to large quantities of diarylstibinic acids. Thus this reaction is a valuable supplement to the above described arylation of compounds $ArSbX_2$.[113]

In contrast to methods in which the organoantimony compounds are prepared from double diazonium and halogenonium salts, a direct decomposition of aryldiazonium[27,83] or diarylhalogenonium[29,85] halides with antimony powder is of no preparative significance.

Also of purely formal interest is a reaction between arylazocarboxylic salts and antimony(III) chloride in acetone, leading to a mixture of organoantimony compounds $ArSbX_2$, Ar_2SbX, and $ArSbX_4$.[119] The yields of organoantimony compounds obtained from ArN_2COOK and antimony(III) chloride in ethyl acetate are shown in Table XXI.

TABLE XXI

Yields of Organoantimony Compounds Obtained from ArN_2COOK[a]

	Yield, %			
Ar in ArN_2COOK	$ArSbO_3H_2$	$ArSbO$	$(Ar_2Sb)_2O$	Total
C_6H_5—[b]		27		27
p-BrC_6H_4—	53.8		10.3	64.1
p-$O_2NC_6H_4$—	50.7			50.7
p-$CH_3C_6H_4$—	11.5	44		55.5
β-$C_{10}H_7$—		90		90

[a] Unless otherwise indicated, all reactions conducted with $SbCl_3$ in ethyl acetate at 16–18°. Data from Ref. 119.

[b] Reaction at 60–70°.

D. Organobismuth Compounds

The method of double onium salts can be used for the preparation of organobismuth as for the other organometallic derivatives of group V elements. The double diazonium salts of bismuth(III) chloride decompose with copper bronze in ethanol[120,121] or bismuth powder in acetone.[122–124] Subsequent symmetrization of the generating aryl and diaryl trivalent bismuth compounds results in Ar_3Bi. Analogous compounds are obtained via the diaryliodonium,[125] diarylchloronium, and diarylbromonium[25] salts.

For preparative purposes it is more convenient to employ, instead of the authentic double salts of bismuth(III) and diaryliodonium chlorides, a mixture of Ar_2ICl and $BiCl_3$, which decomposes with bismuth powder in acetone.[125]

It should be noted that the reaction of diaryliodonium[125] or aryldiazonium[27,83] chlorides with bismuth powder gives no organobismuth derivatives.

Unlike onium chlorides, diazonium,[126] iodonium,[41] and bromonium[28] fluoborates decompose with bismuth in acetone to the organobismuth compounds (Table XXII).

TABLE XXII

Yields of Organobismuth Compounds Obtained from Onium Fluoborates[a,b]

Starting salt	Product	Yield, %
p-BrC$_6$H$_4$N$_2$BF$_4$	(p-BrC$_6$H$_4$)$_3$Bi	40
p-ClC$_6$H$_4$N$_2$BF$_4$	(p-ClC$_6$H$_4$)$_3$Bi	31
m-O$_2$NC$_6$H$_4$BF$_4$	(m-O$_2$NC$_6$H$_4$)$_3$Bi	26
p-O$_2$NC$_6$H$_4$N$_2$BF$_4$	(p-O$_2$NC$_6$H$_4$)$_3$BiCl$_2$[c]	5.5
C$_6$H$_5$N$_2$BF$_4$	(C$_6$H$_5$)$_3$Bi	69
(C$_6$H$_5$)$_2$BrBF$_4$[d,e]	(C$_6$H$_5$)$_3$Bi	7.3
o-CH$_3$C$_6$H$_4$N$_2$BF$_4$	(o-CH$_3$C$_6$H$_4$)$_3$Bi	54
m-CH$_3$C$_6$H$_4$N$_2$BF$_4$	(m-CH$_3$C$_6$H$_4$)$_3$Bi	37
p-CH$_3$C$_6$H$_4$N$_2$BF$_4$	(p-CH$_3$C$_6$H$_4$)$_3$Bi	50
p-C$_2$H$_5$OC$_6$H$_4$N$_2$BF$_4$	(p-C$_2$H$_5$OC$_6$H$_4$)$_3$Bi	27
p-C$_2$H$_5$OCOC$_6$H$_4$N$_2$BF$_4$	(p-C$_2$H$_5$OCOC$_6$H$_4$)$_3$BiCl$_2$[c]	20

[a] Unless otherwise indicated, data are from Ref. 126.

[b] Unless otherwise indicated, the onium fluoborates were decomposed with bismuth powder in acetone at 30–35°.

[c] Ar$_3$BiCl$_2$ prepared after chlorine passage.

[d] Data from Ref. 28.

[e] Reaction temperature 56°.

As seen from the data of Tables XXII and XXIII, the yields of triaryl-bismuth are approximately the same (20–60%) when double diazonium salts of bismuth(III) chloride,[122–124] mixtures of Ar$_2$ICl with BiCl$_3$,[125] as well as aryldiazonium fluoborates decompose with bismuth powder in acetone. But taking into account that diazonium fluoborates are more readily available than diaryliodonium salts, preference should be given to the former.

The possibility of preparing organobismuth compounds via arylazocar-boxylic salts has been demonstrated by Reutov (Table XXIV).[127] However, unlike analogous syntheses of organic mercury,[47] arsenic,[73] and antimony[119] compounds, potassium arylazocarboxylate reacts with bismuth(III) chloride in acetone only in the presence of oxygen and bismuth powder.

In dry acetone or ethyl acetate the arylazocarboxylic salts react readily with bismuth(III) chloride when cooled, in the absence of oxygen, but they give no organobismuth derivatives. For example, besides "diazoresin,"

TABLE XXIII

Yields of Organobismuth Compounds Obtained by the Decomposition of Onium Halides and Double Onium Salts

Starting salt	Catalyst[a]	Product	Yield, %	Ref.
$(p\text{-}BrC_6H_4)_2ICl$	$BiCl_3$, Bi	$(p\text{-}BrC_6H_4)_3Bi$	65	125
$(p\text{-}BrC_6H_4N_2Cl)_2 \cdot BiCl_3$	Cu-bronze[b]	$(p\text{-}BrC_6H_4)_3Bi$	7	121
$(p\text{-}BrC_6H_4N_2Cl)_2 \cdot BiCl_3$	Bi	$(p\text{-}BrC_6H_4)_3Bi$	39	123, 124
$(p\text{-}ClC_6H_4)_2ICl$	$BiCl_3$, Bi	$(p\text{-}ClC_6H_4)_3Bi$	46	125
$(p\text{-}ClC_6H_4N_2Cl)_2 \cdot BiCl_3$	Cu-bronze[b]	$(p\text{-}ClC_6H_4)_3Bi$	8.4	121
	Bi	$(p\text{-}ClC_6H_4)_3Bi$	15	123, 124
$(p\text{-}IC_6H_4N_2Cl)_2 \cdot BiCl_3$	Bi	$(p\text{-}IC_6H_4)_3Bi$	21	124
$(m\text{-}O_2NC_6H_4)_2ICl$	$BiCl_3$, Bi	$(m\text{-}O_2NC_6H_4)_3Bi$	32	125
$(p\text{-}H_2NO_2SC_6H_4N_2Cl)_2 \cdot BiCl_3$	Bi, 3°	$(p\text{-}H_2NO_2SC_6H_4)_3Bi$	20.5	122
$(C_6H_5N_2Cl)_2 \cdot BiCl_3$	Cu-bronze[b]	$(C_6H_5)_3Bi$	22	121
	Bi	$(C_6H_5)_3Bi$	50	123
$(C_6H_5)_2ICl$	$BiCl_3$, Bi	$(C_6H_5)_3Bi$	65	125
$(C_6H_5)_2IBr$	$BiCl_3$, Bi	$(C_6H_5)_3Bi$	62	125
$(C_6H_5)_2II$	$BiCl_3$, Bi	$(C_6H_5)_3Bi$	25	125
$(C_6H_5)_2BrCl \cdot BiCl_3$	Bi	$(C_6H_5)_3Bi$	61	25
$[(C_6H_5)_2ClCl]_2 \cdot BiCl_3$	Bi	$(C_6H_5)_3Bi$	52	25
$(o\text{-}CH_3C_6H_4N_2Cl)_2 \cdot BiCl_3$	Cu-bronze[b]	$(o\text{-}CH_3C_6H_4)_3Bi$	6.4	121
	—	$[(o\text{-}CH_3C_6H_4)_3Bi$	47	123
$(p\text{-}CH_3C_6H_4N_2Cl)_2 \cdot BiCl_3$	—	$(p\text{-}CH_3C_6H_4)_3Bi$	31	123
	Cu-bronze[b]	$(p\text{-}CH_3C_6H_4)_3Bi$	6.7	121
	Bi	$(p\text{-}CH_3C_6H_4)_3Bi$	18	120
$(p\text{-}CH_3C_6H_4)_2ICl$	$BiCl_3$, Bi	$(p\text{-}CH_3C_6H_4)_3Bi$	42	125

$(o\text{-}CH_3OC_6H_4N_2Cl)_2 \cdot BiCl_3$	Cu-bronze[b]	$(o\text{-}CH_3OC_6H_4)_3Bi$	6.4	121
	Bi	$(o\text{-}CH_3OC_6H_4)_3Bi$	47	123
$(p\text{-}CH_3OC_6H_4)_2ICl$	$BiCl_3$, Bi	$(p\text{-}CH_3OC_6H_4)_3Bi$	18.5	125
$(p\text{-}CH_3OC_6H_4N_2Cl)_2 \cdot BiCl_3$	Cu-bronze[b]	$(p\text{-}CH_3OC_6H_4)_3Bi$	1	121
$(m\text{-}C_2H_5OCOC_6H_4)_2ICl$	$BiCl_3$, Bi	$(m\text{-}C_2H_5OCOC_6H_4)_2BiCl$	36	125
$(\alpha\text{-}C_{10}H_7N_2Cl)_2 \cdot BiCl_3$	Bi	$(\alpha\text{-}C_{10}H_7)_3Bi$	15	123

[a] Unless otherwise indicated, all reactions conducted in acetone.
[b] Reaction conducted in ethanol.

117

TABLE XXIV
Yields of Organobismuth Compounds Obtained from
ArN_2COOK^a

Ar in ArN_2COOK	Yield of Ar_3Bi, %
$p\text{-}BrC_6H_4-$	18
$p\text{-}ClC_6H_4-$	7
C_6H_5-	23
$p\text{-}CH_3C_6H_4-$	16.5

[a] All reactions conducted in acetone with bismuth powder in the presence of $BiCl_3$. Data from Ref. 127.

benzene was the only organic product of the reaction between bismuth(III) chloride and potassium phenylazocarboxylate in acetone.

The data obtained testify that arylazocarboxylic salts reacting with bismuth(III) chloride generate aryldiazonium chloride, which further gives double salts with bismuth(III) chloride. It is via decomposition of this salt by bismuth that the organobismuth compounds are obtained.

E. Other Reactions

At the conclusion of this section attention is drawn to the reactions of onium salts with triaryl compounds of the type Ar_3E (E = P, As, Sb, Bi), leading to their arylation products. For example, diazonium salts and triphenylphosphine taken in equimolar quantities react in aqueous alcohol or acidic solutions in the presence of sodium acetate buffer, giving phosphonium salts $(C_6H_5)_3ArPX$:[128,129]

$$(C_6H_5)_3P + ArN_2Cl \longrightarrow (C_6H_5)_3ArPCl + N_2 \qquad (33)$$

A common procedure for the preparation of phosphonium salts $(C_6H_5)_3$ $ArPBF_4$ is the photochemical decomposition of diaryliodonium fluoborates in acetone in the presence of triphenylphosphine:[130-132]

$$(C_6H_5)_3P + Ar_2IBF_4 \xrightarrow{h\nu} (C_6H_5)_3ArP^+BF_4^- + ArI \qquad (34)$$

The yields of phosphonium salts prepared by the arylation of triphenylphosphine with the diazonium and iodonium salts are listed in Table XXV.

Makarova and Nesmeyanov[30,133] have found that not only triphenylphosphine but also the corresponding arsenic and antimony derivatives can be successfully arylated with diphenyliodonium fluoborate:

$$(C_6H_5)_3E + (C_6H_5)_2IBF_4 \longrightarrow (C_6H_5)_4\overset{+}{E}BF_4^- + C_6H_5I \qquad (35)$$
$$(E = P, As, Sb)$$

TABLE XXV
Yields of Tetraarylonium Salts of Group V Elements

Starting materials	Reaction conditions	Product	Yield, %	Ref.
$C_6H_5N_2Cl + (C_6H_5)_3P$	CH_3OH, CH_3COONa, HBr	$(C_6H_5)_4PBr$	32	129
$(C_6H_5)_2ICl + (C_6H_5)_3P$	$h\nu$, 3 hr, ethanol, 20°	$(C_6H_5)_4PCl$	56	130
$(C_6H_5)_2IBF_4 + (C_6H_5)_3P$	$h\nu$, acetone, 20°	$(C_6H_5)_4PBF_4$	85	131
	Ethanol, 97°, 5 hr.	$(C_6H_5)_4PBF_4$	88	30, 133
	213°, without solvent	$(C_6H_5)_4PBF_4$	81	30, 133
$(p\text{-}ClC_6H_4)_2IBF_4 + (C_6H_5)_3P$	$h\nu$, acetone, 20°	$p\text{-}ClC_6H_4(C_6H_5)_3PBF_4$	61	132
$(m\text{-}O_2NC_6H_4)_2IBF_4 + (C_6H_5)_3P$	$h\nu$, acetone, 20°	$m\text{-}O_2NC_6H_4(C_6H_5)_3PBF_4$	47	131
$p\text{-}O_2NC_6H_4N_2ONa + (C_6H_5)_3P$	Ethyl acetate, CH_3COOH, then $HClO_4$	$p\text{-}O_2NC_6H_4(C_6H_5)_3PClO_4$	58	129
$(p\text{-}CH_3C_6H_4)_2IBF_4 + (C_6H_5)_3P$	$h\nu$, acetone, 20°	$p\text{-}CH_3C_6H_4(C_6H_5)_3PBF_4$	40	131
$(m\text{-}C_2H_5O_2CC_6H_4)_2ICl + (C_6H_5)_3P$	$h\nu$, methanol, 20°, then HBF_4	$m\text{-}C_2H_5O_2CC_6H_4(C_6H_5)_3PBF_4$	51	131
$(C_6H_5)_2IBF_4 + (C_6H_5)_3As$	213°, without solvent	$(C_6H_5)_4AsBF_4$	74	30, 133
$(C_6H_5)_2IBF_4 + (C_6H_5)_3Sb$	213°, without solvent	$(C_6H_5)_4SbBF_4$	69	30, 133

Without solvent at 213–220° for triphenylphosphine only does the reaction proceed readily in boiling propanol. Diphenyliodonium fluoborate does not arylate triphenylbismuth.

VI. PREPARATION OF ORGANIC COMPOUNDS OF GROUPS VI AND VII ELEMENTS VIA ONIUM COMPOUNDS

Waters[134] has shown that organic derivatives of sulfur, selenium, and tellurium can in principle be obtained via diazo compounds.* These elements, react with phenyldiazonium chloride in acetone in the presence of chalk, leading to diphenyl sulfide, diphenyl selenide, and diphenyltellurium dichloride, respectively. A higher yield is attained for the latter compound when the double diazonium salt with zinc chloride is decomposed with tellurium.

A general procedure for the preparation of diaryl selenides consists in the decomposition of diazonium fluoborates with zinc powder in absolute acetone, at 0°, in the presence of $SeCl_4$.[135] Diphenyl selenide is obtained in 33% yield; other diaryl selenides are produced in lower yields (4–16%) (Table XXVI).

Arylation of Ar_2E (E = O, S, Se) with diazonium and iodonium salts leads to the onium compounds $Ar_3E^+X^-$. For example, triphenylsulfonium and triphenylselenonium fluoborates are formed by the reaction of diphenyliodonium fluoborates with diphenyl sulfide or diphenyl selenide without solvent at 220–230°:[30]

$$(C_6H_5)_2E + (C_6H_5)_2IBF_4 \longrightarrow (C_6H_5)_3EBF_4 + C_6H_5I \tag{36}$$

In diphenyl ether phenyldiazonium fluoborate decomposes and reacts to give triphenyloxonium fluoborate at 80–90°:[136]

$$(C_6H_5)_2O + C_6H_5N_2BF_4 \longrightarrow (C_6H_5)_3O^+BF_4^- \tag{37}$$

Diphenylchloronium[137] and diphenylbromonium[35] salts have been prepared similarly:

$$C_6H_5Hal + C_6H_5N_2BF_4 \longrightarrow (C_6H_5)_2Hal^+BF_4^- + N_2 \tag{38}$$
$$(Hal = Cl, Br)$$

Use of substituted diazonium salts instead of phenyldiazonium fluoborates gives rise to asymmetrical chloronium and bromonium salts.[40]

Reaction (38) provides no diphenyliodonium salt, which, however, can be obtained from phenyl diazoacetate in iodobenzene[35] or by the simultaneous decomposition of the double diazonium salt $(C_6H_5N_2I)_2 \cdot HgI_2$:[138]

$$(C_6H_5N_2I)_2 \cdot HgI_2 \longrightarrow (C_6H_5)_2I^+HgI_3^- + 2N_2 \tag{39}$$

* Numerous published data describe the introduction of OH, SH, and SeH groups by means of aryldiazonium or diarylhalogenonium salts, but this is beyond the scope of the present review.

TABLE XXVI

Yields of Organoelement Compounds of Group VI Obtained from Onium Salts

Starting material	Reaction conditions	Product	Yield, %	Ref.
$C_6H_5N_2Cl$	S, $CaCO_3$, acetone, 50–56°	$(C_6H_5)_2S$	(a)	134
	Se, $CaCO_3$, acetone, 56°	$(C_6H_5)_2Se$	(a)	134
$C_6H_5N_2BF_4$	$SeCl_4$, Zn, acetone, 0°	$(C_6H_5)_2Se$	33	135
m-$ClC_6H_4N_2BF_4$	$SeCl_4$, Zn, acetone, 0°	$(m$-$ClC_6H_4)_2Se$	16	135
o-$CH_3C_6H_4N_2BF_4$	$SeCl_4$, Zn, acetone, 0°	$(o$-$CH_3C_6H_4)_2Se$	4	135
p-$CH_3C_6H_4N_2BF_4$	$SeCl_4$, Zn, acetone, 0°	$(p$-$CH_3C_6H_4)_2Se$	10	135
p-$CH_3OC_6H_4N_2BF_4$	$SeCl_4$, Zn, acetone, 0°	$(p$-$CH_3OC_6H_4)_2Se$	16	135
$C_6H_5N_2Cl$	Te, $CaCO_3$, acetone	$(C_6H_5)_2TeCl_2$	2	134
$(C_6H_5N_2Cl)_2 \cdot ZnCl_2$	Te, $CaCO_3$, acetone	$(C_6H_5)_2TeCl_2$	8	134
$(C_6H_5)_2IBF_4 + (C_6H_5)_2S$	220–230°	$(C_6H_5)_3SBF_4$	60	133
$(C_6H_5)_2IBF_4 + (C_6H_5)_2Se$	210°	$(C_6H_5)_3SeBF_4$	80	133

ᵃ Not indicated.

It should be noted that at present the above-mentioned preparations of diarylchloronium and bromonium salts are the only reliable procedures, whereas the preparation of diphenyliodonium salts via diazonium salts is of only formal interest.

Unlike phenyldiazonium fluoborate, diaryliodonium salts may react with aryl iodides (traced with ^{131}I). The reaction is usually carried out at the temperature of the iodonium-salt decomposition (180–200°) and leads to tagged diaryliodonium salts unattainable by other methods:[139,140]

$$ArI^* + Ar_2IBF_4 \rightleftharpoons Ar_2I^*BF_4 + ArI \qquad (40)$$

VII. MECHANISM OF FORMATION OF ORGANOELEMENT COMPOUNDS VIA ONIUM COMPOUNDS

The preceding discussion shows the following:

1. A variety of organoelement compounds prepared via diazonium or halogenonium salts have many common synthetic features.

2. Onium salts may lead to a variety of organoelement compounds, and for some elements (mercury, tin, arsenic, antimony, bismuth, selenium) these methods are most important. Hence it is quite natural that the mechanism of the preparation of organometallic compounds via onium and, above all, diazonium salts was for a long time the subject of chemical investigation. In spite of numerous studies, however, a complete mechanism has still not been elicited.

The difficulty is that the data, being often indirect, testify either to homolytic or heterolytic mechanisms for the decomposition of onium salts in organoelement synthesis. Thus the mechanism of the synthesis of the organometallic compounds can be interpreted in two ways, but neither explanation is determinative.

A. Homolytic Decomposition

The homolytic decomposition of diazonium and iodonium salts is defined by the nature of the by-products as follows:

1. Substitution products of the diazo group by H—ArH.[1,14,27,49,54,55,60,123,141] Analogous compounds (e.g., ArH) are also formed from diaryliodonium salts.[125,142,143]

2. Acetaldehyde is produced when the reaction is conducted in ethanol.[27,123,142,143]

3. Biaryls (biphenyl in particular) are generated from the phenyldiazonium salt.[49,54,55,60,123]

4. Solvent chlorination products usually are formed in acetone or ethyl acetate.[27,28]

All these compounds undoubtedly are the products of radical reactions. For example, ArH is generated by the interaction of an aryl radical and the solvent:

$$Ar\cdot + RH \longrightarrow ArH + R\cdot \qquad (RH = solvent) \qquad (41)$$

Nesmeyanov et al.[54,55,123] have found that the formation of ArH is stimulated in hydroxylic solvents or in those able to exist in enolic form, in which alcohol can be oxidized to the aldehyde.

The homolytic decomposition of onium salts gives, along with atomic chlorine, the aryl radical as well:[30,144]

$$Ar\!:\!N\!=\!N\!:\!Cl \longrightarrow Ar\cdot + N_2 + \cdot Cl \qquad (42)$$

$$\begin{array}{c} Ar \\ Hal\!:\!Cl \\ Ar \end{array} \longrightarrow ArHal + Ar\cdot + \cdot Cl \qquad (43)$$

The homolytic course is substantially supported by the formation of heavy-metal chlorides in some cases, along with organometallic compounds in the reaction between metals and phenyldiazonium chloride.[27,49,83] Heavy-metal chlorides are also formed in the presence of chalk,[27,83] in the presence of which metals and hydrogen chloride (one of the by-products) would not react. Moreover, even for metals that on reacting with acid never give chlorides, chlorides have been isolated, e.g., AgCl.[27] On the basis of these data Waters[27] concluded that the metal chlorides are produced when atomic chlorine reacts with metals.

However, recent studies on the formation mechanisms of organotin and organomercury compounds,* in particular from iodonium salts, demonstrate the need for another viewpoint. We assume that the metal chlorides are produced in oxidative–reductive reactions: the diazonium cation is reduced to a radical by the metal, which in turn is transformed to a cation. The latter reacts with chlorine, giving the metal chloride. According to widespread opinion,[1,27,28,49,83,145,146] for a successful reaction with the metal, the onium salt should change from ionic to covalent form. The following example provides such evidence: organomercury compounds are successfully obtained from metallic mercury and aryldiazonium chloride[1,27,28,144,146] or diphenyl-halogenonium halides,[27,29,30,144–146] but no organomercury compound can be obtained from the fluoborates of the same onium salts.[28,30,144] However, as shown in the preceding sections, other metals behave otherwise. For example, organometallic compounds of thallium, germanium, and bismuth

* Discussed in subsections C and D, respectively.

cannot be obtained from diazonium and halogenonium halides but are successfully produced from the fluoborates.

In such cases the homolytic course of reaction can be explained in the following manner:[28] as a nucleophilic species, the metal reacts with the diazonium or halogenonium cations, converting them to unstable forms combined with the metal by covalent bonding:*

$$\overset{+}{Ph-N\equiv N} + :M \longrightarrow Ph_{\vdots}'N{=}N_{\vdots}'M \longrightarrow N_2 + PhM^+ \qquad (44)$$

$$\underset{Ph}{Ph:Hal^+} + :M \longrightarrow \underset{Ph}{Ph_{\vdots}'Hal_{\vdots}'M} \longrightarrow PhHal + PhM^+ \qquad (45)$$

Thus organometallic syntheses via aryldiazonium and diarylhalogenonium halides and fluoborates (as well as via double onium salts) are homolytic but all involve substantially different mechanisms. It thus seems that in the case of halides the onium salt is in the covalent, but in fluoborates in the ionic, form while participating in the reaction. On the other hand, no spectral difference was found between diazonium† halides and fluoborates[148-151] nor between halogenonium halides and fluoborates;[152-156] thus all the salts are ionic. However, if the structures of diazonium and halogenonium halides and fluoborates are similar in solution, then there are no grounds for substantially different mechanisms for the formation of organometallic compounds via these salts.

B. Heterolytic Decomposition

For the ionic structures of the onium salts heterolytic mechanisms may be suggested.

This may be supported by polar effects in organometallic syntheses via diazonium or iodonium salts. For example, Reutov, Markovskaya, and Mardaleishvili[157] investigated the reaction kinetics. On decomposing the double salts $p\text{-}XC_6H_4SbCl_4 \cdot C_6H_5N_2Cl$ with iron in acetone, the reaction rate was found to increase with increasing electron-releasing effect of a substituent X in these double salts and to decrease in the series $C_2H_5O >$ $CH_3 > H > Cl > NO_2$. On the other hand, under the same conditions for the decomposition of the double salts $C_6H_5SbCl_4 \cdot p\text{-}YC_6H_4N_2Cl$ the substituent effects were just the opposite; i.e., the stronger the electron-releasing effect of a substituent, the slower the reaction rate, decreasing in the order $H > CH_3 > OCH_3$.[158] The stabilities of the double diazonium salts

---

* An analogous mechanism is suggested for organometallic syntheses via double diazonium salts.

† According to spectral data the double diazonium salts are also ionic.[147-149]

TABLE XXVII

Stability of Double Diazonium Salts of the Type
$Ar'N_2Cl \cdot ArSbCl_2$[a,b]

Ar'	Ar			
	$p\text{-}O_2NC_6H_4$—	$p\text{-}H_2NO_2SC_6H_4$—	C_6H_5—	$p\text{-}CH_3C_6H_4$—
$p\text{-}O_2NC_6H_4$—	−	−	−	−
$m\text{-}O_2NC_6H_4$—	−	−	−	−
$p\text{-}C_2H_5OCOC_6H_4$—	−	−	−	−
$p\text{-}CH_3COC_6H_4$—	+	−	−	−
C_6H_5—	+	+	+	−
$p\text{-}CH_3C_6H_4$—	+	+	+	+
$o\text{-}CH_3OC_6H_4$—			+	
$o\text{-}C_2H_5OC_6H_4$—			+	
$p\text{-}CH_3OC_6H_4$—	+		+	+
$p\text{-}C_2H_5OC_6H_4$—		+	+	
$p\text{-}(CH_3)_2NC_6H_4$—	+	+	+	+

[a] Data from Ref. 159.

[b] Key: a minus sign indicates that the double diazonium salt is unstable (decomposes); a plus sign indicates that a double diazonium salt is obtained; a blank space means that such a salt has not been investigated.

$p\text{-}XC_6H_4SbCl_2 \cdot p\text{-}YC_6H_4N_2Cl$ show that substituent effects in these salts are analogous.[159] As seen from Table XXVII, their stabilities decrease when the electron-releasing effect of X and the electron-withdrawing ability of Y both increase. For example, when Y is a nitro or carboxy group, the double diazonium salts decompose *in statu nascendi* during exchange reactions:

$$YC_6H_4N_2Cl \cdot FeCl_3 + XC_6H_4SbCl_2 \rightleftarrows YC_6H_4N_2Cl \cdot XC_6H_4SbCl_2 + FeCl_3 \qquad (46)$$

In contrast, *p*-nitrophenyldichlorostibine gives a double diazonium salt even with *p*-acetophenyldiazonium chloride.

The evidence presented for the stabilities of the double diazonium salts $YC_6H_4N_2Cl \cdot XC_6H_4SbCl_2$ and the nature of the substituents X and Y as well as kinetic data on the decomposition of the double diazonium salts $p\text{-}XC_6H_4SbCl_4 \cdot C_6H_5N_2Cl$ and $C_6H_5SbCl_4 \cdot p\text{-}YC_6H_4N_2Cl$ are in agreement with the concept of a heterolytic mechanism.[6–8,160]*

Reutov et al.[161] decomposed asymmetrical diaryliodonium salts. They found that polar effects alone can provide no unequivocal conclusion on the mechanism of onium-salt decomposition. One may note that the evident

* Note should be made that at the time of these investigations no data had been published on the strong polar effect in homolytic reactions.

radical by-products mentioned above can be explained by homolytic cleavage of the free aryldiazonium chlorides[6]

$$ArN_2MX_{n+1} \rightleftarrows ArN_2X + MX_n \qquad (47)$$

parallel with the major reaction. Hence one may again assume for the diazonium salt that its ionic form is converted to a covalent one.

Thus both homolytic or heterolytic mechanisms are in accord with some experimental data and in disagreement with other findings. None of these mechanisms, however, provides an understanding of the fact that for the successful preparation of organometallic compounds one may employ in some cases (antimony, bismuth) either double onium salts or fluoborates, but not halides; in other cases (thallium, germanium, lead) only fluoborates; and in the case of mercury double onium salts or halides, but not fluoborates. This inconsistency is to some extent covered by the studies of mechanisms of organoelement syntheses via diaryliodonium salts.

C. Organotin Compounds

As we have already mentioned, organotin compounds can be obtained in approximately the same yields either from a mixture of diaryliodonium and tin(II) chlorides decomposing with tin powder in acetone or by reacting diaryliodonium and tin(II) chlorides in methanol. Analogous results have been obtained for asymmetrical diaryliodonium salts (Table XXVIII).

TABLE XXVIII

Chromatographic Analysis of the Mixture of Organotin Compounds Obtained by the Decomposition of Asymmetrical Diaryliodonium Salts[a]

Starting diaryliodonium salt	Organotin products and their relations[b]
p-ClC$_6$H$_4$(C$_6$H$_5$)ICl	(p-ClC$_6$H$_4$)$_2$SnCl$_2$ (1)
p-BrC$_6$H$_4$(C$_6$H$_5$)ICl	(p-BrC$_6$H$_4$)$_2$SnCl$_2$ (1)
p-IC$_6$H$_4$(C$_6$H$_5$)ICl	(p-IC$_6$H$_4$)$_2$SnCl$_2$ (1)
p-CH$_3$OC$_6$H$_4$(C$_6$H$_5$)ICl[c]	(p-CH$_3$OC$_6$H$_4$)$_2$SnCl$_2$ (0.5)
p-C$_2$H$_5$OCOC$_6$H$_4$(p-CH$_3$OC$_6$H$_4$)ICl[c]	(p-C$_2$H$_5$OCOC$_6$H$_4$)$_2$SnCl$_2$ (1)
p-C$_2$H$_5$OCOC$_6$H$_4$(C$_6$H$_5$)ICl	(p-C$_2$H$_5$OCOC$_6$H$_4$)$_2$SnCl$_2$ (1)
p-C$_2$H$_5$OCOC$_6$H$_4$(p-CH$_3$C$_6$H$_4$)ICl	(p-C$_2$H$_5$OCOC$_6$H$_4$)$_2$SnCl$_2$ (0.2)
m-C$_2$H$_5$OCOC$_6$H$_4$(C$_6$H$_5$)ICl	(m-C$_2$H$_5$OCOC$_6$H$_4$)$_2$SnCl$_2$[d]
m-C$_2$H$_5$OCOC$_6$H$_4$(p-CH$_3$C$_6$H$_4$)ICl	(m-C$_2$H$_5$OCOC$_6$H$_4$)$_2$SnCl$_2$ (0.7)

[a] Either with tin(II) chloride or with tin powder and tin(II) chloride. Data from Ref. 162.
[b] In parentheses.
[c] Determination after 1 hr.
[d] Other compounds have not been discovered.

The relations between organotin compounds prepared from asymmetrical iodonium salts were quantitatively determined by means of paper chromatography[162] and are shown in Table XXVIII (in parentheses). As can be seen from this table, the structural dependency of a given radical on the extent of its transfer from an asymmetrical diaryliodonium salt to the tin atom is rather complicated and comparatively little related to its electron-releasing or electron-withdrawing effects. Such a negligible polar contribution to the course of a C—I bond cleavage in the preparation of organotin compounds via iodonium salts made possible the suggestion of a homolytic reaction mechanism.* This suggestion was later supported by our kinetic data on the reaction of diphenyliodonium and tin(II) chlorides in methanol.

The reaction rate has been found to depend considerably on the presence of oxygen.† In a nitrogen atmosphere or in the presence of antioxidants for tin(II) chloride (hydroquinone or *m*-dinitrobenzene) the reaction rate has been found to be much lower. However, passing air through the mixture considerably increases the reaction rate, and illumination with ultraviolet light (mercury lamp PRK-4 as the source) makes it practically instantaneous. All these data are evidence for the chain radical reaction between diphenyliodonium and tin(II) chlorides. The effect of oxygen on the reaction rate

---

* Absence of polar effects is usually regarded as evidence of a homolytic course.[163]

† This is probably evidenced by the comparatively poor reproducibility of the kinetic data measured in methanol at reagent concentrations of about 25–100 mM.

Organotin products and their relations[b]	
$ClC_6H_4(C_6H_5)SnCl_2$ (2)	$(C_6H_5)_2SnCl_2$ (1)
$BrC_6H_4(C_6H_5)SnCl_2$ (2)	$(C_6H_5)_2SnCl_2$ (1)
$IC_6H_4(C_6H_5)SnCl_2$ (2)	$(C_6H_5)_2SnCl_2$ (1)
$CH_3OC_6H_4(C_6H_5)SnCl_2$ (2)	$(C_6H_5)_2SnCl_2$ (1)
$C_2H_5OCOC_6H_4)(p\text{-}CH_3OC_6H_4)SnCl_2$ (1.9)	$(p\text{-}CH_3OC_6H_4)_2SnCl_2$ (0.25)
$C_2H_5OCOC_6H_4(C_6H_5)SnCl_2$ (2)	$(C_6H_5)_2SnCl_2$ (0.5)
$C_2H_5OCOC_6H_4(p\text{-}CH_3C_6H_4)SnCl_2$ (2)	$(p\text{-}CH_3C_6H_4)_2SnCl_2$
$C_2H_5OCOC_6H_4(p\text{-}CH_3C_6H_4)SnCl_2$ (2)	$(p\text{-}CH_3C_6H_4)_2SnCl_2$ (1)

was investigated at constant air flow through the reaction mixture. Since the reaction was found to be very rapid in methanol with predominant oxidation of tin(II) chloride, use was made of 80% aqueous methanol, in which the rates of both processes (the iodonium salt reaction with tin(II) chloride and its oxidation) are commensurable and lower than in absolute methanol. The results were satisfactorily reproducible under these conditions.

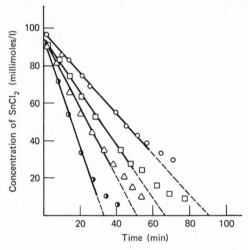

Fig. 1. Rate of oxidation of tin(II) chloride as a function of air flow through the reaction mixture. Rates of air throughput (ml/min): ○, 3; □, 9; △, 15; ◗, 32.

Figures 1 and 2 show the dependence of the rate of oxidation of tin(II) chloride and that of the reaction of diphenyliodonium and tin(II) chlorides on air flow through the reaction mixture. Increasing the air flow not only facilitates the oxidation of tin(II) chloride but also accelerates the iodonium-salt reaction with tin(II) chloride. These data show that both reactions proceed via the same intermediate and thus are conjugate.

Although experiments with air flow led to certain conclusions on the function of oxygen in this reaction, the heterogeneous medium, the concurrent oxidation of tin(II) chloride, and the simultaneous formation of two organotin compounds (diphenyltin dichloride and phenyltin trichloride) all together made more detailed kinetic investigation difficult. Hence in subsequent kinetic studies diphenyliodonium and tin(II) chlorides interacted in aqueous methanol in the presence of hydrochloric acid (200 ml of 1 N HCl diluted with absolute methanol to 1 liter). Such conditions led to phenyltin trichloride as the only reaction product in almost quantitative yield.

In order to attain reproducibility the kinetic experiments were carried out

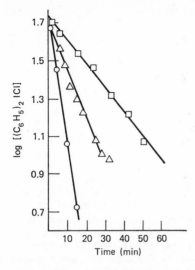

Fig. 2. Rate of reaction between diphenyl-iodonium and tin(II) chlorides as a function of air flow through the reaction solution. Rates of air throughput (ml/min): □, 3; △, 15; ○, 32.

under nitrogen, and di-*tert*-butyl peroxide was employed as initiator. Special experiments showed the latter to be a good initiating agent for the reaction. On the other hand, the rate of tin(II) chloride oxidation is so negligible that it cannot even be measured. The kinetic data of two runs carried out with and without di-*tert*-butyl peroxide are shown in Fig. 3, from which can be seen the speed of the reaction between diphenyliodonium and tin(II) chlorides in the presence of peroxide.

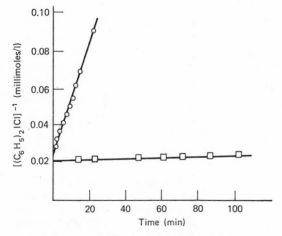

Fig. 3. Rate of reaction between diphenyliodonium and tin(II) chlorides in a nitrogen atmosphere with (○) and without (□) di-*tert*-butyl peroxide in a concentration of 50 millimoles/l.

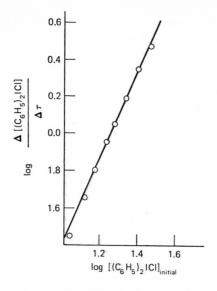

Fig. 4. General order of reaction between diphenyliodonium and tin(II) chlorides (τ = time). Starting reagent concentrations (millimoles/l): tin(II)chloride, 58; diphenyliodonium chloride, 50; di-*tert*-butyl peroxide, 50. The order of reaction is equal to the tangent of the slope—2.2.

As mentioned in the preceding discussion, the kinetics of reaction between an iodonium salt and tin(II) chloride are rather complicated. Although the reaction is of general second order, its component orders were found to be fractional: the order of tin(II) chloride was about 1.5, that of diphenyliodonium about 1 (Figs. 4–6). Such complex kinetics are not surprising if account is taken of the chain radical process mentioned previously.

Reaction-chain length was estimated by rate measurements at varying

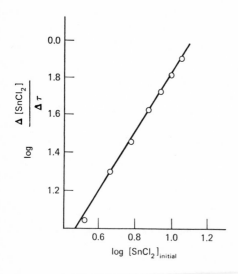

Fig. 5. Reaction order with respect to tin(II) chloride (τ = time). Reagent concentrations (millimoles/l): tin(II) chloride, 26; diphenyliodonium chloride, 100; di-*tert*-butyl peroxide, 25. The order of reaction is equal to the tangent of the slope—1.6.

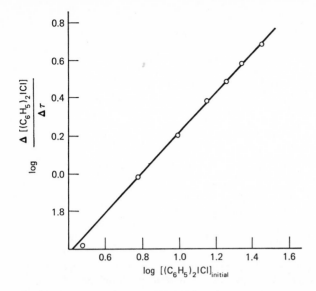

Fig. 6. Reaction order in respect to diphenyliodonium chloride (τ = time). Reagent concentrations (millimoles/l): tin(II) chloride, 550; diphenyliodonium chloride, 75; di-*tert*-butyl peroxide, 50. The order of reaction is equal to the tangent of the slope—1.

amounts of inhibitor (*m*-dinitrobenzene) (Fig. 7).[167] Taking as "inhibition time" the time when almost all inhibitor is exhausted, its rate of consumption can be found. Naturally one may suggest that chain breaking occurs mainly at the inhibitor molecule (one such molecule is usually assumed to cut off two chains). By definition the ratio of the reaction rate in the presence of inhibitor to that of its consumption is called the chain length of reaction in the presence of inhibitor. On the other hand, the ratio of the reaction rates with and without inhibitor is equal to the ratio of chain lengths.

Thus the chain length of reaction under study was determined by this method to be about 10^4. Although its magnitude is much increased, it is quite evident that the chain is rather long.

This conclusion is partially supported by the fact that the rate of reaction between di-*tert*-butyl peroxide and tin(II) chloride corresponding to that of initiation is very small and cannot even be measured.

Thus the decomposition of asymmetrical diaryliodonium salts, the initiation of reaction by means of ultraviolet-light illumination, and the action of oxygen, peroxides, and inhibitors taken all together testify that diaryliodonium and tin(II) chlorides react via a chain radical mechanism.

Unfortunately no direct data are available on the reaction intermediates. However, one may make certain hypotheses as to their nature. The results

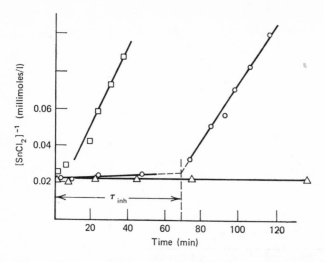

Fig. 7. Effect of *m*-dinitrobenzene concentration on the rate of reaction between diphenyliodonium and tin(II) chlorides. Reagent concentrations (millimoles/l): tin(II) chloride, 58; diphenyliodonium chloride, 50; di-*tert*-butyl peroxide, 50. Concentration of *m*-dinitrobenzene (millimoles/l): □, 0.10; ○, 0.01; △, 0.001. (τ_{inh} = time of inhibition.)

presented above show that stimulus to the interaction between diphenyliodonium and tin(II) chlorides were the intermediate oxidation products of the latter. According to published data,[166,168] the radicallike trivalent tin compound was one such product. Probably compounds of trivalent tin take part in the reaction discussed. The mechanism involving such an intermediate may be interpreted within the following terms:

$$:SnCl_2 + X\cdot \longrightarrow \cdot SnXCl_2 \qquad (A)$$
$$(C_6H_5)_2ICl + \cdot SnXCl_2 \longrightarrow (C_6H_5)_2I\cdot + SnXCl_3 \qquad (B)$$
$$(C_6H_5)_2I\cdot + :SnCl_2 \longrightarrow \cdot SnC_6H_5Cl_2 + C_6H_5I \qquad (C)$$
$$(C_6H_5)_2ICl + \cdot SnC_6H_5Cl_2 \longrightarrow (C_6H_5)_2I\cdot + C_6H_5SnCl_3 \qquad (D)$$
$$(\cdot X = RO\cdot \text{ or } \cdot O{-}O\cdot)$$

(48)

At the stage of initiation trivalent tin derivatives are generated by the reaction of peroxide with tin(II) chloride (stage A). Then trivalent tin reduces the diaryliodonium cation to a radical (stage B). The latter in turn reacts with tin(II) chloride, giving rise to the phenyl derivative of trivalent tin (stage C). This compound further reduces the iodonium cation (stage D). Thus the chain is initiating and propagating. It then breaks off during the recombination of radicals (as usually assumed for liquid-phase reactions) or at the inhibitor molecules.

Diphenyltin dichloride may also arise during the reaction of the phenyltin dichloro radical with diphenyliodine

$$(C_6H_5)_2I\cdot + \cdot SnC_6H_5Cl_2 \longrightarrow (C_6H_5)_2SnCl_2 + C_6H_5I \qquad (49)$$

as well as during the disproportionation reaction of the phenyltin dichloro radical

$$2\cdot SnC_6H_5Cl_2 \longrightarrow (C_6H_5)_2SnCl_2 + SnCl_2 \qquad (50)$$

Both reactions should lead to chain breaking.

Probably the higher the starting concentrations of reagents, the more should reactions (49) and (50) be facilitated and the higher should be the yield of diphenyltin dichloride. Indeed, as we mentioned in Section IV-B, at concentrations above 0.5 M diphenyliodonium and tin(II) chlorides give predominantly diphenyltin dichloride, whereas below this concentration phenyltin trichloride is the major product.

Although it agrees well with experiment, note should be made that reaction scheme (48) has no rigorous proof and seems to be no more than just probable.

D. Organomercury Compounds

Investigations confined to the mechanisms of the formation of organo-mercury compounds via diaryliodonium salts are of considerable interest. Diphenyliodonium salts have been shown[142] to decompose and react with mercury in a major reaction

$$Ar_2IX + Hg \longrightarrow ArHgX + ArI \qquad (51)$$

and two side reactions

$$2Ar_2IX + CH_3CH_2OH + 2Hg \longrightarrow 2ArI + CH_3CHO + 2ArH + Hg_2X_2 \quad (52)$$

$$Ar_2IX \longrightarrow ArI + ArX \qquad (53)$$

Reaction (53) comprises the thermal decomposition of the iodonium salt, being most facile for diphenyliodonium iodide and not occurring in the case of the chloride. The reaction also takes place without mercury, as was found in model closed experiments (reaction products were identified by means of gas–liquid chromatography). On the contrary, the presence of mercury is required in reactions (51) and (52). Since it is undoubtedly the radical-generated product, benzene can thus be obtained only in the homolytic decomposition of the diphenyliodonium salt, in which mercury behaves as an agent somewhat stimulating this decay, because reaction (52) does not take place without mercury. In the presence of mercury the formation of benzene and organomercury compounds in the homolytic decomposition of the iodonium salt is excluded for the following reasons: First, spectral

data (p. 124) testify that there is no significant difference between diphenyliodonium halides and fluoborates;[152-156] thus these salts all have ionic structures.

On the other hand, if the covalent form of an iodonium salt is decomposed, the reaction should be more facile when the I—X bond in $(C_6H_5)_2I$—X is more covalent. In fact, however, the lower dissociation constant of diphenyl-iodonium acetate in methanol (Table XXIX), and hence higher covalency*

TABLE XXIX
Degrees of Dissociation of Diphenyliodonium
Salts in Water and Methanol[169]

Iodonium salt	Degree of dissociation α at $25 \pm 0.1°$	
	In water	In methanol
$(C_6H_5)_2IBF_4$	97.79	98.45
$(C_6H_5)_2ICl$	90.85	89.21
$(C_6H_5)_2IBr$	88.20	85.20
$(C_6H_5)_2IOCOCH_3$	86.34	80.94

with respect to diphenyliodonium chloride or bromide, makes it more difficult to decompose with mercury. With regard to their ease of decomposi-tion with mercury (Table XXX), diphenyliodonium salts can be arranged in

TABLE XXX
Anion Dependence of the Rate of Diphenyliodonium Salt
Decomposition by Mercury[143]

X^- in $(C_6H_5)_2IX$	Time of full decomposition, hr		
	In ethanol at 56°	In methanol at 56°	In water at 90°[a]
CH_3COO^-	15		25
Cl^-	11	27	9
Br^-	7	9.5	1
I^-	5		0.5
CN^-	3		

[a] In the presence of a twofold excess of the same anion.

the following series: $CN^- > I^- > Br^- > Cl^- > CH_3COO^-$.[143] Therefore not the previously assumed covalent, but probably an ionic, form of the

---

* Nondissociated molecules can exist either as ionic pairs or in the form of a covalent iodonium salt.

iodonium salt is responsible for the reaction. Perhaps the reaction involves the following mechanism: mercury first reduces the iodonium cation to the radical, simultaneously giving rise to mercury–anion bonding and the

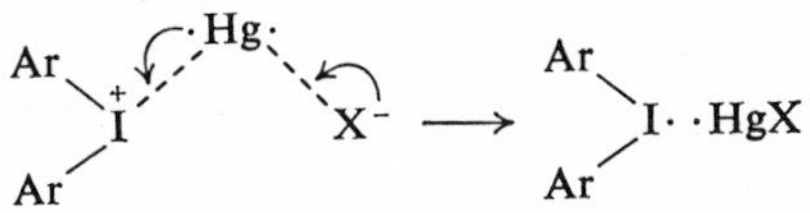

$$\text{(54)}$$

"radical pair." The diphenyliodine radical, reacting with $\cdot HgX$, gives an organomercury compound and an aryl iodide, e.g., in accord with reaction (51). If the diphenyliodine radical reacts with the solvent, it should produce benzene [reaction (52)]. In this case the $\cdot HgCl$ radical should give monovalent mercurous salts Hg_2Cl_2, which indeed have been isolated. The anion should essentially affect the first stage [reaction (54)] because the mercury oxidation–reduction potential is anion dependent[170] in the system

$$2Hg + 2X^- \longrightarrow Hg_2X_2 + 2e$$

This can be seen from the data in Table XXXI. Although the data in this table are for aqueous solutions and inorganic salts of mercury only, and absolute values of potentials certainly change in various organic solvents and for different organomercury compounds, the general pattern is probably the

TABLE XXXI

Oxidation Potentials[170]

Process	Potential $E_{1/2}$, V
$2Hg \rightarrow Hg_2^{2+} + 2e$	-0.789
$2Hg + 2CH_3COO^- \rightarrow Hg_2(OCOCH_3)_2 + 2e$	-0.51
$Hg + 4Cl^- \rightarrow HgCl_4^{2-} + 2e^-$	-0.48
$2Hg + 2Cl^- \rightarrow Hg_2Cl_2 + 2e^-$	-0.2676
$2Hg + 2Br^- \rightarrow Hg_2Br_2 + 2e^-$	-0.1397
$2Hg + 2I^- \rightarrow Hg_2I_2 + 2e^-$	$+0.0405$
$Hg + 4I^- \rightarrow HgI_4^{2-} + 2e^-$	$+0.04$
$Hg + 4CN^- \rightarrow Hg(CN)_4^{2-} + 2e^-$	$+0.37$

same. The very facile decomposition of diphenyliodonium cyanide, as one would expect, may support this idea (Table XXX). The dependence of the reaction rate on the anion X^- was again analogous in water (Table XXX).*

* Since reactions proceed very slowly in water, the decomposition of iodonium salts was carried out in the presence of a twofold excess of anion X^-. (This is subsequently considered in more detail.)

Thus a high reduction potential is probably responsible for the fact that the rate of decomposition with mercury is lowest for diphenyliodonium acetate. Diphenyliodonium fluoborate, which does not decompose with metallic mercury, should have a higher potential. This has been confirmed by the fact that organomercury derivatives are obtained from diaryliodonium fluoborates[42] in the presence of mercury and a reducing agent stronger than mercury (e.g., iron). This provides large quantities of symmetrical organomercury compounds (see p. 84) according to the following scheme:

$$2Ar_2I^+BF_4^- + Fe \longrightarrow 2Ar_2I\cdot + Fe(BF_4)_2 \qquad (55)$$

$$2Ar_2I\cdot + 2Hg \longrightarrow 2ArI + 2ArHg\cdot \qquad (56)$$

$$2ArHg\cdot \longrightarrow Ar_2Hg + Hg \qquad (57)$$

Thus, in spite of some differences, the formation of organomercury compounds via both diaryliodonium fluoborates and halides involves a common stage of oxidation–reduction [reactions (55) and (54), respectively] converting the diaryliodonium cation to diaryliodine and then to organomercury compounds.

TABLE XXXII

Decomposition of Diaryliodonium Bromide by Mercury in Absolute Methanol

Iodonium salt	Quantity of KBr, mole %	Time of reaction, hr	Yield, %
$(C_6H_5)_2IBr$	100	1	62
$(p\text{-}CH_3C_6H_4)_2IBr$	100	2.75	62
$(p\text{-}CH_3OC_6H_4)_2IBr$	100	10	59
$p\text{-}CH_3OC_6H_4(C_6H_5)IBr$	100	6	(a)
$(C_6H_5)_2IBr$	—	9.5	52
$(m\text{-}HOCOC_6H_4)_2IBr$	—	0.15	40
$m\text{-}O_2NC_6H_4(C_6H_5)IBr$	—	1.75	46
$m\text{-}O_2NC_6H_4(C_6H_5)IBr$	100	(a)	54
$o\text{-}O_2NC_6H_4(C_6H_5)IBr$	—	0.5	48
$o\text{-}O_2NC_6H_4(C_6H_5)IBr$	100	0.15	60

[a] Undetermined.

From the mechanism discussed one would expect that substituents in the diphenyliodonium salt must influence the oxidation–reduction stage and hence the rate at which the organomercury compound is formed. Electron-withdrawing substituents, which increase the positive charge on iodine in the iodonium cation, should increase the reaction rate of diaryliodonium salts relative to that of unsubstituted salts. An opposite effect would be expected from electron-releasing substituents.* Experimental data agree with this hypothesis (Table XXXII). The reactions of salts containing electron-releasing substituents were conducted in the presence of the common anion (equimolar amounts of potassium bromide). This increased the rate of decomposition of diphenyliodonium chloride and bromide with mercury[172] (Table XXXIII). This effect of the common anion may be a result of the

TABLE XXXIII

Influence of the Common Anion on the Reaction between Diphenyliodonium Salts and Metallic Mercury[172]

X⁻ = Cl⁻		Quantity of X^- at 1 M $(C_6H_5)_2IX$, moles	X⁻ = Br⁻	
Reaction time, hr	Yield of C_6H_5HgCl, %		Reaction time, hr	Yield of C_6H_5HgBr, %
27	65	0	9.5	51
—	—	0.05	9.5	(a)
23	73	0.20	2.25	60
—	—	0.28	1.75	(a)
21	77	0.50	1.25	61
17	84	1.0	1	62
—	—	1.5	0.5	61
9.5	84	2.0	—	—
6	80	4.0	—	—
2.5	80	6.0	—	—

ᵃ Undetermined.

higher concentration of ionic pairs and the lower oxidation–reduction potential.

The time of reaction of diphenyliodonium chloride and bromide with mercury versus the concentration of the common anion is plotted in Fig. 8. These curves recall the dependence of electrical conductivity of strong electrolytes on the degree of dilution. Ionic pair generation should cause sharp changes in the reaction rate with an increase in anion concentration, then, as the latter slowly attains the limit, the rate does not alter more than negligibly.

As can be seen from Tables XXXII and XXXIII, addition of the common anion increases not only the rate but also the yield of the organomercury

* Electron-withdrawing substituents in molecules with electrophilic groups are known[171] to facilitate their reduction due to decreased electron density. In contrast, electron-releasing substituents hinder the reduction.

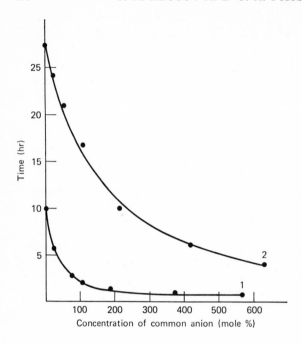

Fig. 8. Time of decomposition of diphenyliodonium bromide (curve 1) and chloride (curve 2) with mercury versus the concentration of the common anion (mole %).

compound. In fact it may be pointed out that along with these effects there is almost complete absence of the radical-originated products, in particular cuprous salts and formaldehyde[172] are observed. In our opinion these data indicate that species more active than the radical $\cdot HgX$ take part in the synthesis of organomercury compounds, and their ability to dimerize may be a criterion of comparative stability. We assume that this may be the radical anion $\cdot HgX_2^-$. It seems probable that, on interacting with the diaryliodine radical, such a more active species should be responsible for the higher yield of the organomercury compound, whereas generation of the radical-originated by-products is less probable. However, model experiments show that, addition of the common anion to the reaction mixture facilitates the side reaction (53).

Participation of the radical anion $\cdot HgX_2^-$ advanced for the reaction is adequate with the results obtained for asymmetrical diaryliodonium salts decomposed with mercury. The latter gives preference to a combination with a more electron-withdrawing radical.

On the basis of these data, the synthesis of organomercury compounds via diaryliodonium salts may be suggested to involve the following mechanism:

$$Ar_2I^+ + X^- \rightleftharpoons Ar_2I^+X^-$$
$$\text{ions} \qquad \text{ionic pair}$$

$$Ar_2I \overset{\cdot Hg}{\underset{X^-}{\diagdown}} \xrightarrow{\text{slow}} Ar_2I \cdot \cdot HgX \qquad\qquad (58)$$
$$\text{radical pair}$$

$$Ar_2I \cdot \cdot HgX + X^- \xrightarrow{\text{fast}} Ar_2I \cdot \cdot HgX_2^- \xrightarrow{\text{fast}} ArI + ArHgX + X^-$$

The results on the decomposition of diphenyliodonium chloride with mercury in various solvents are in agreement with the mechanism presented (Table XXXIV). As seen from this table, the reaction rate is the reciprocal of the amount of unreacted iodonium salt (at a constant reaction time of 3 hr) and is independent of either the dielectric constant of the solvent or the solubility of the iodonium salt. It decreases in the order ethanol > water > dioxane > acetone > benzene. However, the data of Table XXXIV are in

TABLE XXXIV

Decomposition of Diphenyliodonium Chloride by Mercury in Various Solvents[a]

Solvent and its dielectric constant[b]		Yield of C_6H_5HgCl, %	Iodonium Salt recovered, %	Yield of C_6H_5HgCl, %, based on reacted salt
Dioxane	2.20	8.6	89.5	83
Benzene	2.28	15.4	76.0	64
Water	80.0	16.6	76.0	70
Ethanol	24.3	45.6	23	60
Acetone	20.70	86.0	—	86

[a] Reaction time of 3 hr.
[b] Dielectric constants are from Ref. 173.

agreement with the idea that the oxidation–reduction stage is decisive. Reduction of the cation is known to be more difficult when it is more strongly solvated.[174] The solvating power increases in the order acetone < ethanol < water; thus the rates of iodonium-salt decomposition with mercury should decrease in the same sequence.

The slow reaction observed in dioxane seems to be a result of its tendency to complex diaryliodonium salts.[175]* Naturally, the reactivity of iodonium salts toward mercury should decrease with complexation. Complexation is probably the reason† that diaryliodonium fluoborate and iron do not react in acetone but do react in alcohol (see p. 84).

No solvation of the iodonium salt takes place in benzene, but it is almost insoluble in this solvent, which makes the reaction very slow.

Thus, although the formation of organotin and of organomercury compounds via diaryliodonium salts has different mechanisms, both reactions involve the reduction of the diaryliodonium cation to the diaryliodine radical; the latter by one or another route leads to the corresponding organometallic compound. We assume that syntheses of organometallic compounds via diazonium (including double diazonium salts) and other diarylhalogenonium salts involve the reduction of a diazonium (halogenonium) cation to a radical as one of the major stages. Then the generation of the radical-originated by-products may be interpreted without the need of a mechanism that somewhat artificially converts an ionic diazonium salt to a covalent one.

However, methods of generation of the radicals ($ArN_2\cdot$ and $Ar_2Hal\cdot$) and then conversion to the organoelement compounds must probably change from metal to metal or from one to another group of the periodic table. In our opinion this may be supported by the mechanism of formation of organotin and organomercury compounds via diaryliodonium salts discussed above.

E. Mechanisms of Reaction between Diaryliodonium Fluoborates and Triphenylphosphine

Makarova and Nesmeyanov[30] assumed that diphenyliodonium fluoborate, which is never covalent, may decompose heterolytically, giving rise to the phenyl cation, which attacks the lone electron pair of triphenylphosphine:

$$C_6H_5 \diagdown I^+BF_4^- + :P(C_6H_5)_3 \longrightarrow C_6H_5I + (C_6H_5 : P^+(C_6H_5)_3BF_4^- \qquad (59)$$
$$C_6H_5 \diagup$$

It seems quite probable indeed that at high temperatures (200°) diphenyliodonium fluoborate decomposes heterolytically in the presence of nucleo-

---

* We have obtained a dioxane–diphenyliodonium fluoborate complex by recrystallizing the iodonium salt from dioxane (m.p. 123–129°).

† No direct proof of the complexation of diaryliodonium fluoborates with acetone is known. However, Ar_2IBF_4 has an unusually high solubility in acetone. The addition of ether to a solution of diphenyliodonium fluoborate in acetone precipitated crystals whose melting point was lower than that of the starting compound, which only after heating in water attained the melting point of $(C_6H_5)_2IBF_4$.

philic agents (in particular triphenylphosphine). On the other hand, the reaction of triphenylphosphine with $(C_6H_5)_2IBF_4$ in boiling propanol has been shown to involve two processes: thermal and photochemical.[130,173] According to the authors,[132] they are both chain radical processes:

$$(C_6H_5)_2IBF_4 + :P(C_6H_5)_3 \longrightarrow [(C_6H_5)_2I:P(C_6H_5)_3]^+BF_4^-$$

$$[(C_6H_5)_2I:P(C_6H_5)_3]^+BF_4^- \longrightarrow (C_6H_5)_2I\cdot + \cdot\overset{+}{P}(C_6H_5)_3 + BF_4^-$$

$$(C_6H_5)_2I\cdot + :P(C_6H_5)_3 \longrightarrow C_6H_5I + (C_6H_5)_4P\cdot \qquad (60)$$

$$(C_6H_5)_4P\cdot + (C_6H_5)_2IBF_4 \longrightarrow (C_6H_5)_4PBF_4 + (C_6H_5)_2I\cdot, \text{ etc.}$$

This mechanism is supported by the following results: First, inhibitors of radical reactions, such as hydroquinone and m-dinitrobenzene, influence these reactions considerably. They greatly decrease the yield of tetraphenylphosphonium fluoborate. Second, with alcohol as solvent,* benzene and acetaldehyde are formed as by-products. These compounds could result only from the homolytic decomposition of the iodonium salt and from the reaction of the diphenyliodine radical (or its phenyl radical) with the solvent (alcohol):

$$(C_6H_5)_2I\cdot + RCH_2OH \longrightarrow C_6H_5I + C_6H_6 + R\overset{\cdot}{C}HOH \qquad (61)$$

Then the radical $R\overset{\cdot}{C}HOH$ converts to the aldehyde. It may be pointed out that the aforementioned by-products are generated only in the presence of triphenylphosphine. Hence it is the latter that takes part in the formation of the diphenyliodonium radical.

Another manifestation of the reaction's chain radical nature is that the quantum yield of the photochemical reaction is 180.

Ultraviolet spectroscopy gives further evidence of the diphenyliodonium fluoborate–triphenylphosphine complex. Acetone solutions of $(C_6H_5)_3P$ and $(C_6H_5)IBF_4$ exhibit a new band in the ultraviolet, with a maximum at 336 mμ, whereas the starting compounds and reaction products do not absorb above 300 mμ. Thus the band at 336 mμ in the spectrum of an acetone solution of triphenylphosphine and diphenyliodonium fluoborate appears to be due to some new compound—probably the complex $(C_6H_5)_2IBF_4 \cdot (C_6H_5)_3P$.†

Moreover, the formation of the complex $[(C_6H_5)_2I \leftarrow :P(C_6H_5)_3]^+BF^4$ is manifested by the fact that 336 mμ is the most effective wavelength photochemically. Thus the complex $[(C_6H_5)_2I \leftarrow :P(C_6H_5)_3]^+ BF_4^-$ decomposes with light or temperature (in boiling propanol) to form the diphenyliodonium radical, which further reacts in accord with the scheme suggested. We assume

---

* The photochemical reaction was conducted in ethanol and acetone, as well as in propanol.

† It should be noted that the complex $(C_6H_5)_2IBF_4 \cdot H_2NC_6H_5$ absorbs at 329 mμ.[176]

that this course of reaction is supported by the reaction of triphenylphosphine and diphenyliodonium fluoborate in acetone, at room temperature, in darkness, and with reduced iron powder:

$$2(C_6H_5)_2I^+BF_4^- + Fe \longrightarrow 2(C_6H_5)_2I\cdot + Fe(BF_4)_2$$

$$(C_6H_5)_2I\cdot + (C_6H_5)_3P: \longrightarrow (C_6H_5)_4P\cdot + C_6H_5I \qquad (62)$$

$$(C_6H_5)_4P\cdot + (C_6H_5)_2IBF_4 \longrightarrow (C_6H_5)_4PBF_4 + (C_6H_5)_2I\cdot$$

The diphenyliodonium radical is generated in this case by the reduction of the iodonium cation with iron.* As in the photochemical reaction, hydroquinone decreases the yield of tetraphenylphosphonium fluoborate.

Thus all these results testify to the radical mechanism in the reactions of diaryliodonium fluoborate and triphenylphosphine. However, the use of asymmetrical diaryliodonium salts shows that, as in the case of organomercury compounds,[177] the more electron-withdrawing substituent usually transfers to triphenylphosphine.[161]

$$C_6H_5(o\text{-}O_2NC_6H_4)IBF_4 + (C_6H_5)_3P \longrightarrow (C_6H_5)_3(o\text{-}O_2NC_6H_4)PBF_4 + C_6H_5I \quad (63)$$

Hence in radical reactions polar effects play an important function in the cleavage of the C—I bond in asymmetrical diaryliodonium salts.† This reaction is one of the few examples in which investigation of the polar effects alone is not sufficient to determine whether the reaction mechanism is homolytic or heterolytic.

VIII. EXAMPLES OF ORGANOELEMENT SYNTHESES VIA ARYLDIAZONIUM AND DIARYLHALOGENONIUM SALTS

A. Organomercury Compounds

1. Asymmetrical Organomercury Compounds

a. Preparation by Nesmeyanov's Method. The procedure can be divided into three steps:

(i) Preparation of the double diazonium salt. One mole of amine is mixed with 300 ml of concentrated hydrochloric acid, heated, and stirred until completely converted to the salt. After cooling, 300 g of crushed ice is added, and the mixture is rapidly diazotized with a saturated sodium nitrite solution (1 mole) with efficient stirring. If necessary, the diazo solution is filtered.

---

* Model experiments show that iron decomposes diphenyliodonium fluoborate under these conditions to benzene and iodobenzene.

† A number of recent papers by Hey and co-workers[178-183] report substantial polar effects in free-radical reactions.

The resulting clear solution of diazonium salt is added quickly with stirring and cooling to 270 g of mercury(II) chloride in 270 ml of concentrated hydrochloric acid mixed with 300 g of ice. The double diazonium salt precipitates and is filtered, washed with water, alcohol, and ether, and dried in air.

(ii) Preparation of copper powder. Zinc powder (60 g) is sifted into a vigorously stirred cold solution of 250 g of cupric sulfate in 1.5–2.0 l of water. The solid that precipitates is filtered, washed thoroughly with water, alcohol, and ether, and dried in air. The copper powder should have a metallic copper color.

(iii) Common procedure for the preparation of arylmercury halides. The double diazonium salt is added in small portions to a well-stirred suspension of copper powder (50% excess) in the corresponding solvent, cooling with snow and salt (see Table III). A 30–50 ml quantity of solvent is usually taken for 10 g of the double salt. Decomposition temperature is maintained at about −5 to −15°. On completion of decomposition the solvent is evaporated, the precipitated solid is washed with a small portion of ether, and the arylmercury halide is extracted with a suitable solvent (usually acetone, benzene, or xylene). The organomercury compound is recrystallized from the same solvent.

Compounds prepared by this procedure are listed in Section II-A, Table III.

When the reaction is carried out in water, 10 g of the double salt is taken per 35–70 ml of water at 0°. The reaction is completed after 4–5 hr. The mixture is allowed to sit overnight. The precipitate is filtered and washed with small portions of alcohol and ether. The organomercury compound is extracted with a suitable solvent (usually acetone, benzene, chloroform, or ethyl acetate) and recrystallized from one of these solvents.

b. Preparation via Diaryliodonium Salts.   Diaryliodonium chloride (0.01 mole) is vigorously stirred with 2 ml of metallic mercury in 100 ml of acetone at 56° for 3 hr. The solid is filtered off and extracted with acetone, combining the extract with the filtrate. The solvent is evaporated, the organomercury compound is separated from aryl iodide by washing with light petroleum. The yields of compounds obtained by this method are shown in Table II (Section II-A).

c. Preparation via Arylazocarboxylic Salts.   Potassium arylazocarboxylate (usually ca. 2 g) is added at room temperature during 30 min to 8.7 g of mercury(II) chloride (threefold excess) in 100 ml of acetone, with mechanical stirring. Stirring is continued for another 30 min. After evaporating the solvent, the dry residue is washed free from the mercury(II) chloride with sodium chloride solution and water. The organomercury compound is extracted with acetone. The yields of organomercury halides obtained by this method are shown in Table V (Section II-A).

2. Symmetrical Organomercury Compounds

a. Preparation by Nesmeyanov's Diazo Method. The double diazonium salt (10 g) is added in small portions to 8 g of copper powder suspended in 50 ml of acetone while stirring and cooling at -5 to $-10°$. Five minutes after the completion of vigorous gas evolution, an equal volume of aqueous ammonia is added; the mixture is thoroughly stirred for several minutes, allowed to stand for 24 hr at room temperature, and refluxed for 1–2 hr. Addition of a large excess of water precipitates the organomercury compound. The solid is filtered, washed with water, and a small portion of ether. The diarylmercury compound is extracted with a suitable solvent (alcohol, benzene, chloroform) and recrystallized from the same solvent.

b. Preparation via Diaryliodonium Fluoborates. Diaryliodonium fluoborate, reduced iron powder, and metallic mercury (in the molar ratio 0.02:0.27:0.135) are placed in a reaction flask and covered with 40 ml of absolute methanol. Effective stirring is provided by using a reaction vessel with a working volume twice that of the reaction mixture. The mixture is then shaken at room temperature during the time indicated in Table IV (Section II-A). After completion of reaction, the unreacted iron and mercury are filtered and washed with chloroform. Inorganic iron salts are separated by pouring the alcohol–chloroform solution into water. The chloroform layer is separated, and the water part is extracted three times with fresh portions of chloroform for a complete extraction of diarylmercury. The combined chloroform extracts are dried over calcium chloride, and the solvent is evaporated. Light petroleum is added to the residue for separating the aryl iodide from the organomercury compound. The precipitate is filtered, giving practically pure diarylmercury.

B. Thallium Organic Compounds: Synthesis of Diphenylthallium Chloride[51]

A suspension of 5 g (0.025 mole) of phenyldiazonium fluoborate in 50 ml of acetone is placed into a high, narrow glass vessel provided with a turbo-stirrer (3000 rpm) and cooled with an ice–salt bath to $-14°$. Thallium powder, 8 g (0.039 g-atom), prepared by the reaction of zinc powder with an aqueous solution of thallous sulfate and washed with water, is added during 15–20 min in small portions to this mixture. The temperature is allowed to increase to $-3°$. After the addition of all the thallium, the mixture is stirred for 2 hr in an ice–salt bath. The next day the acetone is evaporated *in vacuo*, the residue is treated with 40 ml of hydrochloric acid (1:1), with slight heating, and then the solid is filtered, washed first with water and then acetone, and extracted with pyridine in a Soxhlet apparatus. Evaporation of the pyridine extract afforded 1.04 g (20%) of diphenylthallium chloride.

C. Germanium Organic Compounds: Decomposition of Phenyldiazonium Fluoborate with Zinc Powder in Acetone in the Presence of GeCl₄

The reaction is carried out in a tall, narrow glass vessel provided with a Witt stirrer and a thermometer. Phenyldiazonium fluoborate, 50 g (0.26 mole), is added in small portions during 20 min at $-8°$ to a suspension of 17.4 g (0.26 g-atom) of zinc powder in a solution of 25.15 g (0.35 mole) of $GeCl_4$ in 80 ml of acetone while vigorously stirring the mixture. Even the first portions of diazonium cause the temperature to increase to $5°$. The addition is further conducted at a rate that will maintain the temperature below $5°$. After completion of the addition, the stirring is continued for 5 hr with cooling. The next day 40 ml of dry acetone is added to the reaction mixture, and stirring is conducted until the diazonium salt is completely decomposed (no reaction with β-naphthol).

The reaction mixture is worked up with 20% sodium hydroxide solution. The solid that precipitates in 3 hr is filtered and washed with acetone (filtrate I). A substantial quantity of phenylgermanic acid anhydride is extracted from the solid with 20% sodium hydroxide solution with heating and subsequent acidification of the alkaline filtrates with concentrated hydrochloric acid. The remaining residue contains no organogermanium compounds.

Filtrate I is separated into two layers: the organic layer after the addition of ether and the alkaline aqueous layer from which an additional quantity of phenylgermanic acid is isolated on acidification (after ether addition). No organogermanium compound was found in the organic layer. The total yield of phenylgermanic acid anhydride is 5.58 g (27%). It is repeatedly precipitated with hydrochloric acid from 10% sodium hydroxide solution with heating and subsequent washing with pyridine (once), water, alcohol, and ether.

An analogous procedure is employed for the preparation of other arylgermanic acids (see Table VII in Section IV-A).

D. Organotin Compounds

1. Preparation of Organotin Compounds via Aryldiazonium Fluoborates[53]

Small portions of 0.0375 g-atom of zinc powder and 0.025 mole of freshly prepared aryldiazonium fluoborate are added alternately to a stirred solution of 0.0375 mole of $SnCl_2 \cdot 2H_2O$ in 50 ml of acetone contained in an open flask (diameter 45 mm, height 250 mm), provided with a thermometer, efficient bell-shaped turbostirrer, and external ice cooling. The temperature increases immediately, and the evolution of nitrogen evolution starts. For 1–1.5 hr after the evolution of nitrogen stops stirring is continued at room temperature.* The next day the acetone is evaporated on a water bath, the residue is exhaustively extracted with light petroleum (b.p. 70–110°), and the solvent is evaporated. The liquid residue is diluted with ethanol, and an excess of 25% aqueous ammonia solution is added. Organotin oxides precipitate and are filtered off and washed with alcohol and ether. The solid insoluble diaryltin oxide was identified by conversion to diarylmercury or diaryltin dichloride by reaction with thionyl chloride.

The residue of solvent evaporation from the alcohol–ether solution containing triaryltin oxide and arylstannonic acid is worked up with 10% sodium hydroxide solution. Triaryltin oxide is precipitated. Arylstannonic acid is precipitated by carbon dioxide from the alkaline solution. Both compounds were identified by conversion to diarylmercury.

Usually this method cannot give tetraaryl compounds. The total yield of organotin compounds obtained is shown in Table IX in Section IV-B.

2. Synthesis of organotin compounds via diaryliodonium salts[56]

a. Synthesis of Diphenyltin Oxide. Diphenyliodonium chloride, 20 g (0.063 mole), is added to 25 ml of acetone. Then 20 g (0.1 mole) of anyhdrous tin(II) chloride and 10 g (0.084 g-atom) of freshly prepared tin powder are added to the solution with vigorous stirring. After several minutes, the temperature spontaneously rises almost to the boiling point. After vigorous stirring for 4 hr, the inorganic material is filtered off, and the solvent is evaporated. The oil remaining after acetone evaporation is washed with hydrochloric acid to remove the inorganic tin compounds and dissolved in alcohol. The alcohol solution is poured into 10% sodium hydroxide solution with cooling. Diphenyltin oxide precipitates, is filtered, and washed with water, alcohol, and ether to give 7 g (76%) of product.

b. Synthesis of Di-p-tolyltin Oxide. A 7-g quantity (0.02 mole) of di-*p*-tolyliodonium chloride and 4 g (0.002 mole) of anhydrous tin(II) chloride in 20 ml of acetone are decomposed with 3 g (0.025 g-atom) of tin. After stirring the reaction mixture for 2 hr, treatment similar to that described for diphenyltin oxide gives 2.15 g (67%) of di-*p*-tolyltin oxide.

E. Organolead Compounds

1. Synthesis of Tetraphenyllead via Phenyldiazonium Fluoborate[59]

To a vigorously stirred suspension of 7.7 g (0.04 mole) of freshly prepared, dry phenyldiazonium fluoborate in 60 ml of acetone cooled to 6–7°, is added

---

* The decomposition of *p*-nitrophenyldiazonium fluoborate is carried out with cooling in an ice–salt bath, and the reaction mixture is allowed to stand overnight in the melting, cooling mixture.

during 8–10 min 12.4 g (0.06 g-atom) of metallic lead powder. The reaction is accompanied by heat evolution. The temperature is kept at 15–17° by cooling the flask with ice water. The mixture is stirred for another hour while cooling with ice water and allowed to stand overnight. The solid is filtered, washed with ether, and extracted with chloroform in a Soxhlet apparatus. Recrystallization from a chloroform–absolute alcohol mixture gives 0.85 g (15%) of tetraphenyllead, m.p. 226°.

2. Synthesis of Tetraphenyllead via Diphenyliodonium Fluoborate[41]

a. Preparation of Lead Powder. Lead acetate, 38 g (0.1 mole), and zinc powder, 6 g (0.09 g-atom), are thoroughly triturated in a mortar with 2–3 ml of water. The reaction is accompanied by the vigorous evolution of heat. The mixture is washed by decanting with acetone and then repeatedly with water (until complete removal of lead acetate) and dilute hydrochloric acid (for zinc removal). The lead sponge obtained is washed with methanol and ether. The sponge is readily dispersed to a fine powder.

b. Synthesis of Tetraphenyllead. A 7.4-g quantity (0.02 mole) of diphenyliodonium fluoborate, 80 ml of absolute alcohol, and 8 g (0.038 g-atom) of lead powder are placed in a round-bottomed flask equipped with an effective stirrer. Reaction temperature increases slightly. Stirring is continued for 6 hr whereupon the solid is filtered, washed with methanol, and extracted with benzene. Evaporation of the benzene, gave 0.65 g (25%) of tetraphenyllead, m.p. 226° (after recrystallization from toluene) (reported m.p. 226°).[59]

F. Organoarsenic Compounds

1. Reaction of Potassium Phenylazocarboxylate with Arsenic(III) Chloride[73]

Potassium phenylazocarboxylate, 7 g (0.037 mole), is added with mechanical stirring during 10 min to 10.2 g (50% excess) of arsenic chloride in 150 ml of absolute acetone at room temperature. Sitrring is continued for another 20 min. The precipitate is filtered off and washed with a small portion of acetone. The filtrate is evaporated *in vacuo* at 35–40°, and the thick, brown residue is washed twice with cold hydrochloric acid [(1:1) (30 and 15 ml] and water (15 ml), poured into 15 ml of 40% potassium hydroxide solution, and heated in a porcelain dish on a water bath to 90–100°. The hot mixture is filtered through a sintered glass filter to give 0.8 g of solid diphenylarsine oxide contaminated with resin. Recrystallization from light petroleum gave a melting point 86–88°.

A mixture of potassium chloride and diphenylarsine oxide precipitates from the filtrate after cooling with snow and salt. The potassium chloride is washed out with water to give 0.15 g of diphenylarsine oxide for a total yield of 0.95 g (21%); m.p. 88–90° (reported m.p. 91–92°).[184]

Phenylarsine oxide (2.6 g, 42%) is precipitated from the filtrate with a saturated aqueous solution of ammonium chloride. Phenylarsine oxide is precipitated three times from chloroform with ether; m.p. 127–130° (reported m.p. 119–121°,[184] 142–144°).[185]

Other arylazocarboxylic salts are decomposed similarly (see Table XV in Section V-B).

2. Decomposition of Double Diazonium Salts with Iron

a. Reaction of the Double Salt of Phenyldiazonium and Iron(III) Chlorides with Arsenic(III) Chloride.[70]   The double salt of phenyldiazonium and iron (III) chlorides (13.5 g, 0.044 mole) is added with stirring over a 30-min period to 8 g (0.044 mole) of arsenic(III) chloride and 14 g (0.25 g-atom) of iron powder in 50 ml of absolute acetone. The reaction vessel is cooled with ice water. After gas evolution has ceased, the mixture is filtered from the unreacted iron, the acetone is evaporated from the filtrate and the residue (a viscous dark liquid) is washed first with hydrochloric acid (1:1) and then water and hydrolyzed with 40 ml of potassium hydroxide (1:1) to give a viscous mixture. After 1 hr, the solid is filtered off. After the addition of a saturated aqueous solution of ammonium chloride, traces of phenylarsine oxide are found in the filtrate. The solid is washed with water, dried, and extracted with acetone; the solvent is evaporated from the extract to give solid diphenylarsenic oxide, m.p. 92–93° (from light petroleum) (reported m.p. 91–92°).[186]

b. Reaction of the Double Salt of Phenyldiazonium and Zinc Chlorides with Arsenic(III) Chloride.[70] The double salt of phenyldiazonium and zinc chlorides (45 g, 0.11 mole) is suspended in 130 ml of absolute acetone containing 40 g (0.22 mole) of arsenic(III) chloride. The mixture is cooled to −5°, and 12.3 g (0.22 g-atom) of iron powder is added during 1.5 hr with vigorous stirring. After gas evolution has ceased, the reaction mixture is filtered, the inorganic solid is washed with acetone, and the combined filtrates are evaporated at 30–40° at reduced pressure. The residue is thoroughly washed with hydrochloric acid (1:1), then with dilute hydrochloric acid. The organic layer is extracted with chloroform and dried over anhydrous calcium chloride. Evaporation of the solvent gives as a residue a mixture of phenyldichloroarsine and diphenylchloroarsine, which is distilled. The following fractions were collected:

1. 120–160° (12 mm): phenyldichloroarsine with an impurity of diphenyl-chloroarsine.
2. 160–200° (12 mm): pure diphenylchloroarsine.

Repeated distillation of each fraction gave 14 g (29%) of phenyldichloro-arsine, b.p. 125–130° (12 mm) and 10 g (35% based on the double salt; 17% on $AsCl_3$) of diphenylchloroarsine, m.p. 130–180° (12 mm) [reported: phenyl-dichloroarsine,[187] b.p. 250–255° (760 mm); diphenylchloroarsine,[184] b.p. 233° (760 mm)].

The total yield of the organoarsenic compounds is 46% based on $AsCl_3$ and 64% based on the double salt.

3. Arylation of Aryl and Diaryl Arsenic Chlorides with the Double Salts of Iron(III) or Zinc Chloride

a. Reaction of Phenyldichloroarsine with the Double Salt of Phenyldiazonium and Zinc Chlorides in the Presence of Sodium Iodide.[71] The double salt of phenyldiazonium and zinc chlorides (9.6 g, 0.013 mole) is suspended in 30 ml of acetone containing 8 g (0.036 mole) of dissolved phenyldichloroarsine. The mixture is cooled to 0°, and 9 g (0.06 mole) of sodium iodide in 40 ml of acetone is added during 1.5 hr. When no more nitrogen is evolved, the inorganic residue is filtered and washed with a minimal portion of acetone. The combined filtrates are evaporated, giving a residue (a viscous dark liquid), which is washed three times with 20-ml portions of hydrochloric acid (1:1) and hydrolyzed with 30 ml of potassium hydroxide (40%), leaving a solidified mixture.

Diphenylarsine oxide is washed three times with water, dissolved in ether, and filtered from the inorganic impurities. After evaporation of the ether, the oxide crystallizes slowly, affording 46 g (42% based on the double salt and 54% based on phenyldichloroarsine) of product. The oxide is oxidized with hydrogen peroxide (30%) to diphenylarsinic acid. After two recrystalli-zations from water, the melting point is 178° (reported m.p. 178°).[75,188]

b. Reaction of Phenyldichloroarsine with the Double Salt of o-Nitrophenyl-diazonium and Iron(III) Chlorides in the Presence of Sodium Iodide.[71] A solution of 20.3 g (0.059 mole) of the double salt of o-nitrophenyldiazonium and iron(III) chlorides and 10 g (0.045 mole) of phenyldichloroarsine in 50 ml of acetone is cooled to 0°, and 13 g (0.086 mole) of sodium iodide in 30 ml of acetone is added with stirring during 1.5 hr. The mixture is worked up in accord with the procedure described above. Phenyl-o-nitrophenylarsine oxide, isolated after hydrolysis, was identified by conversion to phenyl-o-nitrophenylarsinic acid. This was washed with acetone and ether and re-crystallized three times from water; m.p. 193.5° (reported m.p. 196°,[189] 199°).[188]

c. Reaction of Phenyl-p-chlorophenylarsine Chloride with the Double Salt of p-Tolyldiazonium and Zinc Chlorides in the Presence of Iron Powder.[71]

The double salt of p-tolyldiazonium and zinc chlorides (5.6 g, 0.012 mole) is suspended in 20 ml of acetone containing 5.7 g (0.019 mole) of phenyl-p-chlorophenylarsine chloride. The mixture is cooled to 0°, and 1.4 g (0.025 g-atom) of iron powder is added during 40–50 min while stirring. After all the nitrogen has been evolved, the inorganic solid is filtered, the acetone is evaporated from the filtrate, and the residue is washed thrice with 10-ml portions of hydrochloric acid (1:1) and dissolved in ethanol. Aqueous potassium hydroxide (40%) is added dropwise to the alcohol solution until precipitation of ferric hydroxide is complete. The mixture is filtered, and phenyl-p-tolyl-p-chlorophenylarsine is precipitated with diluted hydrochloric acid, extracted with chloroform, and dried over calcium chloride. Evaporation of the solvent afforded 3.4 g (38% based on phenyl-p-chlorophenylarsine chloride) of viscous oil.

The complex $Ar_3As \cdot HgCl_2$ precipitates on pouring the ethereal triarylarsine solution into an ethereal solution of mercury(II) chloride. Three recrystallizations from glacial acetic acid give m.p. 188–189°. The complex is soluble in ether and poorly soluble in acetone.

d. Reaction of the Double Salt of p-*Nitrophenyldiazonium and Iron(III) Chlorides with Phenyl-*p-*tolylarsine Chloride.*[71] Iron powder (1 g, 0.018 g-atom) is added during 30 min at 5° to a vigorously stirred solution of 2.5 g (0.009 mole) of phenyl-p-tolylarsine chloride and 3.2 g (0.008 mole) of the double salt of p-nitrophenyldiazonium and iron(III) chlorides in 20 ml of acetone. Vigorous evolution of nitrogen occurs. The reaction mixture is treated by a procedure similar to that described in the preceding subsection *c*. After evaporation of the chloroform extract, the residue is extracted with ether, and the solvent is evaporated to give 1.3 g (42%) of phenyl-p-nitrophenyl-p-tolylarsine. The complex with mercuric chloride after two recrystallizations from glacial acetic acid has m.p. 193–194°. It is a light-yellow substance, moderately soluble in acetone and ether.

G. Antimony Organic Compounds

1. Synthesis of Arylstibonic Acids via the Decomposition of the Double Salts of Aryldiazonium and Antimony(V) Chlorides

a. Synthesis of the Double Salts of Aryldiazonium and Antimony(V) Chlorides.[108] The double salt of phenyldiazonium and iron(III) chlorides (0.05 mole) is dissolved in a minimal amount of dry acetone. Antimony(V) chloride (0.06 mole) in 75 ml of cold, dry chloroform is added to the mixture while stirring and cooling with snow and salt. A crystalline paste forms. Stirring is continued, and 200 ml of ether is added. The double salt of aryldiazonium and antimony(V) chlorides precipitates. The analytically pure double salt is obtained by reprecipitating from acetone solution with ether and cooling.

 b. *Synthesis of Phenylstibonic Acid.*[102] The double salt of phenyldiazonium and antimony(V) chlorides (10 g, 0.02 mole) is mixed with 15 g (0.09 mole) of cuprous chloride. The mixture is placed in a flask, covered with 100 ml of acetone, and stirred for 6 hr at 25°. The solvent is evaporated, and 80 ml of 5 N NaOH is added to the residue. In 2 hr the solid is filtered and washed with 5 N NaOH. The filtrate is acidified with 5 N HCl (Congo Red), precipitating phenylstibonic acid, which is filtered, thoroughly washed with water, and dried at 80–90° to give 2.6 g (37%). The product is dissolved in concentrated hydrochloric acid and by the addition of a pyridine solution in hydrochloric acid converted to the pyridine complex $C_6H_5SbCl_4 \cdot C_5H_5N \cdot HCl$, m.p. 133°C (from alcohol) (reported m.p. 139°).[99] Other arylstibonic acids are prepared similarly (see Table XIX in Section V-C).

2. Synthesis of Diarylstibinic Acids and Triaryldichlorostibines

 a. *Decomposition of the Double Diazonium Salts of Antimony(V) Chloride with Iron Powder.*[90] To a suspension of 5.6 g (0.1 g-atom) of sieved iron powder (100 mesh) in 50 ml of dry acetone is added 0.025 mole of the double salt of aryldiazonium and antimony(V) chlorides in 40 ml of dry acetone, and the mixture is stirred with a good mechanical stirrer during 15 min. One-third of the solution is added at once. In 5 min, when vigorous nitrogen evolution commences and the mixture becomes warm, the remaining solution is added at a rate providing a continuous vigorous evolution of nitrogen. After complete addition, the mixture is stirred for 30 min.

 The inorganic solid is filtered and the filtrate is evaporated *in vacuo* at room temperature, leaving a brown oil which is washed with 5 N HCl (20 and 15 ml), with stirring, and then mixed with 30 ml of cold 96% alcohol.

 Undissolved triaryldichlorostibine is filtered and recrystallized from an appropriate solvent.

 The alcohol filtrate (after separation of Ar_3SbCl_2) is mixed with 5% aqueous ammonia, precipitating diarylstibinic acid, which is filtered, thoroughly washed with water, and dried in air. By heating with 5 N HCl, the acid was converted to diarylantimony trichloride for identification.

 b. *Decomposition of the Double Salt of Phenyldiazonium and Antimony(III) Chlorides with Iron Powder in Acetone.*[88] To a suspension of 25 g (0.067 mole) of the double salt of phenyldiazonium and antimony(III) chlorides in 75 ml of dry acetone 3.3 g (0.06 g-atom) of iron powder is added at 0° with vigorous stirring with a Witt's stirrer for 35–40 min. After all the iron has been added, the mixture is stirred for 40 min. The inorganic solid is filtered, and the solvent is evaporated. The residue is triturated with 50 ml of 5 N HCl and mixed with 96% alcohol (25–30 ml). The alcohol solution is poured onto an excess of 5% aqueous ammonia mixed with ice, giving 9 g (85%) of diphenyl-stibinic acid. Crystallizing the latter from 5 N HCl converts it to diphenyl-antimony trichloride, 171–172° (reported m.p. 171–177°).[116] A mixture melting point with authentic diphenylantimony trichloride is not depressed.

Other double diazonium salts with antimony(III) chloride are analogously decomposed with iron powder in acetone. When Ar_2SbCl_3 and Ar_3SbCl_2 are formed simultaneously, the latter is precipitated after evaporation of acetone, washing with hydrochloric acid, and addition of alcohol.

c. *Decomposition of the Double Salt of Diphenyliodonium and Antimony(V) Chlorides with Antimony in Acetone.*[91]   The double salt $(C_6H_5)_2ICl \cdot SbCl_5$ is prepared by pouring together solutions of diphenyliodonium chloride [10 g (0.047 mole)] in the minimal amount of concentrated hydrochloric acid and 14.1 g (0.047 mole) of antimony(V) chloride in 25 ml of concentrated hydrochloric acid. The precipitated double salt is filtered, washed with water, and dried in a vacuum desiccator to give a quantitative yield.* The salt is purified by reprecipitation from absolute acetone with absolute ether; m.p. 167–168°.

Freshly precipitated antimony powder, 13 g (0.1 g-atom), is added to 15 g (0.024 mole) of the double salt of diphenyliodonium and antimony(V) chlorides in 150 ml of acetone while cooling with ice water. The mixture is stirred for 25 hr at room temperature. The inorganic solid is filtered and washed with absolute acetone; the solvent is evaporated, and the residue is dissolved in 25 ml of benzene. After extracting twice with 5 N HCl to remove the inorganic compounds of antimony, the benzene is evaporated *in vacuo* and 8 ml of alcohol is added to the residue. The mixture is poured into 5% aqueous ammonia to give a solid, which is filtered, washed with water, alcohol, and thoroughly with ether, to give diphenylstibinic acid (4.2 g, 56%). For identification this was converted to diphenylantimony trichloride by refluxing with 5 N HCl; m.p. 168–169° (reported m.p. 168–169° and 171–172°).[116]

After evaporation of the ether, iodobenzene is separated by steam distillation of the residue. The remaining diphenylantimony oxide is worked up with glacial acetic acid, affording 0.2 g (2.5%), of diphenylstibine acetate, m.p. 131–132° (reported m.p. 132°).[84]

By analogous procedures other double salts are decomposed with antimony in acetone.

---

* This procedure also affords good yields of other double salts $Ar_2ICl \cdot SbCl_5$.

3. Synthesis of Organoantimony Compounds by Nesmeyanov's Diazo Method[84]

a. Synthesis of the Double Diazonium Salts $ArN_2Cl \cdot SbCl_3$ (May's Salts). One mole of amine is mixed with 300 ml of concentrated hydrochloric acid and cooled, followed by 300 g of ice, and then by the equivalent quantity of solid sodium nitrite. To the resulting diazo solution 1 mole of antimony (III) chloride in 150 ml of concentrated hydrochloric acid is added with cooling and vigorous stirring. A precipitate forms and is filtered, washed with 2–3% hydrochloric acid, alcohol, and ether, and dried in air. The yields of double salts are usually high.

b. Decomposition of the Double Diazonium Salts of Antimony(III) Chloride with Zinc. The decomposition of the double salts $ArN_2Cl \cdot SbCl_3$ is carried out in a four-necked conical flask with a hemispherical bottom, equipped with a thermometer, reflux condenser, and powerful Witt's stirrer. Reagents are added through the fourth neck. The decomposition of the double salts is performed in the following way: solvent* (3 ml per 1 g of the double diazonium salt) heated to 60° is quickly poured into a flask, stirring is commenced, and all the zinc powder is added at once (usually 50% excess); then the double diazonium salt is rapidly added. Decomposition starts immediately. The solvent boils, and the refluxing mixture fills most of the flask space. After all the nitrogen has been evolved, the warm solution is filtered from the inorganic material, and the solid is washed with the same solvent. The combined filtrate is evaporated in a slight vacuum giving a thick liquid residue, which is transferred to a funnel and extracted with 5 N HCl (1 ml of acid per 1 g of the double salt). The aqueous acidic solution is separated, and the organic layer is repeatedly treated with half its volume of hydrochloric acid. The oily material is washed free from the inorganic antimony salts and mixed with five volumes of alcohol and cooled with snow and salt. The precipitated triarylstibine and triaryldichlorostibine are filtered, dissolved in hot chloroform, and mixed with an excess of hot alcohol solution of cupric chloride. Triarylantimony is converted to triaryldichloroantimony. The alcohol is evaporated, and the residue is recrystallized from chloroform–alcohol. This affords pure triaryldichlorostibine. In most cases the procedure gives triarylstibine or triaryldichlorostibine and requires none of the treatment described; recrystallization from chloroform is quite sufficient.

The alcoholic mother liquor is poured into an excess of 5% aqueous ammonia mixed with a large quantity of ice. The precipitated mixture of arylstibine and diarylstibine oxides is filtered and washed with water and ether. The diarylstibine oxide is extracted by the etheral solution.

---

* The reaction is usually conducted in ethyl acetate.

After solvent evaporation, the viscous mass of $(Ar_2Sb)_2O$ is dissolved in hot acetic acid. Diarylstibine acetate precipitates on cooling. Arylstibine oxide remaining on the filter is usually analytically pure after washing with ether. However, if it gives a reaction characteristic of inorganic antimony compounds (with hydrogen sulfide), it should be dissolved in glacial acetic acid, filtered from the solid, and repeatedly precipitated with the 5% aqueous ammonia–ice mixture.

4. Arylation of Aryl and Diaryl Compounds of Trivalent Antimony*

a. Reaction of p-*Tolyldichloroantimony with the Double Salt of Phenyldiazonium and Antimony(III) Chlorides.*[113] A 4-g quantity (0.01 mole) of the double salt of phenyldiazonium and antimony(III) chlorides is added to a solution of 2 g (0.007 mole) of p-tolyldichlorostibine in 20 ml of acetone. The reaction is very vigorous at room temperature. After all the nitrogen has been evolved, excess of May's salts is filtered, and the solvent is evaporated. The viscous residue is washed with 5 N HCl and mixed with 25 ml of alcohol, affording an immediate precipitate of 0.5 g of the double salt. Addition of the alcohol solution to 5% aqueous ammonia gives 1 g (45%) of phenyl-p-tolystibinic acid, which was identified via the double salt $C_6H_5(p\text{-}C_7H_7)SbCl_3 \cdot C_6H_5N_2Cl$, m.p. 63–64° (reported m.p. 63–64°).[115]

b. Reaction of Di-o-chlorophenylchlorostibine with the Double Salt of o-*Chlorophenyldiazonium and Antimony(III) Chlorides.*[113] A 4-g quantity (0.01 mole) of the double salt of o-chlorophenyldiazonium and antimony(III) chlorides is added to 2.5 g (0.0065 mole) of di-o-chlorophenylchlorostibine in 40 ml of acetone. The reaction is exothermic and terminates in 30–35 min. The solvent is evaporated, and the residue is washed with 5 N HCl and taken up in cold alcohol. Tri-o-chlorophenylantimony dichloride precipitates from the alcohol (2.5 g, 73%). Recrystallization from acetone gives m.p. 204–206° (reported m.p. 205–206°).[89]

Other Ar_2SbCl compounds can be arylated analogously.

5. Decomposition of the Double Salts $ArN_2Cl \cdot Ar'SbCl_4$†

a. Synthesis of the Double Salt of p-*Tolyldiazonium Chloride and Phenylantimony Tetrachloride.*[118] Phenylstibonic acid, 1.6 g (0.0064 mole), is dissolved in 15 ml of ethanol saturated with hydrogen chloride. The mixture is cooled with ice, and 3.0 g (0.0096 mole) of the double salt of p-tolyldiazonium and iron(III) chlorides in the minimal amount of acetone is added. The double salt of p-tolyldiazonium chloride and phenylantimony tetrachloride

---

* See Table XXI in Section V-C.
† See Table XXI in Section V-C.

precipitates and is filtered, washed with small portions of cold alcohol and then ether, and dried in air to give 2.3 g (72%). After recrystallization from acetone–ether, the salt melted at 111° (decomposition).

Other salts, $ArN_2Cl \cdot Ar'SbCl_4$, can be prepared in the same manner.

b. Decomposition of the double Salt of p-*Tolyldiazonium Chloride and Phenylantimony Tetrachloride.* The double salt of p-tolyldiazonium chloride and phenylantimony tetrachloride (4 g, 0.008 mole) is added in 5 min to a suspension of 0.89 g (0.016 g-atom) of iron powder in 100 ml of dry acetone. The reaction is completed in several minutes, and stirring is continued for 30 min. The inorganic solid is filtered, and the filtrate is evaporated to a viscous residue, which is washed twice with 5 N HCl (10 and 5 ml). After dissolving the mass in 30 ml of alcohol, the solution is filtered and poured into 5% aqueous ammonia, precipitating phenyl-p-tolylstibinic acid, which is filtered, washed with water, and dried in air. Acidification of the aqueous filtrate with acetic acid affords an additional quantity of phenyl-p-tolyl-stibinic acid for a total yield of 1.3 g (50%). Recrystallization from 5 N HCl gives phenyl-p-tolylantimony trichloride, m.p. 153.5–154° (reported m.p. 150–151.5°[112]). A mixture melting point is not depressed with an authentic sample.

Other double salts, $ArN_2Cl \cdot Ar'SbCl_4$, can be decomposed in the same manner.

H. Organobismuth Compounds

1. Decomposition of Aryldiazonium Fluoborates with Bismuth*

a. Preparation of Bismuth Powder. Bismuth powder is prepared by adding zinc powder (20 g) to a solution of bismuth(III) chloride (60 g) in acetone. Metallic bismuth precipitates, is filtered, washed with water, hydrochloric acid (15%), alcohol, and ether, and dried in air to give 37 g of metallic bismuth.

b. Synthesis of Triphenylbismuth. The freshly prepared metallic bismuth (10.5 g, 0.05 g-atom) is added with vigorous stirring to 9.6 g (0.05 mole) of phenyldiazonium fluoborate in 100 ml of dry acetone. The decomposition of the diazonium salt starts immediately and becomes vigorous in 15 min while the reaction temperature increases to 30–35°. To avoid further temperature rise, the mixture is cooled to 25°. Nitrogen evolution is complete in 15 min. After 10 min of stirring, the mixture is successively worked up with 85 ml of concentrated aqueous ammonia and 330 ml of water. After 1-hr standing, a solid precipitates, is filtered, washed with water, dried in air, and extracted with benzene in a Soxhlet apparatus. The residue crystallizes

* See Table XXII in Section V-D.

during evaporation of the benzene, giving a crude yield of 5.05 g (69%). Tar formation is negligible. Recrystallization from methanol gives m.p. 77–78° (reported m.p. 77.5–78°).[123]

2. Decomposition of Diaryliodonium and Bismuth(III) Chlorides with Bismuth Powder*

a. *Synthesis of Triphenylbismuth*.[125] Bismuth powder (27.5 g, 0.12 g-atom) is added with stirring to a mixture of 9.5 g (0.03 mole) of diphenyliodonium chloride and 4.7 g (0.015 mole) of bismuth(III) chloride in 60 ml of dry acetone. The mixture warms (40–50°), and stirring is continued for 2 hr at room temperature. The solid is filtered, washed with acetone, and extracted with hot methanol. On evaporation of methanol no iodonium salt was found, which shows its complete decomposition.

The acetone solution is poured into 50 ml of 25% aqueous ammonia, diluted with water (200 ml), and allowed to stand overnight. The solid that is filtered precipitates and is washed with acetone and ether. The aqueous layer is separated and extracted twice with ether, combining the extracts with the organic layer. The combined organic solvents are evaporated on a water bath, and the residue is distilled with steam to give 3.7 g (60%) of iodobenzene (isolated from the distillate).

Triphenylbismuth is extracted with ether from the residue after steam distillation. Evaporation of the ether gives 2.8 g (65%) of triphenylbismuth, which, on recrystallization from chloroform–alcohol (1:3), gives white crystals, m.p. 77.5–78°[123] (reported m.p. 75°).[190] A mixture melting point with authentic triphenylbismuth was not depressed.

Other organobismuth compounds of the type Ar_3Bi can be prepared similarly.

b. *Synthesis of Di-(m-carboethoxyphenyl)bismuth Chloride*.[125] Bismuth powder (24.5 g, 0.12 g-atom) is added with stirring to a mixture of 13.8 g (0.03 mole) of di-*m*-carboethoxyphenyliodonium chloride and 4.7 g (0.015 mole) of bismuth(III) chloride in 63 ml of dry acetone. After stirring for 3 days at room temperature, the mixture is worked up as in the preceding procedure for triphenylbismuth. The solid precipitating from the ammonia solution is filtered, washed with ether and chloroform, and extracted with hot benzene. Evaporation of the benzene gave 1.8 g (36%) of di-(*m*-carboethoxyphenyl)-bismuth chloride as a fine white crystalline powder, insoluble in ether, alcohol, acetone, and cold chloroform; moderately soluble in hot chloroform and benzene; easily soluble in hot benzene; decomposing at 130–135°.

* See Table XXIII in Section V-D.

I. Tetraarylphosphonium Salts: Synthesis of Tetraphenylphosphonium Fluoborate[131]

A mixture of 0.52 g (0.002 mole) of triphenylphosphine and 0.74 g (0.002 mole) of diphenyliodonium fluoborate is dissolved in 10 ml of absolute acetone and illuminated with a mercury lamp (PRK-4) for 6 hr. By that time the reaction is almost complete. The tetraphenylphosphonium fluoborate precipitates and is filtered, giving 0.48 g; m.p. 345° (reported m.p. 350–355°).[30]

Evaporation of the filtrate, washing repeatedly to remove iodobenzene and unreacted triphenylphosphine, leaves a residue containing fluoborates of diphenyliodonium and tetraphenylphosphonium. Several milliliters of acetone are added, which dissolves only part of the tetraphenylphosphonium fluoborate. The phosphonium salt (0.16 g) is filtered, and the filtrate is subjected to thin-layer chromatography on alumina (3–4-mm layer; solvent: acetone). Such conditions leave diphenyliodonium fluoborate at the starting point, while tetraphenylphosphonium fluoborate moves with the front. The phosphonium salt is eluted with acetone, and the solvent is evaporated to give pure tetraphenylphosphonium fluoborate, 0.07 g, m.p. 343°, for a total yield of 0.71 g (85%).

Other phosphonium salts of the type $(C_6H_5)_3ArPBF_4$ can be prepared by a similar procedure.

REFERENCES

1. *Reactions and Methods of Investigation of Organic Compounds*, Goskhimizdat, Vol. 3, Moscow, 1954, p. 73.
2. A. N. Nesmeyanov, *Uch. Zap. MGU*, **3**, 291 (1934).
3. A. B. Bruker, *Dokl. Akad. Nauk SSSR*, **58**, 803 (1947).
4. A. B. Bruker, *Zh. Obshch. Khim.*, **18**, 1927 (1948).
5. O. A. Reutov, *Usp. Khim.*, **23**, 426 (1954).
6. O. A. Reutov, *Uch. Zap. MGU*, No. 175, *Org. Khim.*, 71 (1956).
7. O. A. Reutov, *Izv. Akad. Nauk SSSR, Otd. Khim. Nauk*, **1956**, 943.
8. O. A. Reutov, *Tetrahedron*, **1**, 67 (1957).
9. *Organic Reactions*, Vol. 2, New York, 1944, p. 448.
10. A. N. Nesmeyanov, *Zh. Russ. Fiz.-Khim. Obshch.*, **61**, 1393 (1929).
11. A. N. Nesmeyanov, *Chem. Ber.*, **62**, 1010 (1929).
12. A. N. Nesmeyanov and L. G. Makarova, *Zh. Obshch. Khim.*, **1**, 598 (1931).
13. A. N. Nesmeyanov and E. M. Toropova, *Zh. Obshch. Khim.*, **4**, 664 (1934).
14. A. N. Nesmeyanov, N. F. Glushnev, P. F. Epiganskii, and A. I. Flegontov, *Zh. Obshch. Khim.*, **4**, 713 (1934).
15. I. T. Eskin, *Izv. Akad. Nauk SSSR, Otd. Khim. Nauk*, **1942**, 297.
16. I. T. Eskin and A. N. Nesmeyanov, *Izv. Akad. Nauk SSSR, Otd. Khim. Nauk*, **1942**, 116.
17. F. Bolth, W. Whaley, and E. Starkey, *J. Amer. Chem. Soc.*, **65**, 1456 (1943).
18. I. T. Eskin, *Izv. Akad. Nauk SSSR, Otd. Khim. Nauk*, **1947**, 405.
19. British Patent 638,565 (1950); *Chem. Abstr.*, **44**, 9478 (1950).

20. V. V. Kozlov, *Zh. Obshch. Khim.*, **18**, 1376 (1948).
21. A. N. Nesmeyanov and I. F. Lutsenko, *Zh. Obshch. Khim.*, **11**, 382 (1941).
22. Austrian Patent 172,320 (1952); *Chem. Abstr.*, **47**, 3343c (1953).
23. A. N. Nesmeyanov, L. G. Makarova, and I. V. Polovyanyuk, *Zh. Obshch. Khim.*, **35**, 681 (1965).
24. O. A. Reutov, O. A. Ptitsyna, and K.-V. Khu, *Dokl. Akad. Nauk SSSR*, **122**, 825 (1958).
25. A. N. Nesmeyanov, O. A. Reutov, T. P. Tolstaya, O. A. Ptitsyna, L. S. Isaeva, M. F. Turchinsky, and G. P. Bochkareva, *Dokl. Akad. Nauk SSSR*, **125**, 1265 (1959).
26. R. McClure and A. Lowy, *J. Amer. Chem. Soc.*, **53**, 319 (1931).
27. W. Waters, *J. Chem. Soc.*, **1937**, 2007.
28. A. N. Nesmeyanov, T. P. Tolstaya, and L. S. Isaeva, *Dokl. Akad. Nauk SSSR*, **125**, 330 (1959).
29. R. Sandin, F. McClure, and F. Irvin, *J. Amer. Chem. Soc.*, **61**, 2944 (1939).
30. L. G. Makarova and A. N. Nesmeyanov, *Izv. Akad. Nauk SSSR, Otd. Khim. Nauk.*, **1945**, 617.
31. M. Dunker and E. Starkey, *J. Amer. Chem. Soc.*, **61**, 3005 (1939).
32. M. Kharasch, H. Pines, and J. Levine, *J. Org. Chem.*, **3**, 347 (1938).
33. M. Dunker, E. Starkey, and G. Jenkins, *J. Amer. Chem. Soc.*, **58**, 2308 (1936).
34. V. Ettel and J. Nosek, *Coll. Czech. Chem. Commun.*, **14**, 74 (1949).
35. A. N. Nesmeyanov, T. P. Tolstaya, and L. S. Isaeva, *Dokl. Akad. Nauk SSSR*, **104**, 872 (1955).
36. S. Lamdan, *Rev. Assoc. Bioquim. Argentina*, **14**, 295 (1947).
37. R. Beattie and F. C. Whitmore, *J. Amer. Chem. Soc.*, **55**, 1567 (1933).
38. F. Hull, *J. Amer. Chem. Soc.*, **60**, 321 (1938).
39. I. Campbell and E. Turner, *J. Chem. Soc.*, **1938**, 37.
40. A. N. Nesmeyanov, N. V. Kruglova, R. B. Materikova, and T. P. Tolstaya, *Zh. Obshch. Khim.*, **26**, 2211 (1956).
41. O. A. Reutov and O. A. Ptitsyna, report at Lomonosov's readings MGU, 1968.
42. O. A. Ptitsyna, S. I. Orlov, M. N. Il'ina, and O. A. Reutov, *Dokl. Akad. Nauk SSSR*, **177**, 862 (1967).
43. A. N. Nesmeyanov and E. I. Kan, *Zh. Russ. Fiz.-Khim. Obshch.*, **61**, 1407 (1929).
44. A. N. Nesmeyanov and E. I. Kan, *Chem. Ber.*, **62**, 1018 (1929).
45. A. N. Nesmeyanov and N. N. Novikova, *Izv. Akad. Nauk SSSR, Otd. Khim. Nauk*, **1942**, 372.
46. I. T. Eskin, *Izv. Akad. Nauk SSSR, Otd. Khim. Nauk*, **1942**, 302.
47. A. N. Nesmeyanov and O. A. Reutov, *Izv. Akad. Nauk SSSR, Otd. Khim. Nauk*, **1948**, 316.
48. A. N. Nesmeyanov and L. G. Makarova, *Izv. Akad. Nauk SSSR, Otd. Khim. Nauk*, **1959**, 2241.
49. W. Waters, *J. Chem. Soc.*, **1939**, 864.
50. A. Roe and J. Graham, *J. Amer. Chem. Soc.*, **74**, 6297 (1952).
51. A. N. Nesmeyanov and L. G. Makarova, *Dokl. Akad. Nauk SSSR*, **87**, 417 (1952).
52. A. N. Nesmeyanov, L. I. Emel'yanova, and L. G. Makarova, *Dokl. Akad. Nauk SSSR*, **122**, 403 (1958).
53. A. N. Nesmeyanov and L. G. Makarova, *Dokl. Akad. Nauk SSSR*, **87**, 421 (1952).
54. K. A. Kocheshkov, A. N. Nesmeyanov, and V. A. Klimova, *Zh. Obshch. Khim.*, **6**, 167 (1936).
55. K. A. Kocheshkov, A. N. Nesmeyanov, and V. A. Klimova, *Chem. Ber.*, **68**, 1877 (1935).

56. O. A. Ptitsyna, O. A. Reutov, and M. F. Turchinsky, *Dokl. Akad. Nauk SSSR*, **114**, 110 (1957).
57. A. N. Nesmeyanov, *Chem. Ber.*, **68**, 1877 (1935).
58. O. A. Ptitsyna, O. A. Reutov, and M. F. Turchinsky, personal communication, 1961.
59. A. N. Nesmeyanov, K. A. Kocheshkov, and M. M. Nad, *Izv. Akad. Nauk SSSR, Otd. Khim. Nauk*, **1945**, 522.
60. K. A. Kocheshkov, A. N. Nesmeyanov, and N. K. Gipp, *Zh. Obshch. Khim.*, **6**, 172 (1936).
61. G. Doak and L. Freedman, U.S. Patent 2,653,160 (1953); *Chem. Abstr.*, **48**, 10764 (1954).
62. G. Doak and L. Freedman, *J. Amer. Chem. Soc.*, **75**, 683 (1953).
63. L. Freedman, H. Tauber, G. Doak, and H. Magnuson, *J. Amer. Chem. Soc.*, **75**, 1379 (1953).
64. L. Freedman and G. Doak, *J. Amer. Chem. Soc.*, **75**, 4905 (1953).
65. A. M. Lukin and I. D. Kalinina, *Dokl. Akad. Nauk SSSR*, **137**, 873 (1961).
66. G. Doak and L. Freedman, *J. Amer. Chem. Soc.*, **73**, 5658 (1951).
67. L. Freedman and G. Doak, *J. Amer. Chem. Soc.*, **74**, 2884 (1952).
68. W. Hanby and W. Waters, *J. Chem. Soc.*, **1946**, 1029.
69. O. A. Reutov and Yu. G. Bundel, *Vestnik MGU*, **10**, 85 (1955).
70. O. A. Reutov and Yu. G. Bundel, *Zh. Obshch. Khim.*, **25**, 2324 (1955).
71. A. N. Nesmeyanov, O. A. Reutov, and Yu. G. Bundel, *Izv. Akad. Nauk SSSR, Otd. Khim. Nauk*, **1957**, 929.
72. K. Takahashi, *J. Pharm. Soc. Japan*, **72**, 533 (1952); *Chem. Abstr.*, **46**, 9791 (1952).
73. O. A. Reutov and Yu. G. Bundel, *Izv. Akad. Nauk SSSR, Otd. Khim. Nauk*, **1952**, 1041.
74. G. Doak and L. Freedman, *J. Amer. Chem. Soc.*, **73**, 5656 (1954).
75. H. Bart, *Ann.*, **429**, 55 (1922).
76. S. Schmidt, *Ann.*, **421**, 159 (1920).
77. E. Scheller, German Patent 522,892 (1931); *Chem. Zentr.*, **II**, 313 (1931).
78. G. Doak, H. Steinman, and H. Eagle, *J. Amer. Chem. Soc.*, **66**, 194 (1944).
79. G. Doak, *J. Amer. Chem. Soc.*, **62**, 167 (1940).
80. A. Binz and O. Schicki, *Chem. Ber.*, **69**, 1527 (1936).
81. E. Scheller, French Patent 642,028 (1926); *Chem. Zentr.*, **II**, 2229 (1927).
82. W. Waters, *Nature*, **142**, 1077 (1938).
83. F. Makin and W. Waters, *J. Chem. Soc.*, **1938**, 843.
84. A. N. Nesmeyanov and K. A. Kocheshkov, *Izv. Akad. Nauk SSSR, Otd. Khim. Nauk*, **1944**, 416.
85. O. A. Ptitsyna, O. A. Reutov, and G. A. Ertel', *Izv. Akad. Nauk SSSR, Otd. Khim. Nauk*, **1961**, 265.
86. O. A. Reutov, O. A. Ptitsyna, and G. A. Ertel', *Chem. Tech.*, **10**, 201 (1958).
87. A. N. Nesmeyanov, N. K. Gipp, L. G. Makarova, and K. K. Mozgova, *Izv. Akad. Nauk SSSR, Otd. Khim. Nauk*, **1953**, 298.
88. A. N. Nesmeyanov, O. A. Reutov, and O. A. Ptitsyna, *Dokl. Akad. Nauk SSSR*, **91**, 1341 (1953).
89. O. A. Reutov, *Dokl. Akad. Nauk SSSR*, **87**, 991 (1952).
90. O. A. Reutov and V. V. Kondrat'eva, *Zh. Obshch. Khim.*, **24**, 1259 (1954).
91. O. A. Ptitsyna, A. N. Kozlova, and O. A. Reutov, *Izv. Akad. Nauk SSSR, Otd. Khim. Nauk*, **1962**, 634.
92. R. Nakai, H. Tomono, and T. Azuma, *Bull. Inst. Chem. Res. Kyoto Univ.*, **26**, 99 (1951).

93. R. Nakai, H. Tomono, and T. Azuma, *Bull. Inst. Chem. Res. Kyoto Univ.*, **22**, 92 (1950).
94. S. Schmidt, *Ann.*, **421**, 174 (1920).
95. S. Schmidt, *Chem. Ber.*, **57**, 1142 (1924).
96. British Patent 244,746 (1925); *Chem. Abstr.*, **21**, 248g (1927).
97. U.S. Patent 1,682,269 (1928); *Chem. Abstr.*, **22**, 3892$_2$ (1928).
98. G. Dayson, *Rec. Trav. Chim.*, **57**, 1016 (1938).
99. G. Doak and H. Steinman, *J. Amer. Chem. Soc.*, **68**, 1987 (1946).
100. British Patent 569,037 (1945); *Chem. Abstr.*, **42**, 217 (1948).
101. British Patent 313,058 (1928); *Chem. Abstr.*, **24**, 861$_4$ (1930).
102. A. N. Nesmeyanov, O. A. Reutov, and P. G. Knoll, *Izv. Akad. Nauk SSSR, Otd. Khim. Nauk*, **1954**, 410.
103. German Patent, 1,064,948 (1959); *Chem. Abstr.*, **55**, 19862a (1961).
104. G. Doak, L. Freedman, and S. Egland, *J. Amer. Chem. Soc.*, **74**, 830 (1952).
105. German Patent 1,069,149 (1959); *Chem. Abstr.*, **55**, 23446c (1961).
106. R. Nakai, H. Tomono, and T. Azuma, *Bull. Inst. Chem. Res. Kyoto Univ.*, **25**, 72 (1951); *Chem. Abstr.*, **46**, 8033c (1952).
107. J.-Y. Chi and T.-C. Sun, *Ko Hsüch Tung Pao*, **1957**, No. 17, 533; *Chem. Abstr.*, **55**, 24620h (1961).
108. O. A. Reutov, *Dokl. Akad. Nauk SSSR*, **87**, 73 (1952).
109. G. Doak, L. Freedman, and S. Egland, *J. Amer. Chem. Soc.*, **74**, 830 (1952).
110. A. Voigt, *Acta Chem. Scand.*, **1**, 118 (1947).
111. O. A. Reutov and O. A. Ptitsyna, *Dokl. Akad. Nauk SSSR*, **79**, 819 (1951).
112. O. A. Reutov and O. A. Ptitsyna, *Dokl. Akad. Nauk SSSR*, **89**, 877 (1953).
113. A. N. Nesmeyanov, O. A. Reutov, O. A. Ptitsyna, and P. A. Tsurkan, *Izv. Akad. Nauk SSSR, Otd. Khim. Nauk*, **1958**, 1435.
114. J. Campbell, *J. Chem. Soc.*, **1950**, 3109.
115. O. A. Reutov and A. Markovskaya, *Dokl. Akad. Nauk SSSR*, **99**, 543 (1954).
116. A. B. Bruker, *Zh. Obshch. Khim.*, **6**, 1823 (1936).
117. O. A. Reutov, A. Markovskaya, and A. N. Lovtsova, *Dokl. Akad. Nauk SSSR*, **99**, 269 (1954).
118. O. A. Reutov and A. Markovskaya, *Dokl. Akad. Nauk SSSR*, **98**, 979 (1954).
119. O. A. Reutov and O. A. Ptitsyna, *Izv. Akad. Nauk SSSR, Otd. Khim. Nauk*, **1952**, 93.
120. H. Gilman and A. Svigoon, *J. Amer. Chem. Soc.*, **61**, 3586 (1939).
121. H. Gilman and H. Yablunky, *J. Amer. Chem. Soc.*, **63**, 949 (1941).
122. A. N. Nesmeyanov, K. A. Kocheshkov, and M. M. Nad, *Izv. Akad. Nauk SSSR, Otd. Khim. Nauk*, **1945**, 524.
123. T. K. Kozminskaya, M. M. Nad, and K. A. Kocheshkov, *Zh. Obshch. Khim.*, **16**, 891 (1946).
124. M. M. Nad, T. K. Kozminskaya, and K. A. Kocheshkov, *Zh. Obshch. Khim.*, **16**, 897 (1946).
125. O. A. Ptitsyna, O. A. Reutov, and Yu. S. Ovodov, *Izv. Akad. Nauk SSSR, Otd. Khim. Nauk*, **1962**, 638.
126. A. N. Nesmeyanov, T. P. Tolstaya, and L. S. Isaeva, *Dokl. Akad. Nauk SSSR*, **122**, 614 (1958).
127. O. A. Reutov, *Vestnik MGU*, **1953**, 119.
128. L. Horner and H. Hoffman, *Angew. Chem.*, **68**, 473 (1956).
129. L. Horner and H. Hoffman, *Chem. Ber.*, **91**, 45 (1958).

130. O. A. Ptitsyna, M. F. Turchinsky, E. A. Sidel'nikova and O. A. Reutov, *Izv. Akad. Nauk SSSR, Ser. Khim.*, **1963**, 1527.
131. O. A. Ptitsyna, M. E. Pudeeva, H. A. Belkevich, and O. A. Reutov, *Dokl. Akad. Nauk SSSR*, **163**, 383 (1965).
132. O. A. Ptitsyna, M. E. Pudeeva, and O. A. Reutov, *Dokl. Akad. Nauk SSSR*, **165**, 838 (1965).
133. A. N. Nesmeyanov and L. G. Makarova, *Uch. Zap. MGU*, **132**, 109 (1950).
134. W. Waters, *J. Chem. Soc.*, **1938**, 1077.
135. A. N. Nesmeyanov, V. N. Vinogradova, and L. G. Makarova, *Izv. Akad. Nauk SSSR, Otd. Khim. Nauk*, **1960**, 1710.
136. A. N. Nesmeyanov and T. P. Tolstaya, *Dokl. Akad. Nauk SSSR*, **117**, 626 (1957).
137. A. N. Nesmeyanov and T. P. Tolstaya, *Dokl. Akad. Nauk SSSR*, **105**, 94 (1955).
138. A. N. Nesmeyanov, *Z. Anorg. Allgem. Chem.*, **178**, 300 (1929).
139. O. A. Reutov, G. Ertel', and O. A. Ptitsyna, *Dokl. Akad. Nauk SSSR*, **133**, 1108 (1960).
141. A. N. Nesmeyanov and O. A. Reutov, *Izv. Akad. Nauk SSSR, Otd. Khim. Nauk*, **1949**, 611.
142. O. A. Ptitsyna, S. I. Orlov, and O. A. Reutov, *Vestnik MGU, Khim.*, Ser. II, **1966**, 105.
143. O. A. Ptitsyna, S. I. Orlov, and O. A. Reutov, *Izv. Akad. Nauk SSSR, Ser. Khim.*, **1966**, 1497.
144. L. G. Makarova, *Izv. Akad. Nauk SSSR, Otd. Khim. Nauk*, **1951**, 741.
145. A. N. Nesmeyanov and L. G. Makarova, *Izv. Akad. Nauk SSSR, Otd. Khim. Nauk*, **1947**, 213.
146. A. N. Nesmeyanov, L. G. Makarova, and T. P. Tolstaya, *Tetrahedron*, **1**, 145 (1957).
147. L. A. Kazitsyna, *Proceedings of the Conference on Physical Methods in the Study of Organic Compounds and Chemical Processes, May 10–17, 1962, Frunze*, 1964, p. 128.
148. L. A. Kazitsyna, O. A. Reutov, and Z. F. Buchkovskii, *Zh. Phys. Khim.*, **34**, 850 (1960).
149. L. A. Kazitsyna, O. A. Reutov, and Z. F. Buchkovskii, *Zh. Obshch. Khim.*, **31**, 2065, 2943 (1961).
150. L. A. Kazitsyna, S. V. Pasynkevich, A. V. Kuznetsova, and O. A. Reutov, *Izv. Akad. Nauk SSSR, Otd. Khim. Nauk*, **1962**, 448.
151. L. A. Kazitsyna, B. S. Kikot, B. V. Rassadin, and O. A. Reutov, *Zh. Obshch. Khim.*, **32**, 3977 (1962).
152. H. Irving, G. Turner, and R. Reid, *J. Chem. Soc.*, **1960**, 2082.
153. I. Lillien, *Dissertation Abstr.*, **20**, 4524 (1960); *Chem. Abstr.*, **54**, 17302c (1960).
154. F. M. Beringer and I. Lillien, *J. Amer. Chem. Soc.*, **82**, 5135 (1960).
155. L. M. Epshtein and N. G. Yaroslavskii, *Dokl. Akad. Nauk SSSR*, **149**, 865 (1963).
156. A. N. Nesmeyanov, L. M. Epshtein, L. S. Isaeva, T. P. Tolstaya, and L. A. Kazitsyna, *Izv. Akad. Nauk SSSR, Ser. Khim.*, **1964**, 613.
157. O. A. Reutov, A. G. Markovskaya, and R. E. Mardaleishvili, *Dokl. Akad. Nauk SSSR*, **104**, 253 (1955).
158. O. A. Reutov, A. G. Markovskaya, and R. E. Mardaleishvili, *Zh. Phys. Khim.*, **30**, 2533 (1956).
159. O. A. Reutov and O. A. Ptitsyna, *Dokl. Akad. Nauk SSSR*, **102**, 291 (1955).
160. A. N. Nesmeyanov and O. A. Reutov, *Uch. Zap. MGU, No. 175, Org. Khim.*, **1956**, 55.

161. O. A. Ptitsyna, M. R. Pudeeva, and O. A. Reutov, *Dokl. Akad. Nauk SSSR*, **165**, 582 (1965).

162. O. A. Reutov, O. A. Ptitsyna, and M. F. Turchinsky, *Dokl. Akad. Nauk SSSR*, **139**, 146 (1961).

163. J. I. G. Cadogan and D. H. Hey, *Quart. Rev.*, **8**, 308 (1954).

164. R. Haring and S. Walton, *J. Amer. Chem. Soc.*, **37**, 135, 375 (1933).

165. G. Filson and S. Walton, *J. Amer. Chem. Soc.*, **34**, 740 (1932).

166. E. Barer, *J. Appl. Chem.*, **3**, 323 (1953).

167. E. T. Denisov and N. M. Emanuel, *Usp. Khim.*, **27**, 365 (1958).

168. T. Bale, W. Wuljkuchen, and R. Winigard, *J. Amer. Chem. Soc.*, **39**, 1729 (1935).

169. O. A. Ptitsyna, G. G. Lyatiev, V. N. Krishchenko, and O. A. Reutov, *Izv. Akad. Nauk SSSR*, Ser. *Khim.*, **1967**, 955.

170. W. M. Latimer, *The Oxidation States of the Elements and Their Potentials in Aqueous Solutions*, Prentice-Hall, New York, 1952, pp. 182, 185.

171. V. B. Avilov, *Teoriya i Praktika Polyarograf. Analiza, Akad. Nauk. Moldavsk. SSR, Materialy Pervogo Vses. Soveshch.*, **1962**, 205.

172. O. A. Ptitsyna, T. V. Levashova, and O. A. Reutov, *Izv. Akad. Nauk SSSR*, Ser. *Khim.*, **1968**, 1651.

173. O. A. Ptitsyna, M. E. Pudeeva, and O. A. Reutov, *Dokl. Akad. Nauk SSSR*, **168**, 595 (1966).

174. J. Coctzee, D. McGuire, and J. Hedrick, *J. Phys. Chem.*, **67**, 1814 (1963).

175. F. M. Beringer, R. Falk, M. Karniol, I. Lillien, and G. Masullo, *J. Amer. Chem. Soc.*, **81**, 342 (1959).

176. O. A. Ptitsyna, G. G. Lyatiev, and O. A. Reutov, *Izv. Akad. Nauk SSSR*, Ser. *Khim.*, **1968**, 2125.

177. O. A. Ptitsyna, S. I. Orlov, and O. A. Reutov, *Vestnik MGU*, Ser. *II, Khim.*, **1966**, 50.

178. J. Hambling, D. Hey, and G. Williams, *J. Chem. Soc.*, **1962**, 487.

179. D. Hey, H. Maulden, and G. Williams, *J. Chem. Soc.*, **1960**, 3769.

180. D. Augood, D. Hey, and G. Williams, *J. Chem. Soc.*, **1952**, 2095.

181. J. Hambling, D. Hey, and G. Williams, *J. Chem. Soc.*, **1960**, 3782.

182. D. Hey and A. Hechvatal, *J. Chem. Soc.*, **1951**, 2892.

183. D. Hey, S. Orman, and G. Williams, *J. Chem. Soc.*, **1965**, 101.

184. A. Michaelis and W. La Coste, *Ann.*, **201**, 184 (1880).

185. F. Blicke and F. Smith, *J. Amer. Chem. Soc.*, **52**, 2946 (1930).

186. W. La Coste and A. Michaelis, *Chem. Ber.*, **11**, 1883 (1878).

187. G. Roeder and N. Blasi, *Chem. Ber.*, **47**, 2748 (1914).

188. K. Takahashi, *J. Pharm. Soc. Japan*, **72**, 523 (1952); *Chem. Abstr.*, **46**, 9790 (1952).

189. E. Sakellarios, *Chem. Ber.*, **57** (B), 1514 (1924).

190. A. Michaelis and A. Marquardt, *Ann.*, **251**, 323 (1883).

Reactions of Bis(π-cyclopentadienyl) Transition-Metal Compounds

E. G. PEREVALOVA AND T. V. NIKITINA

Department of Chemistry, Moscow University, Moscow, U.S.S.R.

Introduction

Ferrocene was discovered accidentally in 1951 by Kealy and Pauson,[1] who were trying to obtain bis(cyclopentadienyl), $(C_5H_5)_2$. They reacted cyclopentadienylmagnesium bromide with iron(III) chloride, but instead of the bis(cyclopentadienyl) expected (on the assumption that cyclopentadienylmagnesium bromide would react like phenylmagnesium bromide) they obtained a stable, orange-colored compound whose composition corresponded to that of bis(cyclopentadienyl)iron. Miller, Tebboth, and Tremaine[2] independently obtained bis(cyclopentadienyl)iron by reacting iron with cyclopentadiene in the presence of some metallic oxides. The iron organic compound obtained was remarkable for its stability. In 1952 Woodward and co-workers[3] discovered that, like aromatic hydrocarbons, bis(cyclopentadienyl)iron is Friedel–Crafts acylated. They assumed[4] that bis(cyclopentadienyl)iron has the sandwich structure with equivalent C—H bonds as well as equivalent Fe—C_5H_5 bonds and suggested the name "ferrocene" for it.

Two brief papers by Woodward et al.[3,4] established the lines of research on the cyclopentadienyl derivatives of the transition metals for several years to come: a general study of ferrocene reactions (first of all those of "aromatic substitution"), synthesis of bis(cyclopentadienyl) (and later monocyclopentadienyl) compounds of other transition metals, and investigation into the physical properties and electronic structure of these compounds. Research on transition-metal compounds with other organic ligands (olefins, acetylenes, arenes) began somewhat later.

The number of papers on the organic compounds of the transition metals has increased from year to year and has begun to surpass that on the organic compounds of other groups of metals (with the exception of silicon and boron). For example, Seyferth and King[5] cite about 450 papers on the chemistry of the organic derivatives of nontransition metals and more than 500 papers on the derivatives of transition metals in their review of organometallic chemistry in 1964. The most attention has been devoted to the derivatives of metals of the group VIII, chiefly iron (almost 300 publications in 1964, about half of them concerning iron compounds).

The structure and properties of metallocenes have been discussed in a number of reviews,[6-24] but most of them are either 5 to 10 years old or else concerned only with specific aspects of these compounds. The first part of the book by Rosenblum,[22] published in 1965, is the nearest to this review. It describes the preparation, structure, and properties of ferrocene, rutheno-cene, and osmocene. Our review covers all metallocenes. The material in this work is classified by types of reaction instead of by types of compound, as in the book by Rosenblum. The methods of preparation and the physical properties of metallocenes are not discussed in this review.*

Research into the reactions of metallocenes started with ferrocene. This was the first representative of the metallocenes, both in time of discovery and in variety of hydrogen-substitution reactions. Electrophilic substitution reactions were also sought among other metallocenes, but only ruthenocene and osmocene have shown them. In other metallocenes reactions involving the metal–ring bond prevail. One property common to all metallocenes is oxidation to the corresponding bis(cyclopentadienyl) cations. Depending on the metal, the bis(cyclopentadienyl) compounds are stable in air as either neutral compounds or cations.

The following chapters of this review discuss the properties of metallocenes by types of reaction:

Chapter 1. Hydrogen-substitution reactions of five-membered metallocene rings.

Chapter 2. Substituent-exchange reactions on the cyclopentadienyl ring, C_5H_4X (X $\neq$ H).

Chapter 3. Reactions involving the metal–ring bond.

Chapter 4. Oxidation–reduction reactions of the metallocenes.

Examples of some of the most typical reactions are described in each chapter.

The numerous transformations of ferrocene derivatives that do not affect the five-membered ring (i.e., changes of substituents without rupture of a bond connected to the five-membered ring) are not discussed because in most cases these reactions are not exclusively characteristic of ferrocene.

Most of the papers cited were published before January 1, 1968. A short review of results published in 1968 and 1969 and partly in 1970 is given in the supplement.

The writers have tried to achieve complete coverage of the literature on the problems under discussion, but they do not claim their references to be totally complete and apologize to the authors whose papers passed unmentioned.

This review was written at the suggestion of Academician A. N. Nes-

---

* Bis(π-cyclopentadienyl) metal hydrides are also not discussed because they are the subject of a recent review by Green and Jones.[23]

meyanov. The writers, who are happy to have been his students, wish to thank him sincerely for his continuous interest in their work, valuable discussions, and corrections.

In writing this review great help was received from E. I. Smyslova, T. T. Tsiskaridze, L. L. Leont'eva, T. V. Baukova, and K. I. Grandberg. We express our deep gratitude for their help. Without the active and friendly help of these colleagues we would still be a long way from completion of this work.

This review was translated into English by A. V. Grib and A. V. Parnakh. We are thankful to them for taking up this work and for the patience with which they made numerous changes in the translation from the Russian manuscript.

References

1. T. J. Kealy and P. L. Pauson, *Nature*, **168**, 1039 (1951).
2. S. A. Miller, J. A. Tebboth, and J. F. Tremaine, *J. Chem. Soc.*, **1952**, 632.
3. R. B. Woodward, M. Rosenblum, and M. C. Whiting, *J. Amer. Chem. Soc.*, **74**, 3458 (1952).
4. G. Wilkinson, M. Rosenblum, M. C. Whiting, and R. B. Woodward, *J. Amer. Chem. Soc.*, **74**, 2125 (1952).
5. D. Seyferth and R. B. King, *Annual Surveys of Organometallic Chemistry*, Vol. 1, North-Holland, Amsterdam–London–New York, 1965.
6. F. Hein, *Chem. Technol.*, **9**, 198 (1957).
7. P. L. Pauson, *Quart. Rev.*, **9**, 391 (1955).
8. E. O. Fischer, *Angew. Chem.*, **67**, 475 (1955).
9. M. Rausch, M. Vogel, and H. Rosenberg, *J. Chem. Educ.*, **34**, 268 (1957).
10. A. N. Nesmeyanov and E. G. Perevalova, *Usp. Khim.*, **27**, 3 (1958).
11. M. E. Diatkina, *Usp. Khim.*, **27**, 57 (1958).
12. K. Schlögl, *Österreich. Chem.-Ztg.*, **59**, 93 (1958).
13. G. Wilkinson and F. A. Cotton, *Progress in Inorganic Chemistry*, Vol. 1, Interscience, New York, 1959, p. 1.
14. P. L. Pauson, in *Non-Benzenoid Aromatic Compounds*, D. Ginsburg, Ed., Interscience, New York, 1959.
15. E. O. Fischer and H. P. Fritz, *Advances in Inorganic Chemistry and Radiochemistry*, Vol. 1, New York, 1959, pp. 55–115.
16. P. L. Pauson, in *Organometallic Chemistry*, H. Zeiss, Ed., Reinhold, New York, 1960, p. 346.
17. K. Plesske, *Angew. Chem.*, **74**, 301 (1962).
18. W. F. Little, in *Survey of Progress in Chemistry*, A. F. Scott, Ed., Vol. 1, Academic Press, New York, 1963, pp. 133–210.
19. R. D. Fischer, *Theor. Chim. Acta (Berlin)*, **1**, 418 (1963).
20. H. D. Kaesz, *J. Chem. Educ.*, **40**, 159 (1963).
21. F. G. A. Stone, *Pure Appl. Chem.*, **10**, 37 (1965).
22. M. Rosenblum, *Chemistry of the Iron Group Metallocenes: Ferrocene, Ruthenocene, Osmocene*, Part 1, Wiley, New York, 1965.
23. M. L. H. Green and D. J. Jones, *Advances in Inorganic Chemistry and Radiochemistry*, Vol. 1, New York, 1965, pp. 115–184.
24. A. N. Nesmeyanov and E. G. Perevalova, *Ann. N.Y. Acad. Sci.*, **125**, 67 (1965).

Chapter 1

Hydrogen-Substitution Reactions of Five-Membered Metallocene Rings

I. GENERAL

Under the influence of electrophiles, metallocenes (with the exception of ferrocene, ruthenocene, and osmocene) are either oxidized to the corresponding bis(cyclopentadienyl) cations or destroyed. These three compounds generally undergo hydrogen-substitution reactions of the five-membered rings. Nitrating and halogenating agents, however, oxidize them to the cations. Recently Bykova and Setkina[1] reported that the hydrogen atoms of nickelocene are exchanged for deuterium atoms under protophilic substitution conditions. However, it is for ferrocene and its derivatives that hydrogen substitutions are the most diverse and widely studied.

With the exception of bis(cyclopentadienyl)zirconium cations $(C_5H_5)_2Zr^{2+}$, metallocene cations do not enter electrophilic substitution reactions.[2-5]

Topics discussed in more detail are as follows:

1. Hydrogen-substitution reactions of the cyclopentadienyl rings in ferrocene and its derivatives.

2. Hydrogen-substitution reactions of the cyclopentadienyl rings of ruthenocene and osmocene, with comparison of the reactivity of metallocenes and that of other aromatic systems.

3. Hydrogen-substitution reactions in bis(cyclopentadienyl)zirconium derivatives.

References

1. E. V. Bykova and V. N. Setkina, *Izv. Akad. Nauk SSSR, Ser. Khim.*, **1967**, 1628.
2. G. Wilkinson and J. M. Birmingham, *J. Amer. Chem. Soc.*, **76**, 4281 (1954).
3. E. O. Fischer and R. Jira, *Z. Naturforsch.*, **8b**, 1 (1953).
4. G. Wilkinson, *J. Amer. Chem. Soc.*, **74**, 6148 (1952).
5. A. N. Nesmeyanov and E. G. Perevalova, *Usp. Khim.*, **27**, 42, 43 (1958).

II. HYDROGEN-SUBSTITUTION REACTIONS OF C_5H_5-RINGS IN FERROCENE AND ITS DERIVATIVES

A. General

This section covers all hydrogen-substitution reactions in ferrocene rings regardless of their mechanism.

Under the influence of electrophilic agents a ferrocene hydrogen atom is substituted under mild conditions (much more readily than in benzene).

171

Depending on the amount of the agent and other conditions, monosubstituted and/or disubstituted derivatives of ferrocene are formed. More rarely—e.g., in Friedel–Crafts alkylation—polysubstituted ferrocenes are formed.

The classical reactions of electrophilic substitution, i.e., nitration and halogenation, are unknown for ferrocene and its derivatives. Nitrating and halogenating agents oxidize the ferrocene iron. The cation thus formed is inert to electrophilic substitution reactions.

The hydrogen atoms on the ferricinium ion do react, however, with diazonium salts as well as with liquid hydrogen cyanide. Arylation of ferrocene presumably passes through the step of ferrocene oxidation to ferricinium. As in the case of benzene, arylation is assumed to be a homolytic reaction.

The effect of substituents on a ferrocene nucleus is similar to the effect in the benzene series: electron-withdrawing substituents inhibit electrophilic substitution reactions, whereas electron-donating substituents facilitate them. However, the boundary between electron-donating and electron-withdrawing substituents is not the same as in the benzene series. Orientation rules in homoannular substitution are not yet known in detail, but they are possibly less pronounced than in the benzene series.

The effect of substituents on the oxidation of the iron atom has been studied for a great number of ferrocene derivatives. The results are described in Section II-A of Chapter 4.

We discuss hydrogen-substitution reactions in the ferrocene nucleus by types of reaction (acylation, formylation, alkylation, sulfonation, dialkylaminomethylation, metalation, arylation, condensation, and cyanation). The discussion starts with the simplest reaction—that of hydrogen–deuterium exchange. The mechanism of the electrophilic substitution reaction in the ferrocene series is discussed under the headings "Deuteration" and "Acylation and Formylation" because it is from these reactions that data on the mechanism of electrophilic aromatic substitution have been obtained. These data, however, are very scarce and do not permit one to answer the basic question that arises in studying the mechanism of electrophilic substitution: which of the two nucleophile centers of the ferrocene molecule, carbon or iron, is the object of the initial attack of the electrophilic particle?

Information on the mechanism of the electrophilic substitution of mercury bonded to the ferrocene nucleus is presented in Chapter 2.

B. Deuteration

1. General

As the simplest example of electrophilic substitution, isotopic exchange is a convenient model to use in the study of electrophilic substitution in aromatic systems.

A kinetic study of this reaction in ferrocene and its derivatives makes it possible to estimate quantitatively the change in reactivity caused by various substituents and to make a quantitative comparison with benzene and its derivatives as well as with other aromatic systems.

The only other kinetic study of an electrophilic hydrogen-substitution reaction in the ferrocene series has been Friedel–Crafts acylation. However, due to the conditions of the reaction, the set of substituents is limited (see Section C).

In studying the kinetics of deuteration it is the total rate at all ring positions that is measured rather than the reactivity at each individual site. However, a comparison of the total rates of isotopic exchange in a series of ferrocene derivatives with those of the corresponding benzene derivatives describes in sufficient detail the effect of substituents on the reactivity of the ferrocene nucleus and reveals some features of the ferrocene system unknown in the benzene system.

In the case of methoxyferrocene and chloroferrocene a nuclear-magnetic-resonance (NMR) study revealed the rates of hydrogen exchange in each position: 1', 2, or 3.

In deuteration reactions halogenated ferrocenes behave peculiarly. Under treatment with deuterotrifluoroacetic acid an iodine atom in iodoferrocene is replaced by a deuterium atom. An analogous reaction also occurs with chloroferrocene and bromoferrocene, but to a significantly smaller degree.

2. Deuteration of Ferrocene and Its Derivatives

Ferrocene is deuterated in both acid and alkaline media.[1-3] It quickly exchanges some hydrogen atoms for deuterium when dissolved in anhydrous deuterosulfuric acid.[1] At the same time, however, it is oxidized to the ferricinium cation, which cannot enter the isotopic exchange reaction. No side reaction takes place when other acids (e.g., deuteroacetic, deuterophosphoric, deuterated hydrochloric, and deuterotrifluoroacetic acids) are used.[1,2] The latter, which has a high acidity, is the most convenient.

The rate constant of hydrogen exchange by ferrocene in a benzene solution of deuterotrifluoroacetic acid (the ratio of ferrocene, deuterotrifluoroacetic acid, and benzene being 1:3:20) at 25° is 1.6×10^{-4} sec^{-1}. The benzene hydrogen is not exchanged under these conditions. The rate constant of hydrogen exchange in toluene under the same conditions is 3×10^{-8} sec^{-1}. In other words, the rate of hydrogen exchange in ferrocene is more than three orders of magnitude higher than that in toluene.

It has been shown that deuterated or tritiated ferrocene enters isotopic exchange with liquid ammonia in the presence of potassium amide. The rate of exchange is 25–30 times greater than that of benzene.[3]

The reaction of isotopic hydrogen exchange has been studied[1,2,4-8] in a great number of both monosubstituted and disubstituted ferrocenes with various substituents [CH_3, C_2H_5, OCH_3, Cl, C_6H_5, $COOCH_3$, $COCH_3$, $PO(C_5H_4FeC_5H_5)_2$]. Electron-withdrawing substituents markedly reduce the rate of isotopic hydrogen exchange of a ferrocene nucleus.[1,2,4-8] For example, in acetylferrocene the hydrogens of the five-membered rings are exchanged 1000 times more slowly than in ferrocene.[1,2]

The effect of all substituents that have been studied (excluding chlorine) on the deuteration rate in the ferrocene series is substantially weaker than that in the benzene series. For example, a methyl group increases the rate of deuteration of ferrocene 10.7 times,[7] but it increases that of benzene 155 times.[9] The difference is the greatest for the methoxy group. In methoxyferrocene the exchange is 6.7 times faster than it is in ferrocene,[7] whereas in anisole it is 2×10^4 times as fast as it is in benzene.[10] The effect of the methoxy group on the deuteration rate in ferrocene is comparable to the similar effect caused by alkyl groups. This fact seems to suggest that, although the conjugation effect of the methoxy group with the ferrocene nucleus is much weaker than the corresponding effect in the benzene series, it still surpasses the negative inductive effect of that substituent.* In the reaction under study, as well as in acylation (see Section C), the phenyl group acting as the substituent in the ferrocene nucleus produces an electron-withdrawing effect.[6,7] The effect of a chlorine atom on isotopic hydrogen exchange is about the same in both ferrocene and benzene nuclei.[7,11]

Thus an analysis of data obtained proves that the effect of a substituent on the rate of hydrogen exchange in ferrocene can be described as a combination of the inductive effect and the conjugation effect; however, the contribution of the latter is much smaller with ferrocene derivatives than it is with those of benzene.

An analysis of kinetic data has shown[6,7] that the logarithm of the total hydrogen-exchange rate for a ferrocene derivative is linearly dependent on the σ_p° constants of its substituents. If doubled values of σ_p° are taken for heteroannular disubstituted derivatives, the logarithms of the total hydrogen-exchange rate fall on the same straight line. Thus there is no substantial interaction between the two substituents on different rings. A similar correlation has also been found for the equilibrium oxidation–reduction constants of substituted ferrocenes (see Section II-A-4 in Chapter 4).

Some preliminary data on the reactivity of different positions in substituted ferrocenes have been obtained by NMR studies. The relative intensities of the signals of (1'), (2), and (3) protons in NMR spectra were measured in the course of isotopic exchange.[8,12]

---

* The comparison of the conjugation effect in ferrocene and benzene systems is certainly of a formal nature since the electronic mechanism of conjugation in the ferrocene system is unknown.

In methoxyferrocene and chloroferrocene all of the three types of hydrogen atom are exchanged at comparable rates. For methoxyferrocene the following deuterium distribution was found: 33% of the total deuterium was in the free ring; 30% was in position 2; 37% was in position 3. The partial factors of the deuteration rate were 4.0, 9.1, and 11.5, respectively.

In the case of a strong electron-withdrawing substituent, such as the carbomethoxy group, the difference in reactivity is more pronounced between the free and the substituted rings. In a sample of carbomethoxyferrocene containing 2.3 atoms of deuterium (50% of the amount due to equilibrium exchange) two atoms of deuterium (87%) were in the free ring and 0.3 atom (13%) was in the substituted ring.[6]

However, the accuracy of such findings is considerably less than that of measuring the exchange-rate constants; therefore the numerical data thus obtained must be considered to be rather approximate.

3. Deuteration Mechanism

The mechanism of the isotopic hydrogen-exchange reaction has not been explained. Nesmeyanov, Kursanov, and co-workers believe that the reaction proceeds by deuteronation of the metal atom, with subsequent migration of the deuterium to the ring. This has been called a "ricochet" substitution[3,6] (see pp. 262, 263). If $k_1/k_2 < k_3$, the equilibrium concentration of deuterated cation (1) determines the overall rate of the reaction. The above data on correlation analysis agree with the mechanism suggested but cannot be considered as proof of its validity.

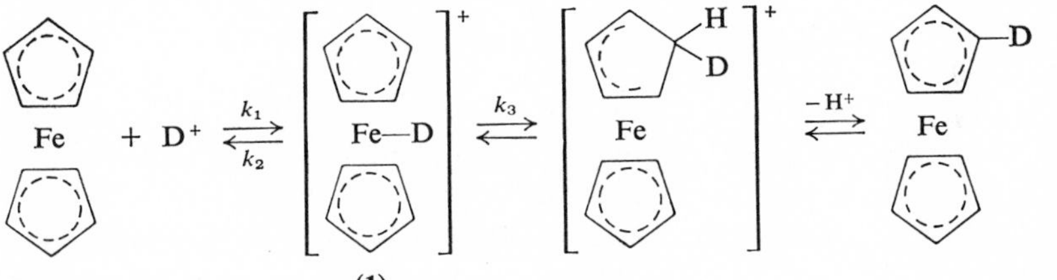

(1)

The mechanism of electrophilic substitution is also described in Section C.

4. Reaction of Halogenated Ferrocenes with Deuterotrifluoroacetic Acid

A study of iodoferrocene gave surprising results.[13] When deuterotrifluoroacetic acid was reacted with iodoferrocene solutions in such organic solvents as benzene and methylene chloride, the products were ferricinium cations (which do not enter isotopic exchange) and complexes of iodoferrocene with molecular iodine ($C_5H_5FeC_5H_4I \cdot nI_2$). (Such complexes are also formed when iodoferrocene is treated with iodine.[14]) The complexes of iodoferrocene with iodine, after treatment with sodium thiosulfate, are converted into iodoferrocene containing no deuterium. After reduction with sodium sulfite, the ferricinium cation produces ferrocene containing 9.5% deuterium, which exactly corresponds to replacement of one atom of iodine by deuterium. It follows that the deuterium enters the ferrocene nucleus as a result of replacement of an iodine atom rather than as a result of isotopic hydrogen exchange.

In the benzene series a reduction of substituted iodobenzenes by hydroiodic acid to the corresponding benzene derivatives is known.[15,16] This reaction, termed protodeiodination, is actually an electrophilic replacement of iodine by a proton of the acid, with an iodine cation splitting off. The reaction proceeds only in the presence of agents that remove the abstracted iodine cation.

Evidently deiodination in the ferrocene series is accompanied by an intramolecular oxidation–reduction reaction in which iodine is abstracted and a ferricinium cation is formed. The reaction must follow a ricochet substitution according to the scheme

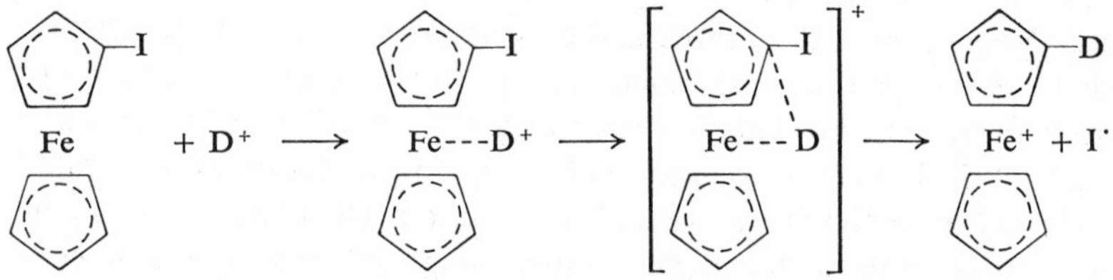

$$2I^{\cdot} \longrightarrow I_2 \tag{3}$$

$$C_5H_5FeC_5H_4I + nI_2 \longrightarrow C_5H_5FeC_5H_4I \cdot nI_2 \tag{4}$$

No iodine cation forms in this case, but atomic iodine and deuterated ferricinium cations are found. This is confirmed by the fact that no reduced deuteroferrocene or oxidized iodoferrocene has been found.

Unlike chloro and bromo benzenes, for which the protodehalogenation reaction is unknown, chloro and bromo ferrocenes can exchange their halogens for deuterium. When chloro and bromo ferrocenes interact with acids, isotopic hydrogen exchange and oxidation to a halogenated ferricinium cation proceed simultaneously with protodehalogenation; isotopic hydrogen exchange is the prevailing reaction (80–90%).[13]

REFERENCES

1. A. N. Nesmeyanov, D. N. Kursanov, V. N. Setkina, N. V. Kislyakova, and N. S. Kochetkova, *Tetrahedron Letters*, **1961**, 41.
2. A. N. Nesmeyanov, D. N. Kursanov, V. N. Setkina, N. V. Kislyakova, and N. S. Kochetkova, *Izv. Akad. Nauk SSSR, Otd. Khim. Nauk*, **1962**, 1332.

3. F. S. Yakushin, V. N. Setkina, E. A. Yakovleva, A. N. Shatenstein, and D. N. Kursanov, *Izv. Akad. Nauk SSSR, Ser. Khim.*, **1967**, 206.
4. A. N. Nesmeyanov, D. N. Kursanov, V. D. Vil'chevskaya, N. S. Kochetkova, V. N. Setkina, and Yu. N. Novikov, *Dokl. Akad. Nauk SSSR*, **160**, 1090 (1965).
5. D. N. Kursanov, V. N. Setkina, M. N. Nefedova, and A. N. Nesmeyanov, *Izv. Akad. Nauk SSSR, Ser. Kkim.*, **1965**, 2218.
6. M. N. Nefedova, V. N. Setkina, E. G. Perevalova, D. N. Kursanov, and A. N. Nesmeyanov, *Reakcionnaya Sposobnost' Organicheskikh Soyedinenij*, Tartu, SSSR., **2**, No. 3, 69 (1965).
7. M. N. Nefedova, D. N. Kursanov, V. N. Setkina, E. G. Perevalova, and A. N. Nesmeyanov, *Dokl. Akad. Nauk SSSR*, **166**, 374 (1966).
8. J. A. Mangravite and T. G. Traylor, *Tetrahedron Letters*, **1967**, 4457.
9. W. M. Lauer and G. Stedman, *J. Amer. Chem. Soc.*, **80**, 6439 (1958).
10. D. P. W. Satchell, *J. Chem. Soc.*, **1956**, 911.
11. C. Eaborn and R. Taylor, *J. Chem. Soc.*, **1961**, 2388.
12. D. N. Kursanov, V. N. Setkina, and M. N. Nefedova, unpublished data.
13. A. N. Nesmeyanov, D. N. Kursanov, M. N. Nefedova, V. N. Setkina, and E. G. Perevalova, *Dokl. Akad. Nauk SSSR*, **161**, 1349 (1965).
14. A. N. Nesmeyanov, E. G. Perevalova, and O. A. Nesmeyanova, *Dokl. Akad. Nauk SSSR*, **100**, 1099 (1955).
15. H. S. Choquill and J. H. Ridd, *J. Chem. Soc.*, **1961**, 822.
16. B. D. Batts and V. Gold, *J. Chem. Soc.*, **1964**, Suppl. 1, 5753.

C. Acylation and Formylation

1. General

The discovery of ferrocene acylation by acyl halides in the presence of aluminum chloride was made by Woodward, Rosenblum, and Whiting[1] in 1952 and stimulated active investigations into the reactivity and structure of ferrocene. At present this reaction is known for some other metallocenes, as well as for monocyclopentadienyl compounds of the transition metals. It can be described as a qualitative test for "aromatic" reactivity of metal cyclopentadienyls. If there is no Friedel–Crafts acylation, other electrophilic substitution reactions cannot be effected either [except in zirconium bis(cyclopentadienyl) compounds—see Section IV]. The acylation reaction has been extensively studied in the ferrocene series. In ferrocene acylation monoacyl or diacyl ferrocenes are obtained, depending on the nature and the amount of the catalyst. In this section we also discuss the cyclization of ω-ferrocenylcarboxylic acids (intramolecular acylation), formylation of ferrocene, and other reactions (interaction in the presence of aluminum chloride with phenyl isocyanates, phosphorus halides, etc.).

The catalyst generally used in ferrocene acylation is aluminum chloride. It also catalyzes a number of other transformations of the ferrocene nucleus. For example, if ferrocene is treated with acyl chlorides that have electron-withdrawing substituents (like terephthalyl, *p*-nitrobenzoyl, and chloroacetyl chlorides), ferrocene is oxidized to the ferricinium cation and acyl-

TABLE I

Monoacylation of Ferrocene[a]

Acylation agent	Solvent	Acyl in reaction product $AcC_5H_4FeC_5H_5$	Yield,[b] %	Ref.[c]
CH_3COCl	CH_2Cl_2	—$COCH_3$	70	84, 2, 17
	CS_2	—$COCH_3$	25	56
	$CHCl_3$	—$COCH_3$	54	5
$(CH_3CO)_2O$[d]	CH_2Cl_2	—$COCH_3$	70	84, 49, 85
	$CHCl_3$[e]	—$COCH_3$	73	5
	CH_2Cl_2[e]	—$COCH_3$	90	6, 7
	$CH_3COOC_2H_5, C_2H_4Cl_2$[e]	—$COCH_3$	88	6
	$(CH_3CO)_2O$[f]	—$COCH_3$	71	3, 4
	$(CH_3CO)_2O$[g]	—$COCH_3$	—	85
$(CH_3COO)_4Si$	C_6H_6[h]	—$COCH_3$	40	8
$ClCH_2COCl$	CH_2Cl_2	—$COCH_2Cl$	37[i]	10, 86
$Cl_2CHCOCl$	CH_2Cl_2	—$COCHCl_2$	11[i]	10
	CH_2Cl_2	(j)	—	11
	CH_2Cl_2[e]	(j)	—	11
Cl_3CCOCl	CH_2Cl_2	—$COCHCl_2$	25[i]	10
	CH_2Cl_2	(j)	—	11
CH_3CH_2COCl	CH_2Cl_2	—$COCH_2CH_3$	48	87
$(CH_3CH_2CO)_2O$	$(CH_3CH_2CO)_2O$[f]	—$COCH_2CH_3$	48	19
	CH_2Cl_2	—$COCH_2CH_3$	53	60
$CH_3(CH_2)_2COCl$	CH_2Cl_2	—$CO(CH_2)_2CH_3$	72	88
$i\text{-}C_3H_7COCl$	$(C_2H_5)_2O$[k]	—$COCH(CH_3)_2$	—	89
	$(CH_3)_2CHCH_2Cl$	—$COCH(CH_3)_2$	—	90
$CH_3(CH_2)_3COCl$	CH_2Cl_2	—$CO(CH_2)_3CH_3$	55	91

$(CH_3)_3CCOCl$	—[g]	$-COC(CH_3)_3$	—	90
	$C_2H_4Cl_2$	$-COC(CH_3)_3$	—	90, 92
	$(C_2H_5)_2O$ or $(C_4H_9)_2O$[k]	$-COC(CH_3)_3$	—	89
	$C_2H_4Cl_2$ or $(i\text{-}C_3H_7)_2O$	$-COC(CH_3)_3$	—	89
	—[l]	$-COC(CH_3)_3$	—	90
$[(CH_3)_3CCO]_2O$	$[(CH_3)_3CCO]_2O$	$-COC(CH_3)_3$	—	90
$CH_3(CH_2)_4COCl$	CH_2Cl_2	$-CO(CH_2)_4CH_3$	88	88, 93
$CH_3(CH_2)_6COCl$	CH_2Cl_2	$-CO(CH_2)_6CH_3$	91	88
$CH_3(CH_2)_8COCl$	CH_2Cl_2	$-CO(CH_2)_8CH_3$	84	88
$CH_3(CH_2)_{10}COCl$	CH_2Cl_2	$-CO(CH_2)_{10}CH_3$	79	88
$CH_3(CH_2)_{14}COCl$	CH_2Cl_2	$-CO(CH_2)_{14}CH_3$	46	93
$C_6H_{11}COCl$	—	$-COC_6H_{11}$	30	94, 90
$C_6H_{11}CH_2COCl$	$C_2H_4Cl_2$	$-COCH_2C_6H_{11}$	—	95
C_6H_5COCl	CH_2Cl_2	$-COC_6H_5$	75	96
	CS_2	$-COC_6H_5$	67	97, 27, 38, 98, 99
$p\text{-}NO_2C_6H_4COCl$	CH_2Cl_2	(l)	22	11
$o\text{-}HOC_6H_4COCl$	CH_2Cl_2	$-COC_6H_4OH\text{-}o$	43	71
$o\text{-}CH_3OC_6H_4COCl$	C_6H_6	$-COC_6H_4OCH_3\text{-}o$	45	100
	CH_2Cl_2	$-COC_6H_4OCH_3\text{-}o$	85	100
$p\text{-}CH_3OC_6H_4COCl$	CH_2Cl_2	$-COC_6H_4OCH_3\text{-}p$	23	101
	CS_2[m]	$-COC_6H_4OCH_3\text{-}p$	57	27
$m,m'\text{-}(CH_3O)_2C_6H_3COCl$	CH_2Cl_2	$-COC_6H_3(OCH_3)_2\text{-}m,m'$	57	100
$o\text{-}CH_3C_6H_4COCl$	CH_2Cl_2	$-COC_6H_4CH_3\text{-}o$	—	102
$m\text{-}CH_3C_6H_4COCl$	CH_2Cl_2	$-COC_6H_4CH_3\text{-}m$	—	102
$p\text{-}CH_3C_6H_4COCl$	CH_2Cl_2	$-COC_6H_4CH_3\text{-}p$	80	102
$C_6H_5CH_2COCl$	CH_2Cl_2	$-COCH_2C_6H_5$	80	102–106
	$(C_2H_5)_2O$[k]	$-COCH_2C_6H_5$	—	107

(continued)

TABLE 1 (continued)

Acylation agent	Solvent	Acyl in reaction product AcC5H4FeC5H5	Yield,[b] %	Ref.[c]
C6H5CH2CH2COCl	C2H4Cl2	—COCH2CH2C6H5	41	108
trans-C6H5CH=CHCOCl	CH2Cl2	—COCH=CHC6H5	81	87
(pyrrole)—COCl	CH2Cl2	—CO—(pyrrole, N—H)	—	102
(furan)—COCl	CH2Cl2	—CO—(furan, O)	—	102
(thiophene)—COCl	CH2Cl2	—CO—(thiophene, S)	15	91, 102
FeC10H9COCl	CH2Cl2	—COC10H9Fe	25	12
FeC10H9CH2COCl	CH2Cl2	—COCH2C10H9Fe	—	109
FeC10H9CH=CHCOCl	CH2Cl2	—COCH=CHC10H9Fe	17	10
(CO)3MnC5H4COCl	?	—COC5H4Mn(CO)3		110, 111
COCl2	?	—COC10H9Fe	31	112, 113
NH2COCl	?	—CONH2	71	29, 28
(COCl)2	?¹	[FeC10H9C=N—]n	87	114
	CH2Cl2	—COC10H9Fe	0.5	115
CH3OOCCOCl	?	—COCOOCH3	—	98

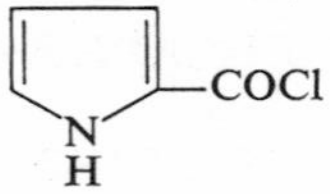

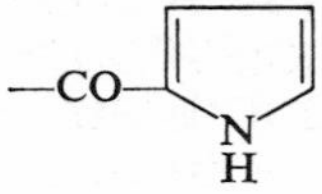

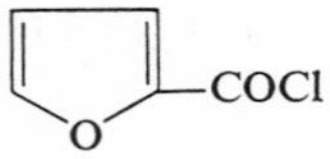

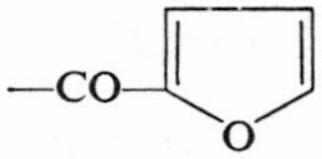

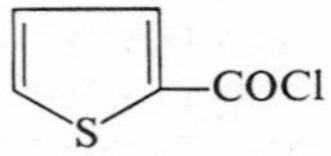

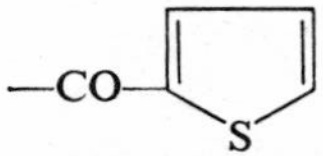

Acyl chloride	Product	Solvent	Yield	Ref.
$C_2H_5OOCCOCl$	(j)	CH_2Cl_2	—	11
$(CH_3)_2C(COCl)_2$	$-COCH(CH_3)CH_3;$ CH_3 $-COCOC_{10}H_9Fe$ CH_3	CH_2Cl_2	—	116
$CH_3OOCCH_2CH_2COCl$	$-COCH_2CH_2COOCH_3$	CH_2Cl_2	78	117, 118
	$-COCH_2CH_2COOCH_3$	CS_2	32	58
$ClCOCH_2CH_2COCl$	$-COCH_2CH_2COOH$	CH_2Cl_2	—	103
	$-COCH_2CH_2COC_{10}H_9Fe;$ $(FeC_{10}H_9)_2CCH_2CH_2$ [—O—CO ring]		—	103
$\begin{array}{c} CH_2CO \\ \mid \quad\diagdown O \\ CH_2CO \end{array}$	$-COCH_2CH_2COOH$	H_2Cl_2C	87	60
$\begin{array}{c} CH_3CHCO \\ \mid \quad\quad\diagdown O \\ CH_2CO \end{array}$	$-COCH_2CH(CH_3)COOH;$ $-COCH(CH_3)CH_2COOH$	CH_2Cl_2	80^n	104, 102,119
$\begin{array}{c} CH_2CO \\ (CH_3)_2C-CO \diagup O \end{array}$	$-COCH_2C(CH_3)_2COOH$	CH_2Cl_2	—	104
$\begin{array}{c} C_6H_5CHCO \\ \mid \quad\quad\diagdown O \\ CH_2CO \end{array}$	$-COCH(C_6H_5)CH_2COOH;$ $-COCH_2CH(C_6H_5)COOH$	CH_2Cl_2	60–70^n	104, 119

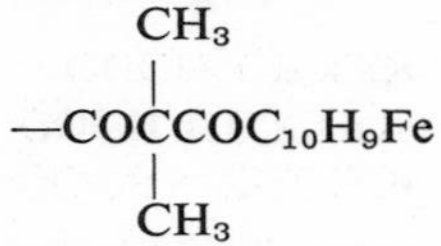

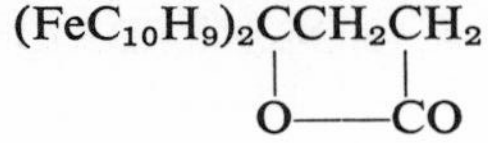

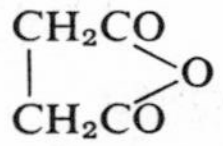

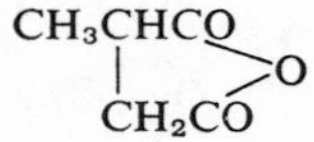

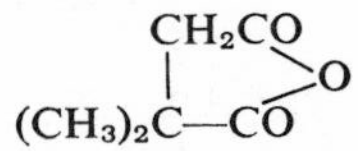

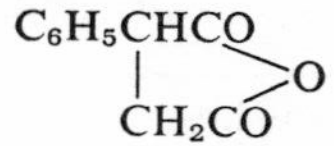

(continued)

181

TABLE I (continued)

Acylation agent	Solvent	Acyl in reaction product $AcC_5H_4FeC_5H_5$	Yield,[b] %	Ref.[c]
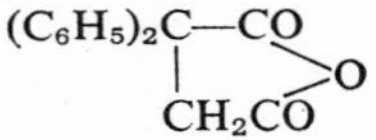 $(C_6H_5)_2C{-}CO$ / CH_2CO (anhydride, O)	CH_2Cl_2	$-COC(C_6H_5)_2CH_2COOH$	—	104
CH_2CO / CH_2 / CH_2CO (anhydride, O)	CH_2Cl_2	$-CO(CH_2)_3COOH$	92	60
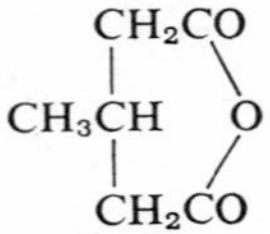 CH_2CO / CH_3CH / CH_2CO (anhydride, O)	CH_2Cl_2	$-COCH_2CH(CH_3)CH_2COOH$	65	104
$ClOC(CH_2)_4COOC_2H_5$	CH_2Cl_2	$-CO(CH_2)_4COOH$	71	60
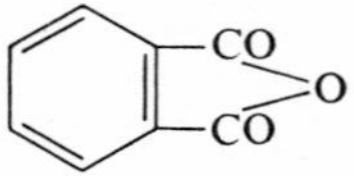 (phthalic anhydride)	CH_2Cl_2	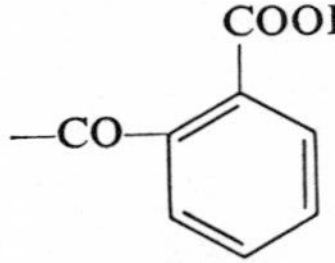 benzene ring bearing $-CO-$ and $COOH$	—	102
$CH_3OOCCH{=}CHCOCl$	CH_2Cl_2	$-COCH{=}CHCOOCH_3$	—	120
$ClCOCH{=}CHCOCl$	CH_2Cl_2	$-COCH_2CH_2COOH$; $-COCH_2CH_2COC_{10}H_9Fe$	—	121
$CH{-}CO$ / $CH{-}CO$ (maleic anhydride, O)	CH_2Cl_2	$-COCH{=}CHCOOH$	—	102

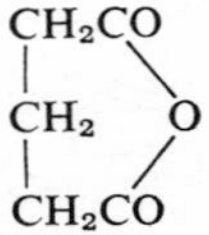

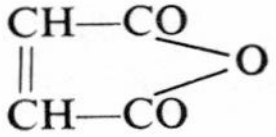

182

	—COCH₂CH(CH₃)COOH;	CH₂Cl₂	—	121
CHCOCl ‖ CH₃CCOCl	—COCH₂CH(CH₃)COC₁₀H₉Fe			
o-CH₃OOCC₆H₄COCl	(d) —COC₆H₄COOCH₃-o	CS₂,(C₂H₅)₂O	83	58
p-ClCOC₆H₄COCl		CH₂Cl₂	—	11
[phthalic anhydride structure]	—COC₆H₄COOH-o	CH₂Cl₂	—	105, 59, 106
[homophthalic anhydride structure]	—COCH₂C₆H₄COOH-o —COC₆H₄CH₂COOH-o	CH₂Cl₂	— —	105, 106

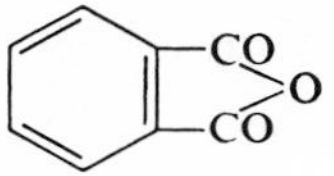

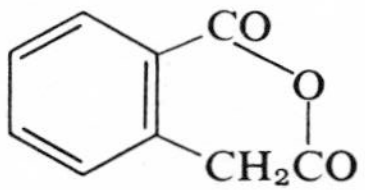

[a] Unless otherwise indicated, all reactions conducted with $AlCl_3$.

[b] Unless otherwise indicated, the yield refers to the amount of ferrocene taken for reaction.

[c] This table presents the best of all yields cited in the papers under review, with the reference corresponding to the best yield given first.

[d] A description of the procedure for obtaining the product is given in Section II-C-9.

[e] BF_3 catalyst.

[f] H_3PO_4 catalyst.

[g] HF catalyst.

[h] $SnCl_4$ catalyst.

[i] Yield refers to the amount of ferrocene reacted.

[j] Product was the ferricinium cation.

[k] $AlCl_3$ and Al used in reaction.

[l] $ZnCl_2$ catalyst.

[m] $AlBr_3$ catalyst.

[n] The yield refers to a mixture of compounds with no individual products isolated.

ferrocene is formed in a small yield or not at all (see following subsection). Moreover, aluminum chloride catalyzes reactions that result in an iron–ring bond, such as replacement of a cyclopentadienyl ring by an arene ring, exchange of cyclopentadienyl rings between ferrocene and alkyl ferrocenes, and partial destruction of the ferrocene nucleus. These reactions are described in Chapter 3.

2. Ferrocene Monoacylation

There are many cases of ferrocene monoacylation (see Table I). This is the basic technique for the synthesis of acylferrocenes. These compounds are, in turn, the parent compounds of various ferrocene derivatives.

Monoacyl ferrocenes (2) are obtained in ferrocene acylation reactions by acyl halides or anhydrides of carboxylic acids in the presence of aluminum chloride when equimolecular ratios of reactants are used. However, along with the monoketone, a diketone always forms (see next subsection).

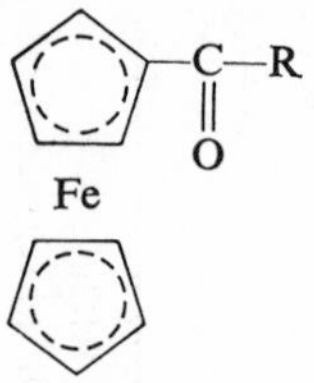

(2)

If there is an excess of aluminum chloride, only the diketone forms—even with equimolecular amounts of ferrocene and acyl halide. Rosenblum and Santer[2] believe that in such a case ferrocene is protonated by the hydrogen chloride formed. In the presence of aluminum chloride the tetrachloro-aluminate ion is formed and then precipitates as an insoluble salt, which is not acylated.

$$(C_5H_5)_2Fe + AlCl_3 + HCl \longrightarrow (C_{10}H_{11}Fe)^+(AlCl_4)^- \tag{5}$$

Ferrocene is monoacylated better in the presence of catalysts milder than aluminum chloride, such as tin(IV) chloride and phosphoric acid. It has been acetylated to monoacetylferrocene by acetic anhydride in the presence of phosphoric acid after brief heating.[3,4] Monoacetylation of ferrocene by acetic anhydride in the presence of boron trifluoride has also been described.[5-7] Monoacetylferrocene is obtained when ferrocene is reacted with acetic acid silicoanhydride and tin(IV) chloride.[8]

$$4(C_5H_5)_2Fe + Si(OCOCH_3)_4 \xrightarrow{\text{SnCl}_4} 4C_5H_5FeC_5H_4COCH_3 + Si(OH)_4 \tag{6}$$

The technique is analogous to that developed by Yur'ev and co-workers[9] for the acylation of five-membered heterocyclics.

When ferrocene is reacted with the anhydrides of dicarboxylic acids or with the corresponding monoesterified diacyl monohalides, ketocarboxylic acids of ferrocene (3) are formed (see Table I). The reaction is carried out in the presence of aluminum chloride.

$$-CO(CH_2)_2COOH$$

Fe

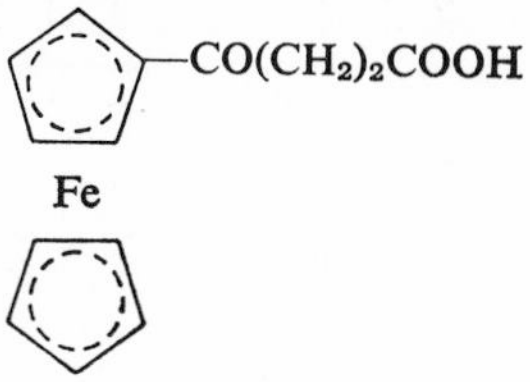

(3)

When it is reacted with acyl chlorides that have electron-withdrawing substituents (*p*-nitrobenzoyl, chloroacetyl chlorides, terephthalyl dichloride, or ethyl oxalyl chloride) in the presence of aluminum chloride, ferrocene is oxidized to ferricinium and acylferrocene is formed in low yield[10] or not at all.[11]

$$(C_5H_5)_2Fe \xrightarrow[\text{AlCl}_3]{\text{RCOCl}} (C_5H_5)_2Fe^+ \xrightarrow{\text{H}_2\text{O,Zn}} (C_5H_5)_2Fe \quad (37\text{–}64\%) \quad (7)$$
$$R = -p\text{-}C_6H_4NO_2, -CCl_3, -CHCl_2, -p\text{-}C_6H_4COCl, -COOC_2H_5$$

The reaction of ferrocene with chlorinated acetyl chlorides in the presence of aluminum chloride leads to a side reaction in which chlorine is partially replaced by hydrogen. Thus in the case of chloroacetyl chloride, along with the expected product chloroacetylferrocene, acetylferrocene is formed and in the case of the dichloroacetyl chloride reaction, dichloroacetyl and monochloroacetyl ferrocenes are produced. Reaction with trichloroacetyl chloride gives only dichloroacetylferrocene.[10]

$$(C_5H_5)_2Fe \xrightarrow[\text{AlCl}_3]{\text{Cl}_3\text{CCOCl}} Cl_2CHCOC_5H_4FeC_5H_5 \quad (8)$$

The Friedel–Crafts technique gives a low yield of diferrocenyl ketone,[12] so that this is better obtained by oxidizing diferrocenylcarbinol[13] or diferrocenylmethane,[14] or from ferrocenecarboxylic acid nitrile.[15]

3. Ferrocene Diacylation

Ferrocene is diacylated by acyl halides or the anhydrides of carboxylic acids in the presence of aluminum chloride* with the reactant ratio 1:2:2 or 1:3:3. Normally the reaction is carried out in dichloromethane or carbon disulfide. The diacyl ferrocenes (4) so obtained are heteroannular.

Friedel–Crafts acylation of ferrocene provides a method of synthesizing various heteroannular diacyl ferrocenes. Ferrocene acylation by dicarboxylic

---

* There are separate instances of the use of BF$_3$ or ZnCl$_2$ catalysts (see Table II).

TABLE II
Diacylation of Ferrocene[a]

Acylation agent	Solvent	—COC$_5$H$_8$(CH$_3$)$_3$—3,5,5	Yield,[b] %	Ref.[c]
CH$_3$COCl[d]	CH$_2$Cl$_2$	—COCH$_3$	76	17, 1, 2, 5, 12, 53
	CH$_2$Cl$_2$	—COCH$_3$[e]	1	17, 16
	CS$_2$	—COCH$_3$	74	17, 1, 5, 38, 122
CH$_3$COBr	CS$_2$	—COCH$_3$	38	38
(CH$_3$CO)$_2$O	CS$_2$	—COCH$_3$	54	38
CH$_3$CH$_2$COCl	CS$_2$	—COCH$_2$CH$_3$	40	97
(CH$_3$CH$_2$CO)$_2$O	CH$_3$COOC$_2$H$_5$, C$_2$H$_4$Cl$_2$[f]	—COCH$_2$CH$_3$	—	6
	(CH$_3$CH$_2$CO)$_2$O[g]	—COCH$_2$CH$_3$[h]	5	19
ClCH$_2$CH$_2$COCl	CS$_2$	—COCH$_2$CH$_2$Cl	—	1, 98
CH$_3$CH$_2$CH$_2$COCl	CS$_2$	—COCH$_2$CH$_2$CH$_3$	70	11, 97
(CH$_3$)$_2$CHCOCl	(CH$_3$)$_2$CHCHCH$_2$Cl	—COCH(CH$_3$)$_2$	—	90
CH$_3$(CH$_2$)$_3$COCl	CH$_2$Cl$_2$	—CO(CH$_2$)$_3$CH$_3$	80	91
(CH$_3$)$_2$CHCH$_2$COCl	C$_2$H$_4$Cl$_2$	—COCH$_2$CH(CH$_3$)$_2$	—	95
(CH$_3$)$_3$CCOCl	CH$_2$Cl$_2$[i]	—COC(CH$_3$)$_3$	—	90, 92
	C$_2$H$_4$Cl$_2$	—COC(CH$_3$)$_3$	—	90
	C$_2$H$_4$Cl$_2$[j]	—COC(CH$_3$)$_3$	—	123
[(CH$_3$)$_3$CCO]$_2$O	—	—COC(CH$_3$)$_3$	—	90
(CH$_3$)$_3$CCH$_2$COCl	C$_2$H$_4$Cl$_2$	—COCH$_2$C(CH$_3$)$_3$	—	95
CH$_3$(CH$_2$)$_4$COCl	CH$_2$Cl$_2$	—CO(CH$_2$)$_4$CH$_3$	67	88
CH$_3$(CH$_2$)$_6$COCl	CH$_2$Cl$_2$	—CO(CH$_2$)$_6$CH$_3$	65	93
CH$_3$(CH$_2$)$_8$COCl	CH$_2$Cl$_2$	—CO(CH$_2$)$_8$CH$_3$	41	93

$CH_3(CH_2)_{10}COCl$	CH_2Cl_2	$—CO(CH_2)_{10}CH_3$	44	93
$CH_3(CH_2)_{11}COCl$	CH_2Cl_2	$—CO(CH_2)_{11}CH_3$	15	93
$CH_3(CH_2)_{14}COCl$	CH_2Cl_2	$—CO(CH_2)_{14}CH_3$	12	93
$C_6H_{11}COCl$	$C_6H_{11}COCl$	$—COC_6H_{11}$	—	90
C_6H_5COCl	CH_2Cl_2	$—COC_6H_5$	91	96
	CS_2	$—COC_6H_5$	70	97, 4, 38
		$—COC_6H_5$[e]	—	124, 98
p-ClC_6H_4COCl	CS_2	$—COC_6H_4Cl$-p	52	4
p-FC_6H_4COCl	CH_2Cl_2	$—COC_6H_4F$-p	76	11
$C_6H_5CH_2COCl$	CH_2Cl_2	$—COCH_2C_6H_5$	60	102
2,4-$(CH_3)_2C_6H_3CH_2COCl$	$C_2H_4Cl_2$	$—COCH_2C_6H_3(CH_3)_2$-2,4	—	95
$CH_3C(CH_3)_2CH_2CH(CH_3)CH_2COCl$	$C_2H_4Cl_2$	$—COCH_2CH(CH_3)CH_2C(CH_3)_2CH_3$	—	95
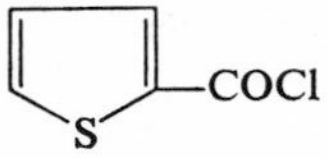	CH_2Cl_2	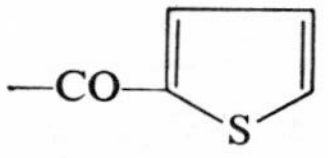	37	91
$CH_3OOCCH_2CH_2COCl$	CS_2	$—CO(CH_2)_2COOCH_3$	27	59
	CH_2Cl_2	$—CO(CH_2)_2COOCH_3$	61	117, 118
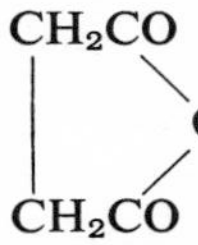	CH_2Cl_2	$—COCH_2CH_2COOH$	38	60, 3
	CS_2	$—COCH_2CH_2COOH$	18	59
$(CH_3)_2C(COCl)_2$	CH_2Cl_2	$—COCH(CH_3)_2$	—	116
$CH_3OOC(CH_2)_3COCl$	CH_2Cl_2	$—CO(CH_2)_3COOCH_3$	70	117, 118
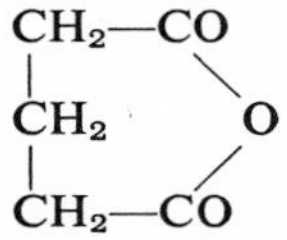	CH_2Cl_2	$—CO(CH_2)_3COOH$	—	118

(*continued*)

TABLE II (*continued*)

Acylation agent	Solvent	$-COC_5H_8(CH_3)_3$-3,5,5	Yield,[b] %	Ref.[c]
$CH_3OOCCH=CHCOCl$	CS_2	$-COCH=CHCOOCH_3$	22	120
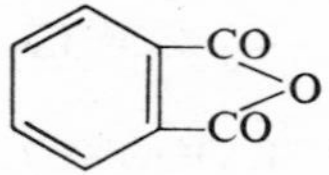	CS_2	$-COC_6H_4COOCH_3$-*o*	—	1
$Fe(C_5H_4COCl)_2$	$CHCl_3$	$-COC_5H_4FeC_5H_4CO-$	—	125

[a] Unless otherwise indicated, all reactions conducted with $AlCl_3$.
[b] The yield refers to the amount of ferrocene taken for reaction.
[c] This table presents the best of all yields cited in the papers under review, with the reference corresponding to the best yield given first.
[d] A description of the procedure for obtaining the product is given in Section II-C-9.
[e] Homoannular 1,2.
[f] BF_3 catalyst.
[g] H_3PO_4 catalyst.
[h] Homoannular.
[i] $ZnCl_2$ catalyst.
[j] $[(CH_3)_3CCOO]_3Fe$ catalyst.

188

acid derivatives produces the corresponding heteroannular keto acids (**5**) (see Table II).

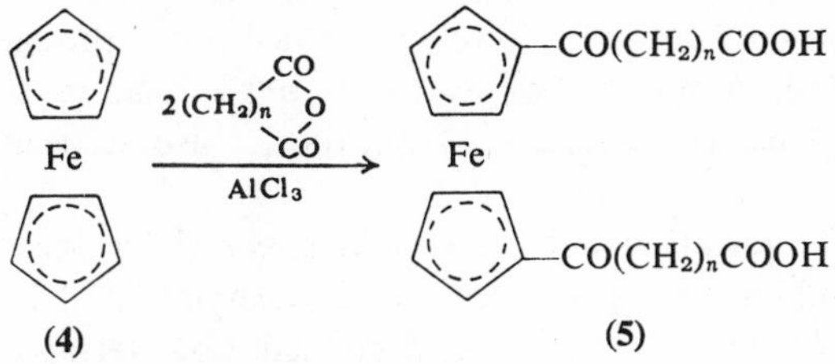

$$\text{(4)} \qquad \xrightarrow[\text{AlCl}_3]{2(\text{CH}_2)_n \begin{smallmatrix} \text{CO} \\ \text{O} \\ \text{CO} \end{smallmatrix}} \qquad \text{(5)}$$

Only small amounts of homoannular isomers are formed. They have been separated from the reaction products in only a few cases: in ferrocene diacetylation[16,17] or dibenzoylation[18] in the presence of aluminum chloride. When propionic anhydride was reacted with ferrocene in the presence of phosphoric acid (in monopropionylferrocene synthesis[19]), a small amount of the homoannular isomer was obtained.

The heteroannularity or homoannularity of the two acyl groups can be established by infrared spectra. X-Ray investigations[20-22] have shown that acyl groups are in the 1,1'-positions in the crystals of heteroannular diacyl ferrocenes. The structure of heteroannular diacylferrocene was originally discovered by Nesmeyanov and co-workers[23] chemically. They used the method of hydrogenating diacetylferrocene: ethylcyclopentane was isolated and diethylcyclopentane was not found.

$$\text{Fe}(\text{C}_5\text{H}_4\text{COCH}_3)_2 \xrightarrow{\text{H}_2/\text{Ni}} \text{C}_5\text{H}_9\text{C}_2\text{H}_5 + \text{Fe} \qquad (9)$$

Of the two homoannular diacetyl ferrocenes that are possible products of ferrocene acetylation, only the 1,2-isomer has been isolated by chromatography. The structure of 1,2-diacetylferrocene was established by Richards and Curphey,[16] who oxidized it with sodium hypochlorite to ferrocenedicarboxylic acid (**6**), which, when treated with N,N'-dicyclohexylcarbodiimide, forms the anhydride (**7**).

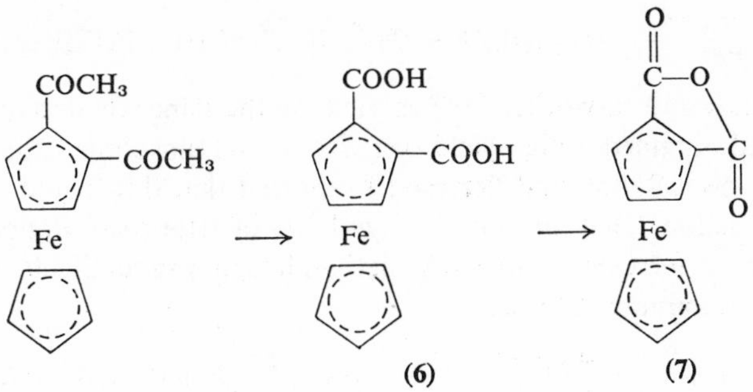

$$\text{(6)} \qquad \text{(7)} \qquad (10)$$

The structure of homoannular dibenzoyl and dipropionyl ferrocenes is not yet known, but by analogy with 1,2-diacetylferrocene the benzoyl groups are believed to be in the 1,2-positions.[18] The possibility of formation of 1,3-diacyl ferrocenes cannot be completely ruled out, although they have not yet been isolated. A number of examples prove that in chromatography the 1,3-isomer is harder to separate from the 1,1'-isomer than from the 1,2-isomer.

Friedel–Crafts acylation does not yield triacetyl ferrocenes.[24] The third acetyl group could not be introduced even by acetylation of 1,2-diacetylferrocene.[17] However, one patent[25] has discussed how tetraacetylferrocene is obtained through ferrocene acylation by a tremendous excess of acetic anhydride at high temperature and in the presence of trifluoroacetic acid.

4. Reactions Similar to Acylation

Ferrocene reacts with alkyl and aryl isocyanates in the presence of aluminum chloride,[26,27] giving N-substituted amides of ferrocenecarboxylic acid (see Table III):

$$(C_5H_5)_2Fe + R-N{=}C{=}O \xrightarrow{\text{AlCl}_3} C_5H_5FeC_5H_4CONH-R \qquad (11)$$

When ferrocene is reacted with carbamyl[29,29] or diphenylcarbamyl[28] chloride in the presence of aluminum chloride, the amide or N,N-diphenylamide of ferrocenecarboxylic acid is obtained in high yield.

$$(C_5H_5)_2Fe + ClCON-R_2 \xrightarrow{\text{AlCl}_3} C_5H_5FeC_5H_4CON-R_2 \qquad (12)$$
$$(R = H, C_6H_5)$$

The bis(N,N-diphenylamide) of 1,1'-ferrocenedicarboxylic acid is also obtained in a similar manner but in low yield (8%).[28]

The Friedel–Crafts reaction has led to the synthesis of ferrocene derivatives containing phosphorus, arsenic, silicon, and germanium. Ferrocene reacts with phosphorus(III) chloride in the presence of aluminum chloride without a solvent to give a mixture of triferrocenyl, diferrocenyl, and monoferrocenyl compounds of phosphorus. The yields are low.[30]

$$(C_5H_5)_2Fe \xrightarrow[\text{2. H}_2\text{O}]{\text{1. PCl}_3,\, \text{AlCl}_3} (FeC_{10}H_9)_3P + (FeC_{10}H_9)_2PO(OH) + FeC_{10}H_9PO(OH)_2 \quad (13)$$

Nesmeyanov and co-workers[31,32] carried out the same reaction in dichloromethane and obtained a high yield of triferrocenylphosphine (isolated as an oxide). However, Sollott and Peterson[33] reported that they could not reproduce this reaction. They proposed a synthesis of triferrocenylphosphine by the reaction of ferrocene with N,N-diethylphosphoramidodichloride in the presence of aluminum chloride.

$$(C_5H_5)_2Fe \xrightarrow[\text{2. H}_2\text{O}]{\text{1. (C}_2\text{H}_5)_2\text{NPCl}_2,\, \text{AlCl}_3} (FeC_{10}H_9)_3P + (FeC_{10}H_9)_3PO \qquad (14)$$

Phenyldichlorophosphine and diphenylchlorophosphine also undergo Friedel–Crafts reaction with ferrocene, giving the corresponding ferrocenyl compounds of phosphorus in high yield[34] (see Table III).

In the Friedel–Crafts reaction of ferrocene with arsenic(III) chloride only one chlorine atom is replaced by ferrocenyl. After hydrolysis arsenosoferrocene is formed.[35]

$$(C_5H_5)_2Fe \xrightarrow[\text{2. H}_2\text{O}]{\text{1. AsCl}_3, \text{ AlCl}_3} C_5H_5FeC_5H_4As\underset{O}{\overset{O}{\diagup\diagdown}}AsC_5H_4FeC_5H_5 \qquad (15)$$

The reaction of phenyldichloroarsine and diphenylchloroarsine with ferrocene in the presence of aluminum chloride does not give arsenic derivatives. In the reaction with arsenic halides ferrocene is surprisingly less reactive than benzene. Sollott and Peterson[35] proposed that this results from steric hindrance in the attack on the iron atom by the voluminous electrophile.

More recently Sollott and Peterson[36] reported that ferrocene could be silylated by chloro and amino silanes under Friedel–Crafts conditions.

$$(C_5H_5)_2Fe + (CH_3)_2Si(Cl)N(CH_3)_2$$
$$\xrightarrow[\text{(H}_2\text{O)}]{\text{AlCl}_3} FeC_{10}H_9Si(OH)(CH_3)_2 + [FeC_{10}H_9Si(CH_3)_2]_2O \quad (16)$$

Germanium derivatives of ferrocene have been also prepared in this manner.[37]

$$(C_5H_5)_2Fe + [(CH_3)_2N]_4Ge \xrightarrow[\text{(H}_2\text{O)}]{\text{AlCl}_3} (FeC_{10}H_9)_3GeCl + [(FeC_{10}H_9)_3Ge]_2O \quad (17)$$

Ferrocenylaryl sulfones could not be obtained under Friedel–Crafts conditions,[38,39] but the synthesis and properties of ferrocenyl sulfones have been described.[40–42]

5. Ferrocene Formylation

The Vilsmeyer reaction, used for the direct formylation of aromatic hydrocarbons of high nucleophilic activity, has been successfully applied to ferrocene, which is formylated by a mixture of N-methylformanilide and phosphorus oxychloride without additional solvent. The yields of ferrocene aldehyde are high (see Table IV). Jutz[43] isolated the intermediate immonium cation (**8**) as the perchlorate.

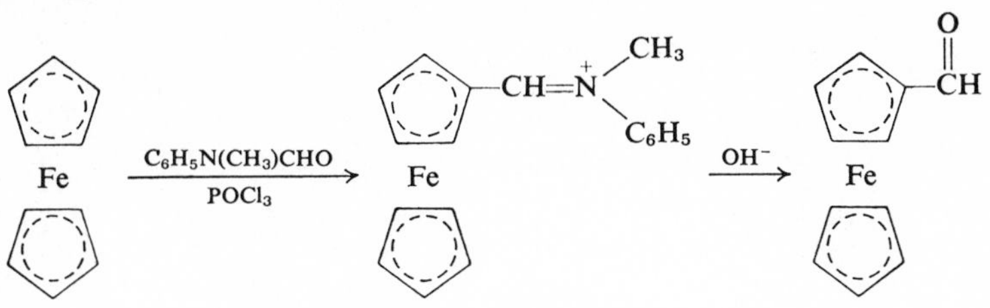

(**8**)

TABLE III
Reactions Closely Related to Acylation[a]

Reactant	Solvent	Reaction products	Yield,[b] %	Ref.
BrCN	CS_2	$FeC_{10}H_9$—CN	—	5
H_2NCOCl	$ClCH_2CH_2Cl$	$FeC_{10}H_9$—$CONH_2$	70	28, 29
$(C_6H_5)_2NCOCl$	$ClCH_2CH_2Cl$	$FeC_{10}H_9$—$CON(C_6H_5)_2$	64	28
	$ClCH_2CH_2Cl$	$Fe[C_5H_4$—$CON(C_6H_5)_2]_2$	8.3	28
$C_2H_5N{=}C{=}O$	CH_2Cl_2	$FeC_{10}H_9$—$CONHC_2H_5$	61[c]	26
$n\text{-}C_{18}H_{37}N{=}C{=}O$	CH_2Cl_2	$FeC_{10}H_9$—$CONHC_{18}H_{37}\text{-}n$	63[c]	26
$C_6H_5N{=}C{=}O$	CH_2Cl_2	$FeC_{10}H_9$—$CONHC_6H_5$	67[c]	26
	CS_2	$FeC_{10}H_9$—$CONHC_6H_5$	25	27
$p\text{-}BrC_6H_4N{=}C{=}O$	CH_2Cl_2	$FeC_{10}H_9$—$CONHC_6H_4Br\text{-}p$	66[c]	26
$p\text{-}C_6H_5C_6H_4N{=}C{=}O$	CH_2Cl_2	$FeC_{10}H_9$—$CONHC_6H_4C_6H_5\text{-}p$	68[c]	26
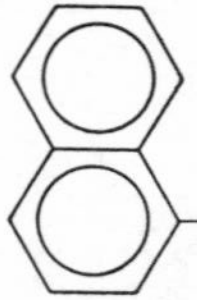 (1-naphthyl)—N=C=O	CH_2Cl_2	$FeC_{10}H_9$—CONH—(1-naphthyl) 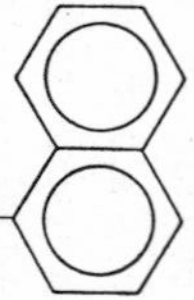	51[c]	26
BCl_3	Petroleum[d]	$FeC_{10}H_9$—$B(OH)_2$	22–54	126
		$Fe[C_5H_4$—$B(OH)_2]_2$	2–14	126
PCl_3	CH_2Cl_2	$(FeC_{10}H_9)_3PO$;	97	31
	—	$(FeC_{10}H_9)_3P$;	11	30
		$(FeC_{10}H_9)_2PO(OH)$;	4.2	
		$FeC_{10}H_9PO(OH)_2$	3.6	
$C_6H_5PCl_2$	$n\text{-}C_7H_{16}$	$(FeC_{10}H_9)_2PC_6H_5$;	67	34
		$(FeC_{10}H_9)_2(C_6H_5)PO$	8.2	
$(C_6H_5)_2PCl$	$n\text{-}C_7H_{16}$	$FeC_{10}H_9P(C_6H_5)_2$;	53	34
		$FeC_{10}H_9(C_6H_5)_2PO$	13	

192

Reagent	Solvent	Products	Yield	Ref.
$(C_2H_5)_2NPCl_2$	$n\text{-}C_7H_{16}$	$(FeC_{10}H_9)_3P$;	47	33
		$(FeC_{10}H_9)_3PO$	23	33
	$n\text{-}C_7H_{16}$	$FeC_{10}H_9PCl_2$;	5	33
		$(FeC_{10}H_9)_2PCl$;	9	
		$(FeC_{10}H_9)_3PO$;	53	
		$(FeC_{10}H_9)_2PO(OH)$;	15	
		$(FeC_{10}H_9)_2P(O)N(C_2H_5)_2$	13	
$AsCl_3$	$n\text{-}C_7H_{16}$	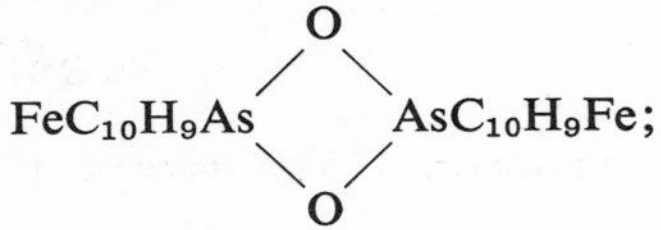 $FeC_{10}H_9As$ $\quad$ $AsC_{10}H_9Fe$; (cyclic structure with O bridges, $FeC_{10}H_9As$—O—$AsC_{10}H_9AsO$)	22	35
		$[FeC_{10}H_9AsO\text{—}]_n$	—	
$(CH_3)_2SiN(CH_3)_2$ $\;$ Cl	$n\text{-}C_7H_{16}$	$FeC_{10}H_9\text{—}Si(OH)(CH_3)_2$;	53	36
		$[FeC_{10}H_9\text{—}Si(CH_3)_2]_2O$	16	
$(CH_3)_2N_2SiCl_2$	$n\text{-}C_8H_{18}$	$(FeC_{10}H_9)_2Si(OH)_2$;	4	37
		$(FeC_{10}H_9)_3SiOH$	5	
$(C_6H_5)_2SiCl_2$	$n\text{-}C_8H_{18}$	$FeC_{10}H_9\text{—}Si(OH)(C_6H_5)_2$	1	36
$(C_6H_5)_2SiN(C_2H_5)_2$ $\;$ Cl	$n\text{-}C_8H_{18}$	$FeC_{10}H_9\text{—}Si(OH)(C_6H_5)_2$;	26	36
		$(FeC_{10}H_9)_2Si(C_6H_5)_2$	4	
$(C_6H_5)_3SiCl$	$n\text{-}C_8H_{18}$	$FeC_{10}H_9\text{—}Si(C_6H_5)_3$	6	36
$(C_6H_5)_3SiN(CH_3)_2$	$n\text{-}C_8H_{18}$	$FeC_{10}H_9\text{—}Si(C_6H_5)_3$	8	36
$[(CH_3)_2N]_2GeCl_2$	$n\text{-}C_8H_{18}$	$[(FeC_{10}H_9)_2GeO]_3$;	50	37
		$[(FeC_{10}H_9)_2Ge]_2O$	1	
$[(CH_3)_2N]_4Ge$	$n\text{-}C_8H_{18}$	$(FeC_{10}H_9)_3GeCl$;	21	37
		$[(FeC_{10}H_9)_3Ge]_2O$	25	

[a] All reactions conducted with $AlCl_3$.
[b] Unless otherwise indicated, the yield refers to the amount of ferrocene taken for reaction.
[c] The yield refers to the amount of ferrocene reacted.
[d] Aluminum powder used in reaction.

TABLE IV
Ferrocene Formylation[a]

Formylation agent	Solvent	R in Reaction product $C_5H_5FeC_5H_4R$	Yield,[b] %	Ref.[c]
$(CH_3)_2NCHO$	$(CH_3)_2NCHO$	—CHO	—	83
$(C_2H_5)_2NCHO$	$(C_2H_5)_2NCHO$	—CHO	—	83
$C_6H_5(CH_3)NCHO$[d]	$C_6H_5(CH_3)NCHO$	—CHO	80	116, 3, 5, 83, 127
	C_6H_5Cl	—CHO	36	86
	C_6H_6	$-CH=\overset{+}{N}(CH_3)C_6H_5\ ClO_4^-$	—	43
$Cl_2CHOC_2H_5$	CH_2Cl_2[e]	—CHO	72[f]	44

[a] Unless otherwise indicated, all reactions conducted with $POCl_3$.
[b] Unless otherwise indicated, the yield given refers to the amount of ferrocene taken for reaction.
[c] The reference citing the best yield is given first.
[d] The procedure for obtaining the product is described in Section II-C-9.
[e] $AlCl_3$ catalyst.
[f] Yield refers to the amount of ferrocene reacted.

TABLE V
Acylation of Monosubstituted Ferrocenes[a]

R in $RC_5H_4FeC_5H_5$	Acylation agent	Solvent	Acyl in reaction products[b] $Ac(R)C_{10}H_8Fe$	Yield,[c] %	Ref.[d]
—CH_3	H_2NCOCl	CH_2Cl_2	1'-$CONH_2$; 3-$CONH_2$; 2-$CONH_2$	48[e] 13	128
	$(C_6H_5)_2NCOCl$	$ClCH_2CH_2Cl$	1'-$CON(C_6H_5)_2$; 2-$CON(C_6H_5)_2$; 3-$CON(C_6H_5)_2$	45[e]	129
	$(CH_3CO)_2O$	CH_2Cl_2[f]	1'-$COCH_3$; 2-$COCH_3$; 3-$COCH_3$	—	51
	C_6H_5COCl	CH_2Cl_2	1'-COC_6H_5; 2-COC_6H_5; 3-COC_6H_5	51[e]	130
	$CH_3OOC(CH_2)_2COCl$	?	1'-$CO(CH_2)_2COOH$; 2-$CO(CH_2)_2COOH$; 3-$CO(CH_2)_2COOH$	—	156
—C_2H_5	CH_3COCl	CH_2Cl_2	1'-$COCH_3$; 2-$COCH_3$; 3-$COCH_3$	—	17
	$(CH_3CO)_2O$	CS_2	1'-$COCH_3$; ?-$COCH_3$	—	48
		CH_2Cl_2[f]	1'-$COCH_3$; 2-$COCH_3$; 3-$COCH_3$	—	51
	$(CH_3CO)_4Si$	C_6H_6[g]	1'-$COCH_3$; 3-$COCH_3$	32[e]	48
	$\begin{array}{c} CH_2CO \\ \diagdown \\ CH_2CO \end{array}\!\!\!O$	?	1',?-$(COCH_3)_2$; 2-$COCH_2CH_2COOH$; 3-$COCH_2CH_2COOH$	— —	131

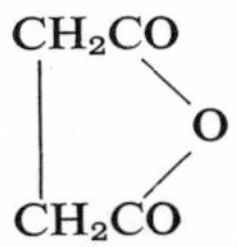

(continued)

TABLE V (continued)

R in $RC_5H_4FeC_5H_5$	Acylation agent	Solvent	Acyl in reaction products[b] $Ac(R)C_{10}H_8Fe$	Yield,[c] %	Ref.[d]
—$CH_2CH_2CH_3$	$CH_3OOCCH_2CH_2COCl$	?	1'-$COCH_2CH_2COOH$; 2-$COCH_2CH_2COOH$; 3-$COCH_2CH_2COOH$	— — —	132
	$(CH_3)_3CCOCl$	$(C_2H_5)_2O$[h]	1'-$COC(CH_3)_3$; 3-$COC(CH_3)_3$	— —	89
—$CH(CH_3)_2$	NH_2COCl	CH_2Cl_2	1'-$CONH_2$; 2-$CONH_2$; 3-$CONH_2$	12 29 35	128
	$(CH_3CO)_2O$	CH_2Cl_2[f]	1'-$COCH_3$; 2-$COCH_3$; 3-$COCH_3$	—	51
—$CH_2CH(CH_3)_2$	$(CH_3)_3CCOCl$	$(C_2H_5)_2O$[h]	1'-$COC(CH_3)_3$; 3-$COC(CH_3)_3$	— —	89, 133
—$C(CH_3)_3$	$(CH_3CO)_2O$	CH_2Cl_2[f]	1'-$COCH_3$; 2-$COCH_3$; 3-$COCH_3$	—[e]	51
—$CH_2C(CH_3)_3$	CH_3COCl	CH_2Cl_2	1'-$COCH_3$; ?-$COCH_3$	— —	134
	C_2H_5COCl	CH_2Cl_2	1'-COC_2H_5	—	134
		$(C_2H_5)_2O$[h]	?-COC_2H_5	—	133
	$i\text{-}C_3H_7COCl$	CH_2Cl_2	1'-$COC_3H_7\text{-}i$; ?-$COC_3H_7\text{-}i$	— —	134
	$(CH_3)_3CCOCl$	$C_2H_4Cl_2$, $(i\text{-}C_3H_7)_2O$	1'-$COC(CH_3)_3$; 3-$COC(CH_3)_3$	— —	89, 133
	$(CH_3)_3CCH_2CH(CH_3)$- CH_2COCl	$(C_2H_5)_2O$	1'-$COCH_2CH(CH_3)CH_2C(CH_3)_3$; 3-$COC(CH_3)_3$; ?-$COCH_2CH(CH_3)CH_2C(CH_3)_3$	— —	133, 134
	$C_6H_{11}COCl$	$(C_2H_5)_2O$	?-COC_6H_{11}	— —	133

R	Acyl chloride	Solvent	Product(s)	Yield (%)	Ref.
$-C_6H_5$	C_6H_5COCl	CH_2Cl_2	$1'-COC_6H_{11}$; $?-COC_6H_{11}$	—	134
	$o-ClC_6H_4COCl$	CH_2Cl_2	$1'-COC_6H_5$	—	134
		$(C_2H_5)_2O$	$?-COC_6H_4Cl-o$	—	133
	$p-ClC_6H_4COCl$	CH_2Cl_2	$1'-COC_6H_4Cl-o$	—	134
	$C_6H_5CH_2COCl$	CH_2Cl_2	$1'-COC_6H_4Cl-p$	—	134
		$C_2H_4Cl_2$	$?-COCH_2C_6H_5$	—	133
		CH_2Cl_2	$1'-COCH_2C_6H_5$; $?-COCH_2C_6H_5$	—	134
	$C_6H_5CH{=}CHCOCl$	CH_2Cl_2	$1'-COCH{=}CHC_6H_5$	—	134
	CH_3COCl	CH_2Cl_2	$1'-COCH_3$; $2-COCH_3$; $3-COCH_3$	—	56, 135
$-CH_2C_6H_5$	CH_3COCl	CH_2Cl_2	$1'-COCH_3$	11	91
	CH_3COCl[l]	CH_2Cl_2	$?-(COCH_3)_3$; $?-(COCH_3)_4$	40	91
$-CH_2CH_2C_6H_5$	$(CH_3)_3CCOCl$	$(C_2H_5)_2O$[h]	$1'-COC(CH_3)_3$; $3-COC(CH_3)_3$	27	89
$-C_6H_4OCH_3\text{-}p$	CH_3COCl	CH_2Cl_2	$2-COCH_3$; $1'-COCH_3$	—	55
$-C_6H_4NO_2\text{-}p$	CH_3COCl	CH_2Cl_2	No acylation	—	24
$-CH_2$(2-thienyl) 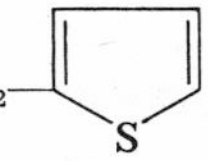	CH_3COBF_4	CCl_4[j]	No acylation	—	24
	CH_3COCl	CH_2Cl_2	$C_5H_5FeC_5H_4CH_2-$(2-thienyl) 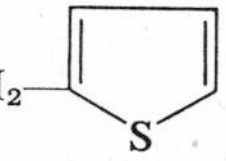	—	91
	CH_3COCl	CH_2Cl_2	$CH_3COC_5H_4FeC_5H_4CH_2-$(5-$COCH_3$-2-thienyl)	—	91

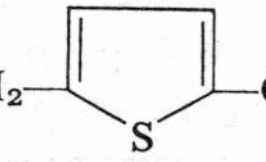

(continued)

TABLE V (continued)

R in $RC_5H_4FeC_5H_5$	Acylation agent	Solvent	Acyl in reaction products[b] $Ac(R)C_{10}H_8Fe$	Yield,[c] %	Ref.[d]
—$C_5H_4FeC_5H_5$ (structure)	CH_3COCl[1]	CH_2Cl_2	$CH_3COC_5H_4FeC_5H_3(COCH_3)CH_2$ 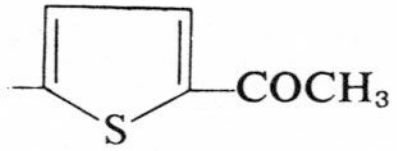 (thiophene with $COCH_3$)	92	91
—$C_5H_4FeC_5H_5$	CH_3COCl	?	?-$(CH_3CO)C_{20}H_{16}Fe_2$	—	136
	CH_3COCl	CH_2Cl_2	$C_5H_5FeC_5H_4C_5H_4FeC_5H_4COCH_3$	13.5	137, 138
			$CH_3COC_5H_4FeC_5H_4C_5H_4FeC_5H_4COCH_3$	46	137, 138
			$CH_3COC_5H_4FeC_5H_4C_5H_3(COCH_3)$-$FeC_5H_4COCH_3$	6.2	137, 138
	$(CH_3CO)_2O$	—[k]	$C_5H_5FeC_5H_4C_5H_3(COCH_3)FeC_5H_5$	—	139, 140
			$CH_3COC_5H_4FeC_5H_4C_5H_4FeC_5H_5$	—	139, 140
			$CH_3COC_5H_4FeC_5H_4C_5H_4FeC_5H_4COCH_3$	—	139, 140
			$CH_3COC_5H_4FeC_5H_4C_5H_3(3\text{-}COCH_3)$-$FeC_5H_5$	—	139, 140
—$CH_2C_5H_4FeC_5H_5$	C_6H_5COCl	CH_2Cl_2	$C_5H_5FeC_5H_4C_5H_4FeC_5H_4COC_6H_5$	6	136
	$C_5H_5FeC_5H_4COCl$	CH_2Cl_2	$2\text{-}COC_5H_4FeC_5H_5$; $3\text{-}COC_5H_4FeC_5H_5$; $1'\text{-}COC_5H_4FeC_5H_5$	4.6 5.9	141
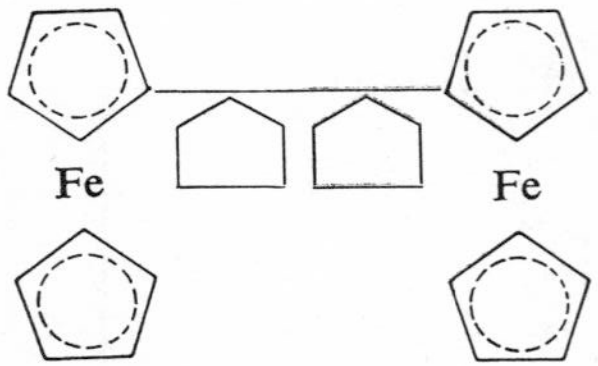 (diferrocenyl structure)	$(CH_3CO)_2O$	CH_2Cl_2	$1'\text{-}COCH_3$	—	142
	CH_3COCl	CH_2Cl_2	$1',1''\text{-}(COCH_3)_2$	—	142

Substituent	Acylating agent	Solvent	Product(s)	Yield (%)	Ref.
$-COCH_3$	CH_3COCl	$CHCl_3$	1'-$COCH_3$	85	5
$-COOCH_3$[n]	CH_3COCl	CS_2	1'-$COCH_3$	89	48
	C_6H_5COCl	CS_2	1'-COC_6H_5	48	48
	C_2H_5COCl	CCl_4	1'-COC_2H_5	80	80, 143, 98
	$CH_3CH_2CH_2COCl$	CCl_4	1'-$COCH_2CH_2CH_3$	88	80
	C_6H_5COCl	CCl_4	1'-COC_6H_5	80	80, 143
$-CO(CH_2)_2COOCH_3$	$CH_3OOC(CH_2)_3COCl$	CCl_4	1'-$CO(CH_2)_3COOCH_3$	85	80
$-CN$	CH_3COCl	CH_2Cl_2	1'-$COCH_3$	65	117, 118
$-CONH_2$	CH_3COCl	CH_2Cl_2	1'-$COCH_3$	100	53
$-CON(C_6H_5)_2$	CH_3COCl	$C_2H_4Cl_2$	1'-$COCH_3$	61	28
	CH_3COCl	$C_2H_4Cl_2$	1'-$COCH_3$	74	28
	C_6H_5COCl	$C_2H_4Cl_2$	1'-COC_6H_5	71.5	28
$-CH_2CONH_2$	CH_3COCl	CH_2Cl_2	1'-$COCH_3$	37	53
	$(CH_3CO)_2O$	CH_2Cl_2[l]	1'-$COCH_3$; 2-$COCH_3$	85; 4	53
	$(CH_3COO)_4Si$	C_6H_6[g]	1'-$COCH_3$; 2-$COCH_3$	50; —	53
$-NHCOCH_3$	CH_3COCl	CH_2Cl_2	1'-$COCH_3$	37	53
	$(CH_3CO)_2O$	CH_2Cl_2[l]	1'-$COCH_3$; 2-$COCH_3$	85[m]; 4[m]	53
$-NHCOOCH_3$	$(CH_3CO)_2O$	—[k]	1'-$COCH_3$	17	53
	$Si(OCOCH_3)_4$	C_6H_6[g]	1'$COCH_3$	50[m]	54
$-NHCOOC_2H_5$	CH_3COCl	CH_2Cl_2	1'-$COCH_3$; 2-$COCH_3$	50; 5	53
	$(CH_3CO)_2O$	CH_2Cl_2[l]	1'-$COCH_3$; 2-$COCH_3$	50; 5	53
$-N\langle^{CO}_{CO}\rangle C_6H_4$ (phthalimido)	$(CH_3CO)_2O$	$(CH_3CO)_2O$[k]	1'-$COCH_3$; 2-$COCH_3$	40; 7	53

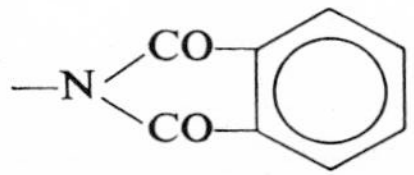

(continued)

TABLE V (continued)

R in $RC_5H_4FeC_5H_5$	Acylation agent	Solvent	Acyl in reaction products[b] $Ac(R)C_{10}H_8Fe$	Yield,[c] %	Ref.[d]
—OCH$_3$	—	CH$_2$Cl$_2$	(C$_5$H$_5$)$_2$Fe; FeC$_{10}$H$_8$(OCH$_3$)$_2$	—	144, 57
—SCH$_3$	—	CH$_2$Cl$_2$	(C$_5$H$_5$)$_2$Fe; FeC$_{10}$H$_8$(SCH$_3$)$_2$	—	57
—Cl[n]	CH$_3$COCl	CH$_2$Cl$_2$	1'-COCH$_3$	81	53, 57, 144
	(CH$_3$CO)$_2$O	(CH$_3$CO)$_2$O[k]	1'-COCH$_3$	61	81
—Br	CH$_3$COCl	CH$_2$Cl$_2$	1'-COCH$_3$	75	53
	(CH$_3$CO)$_2$O	(CH$_3$CO)$_2$O[k]	1'-COCH$_3$	54	145
—I	CH$_3$COCl	CH$_2$Cl$_2$	Fe(C$_5$H$_4$COCH$_3$)$_2$; C$_5$H$_5$FeC$_5$H$_4$COCH$_3$	15 1	53
—COCl	C$_5$H$_5$FeC$_5$H$_4$COCl	CHCl$_3$	C$_5$H$_4$FeC$_5$H$_4$ (CO—CO bridge) C$_5$H$_4$FeC$_5$H$_4$	—	130

[a] Unless otherwise indicated, all reactions conducted with AlCl$_3$.

[b] In most cases only the entering acyls and their position are shown. A substituent present in an initial ferrocene derivative is not rementioned and is always termed as being in the 1-position; for example, compounds arising from the acetylation of methylferrocene are shown as follows: 2-COCH$_3$; 3-COCH$_3$, which means 1-CH$_3$(2-COCH$_3$)—C$_5$H$_3$FeC$_5$H$_5$; 1-CH$_3$(3-COCH$_3$)—C$_5$H$_3$FeC$_5$H$_5$.

[c] Unless otherwise indicated, the yield refers to the amount of ferrocene derivative taken for reaction.

[d] This table presents the best of all yields cited in the papers under review, with the reference corresponding to the best yield placed first.

[e] The yield is that of a mixture of compounds, with no individual products isolated.

[f] BF$_3 \cdot$(C$_6$H$_5$)$_2$O catalyst.

[g] SnCl$_4$ catalyst.

[h] Aluminum powder used with AlCl$_3$.

[i] Excess.

[j] Reaction without catalyst.

[k] H$_3$PO$_4$ catalyst.

[l] BF$_3$ catalyst.

[m] Yield refers to the amount of ferrocene derivative reacted.

[n] Procedure for obtaining product is described in Section II-C-9

TABLE VI
Acylation of Disubstituted and Polysubstituted Ferrocenes[a]

Ferrocene derivative	Acylation agent	Reaction products[b]	Yield,[c] %	Ref.
1,1'-(CH$_3$)$_2$	CH$_3$COCl	2-COCH$_3$; 3-COCH$_3$;	—	146
		2,2'-(COCH$_3$)$_2$;	—	
		3,3'-(COCH$_3$)$_2$;	—	
		2,3'-(COCH$_3$)$_2$	—	
		?-COCH$_3$;[d] ?-(COCH$_3$)$_2$;[d]	—[e]	46
		?-(COCH$_3$)$_3$[d]		
	(CH$_3$CO)$_2$O	2-COCH$_3$; 3-COCH$_3$	72[e]	49
		2,2'-(COCH$_3$)$_2$;	—	147
		3,3'-(COCH$_3$)$_2$		
	C$_6$H$_5$COCl	2-COC$_6$H$_5$; 3-COC$_6$H$_5$	40[e]	130
	(C$_6$H$_5$)$_2$NCOCl	2-CON(C$_6$H$_5$)$_2$;[f]	11	129
		3-CON(C$_6$H$_6$)$_2$[f]	35	
1,1'-(C$_2$H$_5$)$_2$	CH$_3$COCl	2-COCH$_3$; 3-COCH$_3$	—	50, 148
		?-(COCH$_3$)$_2$	70–80	68
	(CH$_3$CO)$_2$O	2-COCH$_3$; 3-COCH$_3$	72[e]	49, 149
	CH$_3$COCl	?-(COCH$_3$)$_n$	—[e]	68
	CH$_2$CO—O—CH$_2$CO	2-COCH$_2$CH$_2$COOH;[g]	—[e]	148, 149
1,1'-(i-C$_3$H$_7$)$_2$		3-COCH$_2$CH$_2$COOH[g]		
	(CH$_3$CO)$_2$O	2-COCH$_3$;3-COCH$_3$	45[e]	49
1,1'-(CH$_2$)$_3$	CH$_3$COCl	2-COCH$_3$; 3-COCH$_3$	—	116, 150
		2,2'-(COCH$_3$)$_2$;	—	65
		3,3'-(COCH$_3$)$_2$;		
		2,3'-(COCH$_3$)$_2$		

(continued)

201

TABLE VI (continued)

Ferrocene derivative	Acylation agent	Reaction products[b]	Yield,[c] %	Ref.
1,1'; 3,3'-[—(CH$_2$)$_3$—]$_2$	(CH$_3$CO)$_2$O	2-COCH$_3$;[h]	21	67
		3-COCH$_3$[h]	34	67
	(CH$_3$CO)$_2$O	2-COCH$_3$;[i]	60	67
		5-COCH$_3$[i]	21	67
1,1'; 3,3'; 4,5-[—(CH$_2$)$_3$—]$_3$	(CH$_3$CO)$_2$O	4'-COCH$_3$;[i]	40	67
		2-COCH$_3$;[i] 2'-COCH$_3$[i]	43[e]	135, 103
1,1'-(C$_6$H$_5$)$_2$	CH$_3$COCl	2-COCH$_3$; 3-COCH$_3$	—	55
1,1'-(C$_6$H$_4$Br-p)$_2$	CH$_3$COCl	2-COCH$_3$; 3-COCH$_3$	—	55
1,1'-(C$_6$H$_4$OCH$_3$-p)$_2$	CH$_3$COCl	2-COCH$_3$; 3-COCH$_3$	—	24
1,1'-(C$_6$H$_5$NO$_2$-p)$_2$	CH$_3$COBF$_4$	No acylation[j]		
1,2-(CH$_2$)$_3$CO	CH$_3$COCl	1'-COCH$_3$	32	151
1,1'-(COCH$_3$)$_2$	CH$_3$COCl	No acylation		24
1,2-(COCH$_3$)$_2$	CH$_3$COCl	No acylation		17
1,1'-(NHCOOC$_2$H$_5$)$_2$	(CH$_3$CO)$_2$O	2-COCH$_3$;[h]	58[k]	53
		3-COCH$_3$[h]	22	

[a] Unless otherwise indicated, all reactions conducted with AlCl$_3$ in CH$_2$Cl$_2$.

[b] Only entering acyls and their position are shown; a substituent present in a ferrocene derivative is not rementioned.

[c] Unless otherwise indicated, the yield refers to the amount taken for reaction.

[d] Reaction with AlCl$_3$ in CS$_2$.

[e] The yield is for a mixture of compounds, with no individual products isolated.

[f] Reaction with AlCl$_3$ in ClCH$_2$CH$_2$Cl.

[g] Reaction with AlCl$_3$ without solvent.

[h] Reaction with BF$_3$ in CH$_2$Cl$_2$. Reaction with AlCl$_3$ in (CH$_3$CO)$_2$O.

[i] Reaction with AlCl$_3$ in (CH$_3$CO)$_2$O.

[j] Reaction without catalyst in CCl$_4$.

[k] Yield refers to the amount of ferrocene derivative reacted.

Ferrocene aldehyde was also obtained under Friedel–Crafts conditions by reacting ferrocene with dichloromethyl ethyl ether.[44] The dialdehyde could not

$$(C_5H_5)_2Fe \xrightarrow[\text{2. } H_2O]{\text{1. } Cl_2CHOC_2H_5, AlCl_3} FeC_{10}H_9CHO \qquad (19)$$

be synthesized by these methods. However, 1,1′-ferrocenedialdehyde was obtained from 1,1′-di-(hydroxymethyl)ferrocene.[45]

6. Acylation and Formylation of Ferrocene Derivatives

Friedel–Crafts acylation is an excellent technique for obtaining ferrocene derivatives (see subsection 3). The diversity of synthetic possibilities is due to both the variety of acylating agents and the numerous further transformations of the acyl ferrocenes.* There are a number of instances of acylation and formylation of ferrocene derivatives. These were carried out with a host

TABLE VII

Formylation of Ferrocene Derivatives with N-Methylformanilide
and Phosphorus Oxychloride[a]

Ferrocene derivative	Reaction products[b]	Yield,[c] %	Ref.
—CH$_3$	2-CHO; 3-CHO; 1′-CHO	93[d]	128, 129
—C$_2$H$_5$	?-CHO	58	65
—CH(CH$_3$)$_2$	1′-CHO; 3-CHO	60[d]	128
—CH$_2$CH$_2$COOCH$_3$	?-CHO	65	65
1,1′-(CH$_3$)$_2$	2-CHO; 3-CHO	84[d]	129
1,1′-(C$_2$H$_5$)$_2$	?-CHO	70	65
	2-CHO[e]; 3-CHO[e]	—	50
1,1′-(i-C$_3$H$_7$)$_2$	3-CHO	64	128
1,1′-(C$_2$H$_5$)$_2$?—CH$_2$CH$_2$COOCH$_3$	?-CHO	69	68
1,1′-(CH$_2$)$_3$	?-CHO	60	65
1,1′; 3,3′-[—(CH$_2$)$_3$—]$_2$	?-CHO	81	68, 67
1,1′; 3,3′; 4,?′-[—(CH$_2$)$_3$—]$_3$	?-CHO	52	68, 67
1,1′; 3,3′; 4,5-[—(CH$_2$)$_3$—]$_3$	2-CHO;[e] 5′-CHO[e]	—	67

[a] Unless otherwise indicated, all reactions conducted in CH$_2$Cl$_2$.
[b] Only the entering group and its position are shown.
[c] The yield refers to the amount taken for reaction.
[d] The yield is for a mixture, with no individual products isolated.
[e] Solvent not specified.

* These transformations are not discussed. They are covered in detail in Rosenblum's book.[18]

of substituents (see Tables V, VI, and VII). Examination of acylation re-actions yielded the largest amount of data on the effect of substituents on electrophilic reactions in the ferrocene nucleus. However, this does not mean that these data are either precise or complete, as is confirmed by further discussion.

Acylation of ferrocene derivatives is of practical value only in the synthesis of heteroannular disubstituted ferrocenes that have electron-withdrawing substituents. Other cases yield mixtures for which there are as yet no effective separation methods.

Of all substituents, only alkyl groups facilitate acylation. For example, 1,1'-dimethylferrocene reacts with acetyl chloride in the presence of aluminum chloride to give monoacetylated and diacetylated as well as triacetylated dimethylferrocene (9), whereas ferrocene is acetylated only to diacetylferro-cene (see subsection 3). Triacetylated dimethylferrocene was not isolated, but its presence in the mixture has been proved by the formation of dimethyl-ferrocenetricarboxylic acid (10) after oxidation and by the formation of dimethyl(triethyl)ferrocene (11) after reduction.[46]

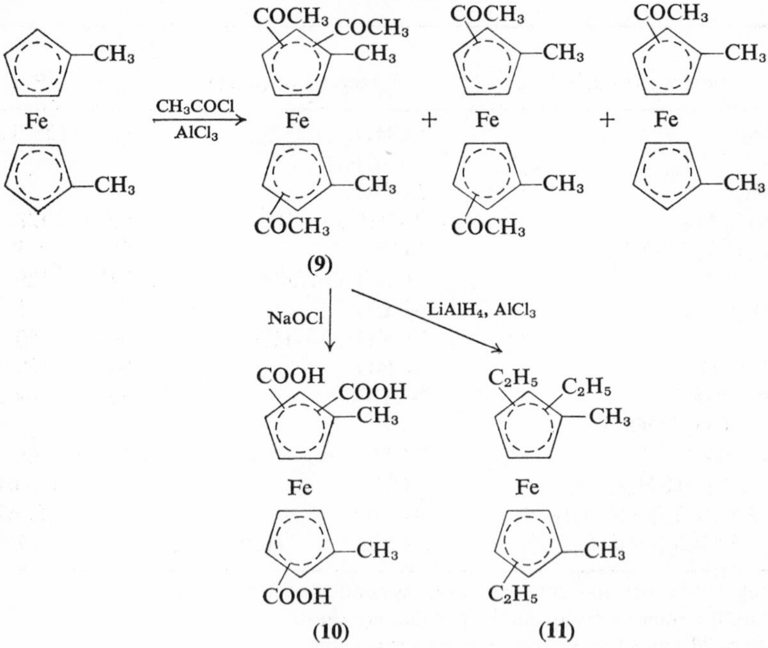

(9)

(20)

(10)   (11)

Nesmeyanov and Vol'kenau[47,48] have shown that when ethylferrocene is acetylated in the presence of aluminum chloride and under the conditions of ferrocene monoacetylation, diacetylated ethylferrocene is formed. When ethyl-ferrocene is subjected to acetic acid silicoanhydride and tin(IV) chloride, both monoacetylated and diacetylated ethyl ferrocenes are formed. The ratio of homoannular and heteroannular monoacetylethylferrocene and diacetylethylferrocene isolated from the mixture is 3.5:1.0:1.0. Ferrocene in the presence of tin(IV) chloride acetylates only to monoacetylferrocene.

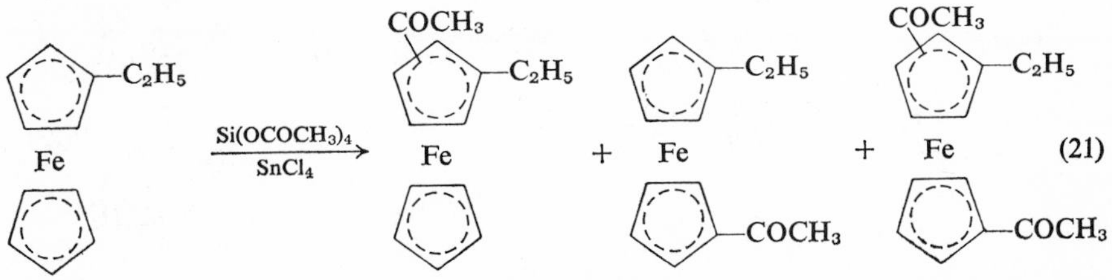

Rosenblum and Woodward[17] have shown that when ethylferrocene is acetylated with acetyl and aluminum chlorides, the amount of homoannular isomers is 2.2 times greater than that of heteroannular ones. The relative activity of the 1′-, 2-, and 3-positions found by Rosenblum and Woodward[17] is 1.0:1.4:4.2. Reaction (22) shows the ratio of isomers and the activity of various positions.

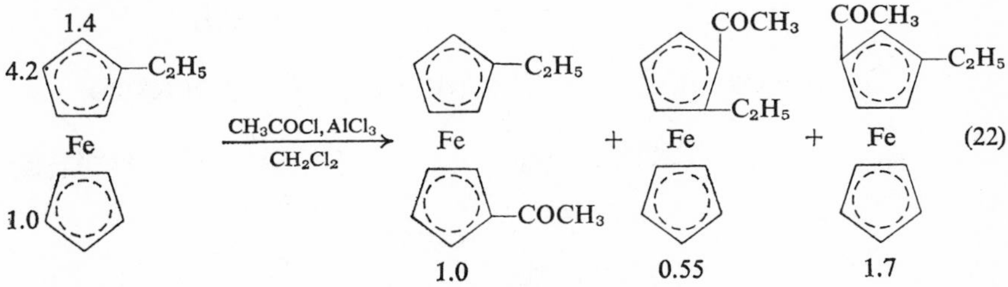

From the above discussion it follows that under the effect of an alkyl group the activity of the ferrocene nucleus subjected to acylation increases. This is particularly true for the five-membered ring to which the alkyl group is connected.

The activity of positions 2 and 3 is noticeably, though not too sharply, different. Substitution in the 3-position is approximately two to four times greater than it is in the 2-position. The above results were obtained for monoalkyl and dialkyl ferrocenes, including the disubstituted ferrocenes with bridge structures. A detailed comparison of the results obtained by different investigators would be pointless because the reactions were carried out under different conditions; moreover, methods of finding the amount of isomers (spectroscopic[49] or separation on alumina[17,50]) are not accurate. One can just note the effect of space factors: with increase in alkyl branching[49,51] or in the volume of the acylating agent (isobutyrylation[52]) the amount of the 1,3-isomer is increased.

In formylating 1,1'-diethylferrocene with N-methylformanilide and phosphorus oxychloride Tainturier and Tirouflet[50] found that the ratio of 2- and 3-isomers was 1:9 (separated on alumina).

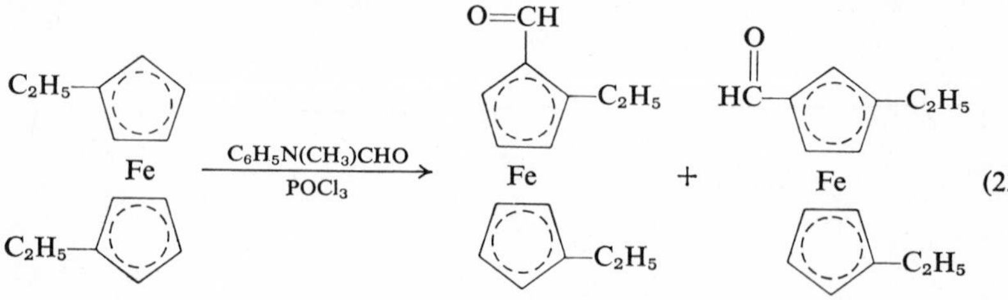

$$\text{(23)}$$

Acylation of ferrocene derivatives other than alkyl ferrocenes is more difficult than it is for ferrocene. Acylation of monosubstituted compounds involves chiefly (or almost exclusively) the free cyclopentadienyl ring (see Tables V and VI). Even N-acylamino ferrocenes are less active than ferrocene, approximately twice so, as found by competing acylation. In this case the substitution involves chiefly the 1'-position, and only small amounts of the homoannular 1,2-isomer are found.[53]

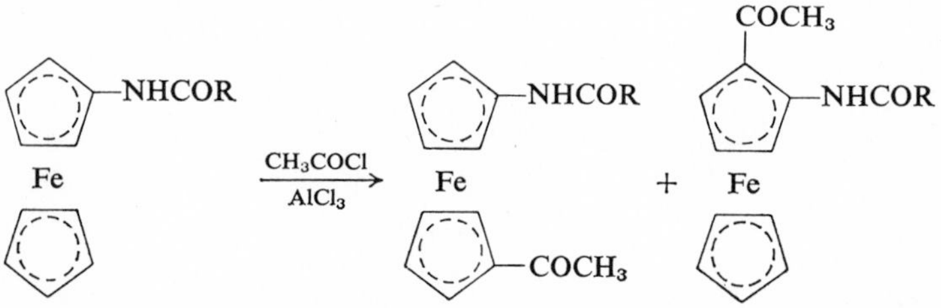

$$\text{(24)}$$

Nesmeyanov, Drozd, and Sazonova[54] acylated N-acylaminoferrocene with acetic anhydride and phosphoric acid and also obtained a predominantly heteroannular isomer. Whether the passivation of the ferrocene nucleus is due to the effect of the N-acylamino group or its complex with acidic agents is not clear.[53]

Position 2 is more active than position 3 in the cyclopentadienyl ring with an electron-withdrawing substituent. This follows both from experimental data and molecular-orbital calculations for ferrocene derivatives with electron-withdrawing substituents.[16,55] It was previously stated that when ferrocene is diacylated, 1,2-diacetylferrocene is formed (in very low yield).

Monoarylferrocene acylation yields a mixture of 1,1'- 1,2-, and 1,3-isomers. The 1,1'-isomer is the major product, the 1,2-isomer is obtained in the next highest yield, and the 1,3-isomer is obtained in the smallest yield. Formula (12) shows the relative activities of the different positions in phenylferrocene according to Rosenblum and Howells.[55]

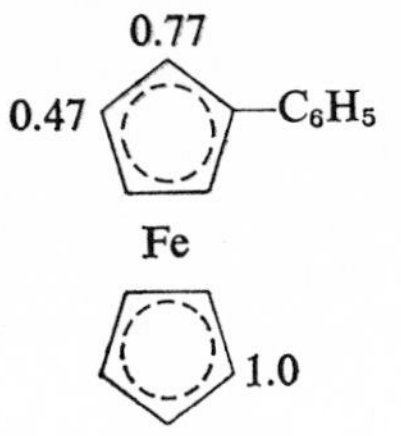

0.77

0.47 (pentagon) —C₆H₅ ... 1.11 ... 1.0 (pentagon) —C₆H₄Br-p

Fe ... Fe

(pentagon) 1.0 ... (pentagon) —C₆H₄Br-p

(12) 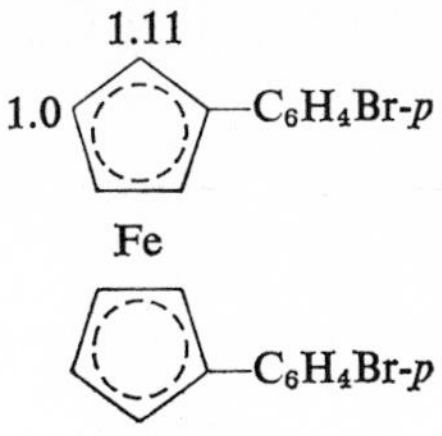 ... (13)

1.66 ... 1.95

1.00 (pentagon) —C₆H₅ ... 1.00 (pentagon) —C₆H₄OCH₃-p

Fe ... Fe

(pentagon) —C₆H₅ ... (pentagon) —C₆H₄OCH₃-p

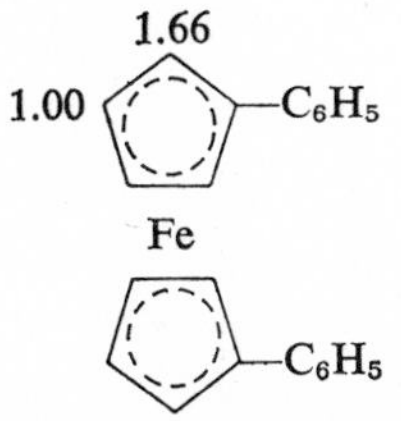

(14) 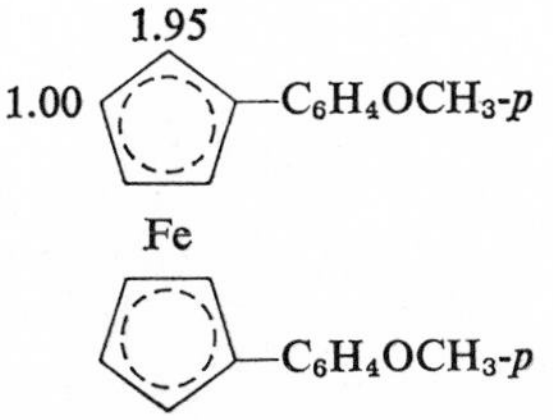 ... (15)

Nesmeyanov and co-workers[56] found that during the competing acetylation of equimolar amounts of ferrocene and phenylferrocene a mixture of acetylferrocene and acetylphenylferrocene in a ratio of 5:1 is obtained.

Heteroannular diaryl ferrocenes form a mixture of 1,2- and 1,3-acetyldiaryl ferrocenes after acylation. The activity of the 2- and 3-positions varies with substituents in the *para* position of the phenyl nucleus[55] [see formulas (13)–(15)].

Acylation of iodoferrocene leads to iodine abstraction, with diacetylferrocene being formed together with a small amount of monoacetylferrocene.[53] Methoxyferrocene gives a mixture of ferrocene and dimethoxyferrocene under Friedel–Crafts conditions. Methylthioferrocene reacts in a similar manner.[57]

7. Intramolecular Acylation of Ferrocene Derivatives

The ferrocenyl keto acids obtained by the reaction of ferrocene with the anhydrides of dicarboxylic acids or with the corresponding acyl monohalides[58–61] are not cyclized[58] as are similarly structured keto acids of the benzene series. The ω-ferrocenylcarboxylic acids that form after the carbonyl group has been reduced to methylene[59,61,62] undergo intramolecular acylation[58,61,63] (see Table VIII).

When cyclized by polyphosphoric acid, ω-ferrocenylbutyric acid (16) gives a homoannular ketone, α-keto-1,2-tetramethyleneferrocene (17).[58,63]

Di-ω-carboxypropylferrocene (18), when heated with polyphosphoric acid, is converted into bis(α-keto-1,2-tetramethylene)ferrocene (19).[58] The

TABLE VIII

Intramolecular Acylation of Ferrocene Derivatives

Ferrocene derivative	Catalyst and solvent[a]	Reaction products	Yield,[b] %	Ref.[c]
—CH₂CH₂COOH	(CF₃CO)₂O, CCl₄	1,1'-(CH₂)₂CO—	90	82, 68
	(CF₃CO)₂O, CH₂Cl₂	1,1'-(CH₂)₂CO—	88	116
	H₃PO₄	1,1'-(CH₂)₂CO—	17	82, 63
	AlCl₃, CH₂Cl₂	1,1'-(CH₂)₂CO—	33	82
—CH(CH₃)CH₂COOH	H₃PO₄	1,1'-CH(CH₃)CH₂CO—	32	152
—CH₂CH(CH₃)COOH	(CF₃CO)₂O	1,1'-CH₂CH(CH₃)CO—	—	153
—CH(CH₃)CH(CH₃)COOH	(CF₃CO)₂O, CCl₄	1,1'-CH(CH₃)CH(CH₃)CO—	41	152
—CH(C₆H₅)CH₂COOH	H₃PO₄	1,1'-CH(C₆H₅)CH₂CO—	21	152
—CH₂CH(C₆H₅)COOH	(CF₃CO)₂O	1,1'-CH₂CH(C₆H₅)CO—	—	153
—CH₂CH(CH₂C₆H₅)COOH	(CF₃CO)₂O	1,1'-CH₂CH(CH₂C₆H₅)CO—	79	154
—CH₂CH(CH₂FeC₁₀H₉)COOH	(CF₃CO)₂O, CH₂Cl₂	1,1'-CH₂CH(CH₂FeC₁₀H₉)CO—	80	154
—CH₂C((CH₃)₂COOH	(CF₃CO)₂O	1,1'-CH₂C(CH₃)₂CO—; 1,2-CH₂C(CH₃)₂CO—	—	116
—CH₂C(CH₂FeC₁₀H₉)(COOH)₂	(CF₃CO)₂O, CH₂Cl₂	1,1'-CH₂CH(CH₂FeC₁₀H₉)CO—;	30	154
		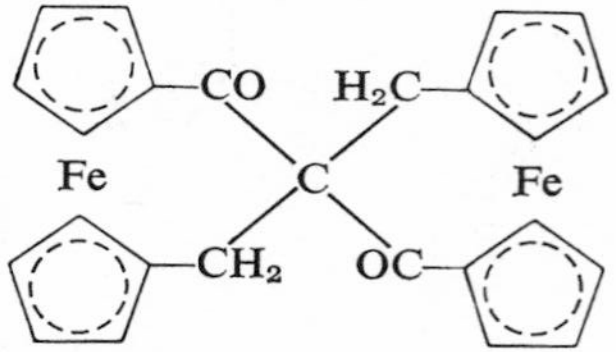	12	
—(CH₂)₃COOH[d]	H₃PO₄	1,2-(CH₂)₃CO—	56	58,82
	(CF₃CO)₂O, CH₂Cl₂	1,2-(CH₂)₃CO—	94	77, 82, 63
—CH₂CH(COCH₃)CH₂COOH	(CF₃CO)₂O, CH₂Cl₂	1,2-CH₂CH(COCH₃)CH₂CO—	23	154
—CH₂CH(C₆H₅)CH₂COOH	H₃PO₄	1,2-CH₂CH(C₆H₅)CH₂CO—	—	119
—CH₂CH₂CH(C₆H₅)COOH	H₃PO₄	1,2-CH₂CH₂CH(C₆H₅)CO—	—	119

Reactant	Reagent	Product	Yield	References
—(CH₂)₄COOH	H₃PO₄	1,2-(CH₂)₄CO—	14	82, 63
	(CF₃CO)₂O	1,2-(CH₂)₄CO—	28	82, 63
—(CH₂)₅COOH	H₃PO₄	??-(CH₂)₅CO—	11	82, 63
—CH₂C₆H₄COOH-o	PCl₅	1,2-CH₂C₆H₄CO—	—	155
—COC₆H₄COOH-o	H₂SO₄ or H₃PO₄	1,2-COC₆H₄CO—	34	58
—COC₆H₄COOCH₃-o	H₂SO₄ or H₃PO₄	1,2-COC₆H₄CO—	54	58
—COC₆H₄CH₂COOH-o	H₃PO₄	C₅H₄FeC₅H₅ [isochromanone structure]	—	105, 106
1-CH₃-2-(CH₂)₃COOH	(F₃CCO)₂O	1-CH₃-2,3-(CH₂)₃CO—	—	156
1-CH₃-3-(CH₂)₃COOH	(F₃CCO)₂O	1-CH₃-2,3-CO(CH₂)₃—; 1-CH₃-3,4-(CH₂)₃CO—	—	156
1-CH₃-1'-(CH₂)₃COOH	(F₃CCO)₂O	1-CH₃-1',2'-(CH₂)₃CO—	—	156
1-C₂H₅-2-(CH₂)₃COOH	(CF₃CO)₂O	1-C₂H₅-2,3-(CH₂)₃CO—	—	132
1-C₂H₅-3-(CH₂)₃COOH	(CF₃CO)₂O	1-C₂H₅-2,3-OC(CH₂)₃—; 1-C₂H₅-1',2'(CH₂)₃CO—	—	132
1-C₂H₅-1'-(CH₂)₃COOH	(CF₃CO)₂O		—	132
[ferrocene structure with CH₂CH₂COOH, Fe, H]	(CF₃CO)₂O, CH₂Cl₂	[ferrocenophanone structure with Fe, H, C=O]	48	77

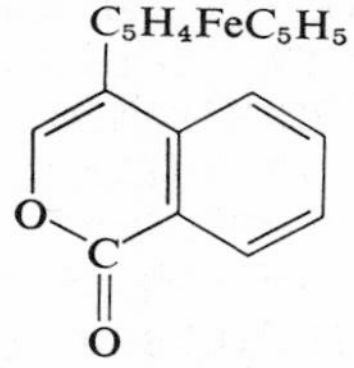

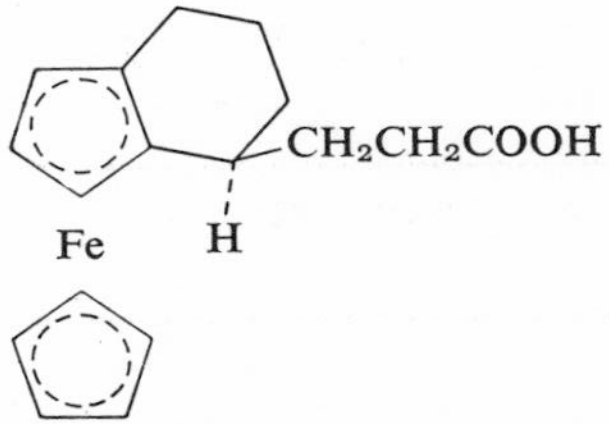

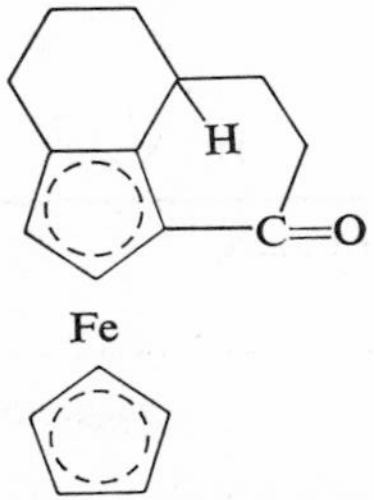

209

(continued)

TABLE VIII (continued)

Ferrocene derivative	Catalyst and solvent[a]	Reaction products	Yield,[b] %	Ref.[c]
	(CF₃CO)₂O, CH₂Cl₂		36	77
1,1'-(C₂H₅)₂-3-(CH₂)₂COOH	(CF₃CO)₂O, CCl₄	3,3'-CH₂CH₂CO—	44	68
1,1'-(C₂H₅)₂-2-(CH₂)₃COOH	H₃PO₄	2,3-CH₂CH₂CH₂CO—	—	148
1,1'—(C₂H₅)₂-3-(CH₂)₃COOH	H₃PO₄	2,3-CH₂CH₂CH₂CO—; 3,4-CH₂CH₂CH₂CO—	—	148
1,1'-(CH₂CH₂COOH)₂	(CF₃CO)₂O, CCl₄	1,1'-(CH₂CH₂CO)-?-CH₂CH₂COOH	80	65
1,1'-(CH₂CH₂COCl)₂	AlCl₃, CH₂Cl₂	1,1'; 3,3'-(—CH₂CH₂CO—)₂	37	65
1,1'-[(CH₂)₃COOH]₂	H₃PO₄	1,2; 1',2'-[—(CH₂)₃CO—]₂; 1,2;1',5'-[—(CH₂)₃CO—]₂	46[e]	59, 131
	(CF₃CO)₂O, CCl₄	1,2;1',2'-[—(CH₂)₃CO—]₂; 1,2;1',5'-[—(CH₂)₃CO—]₂	47[e]	82
1,1'-(C₂H₅)₂-3,3'(?)-(CH₂CH₂COOH)₂	(CF₃CO)₂O, CCl₄	3,?-(—CH₂CH₂CO—)-3'(?)-CH₂CH₂COOH-1,1'-(C₂H₅)₂	30	68

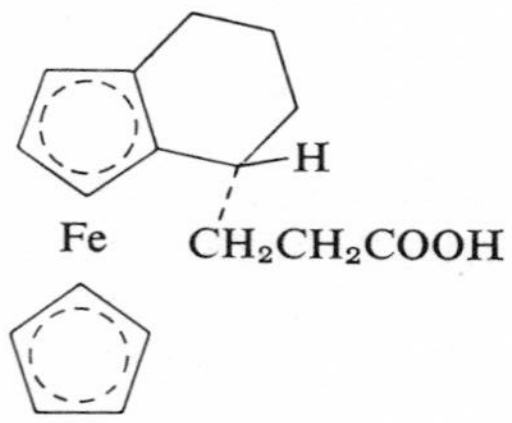

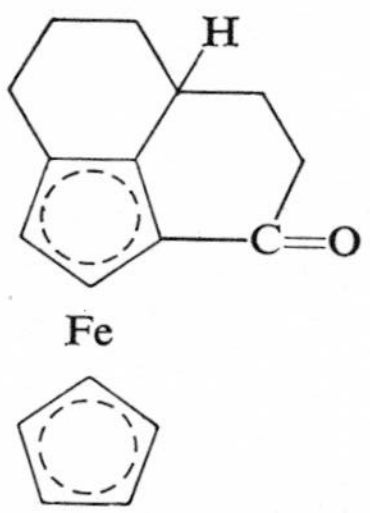

1,1'-[—(CH₂)₃—]-3-CH₂CH₂COOH	$(CF_3CO)_2O$, CCl_4	3,3'-CH₂CH₂CO—	71	65
1,1'-(C₂H₅)₂-3,3'(?)-[—(CH₂)₃—]-4(?)-CH₂CH₂COOH	$(CF_3CO)_2O$, CCl_4	4,4'(?)-CH₂CH₂CH₂CO—	50	68
1,1';3,3'-[—(CH₂)₃—]₂-?-CH₂CH₂COOH	$(CF_3CO)_2O$, CCl_4	?,?-CH₂CH₂CO—	30	67, 68
		4,5-CH₂CH₂CO—	37	67
1,1';3,3';4,4'-[—(CH₂—)]₃-2-CH₂CH₂COOH	PCl_3 or $AlCl_3$	2,2'-CH₂CH₂CO—	—	68
1,1';3,3';?,?-[—(CH₂)₃—]₃-?-CH₂CH₂COOH	$(CF_3CO)_2O$, CCl_4	?,?-CH₂CH₂CO—	7	68
1,1';3,3';4,5-[—(CH₂)₃—]₃-4'CH₂CH₂COOH	$(CF_3CO)_2O$, CCl_4	4',5'-CH₂CH₂CO—	—	67
—C₆H₄COOH-o	$(COCl)_2$, CH_2Cl_2	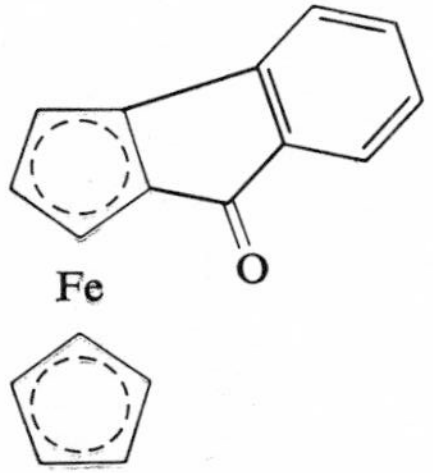	—	69
1-COCl-1'-COC₅H₄FeC₅H₅	$AlCl_3$, $CHCl_3$	1,1'-COC₅H₄FeC₅H₄CO—	—	125

[a] In many cases the reaction was conducted without solvent, and only the catalyst is shown.
[b] The yield refers to the amount taken for reaction.
[c] The reference corresponding to the best yield is placed first.
[d] The procedure for obtaining the product is described in Section II-C-9.
[e] The yield is for a mixture of compounds, with no individual products isolated.

211

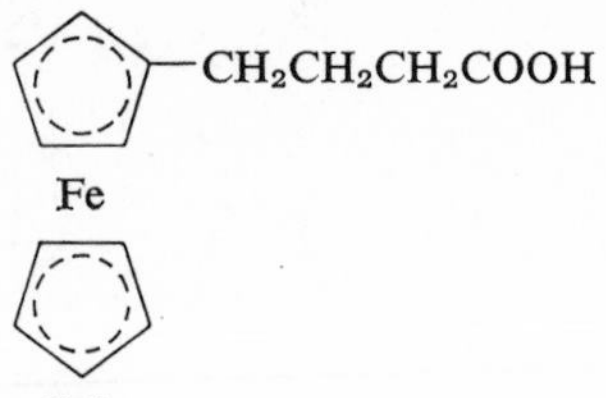

(16)

structure of diketone (19) was proved by Clemmensen reduction to bis(1,2-tetramethylene)ferrocene (20).[58] This is identical with the compound obtained by the hydrogenation of bis(indenyl)iron (21).[64]

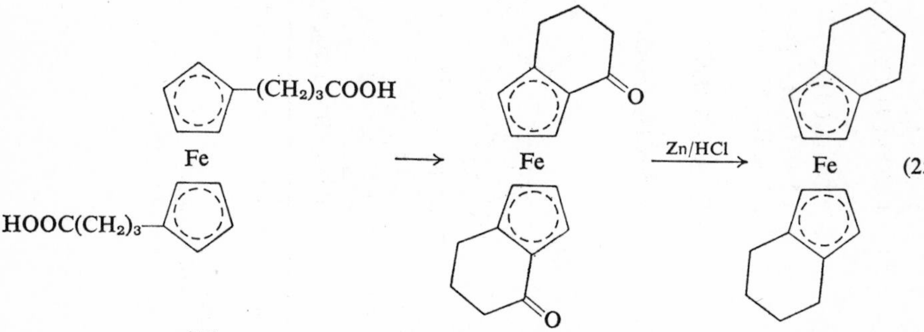

Ferrocenylpropionic acid (22) gives, after intramolecular acetylation, a heteroannular ketone, 1,1'-(α-ketotrimethylene)ferrocene (23).[61,63] The structure of ketone (23) was established spectroscopically.

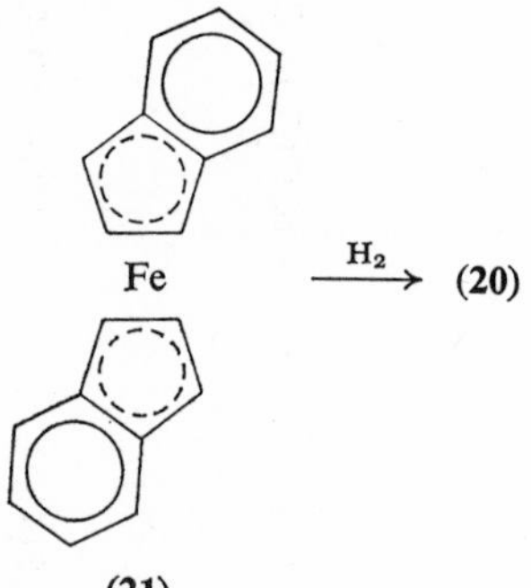

When 1,1'-(trimethylene)ferrocene-3-propionic acid (24) is treated with trifluoroacetic acid, ketone (25) is formed; in this structure the cyclopentadienyl rings are connected by two bridges.[65]

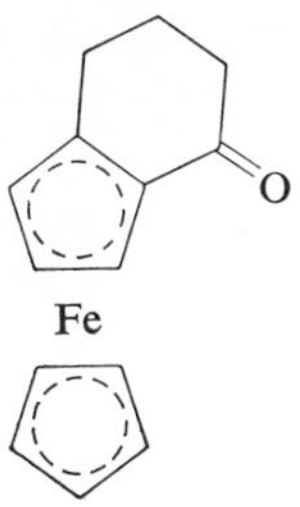

(17) 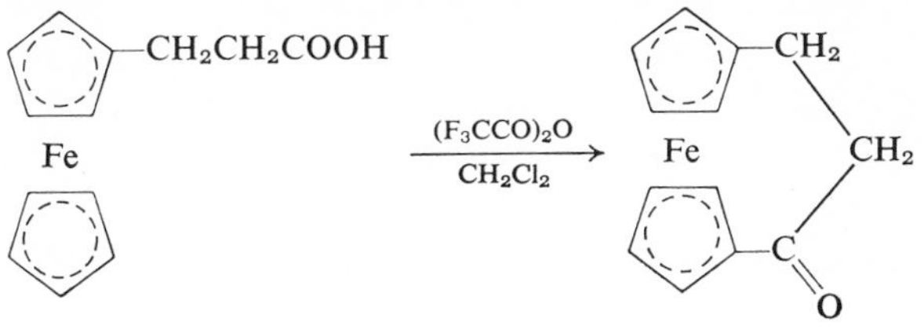   (22)   (23)   (27)

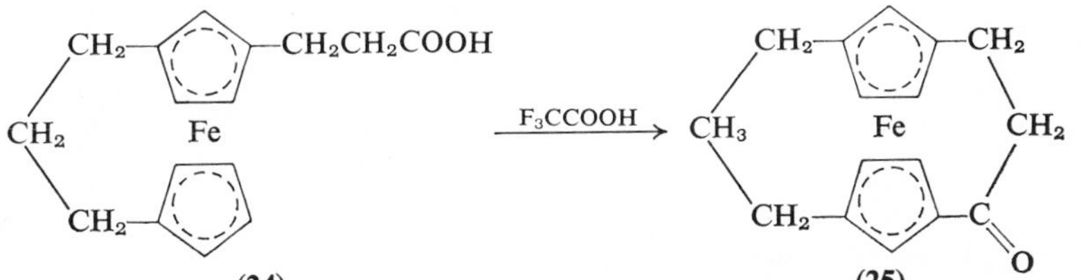

(24)   (25)   (28)

Rinehart, Bublitz, and Gustafson[66] found that in cyclizing 1,1', 3,3'-bis-(trimethylene)ferrocene-4-propionic acid (26) mixtures of homoannular and heteroannular ketones (27) and (28), respectively, are formed.

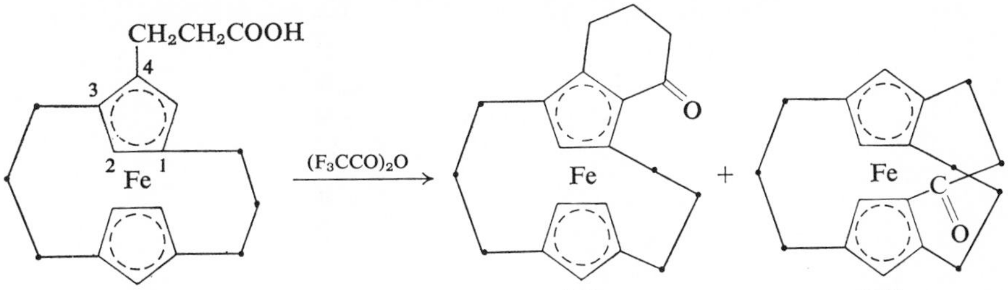

(26)   (27)   (28)

(29)

Bublitz and Rinehart[67] proved that the supposed 1,1'-(α-ketotrimethylene)-2,2'; 4,4'-bis(trimethylene)ferrocene (28), obtained by Schlögl and Peterlik,[68]

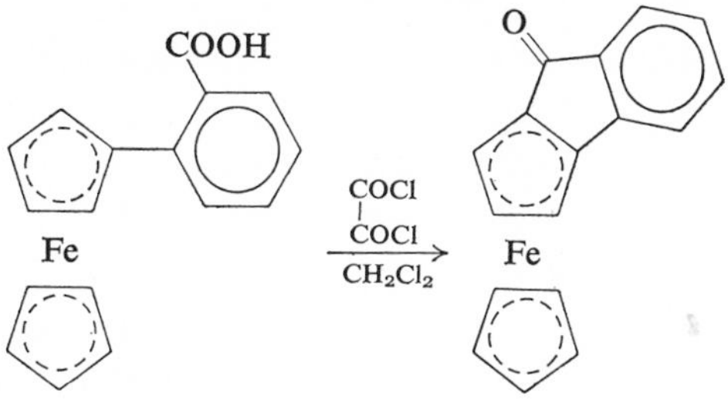

(29)   (30)

(30)

is actually its homoannular isomer (**27**). Therefore all compounds [including 1,1';2,2';3,3';4,4'-tetrakis(trimethylene)ferrocene prepared by Schlögl and Peterlik[68]] based on this ketone had been assigned an incorrect structure.

Cyclization of *o*-ferrocenylbenzoic acid (**29**) by oxalyl chloride to form ketone (**30**) has been described.[69] Attempts to cyclize *o*-carboxybenzoylferrocene (**31**) convert it to 3,3'-diferrocenyl-3,3'-diphthalide (**32**).[70,71]

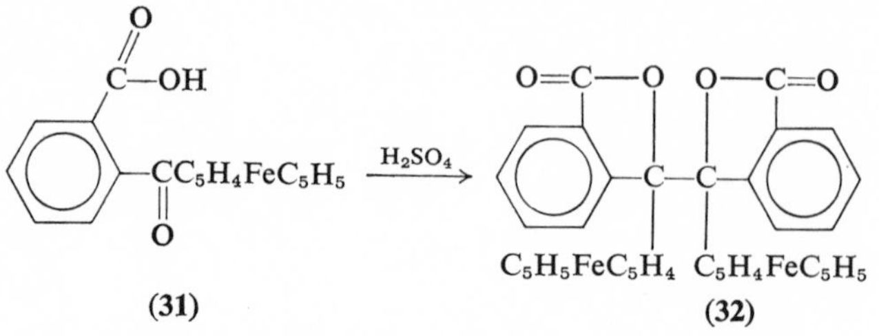

(31)

(31)   (32)

8. Mechanism of Electrophilic Substitution in Ferrocene

In a ferrocene molecule there are two types of nucleophilic center: carbon atoms and the iron atom. At present it has not been established which of the nucleophilic centers is the site of the initial attack in electrophilic substitution. Discussion of this problem has been stimulated by the discovery that the protonation of ferrocene and ruthenocene[2,72] yields a complex (**33**) in which the proton is associated with the metal.

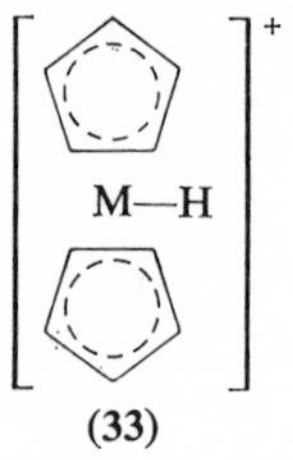

(M = Fe, Ru)

(33)

Richards[73] proposed that the metal atom plays a substantial role in the electrophilic substitution of metallocenes. This idea is the basis of the electrophilic substitution mechanism in metallocenes developed by Rosenblum and co-workers.[74,75] According to this mechanism, the first step in electrophilic substitution in ferrocene is a rapid, reversible addition of an electrophile to the metal atom. During the second step, a slow step, the electrophile transfers to the ring. This leads to the formation of the endocyclic σ-complex (**34**), to which the authors assign a structure similar to that of σ-complexes of the benzene series.* During the third step fast proton abstraction takes

---

* Rosenblum, like other investigators, does not discuss the character of the iron–ring bond in the σ-complex. It should differ greatly from that in ferrocene, since a tetrahedral carbon atom is formed in the σ-complex.

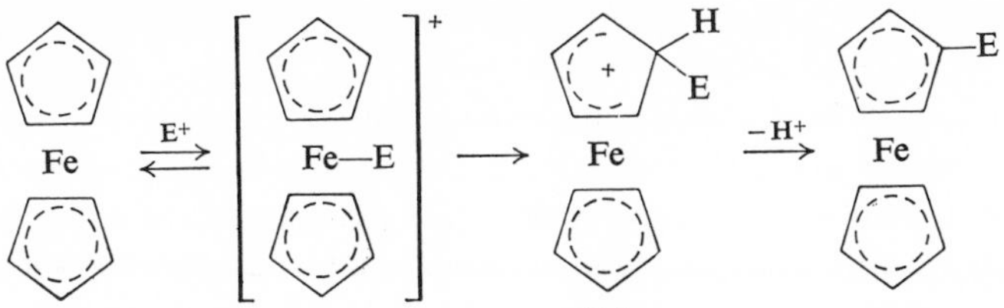

(32)

(34)

place and a substituted ferrocene is formed. A similar mechanism was suggested by Sorokin and Domrachev.[76] A significant feature of these mechanisms is the approach of an electrophile to the five-membered ring from the iron atom. Rosenblum and Abbate[77] investigated the intramolecular acylation of the epimeric pair of acids (35) and (36), in which, for steric reasons, *endo*

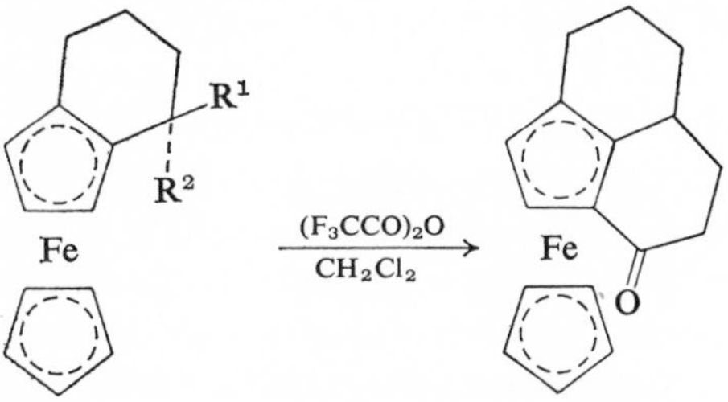

(33)

(35): $R^1 = CH_2CH_2COOH$; $R^2 = H$
(36): $R^1 = H$; $R^2 = CH_2CH_2COOH$

(35) or *exo* (36) cyclic electrophilic attack should be hindered. It appeared, however, that, when treated with trifluoroacetic acid anhydride, both acids were cyclized into the homocyclic ketone (37). The rate of cyclization for the *exo* acid is somewhat higher than that for the *endo* acid. These results led Rosenblum and Abbate to the conclusion that the metal atom does not take any substantial part in ferrocene acylation.

The conclusion made by Rosenblum and Abbate must be considered a preliminary one. They recognized this fact in their later review on the role of the metal atom in iron-group metallocene reactions.[78]

The methanism of electrophilic substitution in metallocenes was discussed in a recent paper by Mangravite and Traylor.[79] The σ-complex was proposed to be formed via a direct attack of an electrophile at a five-membered ring.

9. Examples of Syntheses

a. Monoacetylferrocene (Modified Technique[3]*).* Ferrocene (20 g, 0.11 mole), 5 ml of 85% H_3PO_4, and 150 ml of acetic anhydride are placed into a two-necked flask fitted with a thermometer and a mechanical stirrer. The mixture is stirred for 10 min at 100°, poured on ice, and left overnight.

Saturated sodium carbonate solution is added until precipitation ceases. The precipitate is filtered and treated with small portions of concentrated hydrochloric acid in a mortar until the precipitate almost dissolves. The solution is rapidly filtered through a glass frit and immediately diluted with four to six volumes of ice-cold water. The precipitated acetylferrocene is filtered, washed with water, dried in the air, dried in vacuum over phosphorus pentoxide, and crystallized from n-heptane to give 70–75% of product melting 85–86°.

Purification of acetylferrocene can be accomplished by chromatography on alumina rather than by dissolving it in concentrated hydrochloric acid. Unreacted ferrocene is eluted with petroleum ether; acetylferrocene is eluted with a benzene–ether (1:1) mixture.

*b. 1,1'-Diacetylferrocene.** A mixture of anhydrous aluminum chloride (67 g, 0.50 mole) and 200 ml of dry carbon tetrachloride is placed into a sealed three-necked flask fitted with a reflux condenser; acetyl chloride (30.5 ml, 0.40 mole) dissolved in 30 ml of absolute carbon tetrachloride is added with stirring and cooling with ice. The stirring is continued for 40 min, and ferrocene (37.2 g, 0.20 mole) is gradually added in small (2–3 g) portions. Ferrocene is added from an Erlenmeyer flask connected to the third neck of the flask with a wide rubber tube. The mixture is stirred for 30 min at room temperature, for 1 hr at 40–50°, cooled, and the almost colorless carbon tetrachloride layer is removed by decantation. The residue is treated with a mixture of 10 ml of concentrated hydrochloric acid and 400–500 g of ice. Diacetylferrocene is filtered, carefully washed with water, dried in air (weight 45–50 g), and crystallized from a benzene–petroleum ether mixture (1:1). The yield is 35–40 g (63–70%), m.p. 129–130°.

c. 1,1'-Acyl(carbomethoxy) Ferrocenes.[80]   With stirring and cooling in an ice bath, 20 g (0.148 mole) of aluminum chloride is added to 0.085 mole of the acyl chloride dissolved in 100 ml of absolute carbon tetrachloride. Also ferrocenecarboxylic acid methyl ester (0.037 mole) is dissolved in 90 ml of carbon tetrachloride; this is then added for 30 min to the previous mixture. The stirring is continued for 1 hr at room temperature. The mixture is treated with water and extracted with ether. Ether and carbon tetrachloride are removed, and the residue is dissolved in a petroleum ether–benzene mixture and chromatographed on an alumina column. Methyl esters of substituted ferrocenecarboxylic acids are eluted with ether and crystallized from hexane.

d. 1,1'-Chloro(acetyl)ferrocene.[81]   A mixture of chloroferrocene (5 g), 40 ml of acetic anhydride, 9.6 g of 85% phosphoric acid, and 4.8 g of phosphorus pentoxide is stirred and heated for 10 min in a boiling-water bath.

---

* The technique proposed by N. A. Simukova and E. L. Smyslova (Moscow University, Chemistry Department).

Product	m.p., °C	Yield, %
$CH_3COC_5H_4FeC_5H_4COOCH_3$	102–102.5	80
$C_2H_5COC_5H_4FeC_5H_4COOCH_3$	64–65	88
n-$C_3H_7COC_5H_4FeC_5H_4COOCH_3$	57.5–58.5	80
$C_6H_5COC_5H_4FeC_5H_4COOCH_3$	79.5–80.5	85

The mixture is cooled, poured into a sodium carbonate solution, and extracted with ether. The ether extracts are washed with water and dried over magnesium sulfate. The ether is removed, and the residue is dissolved in hot petroleum ether and chromatographed on alumina. Unreacted chloroferrocene (0.58 g) is eluted with petroleum ether and 1,1'-chloro(acetyl)ferrocene with ether. The yield of the compound is 3.6 g (61%); m.p. 62–63° (crystallized from hexane).

The 2,4-dinitrophenylhydrazone of 1,1'-chloro(acetyl)ferrocene melts at 159–161°.

e. 1,1'-(α-Ketotrimethylene)ferrocene.[82] Trifluoroacetic anhydride (95 g, 0.45 mole) is mixed with β-ferrocenylpropionic acid (9.50 g, 0.037 mole) and 400 ml of carbon tetrachloride. The mixture is then stirred for 4.5 hr under nitrogen at room temperature. The flask is wrapped with aluminum foil. The mixture is poured into a sodium bicarbonate solution. The water layer is extracted with dichloromethane. The combined organic extracts are washed with water, 2 N KOH solution, then with water again, and dried over magnesium sulfate. The solvent is removed, and 1,1'-(α-ketotrimethylene)-ferrocene is obtained, 7.90 g (90%); m.p. 138–143°. After crystallization from hexane, 7.06 g (81%) of the compound is obtained; m.p. 146–147°.

f. Ferrocene Aldehyde.[83] Phosphorus oxychloride (8 ml) is placed into a three-necked flask, and freshly distilled *N*-methylformanilide (11 ml) is added in portions. The reaction is kept under a stream of nitrogen at 8–10°. After 10 min of stirring, the solution is heated to 38–40°, and ferrocene (7.5 g) is gradually added for 30 min. The mixture is stirred for 2 hr at 46–48°, cooled to 15°, and diluted with 25 ml of an ice-cold water mixture. The stirring is continued for 2 hr at room temperature. Ether (100 ml), sodium sulfite (20 g), and sodium bisulfite (40 ml of 40% solution) are then added to the mixture. After a few minutes a dark precipitate of a ferrocene aldehyde bisulfite derivative is formed. The mixture is then stirred for 4 hr at room temperature and left overnight. The precipitate is washed with ether to remove ferrocene (until the filtrate is colorless), transferred to a flask, and stirred with 160 ml of 10% sulfuric acid for 30 min at 40°. The aldehyde is filtered off, washed with saturated sodium carbonate solution and then with water, and dried. The yield of the crude product is 6.7 g. To purify the ferrocene aldehyde, it is dissolved in ether, the ether solution is filtered, and the ether is then removed under vacuum. The yield of ferrocene aldehyde is 5.9 g (69%); m.p. 118–119°.

References

1. R. B. Woodward, M. Rosenblum, and M. C. Whiting, *J. Amer. Chem. Soc.*, **74**, 3458 (1952).
2. M. Rosenblum and J. O. Santer, *J. Amer. Chem. Soc.*, **81**, 5517 (1959).
3. P. J. Graham, R. B. Lindsey, G. W. Parshall, M. L. Peterson, and G. M. Whitman, *J. Amer. Chem. Soc.*, **79**, 3416 (1957).
4. R. Riemschneider and D. Helm, *Ann.*, **646**, 10 (1961).
5. G. D. Broadhead, J. M. Osgerby, and P. L. Pauson, *J. Chem. Soc.*, **1958**, 650.
6. C. R. Hauser and J. K. Lindsay, *J. Org. Chem.*, **22**, 428 (1957).
7. C. R. Hauser and J. K. Lindsay, *J. Org. Chem.*, **22**, 906 (1957).
8. A. N. Nesmeyanov, E. G. Perevalova, R. V. Golovnya, and O. A. Nesmeyanova, *Dokl. Akad. Nauk SSSR*, **97**, 459 (1954).
9. Yu. K. Yur'ev, G. B. Yelyakov, and Z. V. Belyakova, *Dokl. Akad. Nauk SSSR*, **86**, 337 (1952); *ibid.*, **102**, 113 (1955).
10. K. Schlögl and H. Egger, *Monatsh.*, **94**, 376 (1963).
11. R. L. Schaaf and C. T. Lenk, *J. Org. Chem.*, **28**, 3238 (1963).
12. M. D. Rausch, E. O. Fischer, and H. Grubert, *J. Amer. Chem. Soc.*, **82**, 76 (1960).
13. A. N. Nesmeyanov, E. G. Perevalova, L. L. Leont'eva, and Yu. A. Ustynyuk, *Izv. Akad. Nauk SSSR, Ser. Khim.*, **1966**, 556.
14. K. L. Rinehart, Jr., A. F. Ellis, C. J. Michejda, and P. A. Kittle, *J. Amer. Chem. Soc.*, **82**, 4112 (1960).
15. A. N. Nesmeyanov, E. G. Perevalova, L. P. Yur'eva, and L. L. Denisovich, *Izv. Akad. Nauk SSSR, Otd. Khim. Nauk*, **1962**, 2241.
16. J. H. Richards and T. J. Curphey, *Chem. Ind. (London)*, **1956**, 1456.
17. M. Rosenblum and R. B. Woodward, *J. Amer. Chem. Soc.*, **80**, 5443 (1958).
18. M. Rosenblum, *Chemistry of the Iron Group Metallocenes: Ferrocene, Ruthenocene, Osmocene*, Part 1, Wiley, New York, 1965, pp. 67, 95.
19. A. N. Nesmeyanov, E. G. Perevalova, V. D. Tiurin, and S. P. Gubin, *Izv. Akad. Nauk SSSR, Ser. Khim.*, **1966**, 1938.
20. Yu. T. Struchkov, *Dokl. Akad. Nauk SSSR*, **110**, 67 (1956).
21. Yu. T. Struchkov and T. L. Hotsyanova, *Kristallografiya*, **2**, 382 (1957).
22. D. W. Fischer, *Acta Cryst.*, **17**, 619 (1964).
23. A. N. Nesmeyanov, E. G. Perevalova, R. V. Golovnya, T. V. Nikitina, and N. A. Simukova, *Izv. Akad. Nauk SSSR, Otd. Khim. Nauk*, **1956**, 739.
24. A. N. Nesmeyanov, E. G. Perevalova, R. B. Golovnya, N. Y. Simukova, and O. V. Starovskii, *Izv. Akad. Nauk SSSR, Otd. Khim. Nauk*, **1957**, 638.
25. W. M. Sweeney, U.S. Patent 2,852,542 (1961); *Chem. Abstr.*, **53**, 4297 (1959).
26. M. Rausch, P. Shaw, D. Mayo, and A. M. Lovelace, *J. Org. Chem.*, **23**, 505 (1958).
27. N. Weliky and E. S. Gould, *J. Amer. Chem. Soc.*, **79**, 2742 (1957).
28. W. F. Little and R. Eisenthal, *J. Amer. Chem. Soc.*, **82**, 1577 (1960).
29. T. P. Vishnyakova, L. A. Golubeva, and Ya. M. Paushkin, *Vysokomol. Soyedin.*, **7**, 713 (1965).
30. G. P. Sollott and E. Howard, *J. Org. Chem.*, **27**, 4034 (1962).
31. A. N. Nesmeyanov, V. D. Vil'chevskaya, N. S. Kochetkova, and N. P. Palitsyn, *Izv. Akad. Nauk SSSR, Otd. Khim. Nauk*, **1963**, 2051.
32. A. N. Nesmeyanov, V. D. Vil'chevskaya, and A. I. Makarova, *Dokl. Akad. Nauk SSSR*, **169**, 351 (1966).

33. G. P. Sollott and W. R. Peterson, Jr., *J. Organometal. Chem.*, **4**, 491 (1965).
34. G. P. Sollott, H. E. Mertwoy, S. Portnoy, and J. L. Snead, *J. Org. Chem.*, **28**, 1090 (1963).
35. G. P. Sollott and W. R. Peterson, Jr., *J. Org. Chem.*, **30**, 389 (1965).
36. G. P. Sollott and W. R. Peterson, Jr., *J. Amer. Chem. Soc.*, **89**, 5054 (1967).
37. G. P. Sollott and W. R. Peterson, Jr., *J. Amer. Chem. Soc.*, **89**, 6783 (1967).
38. R. Riemschneider and D. Helm, *Chem. Ber.*, **89**, 155 (1956).
39. G. R. Knox and P. L. Pauson, *J. Chem. Soc.*, **1958**, 692.
40. A. N. Nesmeyanov, E. G. Perevalova, and O. A. Nesmeyanova, *Dokl. Akad. Nauk SSSR*, **119**, 288 (1958).
41. E. G. Perevalova, O. A. Nesmeyanova, and L. T. Lukyanova, *Dokl. Akad. Nauk SSSR*, **132**, 853 (1960).
42. A. N. Nesmeyanov, E. G. Perevalova, L. P. Yur'eva, and K. L. Grandberg, *Izv. Akad. SSSR, Otd. Khim. Nauk*, **1962**, 1772.
43. C. Jutz, *Tetrahedron Letters*, **1959**, No. 21, 1.
44. P. L. Pauson and W. E. Watts, *J. Chem. Soc.*, **1962**, 3880.
45. J. M. Osgerby and P. L. Pauson, *J. Chem. Soc.*, **1961**, 4604.
46. A. N. Nesmeyanov, E. G. Perevalova, Z. A. Beynoravichute, and L. L. Malygina, *Dokl. Akad. Nauk SSSR*, **120**, 1263 (1958).
47. A. N. Nesmeyanov and E. G. Perevalova, *Ann. N.Y. Acad. Sci.*, **125**, 67 (1965).
48. A. N. Nesmeyanov and N. A. Vol'kenau, *Dokl. Akad. Nauk SSSR*, **111**, 605 (1956).
49. K. L. Rinehart, Jr., K. L. Motz, and S. Moon, *J. Amer. Chem. Soc.*, **79**, 2749 (1957).
50. G. Tainturier and J. Tirouflet, *Compt. Rend.*, **258**, 5666 (1964); *Bull. Soc. Chim. France*, **1966**, 600.
51. R. A. Benkeser, T. Nagai, and J. Hooz, *J. Amer. Chem. Soc.*, **86**, 3742 (1964).
52. Ref. 18, p. 72.
53. D. W. Hall and J. H. Richards, *J. Org. Chem.*, **28**, 1549 (1963).
54. A. N. Nesmeyanov, V. N. Drozd, and V. A. Sazonova, *Izv. Akad. Nauk SSSR, Otd. Khim. Nauk*, **1965**, 1205.
55. M. Rosenblum and W. G. Howells, *J. Amer. Chem. Soc.*, **84**, 1167 (1962).
56. A. N. Nesmeyanov, E. G. Perevalova, S. P. Gubin, T. V. Nikitina, A. A. Ponomarenko, and L. S. Shilovtseva, *Dokl. Akad. Nauk SSSR*, **139**, 888 (1961).
57. J. G. Morrison and P. L. Pauson, *Proc. Chem. Soc.*, **1962**, 177.
58. A. N. Nesmeyanov, N. A. Vol'kenau, and V. D. Vil'chevskaya, *Dokl. Akad. Nauk SSSR*, **118**, 512 (1958).
59. A. N. Nesmeyanov, N. A. Vol'kenau, and V. D. Vil'chevskaya, *Dokl. Akad. Nauk SSSR*, **111**, 362 (1966).
60. K. L. Rinehart, Jr., R. I. Curby, and P. E. Sokol, *J. Amer. Chem. Soc.*, **79**, 3420 (1957).
61. K. Schlögl and H. Seiler, *Monatsh.*, **91**, 79 (1960).
62. J. B. Thomson, *Chem. Ind. (London)*, **1959**, 1122.
63. K. L. Rinehart, Jr. and R. J. Curby, *J. Amer. Chem. Soc.*, **79**, 3290 (1957).
64. E. O. Fischer and D. Seus, *Z. Naturforsch.*, **9b**, 386 (1954).
65. K. Schlögl and H. Seiler, *Tetrahedron Letters*, **1960**, No. 7, 4; M. Peterlik, K. Schlögl, and H. Seiler, *Monatsh.*, **93**, 1309 (1962).
66. K. L. Rinehart, Jr., D. E. Bublitz, and D. H. Gustafson, *J. Amer. Chem. Soc.*, **85**, 970 (1963).
67. D. E. Bublitz and K. L. Rinehart, Jr., *Tetrahedron Letters*, **1964**, 827.

68. K. Schlögl and M. Peterlik, *Tetrahedron Letters*, **1962**, 573; *Monatsh.*, **91**, 1328 (1962).
69. M. Cais, A. Modiano, and A. Raveh, *J. Amer. Chem. Soc.*, **87**, 5607 (1965).
70. A. N. Nesmeyanov, V. D. Vil'chevskaya, and N. S. Kochetkova, *Dokl. Akad. Nauk SSSR*, **138**, 390 (1961).
71. A. N. Nesmeyanov, N. S. Kochetkova, V. D. Vil'chevskaya, Yu. N. Sheinker, L. B. Senyavina, and M. I. Struchkova, *Izv. Akad. Nauk SSSR, Otd. Khim. Nauk*, **1962**, 1990.
72. T. J. Curphey, J. O. Santer, M. Rosenblum, and J. H. Richards, *J. Amer. Chem. Soc.*, **82**, 5249 (1960).
73. J. H. Richards, in *Abstracts of the 135th National Meeting of the American Chemical Society, April 1959*, pp. 86–90.
74. M. Rosenblum, J. O. Santer, and W. G. Howells, *J. Amer. Chem. Soc.*, **85**, 1450 (1963).
75. Ref. 18, p. 77.
76. Yu. A. Sorokin and G. A. Domrachev, *Trudy po Khim. i Khim. Tekhnol.* (*Gorky, SSSR*), **1961**, vyp. 3, 665; referative journal *Chemistry* (*USSR*), Ref. 10, Zh. 1 (1962).
77. M. Rosenblum and F. W. Abbate, *J. Amer. Chem. Soc.*, **88**, 4178 (1966).
78. M. Rosenblum and F. W. Abbate, *Advances in Chem. Ser.*, **62**, 532 (1967).
79. J. A. Mangravite and T. G. Traylor, *Tetrahedron Letters*, **1967**, 4461.
80. E. G. Perevalova, M. D. Reshetova, K. I. Grandberg, and A. N. Nesmeyanov, *Izv. Akad. Nauk SSSR, Otd. Khim. Nauk*, **1964**, 1901.
81. M. D. Reshetova, L. M. Yarysheva, E. G. Perevalova, and A. N. Nesmeyanov, *Izv. Akad. Nauk SSSR Ser. Khim.*, **1965**, 2198.
82. K. L. Rinehart, Jr., R. J. Curby, D. H. Gustafson, K. G. Harrison, R. E. Bozak, and D. E. Bublitz, *J. Amer. Chem. Soc.*, **84**, 3263 (1962).
83. A. Titov, Ye. S. Lisytsyna, and M. R. Shemtova, *Dokl. Akad. Nauk SSSR*, **130**, 341 (1960).
84. M. Furdic, P. Elecko, S. Toms, and J. Suchy, *Chem. Zvesti*, **14**, 501 (1960).
85. L. Wolf and M. Beer, *Naturwissenschaften* **44**, 442 (1957).
86. K. Schlögl, *Monatsh.*, **88**, 601 (1957).
87. M. D. Rausch and L. E. Coleman, Jr., *J. Org. Chem.*, **23**, 107 (1958).
88. E. L. DeYoung, *J. Org. Chem.*, **26**, 1312 (1961).
89. R. J. Stephenson, British Patent 864,197 (1961); *Chem. Abstr.*, **55**, 17647 (1961).
90. T. Leigh, British Patent 819,108 (1959); *Chem. Abstr.*, **54**, 7732 (1960).
91. K. Schlögl and H. Pelousek, *Ann.*, **651**, 1 (1962).
92. T. Leigh, *J. Chem. Soc.*, **1964**, 3294.
93. M. Vogel, M. Rausch, and H. Rosenberg, *J. Org. Chem.*, **22**, 1016 (1957).
94. N. A. Nesmeyanov and B. N. Strunin, *Dokl. Akad. Nauk SSSR*, **137**, 106 (1961).
95. T. Leigh, British Patent 869,504 (1961); *Chem. Abstr.*, **55**, 24790 (1961).
96. M. Rausch, M. Vogel, and H. Rosenberg, *J. Org. Chem.*, **22**, 903 (1957).
97. A. N. Nesmeyanov and N. A. Vol'kenau, *Dokl. Akad. Nauk SSSR*, **107**, 262 (1956).
98. M. Rosenblum, thesis, Harvard University 1953; see Ref. 18, pp. 92–95.
99. P. L. Pauson, *J. Amer. Chem. Soc.*, **76**, 2187 (1954).
100. R. L. Schaaf, *J. Org. Chem.*, **27**, 107 (1962).
101. M. Cais and A. Eisenstadt, *J. Org. Chem.*, **30**, 1148 (1965).
102. R. Dabard and B. Gautheron, *Compt. Rend.*, **254**, 2014 (1962).
103. N. Sugiyama, H. Suzuki, Y. Shioura, and T. Teitei, *Bull. Chem. Soc. Japan*, **35**, 767 (1962); *Chem. Abstr.*, **57**, 7307 (1962).

104. J. Tirouflet, B. Gautheron, and R. Dabard, *Bull. Soc. Chim. France*, **1965**, 96.
105. J. Boichard and J. Tirouflet, *Compt. Rend.*, **253**, 1337 (1961).
106. J. Boichard and M. Delepine, *Compt. Rend.*, **253**, 2702 (1961).
107. R. J. Stephenson, British Patent 864,197 (1961); *Chem. Abstr.*, **55**, 17647 (1961).
108. T. A. Mashburn, C. E. Cain, and C. R. Hauser, *J. Org. Chem.*, **25**, 1982 (1960).
109. K. L. Rinehart, Jr., C. J. Michejda, and P. A. Kittle, *J. Amer. Chem. Soc.*, **81**, 3162 (1959).
110. M. Cais and M. Feldkimel, *Tetrahedron Letters*, **1961**, 440.
111. M. Cais, U.S. Patent 3,138,625 (1964); *Chem. Abstr.*, **61**, 675 (1964).
112. K. L. Rinehart, Jr., P. A. Kittle, and A. F. Ellis, *J. Amer. Chem. Soc.*, **82**, 2082 (1960).
113. K. Schlögl and A. Maher, *Monatsh.*, **92**, 219 (1961).
114. T. P. Vishnyakova, L. A. Golubeva, and Ya. M. Paushkin, *Vysokomol. Soyedin.*, **8**, 181 (1966).
115. S. I. Goldberg, *J. Org. Chem.*, **25**, 482 (1960).
116. M. Rosenblum, A. K. Banerjee, N. Danieli, R. W. Fish, and V. Schlatter, *J. Amer. Chem. Soc.*, **85**, 316 (1963).
117. K. Schlögl and H. Seiler, *Monatsh.*, **91**, 79 (1960).
118. K. Schlögl and H. Seiler, *Angew. Chem.*, **72**, 38 (1960).
119. J. Tirouflet, R. Dabard, and B. Gautheron, *Compt. Rend.*, **256**, 1315 (1963).
120. A. N. Nesmeyanov, V. D. Vil'chevskaya, and N. S. Kochetkova, *Dokl. Akad. Nauk SSSR*, **152**, 627 (1963).
121. N. Sugiyama and T. Teitei, *Bull. Chem. Soc. Japan*, **35**, 1423 (1962).
122. K. Yamakawa, H. Ochi, and K. Arakawa, *Chem. Pharm. Bull. Tokyo*, **11**, 905 (1963).
123. R. J. Stephenson, British Patent 861,833 (1961); *Chem. Abstr.*, **55**, 25981 (1961).
124. P. L. Pauson, *Quart. Rev.*, **9**, 391 (1955).
125. W. E. Watts, *J. Organometal. Chem.*, **10**, 191 (1967).
126. S. McVey, I. G. Morrison, and P. L. Pauson, *J. Chem. Soc.*, **1967C**, 1847.
127. M. Rosenblum, *Chem. Ind. (London)*, **1957**, 72.
128. K. Schlögl and M. Fried, *Monatsh.*, **95**, 558 (1964).
129. H. Falk, G. Haller, and K. Schlögl, *Monatsh.*, **98**, 592 (1967).
130. K. Schlögl, H. Falk, and G. Haller, *Monatsh.*, **98**, 82 (1967).
131. J. Tirouflet, J. P. Nonin, G. Tainturier, and R. Dabard, *Compt. Rend.*, **256**, 433 (1963).
132. J. Tirouflet and G. Tainturier, *Tetrahedron Letters*, **1965**, 4177; *Bull. Soc. Chim. France*, **1966**, 595.
133. L. A. Day, British Patent 864,198 (1961); *Chem. Abstr.*, **55**, 17647 (1961).
134. S. Birtwell, British Patent 861,834 (1961); *Chem. Abstr.*, **55**, 16565 (1961).
135. M. Rosenblum, *J. Amer. Chem. Soc.*, **81**, 4530 (1959).
136. M. D. Rausch, *J. Amer. Chem. Soc.*, **82**, 2080 (1960).
137. A. N. Nesmeyanov, V. N. Drozd, V. A. Sazonova, V. L. Romanenko, A. K. Prokof'ev, and L. A. Nikonova, *Izv. Akad. Nauk SSSR, Otd. Khim. Nauk*, **1963**, 667.
138. M. D. Rausch, *J. Org. Chem.*, **29**, 1257 (1964).
139. K. Yamakawa, N. Ishibashi, and K. Arakawa, *Chem. Pharm. Bull. (Tokyo)*, **12**, 119 (1964); *Chem. Abstr.*, **60**, 10712 (1964).
140. S. J. Goldberg and J. S. Crowell, *J. Org. Chem.*, **29**, 996 (1964).
141. S. W. Neuse, E. Quo, and W. C. Howells, *J. Org. Chem.*, **30**, 4071 (1965).

142. A. N. Nesmeyanov, N. S. Kochetkova, and R. B. Materikova, *Dokl. Akad. Nauk SSSR*, **136**, 1096 (1961).
143. N. A. Nesmeyanov and O. A. Reutov, *Dokl. Akad. Nauk SSSR*, **115**, 518 (1957).
144. G. R. Knox, I. G. Morrison, P. L. Pauson, M. A. Sandhu, and W. E. Watts, *J. Chem. Soc.*, **1967C**, 1853.
145. A. N. Nesmeyanov, V. A. Sazonova, and V. N. Drozd, *Dokl. Akad. Nauk SSSR*, **137**, 102 (1961).
146. K. L. Motz, *Dissert. Abstr.*, **29**, 958 (1958).
147. K. L. Rinehart, Jr., and K. L. Motz, *Chem. Ind. (London)*, **1957**, 1150.
148. J. Tirouflet, G. Tainturier, and R. Dabard, *Bull. Soc. Chim. France*, **1963**, 2403.
149. D. E. Bublitz, *Can. J. Chem.*, **42**, 2381 (1964).
150. E. A. Hill and I. S. Buck, *J. Amer. Chem. Soc.*, **83**, 4216 (1961).
151. G. Haller and K. Schlögl, *Monatsh.*, **98**, 603 (1967).
152. I. W. Huffman and R. L. Asbury, *J. Org. Chem.*, **30**, 3941 (1965).
153. B. Gautheron and J. Tirouflet, *Compt. Rend.*, **258**, 6443 (1964).
154. A. Dermand, I. P. Rauoux, and I. Decombe, *Compt. Rend.*, **262C**, 940 (1966).
155. A. N. Nesmeyanov, V. D. Vil'chevskaya, and N. S. Kochetkova, *Izv. Akad. Nauk SSSR, Ser. Khim.*, **1966**, 938.
156. R. Dabard and P. Dixneuf, *Compt. Rend.*, **265C**, 324 (1967).

D. Alkylation

1. General Survey

Ferrocene alkylation under Friedel–Crafts conditions leads to a mixture of monoalkyl and polyalkyl ferrocenes, as shown by Nesmeyanov and Kochetkova.[1,2] The second and third alkyl groups enter primarily the five-membered ring that has already acquired substituents. The alkylating agents used are alkyl halides, olefins, and alcohols. Aluminum chloride is normally used as catalyst, but BF_3, H_3PO_4, $H_3PO_4 \cdot BF_3$, and others are also sometimes used (see Table IX).

Ferrocene alkylation is of little synthetic interest, as it is used mainly with highly branched radicals. Alkylation results in mixtures of isomeric alkyl ferrocenes, which are difficult to separate. Alkyl ferrocenes are usually obtained either by the reduction of acyl ferrocenes or by synthesis from alkyl cyclopentadienes.[3]

Ferrocene alkylation in the presence of aluminum chloride results in several side reactions. One side reaction results in the oxidation of ferrocene to the ferricinium ion to such an extent that the yield of alkylferrocene is considerably decreased. Nesmeyanov, Kochetkova, and co-workers[4] have found that, when a reducing agent is added to the reaction mixture, the yield of alkyl ferrocenes is increased twofold or threefold. Other side reactions, in addition to the radical isomerization normal in Friedel–Crafts reactions, are the destruction of the ferrocene nucleus and exchange between cyclopentadienyl rings with different degrees of substitution.

Alkyl ferrocenes containing *iso*-alkyl groups formed during the reaction process have not been isolated (e.g., as in reaction with *n*-butyl chloride[5]).

However, there is little doubt that they are formed. Isomerization occurs even when ferrocene reacts with 1,2-dichloroethane.* The β-ferrocenylethyl cation (**38**) that forms initially is probably isomerized into the stable α-ferrocenylethyl cation (**39**). The main product of the reaction is 1,1-diferrocenylethane (**40**),[7] and only a small amount of 1,2-diferrocenylethane (**41**) is formed.[8]

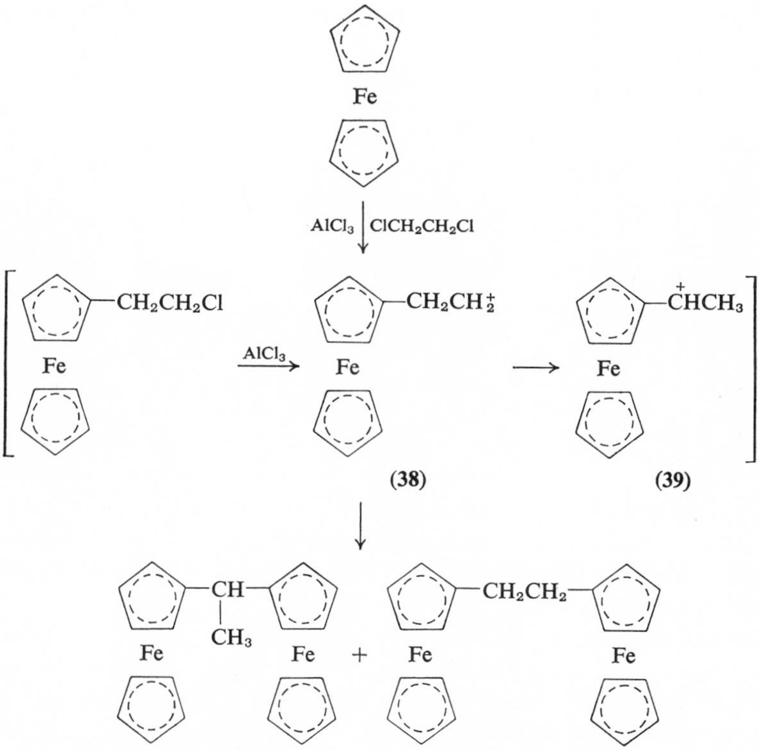

Prolonged heating of ferrocene with aluminum chloride in dichloroethane or benzene[9-13] results in partial decomposition of the ferrocene ring and the formation of a mixture of compounds: one with two ferrocenyl and two cyclopentane groups (**42**),[9-11,13] 1,1'-(1,3-cyclopentyl)ferrocene (**43**), and phenylcyclopentylferrocene.[12] Cyclopentenylferrocene† (**44**) is evidently an intermediate product that dimerizes when treated with aluminum chloride[11,13]

---

* Benzene interaction with 1,2-dichloroethane in the presence of $AlCl_3$ gives only dibenzyl.[6]

† The formation of cyclopentenylferrocene (**44**) or another position of the double bond was observed earlier in ferrocene interaction with hydrogen fluoride.[14]

TABLE IX
Ferrocene Alkylation[a]

Alkylation agent	Solvent	Reaction products[b]	Yield,[c] %	Ref.
CH_3Cl	$n\text{-}C_7H_{16}$	$—CH_3$; $(—CH_3)_2$; $(—CH_3)_n$	—	2
CH_3Br	$n\text{-}C_6H_{14}$	$(—CH_3)_5$[d]	—	17
C_2H_5Br	Petroleum ether	$—C_2H_5$;	18	2
		$—(C_2H_5)_2$	20	
	C_2H_5Br	$—C_2H_5$;	4	1
		$—(C_2H_5)_2$;	3.5	
		$—(C_2H_5)_3$	3.5	
	$n\text{-}C_7H_{16}$[e]	$—C_2H_5$; $—(C_2H_5)_2$; $—(C_2H_5)_3$	76–84[f]	4
$ClCH_2CH_2Cl$	$ClCH_2CH_2Cl$	$—CH_2CH_2C_5H_4FeC_5H_5$	—	8
		$—CH(CH_3)C_5H_4FeC_5H_5$	—	7, 8
$(CH_3)_2CHCl$	Petroleum ether	$—CH(CH_3)_2$;	—	2
		$—(C_3H_7)_2$		
$n\text{-}C_4H_9Cl$	C_4H_9Cl	$n\text{-}C_4H_9—$;	7.6	1
		$(n\text{-}C_4H_9—)_2$[d];	5.2	
		$(n\text{-}C_4H_9—)_5$	16	
$(CH_3)_3CCl$	$ClCH_2CH_2Cl$[g]	$1,1',3,3'\text{-}[—C(CH_3)_3]_4$	68	19
		$—C(CH_3)_3$;		
	$ClCH_2CH_2Cl$	$1,1'\text{-}[—C(CH_3)_3]_2$;	26	19
		$1,3\text{-}[—C(CH_3)_3]_2$	5	
		$1,1',3\text{-}[—C(CH_3)_3]_3$		
	Petroleum ether	$—C(CH_3)_3$; $[—C(CH_3)_3]_2$; $[—C(CH_3)_3]_4$	—	20

Compound	Solvent	Products		Ref.
	$n\text{-}C_7H_{16}{}^e$	—C(CH$_3$)$_3$;	—	4
		1,3-[—C(CH$_3$)$_3$]$_2$?;	16	
		1,1',3-[—C(CH$_3$)$_3$]$_3$?;	12	
		1,1',3,3'-[—C(CH$_3$)$_3$]$_4$?	40	18
	Petroleum ether^h	—C(CH$_3$)$_3$;	18	
		[—C(CH$_3$)$_3$]$_2$?;	7	
		[—C(CH$_3$)$_3$]$_3$?		
(CH$_3$)$_2$C(C$_2$H$_5$)Cl	$n\text{-}C_7H_{16}$	—C(CH$_3$)$_2$C$_2$H$_5$;	14	20
		[—C(CH$_3$)$_2$C$_2$H$_5$]$_2{}^d$	15	
(CH$_3$)$_3$CCH$_2$CH$_2$Cl	ClCH$_2$CH$_2$Cl^g	1,1',3,3'-[—CH$_2$CH$_2$C(CH$_3$)$_3$]$_4$	—	19
$n\text{-}C_{10}H_{21}$Cl	CH$_2$Cl$_2$	$n\text{-}C_{10}H_{21}$—;	—	21
		1,1'-($n\text{-}C_{10}H_{21}$—)$_2$	—	
C$_6$H$_5$CH$_2$Cl	C$_6$H$_5$CH$_2$Cl	—CH$_2$C$_6$H$_5$	42	1
(C$_6$H$_5$)$_3$CCl	CH$_2$Cl$_2$	1,1'-[—C(C$_6$H$_5$)$_3$]$_2$;	—	22
		[—C(C$_6$H$_5$)$_3$]$_n$		
	—	1,1'-[—C(C$_6$H$_5$)$_3$]$_2$	40	22
(C$_6$H$_5$)$_3$CBF$_4$	CH$_2$Cl$_2{}^i$	—C(C$_6$H$_5$)$_3$;	41	23
		1,1'-[—C(C$_6$H$_5$)$_3$]$_2$	44	
CH$_2$=CH$_2$	$n\text{-}C_7H_{16}$	—C$_2$H$_5$;	20	17
		(—C$_2$H$_5$)$_2$,^{d}	5.5	
		(—C$_2$H$_5$)$_n$	4.5	
CH$_3$CH=CH$_2$	$n\text{-}C_7H_{16}$	—CH(CH$_3$)$_2$;	30	17
		[—CH(CH$_3$)$_2$]$_2$,^{d}	14	
		[—CH(CH$_3$)$_2$]$_n$	13	
(CH$_3$)$_2$C=CH$_2$	$n\text{-}C_7H_{16}$	—C(CH$_3$)$_3$;	28	24, 20, 17
		[—C(CH$_3$)$_3$]$_2{}^d$	37	

(continued)

225

TABLE IX (continued)

Alkylation agent	Solvent	Reaction products[b]	Yield,[c] %	Ref.
		$[-C(CH_3)_3]_3$	43	17
		$[-C(CH_3)_3]_n$	35	24
	$n\text{-}C_7H_{16}{}^j$	$-C(CH_3)_3$;	45	24
		$[-C(CH_3)_3]_2$;[d]	26	
	$n\text{-}C_7H_{16}{}^h$	$-C(CH_3)_3$;	50	24
		$[-C(CH_3)_3]_2$;[d]	43	
		$[-C(CH_3)_3]_n$	7	
$(CH_3)_2CHCH=CH_2$	$n\text{-}C_7H_{16}{}^j$	$-CH(CH_3)CH(CH_3)_2$;	25	24
		$[-CH(CH_3)CH(CH_3)_2]_2$[d]	20	
$\underset{\underset{CH_3}{\mid}}{CH}(CH_2)_3CH=CH_2$	$n\text{-}C_7H_{16}{}^j$	$-CH(CH_3)(CH_2)_3CH(CH_3)_2$;	80	25, 24
		$[-CH(CH_3)(CH_2)_3CH(CH_3)_2]_2$;[d]	25	
		$[-CH(CH_3)(CH_2)_3CH(CH_3)_2]_3$	15	25
$\underset{\underset{CH_3}{\mid}}{CH}(CH_2)_7CH=CH_2$	$n\text{-}C_7H_{16}{}^j$	$-CH(CH_3)(CH_2)_7CH(CH_3)_2$;	60	24, 25
		$[-CH(CH_3)(CH_2)_7CH(CH_3)_2]_2$	25	24
		$[-CH(CH_3)(CH_2)_7CH(CH_3)_2]_n$	15	

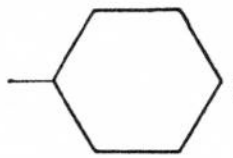

Reactant	Solvent	Product substituent	30	25
(C₆H₅)₂C=CH₂	n-C$_7$H$_{16}$[j]	(methylcyclohexyl)— ; (cyclohexyl)$_2$— ;[d] (cyclohexyl)$_3$—	22	22
(CH₃)₃COH	—[k]		10	22
n-C$_5$H$_{11}$OH	CH₂Cl₂	—CH₂CH(C₆H₅)₂;	15	
		1,1'-[—CH₂CH(C₆H₅)₂]₂	46	22
	—[l]	—C(CH₃)₃;	67	22
		[—C(CH₃)₃]$_n$	—	22
		—C(CH₃)₃;	4	
		[C(CH₃)₃]₃	50	
n-C$_5$H$_{11}$OH	CH₂Cl₂	(—C₅H₁₁)$_n$	—	21
(CH₃)₃CCH₂CH₂OH	CH₂Cl₂	—CH₂CH₂C(CH₃)₃	—	21
	—[m]	(i-C₆H₁₃)$_n$	—	21
n-C$_{10}$H$_{21}$Cl	CH₂Cl₂	n-C$_{10}$H$_{21}$—;	—	21
		1,1'-(n-C$_{10}$H$_{21}$)₂	—	
(CH₃)₂C(OH)C₆H₅	—[g]	1,1'-[—C(CH₃)₂C₆H₅]₂	20	22
		1,1'-[C(CH₃)₂C₆H₅]₂	60	22
(C₆H₅)₂CHOH	—	1,1'-[—CH(C₆H₅)₂]₂;	55	22
		[—CH(C₆H₅)₂]₄	—	

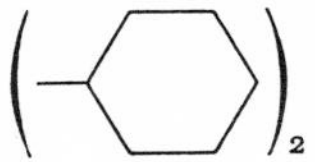

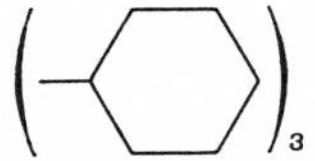

227

(continued)

TABLE IX (continued)

Acylation agent	Solvent	Reaction products[b]	Yield,[c] %	Ref.
	CH_2Cl_2	$1,1'\text{-}[-CH(C_6H_5)_2]_2]_2$;	10	22
		$[-CH(C_6H_5)_2]_6$	72	22
	Dioxane[n]	$1,1'\text{-}[-CH(C_6H_5)_2]_2]_2$;	43	22
		$[-CH(C_6H_5)_2]_n$	12	22
$(C_6H_5)_3COH$	—	$-C(C_6H_5)_3$;	78	22
		$1,1'\text{-}[-C(C_6H_5)_3]_2$	95	
	CH_2Cl_2	$1,1'\text{-}[-C(C_6H_5)_3]_2$	53	22
$C_5H_5FeC_5H_4CH_2OH$	—[o]	$-CH_2C_5H_4FeC_5H_5$	29	26

[a] Unless otherwise indicated, reaction conducted with $AlCl_3$.

[b] Only the entering alkyl groups, their number, and their position in the ferrocene nucleus are indicated. If the position is not specified, it means that it was not established in the reference. A question mark (?) indicates that the structure has not been strictly proved.

[c] The yield refers to the amount of ferrocene taken for reaction.

[d] Homoannular.

[e] Reaction with $AlCl_3$ and $LiAlH_4$.

[f] The yield is for the mixture, with no individual products isolated.

[g] Reaction with $AlCl_3$ or $ZnCl_2$.

[h] Reaction with $BF_3 \cdot O(C_2H_5)_2$.

[i] Reaction without catalyst.

[j] Reaction with $H_3PO_4 \cdot BF_3$.

[k] Reaction with $AlCl_3$ and H_3PO_4.

[l] Reaction with BF_3, without solvent.

[m] Reaction with H_3PO_4, without solvent.

[n] Reaction with $SnCl_4$.

[o] Reaction with H_2SO_4.

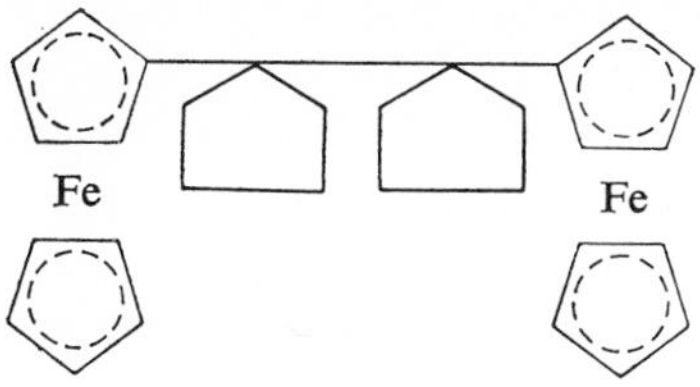

(42) 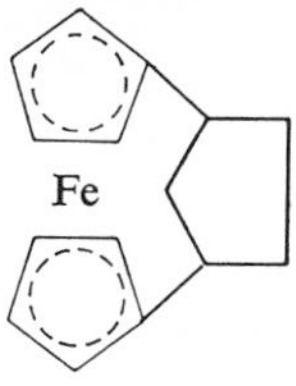   (43) 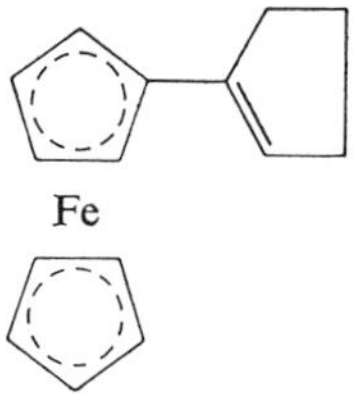   (44)

or undergoes intramolecular alkylation and forms the bridged compound (43).[12]

Nesmeyanov and Kochetkova[11] have shown that heating cyclopentenyl-ferrocene with aluminum chloride in heptane gives compound (42) along with products of higher molecular weights. The structure of compound (42) was suggested by Nesmeyanov and Kochetkova,[11] who studied its NMR spectrum.* When alkyl ferrocenes are heated with aluminum chloride in dichloromethane or with an equimolar mixture of 1,1'-dialkylferrocene and ferrocene, the same equilibrium mixture of all three compounds is found.[16]

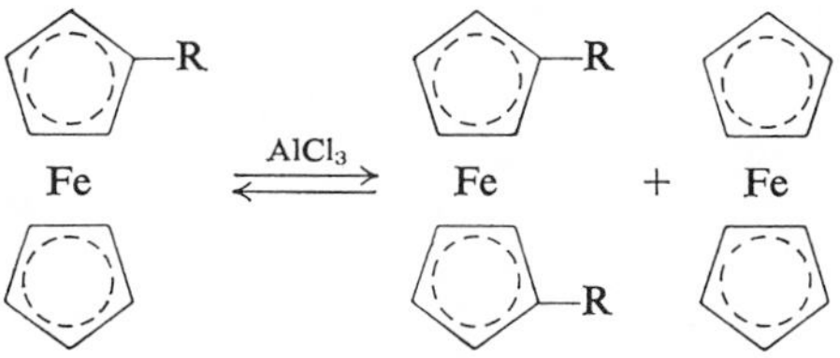

$$[R = CH_3, C_2H_5, n\text{-}C_3H_7, n\text{-}C_4H_9, CH_2CH(CH_3)_2]$$

Neither a homoannular isomer nor alkyl ferrocenes with an isomerized alkyl group have been discovered. Therefore the reaction must involve exchange of cyclopentadienyl rings rather than transalkylation.

2. Examples of Syntheses: tert-Butylferrocene[18]

To a mixture of 186 g (1.0 mole) of ferrocene and 93 g (1.0 mole) of *tert*-butyl chloride in 1 liter of olefin-free petroleum ether (b.p. 65–67°) is added 213 g (1.5 moles) of boron trifluoride etherate. The mixture is heated to reflux for 24 hr with stirring and is then poured into ice water containing potassium carbonate. The ether layer is separated and dried.

---

* The NMR spectrum of compound (42) obtained earlier[15] was misinterpreted. Compound (42) was given the incorrect structure of "pentaethanodiferrocene."[8,9] Ferrocene interaction with benzene in the presence of $AlCl_3$ is also discussed in Chapter 3.

After the solvent is removed, the residue is chromatographed on a short column of Alcoa alumina with petroleum ether (35–37°) as solvent in order to remove some decomposition products. Analysis of this material by vapor-phase chromatography showed that it contained four materials: ferrocene (30%), *tert*-butylferrocene (45%), and two unknowns in 18 and 7% quantities, respectively. The latter two materials may well be bis(*tert*-butyl) and tris(*tert*-butyl) ferrocenes. This mixture is dissolved in 100 ml of petroleum ether (35–37°) and placed in a refrigerator. After a few hours the ferrocene precipitates and is collected by filtration. This technique is repeated until only 5% of the original ferrocene remains.

The red oil that remains is purified by repeated passes through a 4-ft column of Merck alumina. Petroleum ether (35–37°) is used as both developer and eluent. Final purification is effected by distillation through a Todd column. A red liquid (97 g, 40%), b.p. 99–100° (0.5 mm), is collected. (This was shown by vapor-phase chromatography to be pure *tert*-butylferrocene.)

References

1. A. N. Nesmeyanov and N. S. Kochetkova, *Dokl. Akad. Nauk SSSR*, **109**, 543 (1956).
2. A. N. Nesmeyanov and N. S. Kochetkova, *Dokl. Akad. Nauk SSSR*, **114**, 800 (1957).
3. M. Rosenblum, *Chemistry of the Iron Group Metallocenes: Ferrocene, Ruthenocene, Osmocene*, Part 1, Wiley, New York, 1965, p. 120.
4. A. N. Nesmeyanov, N. S. Kochetkova, S. V. Vitt, V. B. Bondarev, and Ye. I. Kovshov, *Dokl. Akad. Nauk SSSR*, **156**, 99 (1964).
5. A. N. Nesmeyanov and N. S. Kochetkova, *Dokl. Akad. Nauk SSSR*, **109**, 543 (1956).
6. G. S. Kolesnikov, V. V. Korshak, and G. V. Smirnova, *Izv. Akad. Nauk SSSR, Otd. Khim. Nauk*, **1955**, 172.
7. K. L. Rinehart, Jr., P. A. Kittle, and A. F. Ellis, *J. Amer. Chem. Soc.*, **82**, 2082 (1960).
8. A. N. Nesmeyanov, N. S. Kochetkova, and R. B. Materikova, *Dokl. Akad. Nauk SSSR*, **136**, 1096 (1961).
9. A. N. Nesmeyanov and N. S. Kochetkova, *Dokl. Akad. Nauk SSSR*, **126**, 307 (1959).
10. S. I. Goldberg, *J. Amer. Chem. Soc.*, **84**, 3022 (1962).
11. A. N. Nesmeyanov, N. S. Kochetkova, P. V. Petrovskii, and E. L. Fedin, *Dokl. Akad. Nauk SSSR*, **152**, 875 (1963).
12. S. G. Cottis and H. Rosenberg, *Chem. Ind. (London)*, **1963**, 860.
13. S. G. Cottis and H. Rosenberg, *Polymer Letters*, **2**, 295 (1964).
14. V. Weinmayr, *J. Amer. Chem. Soc.*, **77**, 3009 (1955).
15. E. Z. Utyanskaya, *Zh. Fiz. Khim.*, **35**, 2611 (1961).
16. D. E. Bublitz, *Can. J. Chem.*, **42**, 2381 (1964).
17. A. N. Nesmeyanov and N. S. Kochetkova, *Izv. Akad. Nauk SSSR, Otd. Khim. Nauk*, **1958**, 242.
18. R. A. Benkeser and J. L. Bach, *J. Amer. Chem. Soc.*, **86**, 890 (1964).

19. T. Leigh, *J. Chem. Soc.*, **1964**, 3294.
20. A. N. Nesmeyanov and N. S. Kochetkova, *Dokl. Akad. Nauk SSSR*, **117**, 92 (1957).
21. M. Vogel, M. Rausch, and H. Rosenberg, *J. Org. Chem.*, **22**, 1016 (1957).
22. E. W. Neuse and D. S. Trifan, *J. Amer. Chem. Soc.*, **84**, 1850 (1962).
23. P. L. Pauson, M. A. Sandhu, and W. E. Watts, *J. Chem. Soc.*, **1966**, 251.
24. Ya. M. Paushkin, T. P. Vishnyakova, T. A. Sokolinskaya, K. I. Zimina, and G. G. Kotova, *Neftekhimiya*, **3**, 280 (1963).
25. T. P. Vishnyakova, Ya. M. Paushkin, and T. A. Sokolinskaya, *Zh. Obshch. Khim.*, **33**, 3685 (1963).
26. P. L. Pauson and W. E. Watts, *J. Chem. Soc.*, **1962**, 3880.

E. Sulfonation

1. Ferrocene Sulfonation

The first attempts at sulfonating ferrocene with concentrated sulfuric acid were unsuccessful. Ferrocene, when dissolved in concentrated sulfuric acid, is oxidized to the ferricinium cation and thus no ferrocenesulfonic acid can be obtained. Later studies on the sulfonation of ferrocene have shown the reaction to proceed in high yield with complexes of sulfur trioxide or with sulfuric or chlorosulfonic acid in acetic anhydride.[1-3]

Ferrocene in dichloroethane is sulfonated by pyridine–sulfur trioxide in a way similar to the sulfonation of five-membered heterocyclics. Depending on the length of heating, ferrocenemonosulfonic or ferrocenedisulfonic acid is formed. Sulfonation by dioxane–sulfur trioxide starts at low temperature and is finished at room temperature. If equimolar amounts of the reactants are taken, ferrocenemonosulfonic acid is obtained (yield 62% on the basis of converted ferrocene) and is isolated as a hydrated crystal.

$$(C_5H_5)_2Fe \quad \begin{array}{c} \xrightarrow[\text{ClCH}_2\text{CH}_2\text{Cl}]{\text{SO}_3 \cdot \text{dioxane}} C_5H_3FeC_5H_4SO_3H \cdot 2H_2O \\[2ex] \xrightarrow[\text{ClCH}_2\text{CH}_2\text{Cl}]{\text{SO}_3 \cdot \text{dioxane}} Fe(C_5H_4SO_3H)_2 \cdot C_4H_8O_2 \end{array} \tag{36}$$

If the ratio of dioxane–sulfur trioxide to ferrocene is 3:1, 1,1'-ferrocenedisulfonic acid is formed (yield 85%, isolated as a complex with dioxane[1]).

In sulfonating with sulfuric[2] or chlorosulfonic[3] acid in acetic anhydride, ferrocenemonosulfonic or 1,1'-disulfonic acid is also formed, depending on the reaction time and the ratios of the reactants.

Ferrocenesulfonic acids are not as hygroscopic as arenesulfonic acids and are more readily isolated as the pure compounds. It should be noted that ferrocenemonosulfonic acid, unlike other sulfonic acids, is only slightly soluble in water. The free acid also readily forms ferrocenesulfonyl chloride with phosphorus(III) chloride. This reaction is not typical of the benzene-series sulfonic acids.

Lead, barium, iron, S-benzylthiuronium, and ammonium salts of ferrocenesulfonic acids have been obtained.[1-3] The synthesis of methyl esters and diethylamides of ferrocenesulfonic acids as well as of the corresponding ferrocenesulfonyl chlorides[1,2,4-6] has been described. The reduction of ferrocenemonosulfonyl chloride to thioferrocenol,[3,4] the reduction of the two ferrocenesulfonyl chlorides to the sulfinic acids,[4,5] and the properties of these acids have been studied.[5]

Exchange of the sulfonic group for other substituents fails in the ferrocene series.

2. Sulfonation of Ferrocene Derivatives

Only ferrocene derivatives with an electron-withdrawing substituent have been sulfonated. Sulfonation of acetylferrocene,[6] ferrocenecarboxylic acid,[7] and phenylferrocene[8] occurs predominantly in the free five-membered ring.

$$R—C_5H_4FeC_5H_5 \xrightarrow[ClCH_2CH_2Cl]{SO_3 \cdot dioxane} R—C_5H_4FeC_5H_4SO_3H \qquad (37)$$

$$(R = —COCH_3, —COOH, —COOCH_3, —C_6H_5)$$

Sulfonation of tris(ferrocenyl)phosphine oxide causes substitution only in the free five-membered rings.[9]

$$(C_5H_5FeC_5H_4)_3PO \xrightarrow[(CH_3CO)_2O]{H_2SO_4} (HO_3SC_5H_4FeC_5H_4)_3PO \qquad (38)$$

Acyl halides, amides, and esters have been obtained from 1-carboxy-1'-ferrocenesulfonic acid, the substitution involving both the carboxy and the sulfonic groups.[7]

A disubstituted ferrocene, 1,1'-di-(carbomethoxy)ferrocene, has been sulfonated by sulfur trioxide in dichloroethane.[6]

$$Fe(CH_3OOCC_5H_4)_2 \xrightarrow[ClCH_2CH_2Cl]{SO_3} CH_3OOCC_5H_4FeC_5H_3(SO_3H)COOCH_3 \quad (39)$$

However, 1,1'-diacylated ferrocenes, 1,1'-ferrocenedisulfonic acid, and the corresponding diacyl dichloride could not be sulfonated. With sulfur trioxide in dichloroethane, 1,1'-diacetylferrocene exchanged its acetyls for sulfonic groups.[6]

$$Fe(C_5H_4COCH_3)_2 \xrightarrow[2. PCl_5]{1. SO_3, ClCH_2CH_2Cl} Fe(C_5H_4SO_2Cl)_2 \qquad (40)$$

3. Examples of Syntheses

a. Ferrocenemonosulfonic Acid.[1] A suspension of 55 g (0.327 mole) of dioxane–sulfur trioxide in 200 ml of dichloroethane is gradually added to 58 g (0.312 mole) of ferrocene dissolved in 250 ml of dry dichloroethane at 0–5°. The mixture is left for 30 min at 0–15°, for 1.5 hr at room temperature, and then poured into cold water. Unreacted ferrocene (31.5 g, 54%) is recovered from the dichloroethane solution. The water solution is evaporated almost to dryness on a water bath. The solid residue, ferrocenemonosulfonic acid, is washed with 40 ml of concentrated hydrochloric acid. The yield is 13.6 g (62% based on the converted amount of ferrocene).

Ferrocenemonosulfonic acid is sparingly soluble in ether, benzene, acetone, and dioxane. It is somewhat more soluble in methanol or ethanol and slightly soluble in cold water. The solid sulfonic acid contains two molecules of water, as shown by elemental analysis and potentiometric measurement of the equivalent weight; m.p. 117–118° in a sealed capillary. When heated to over 200°, the acid decomposes.

   b. Ferrocenedisulfonic Acid. Two sulfonation procedures have been reported:

   (i) Ferrocene Sulfonation with Dioxane–Sulfur Trioxide.[1] A suspension of 29 g (0.172 mole) of dioxane–sulfur trioxide in 50 ml of dichloroethane is added to a suspension of 10.7 g (0.0575 mole) of ferrocene in 10 ml of dichloroethane at 20–30°. The mixture is left overnight at room temperature. A precipitate of pure ferrocenedisulfonic acid is filtered, washed with dioxane and dichloroethane, and dried in a vacuum desiccator for 24 hr. The acid contains one molecule of solvated dioxane. The yield is 21.1 g (85% of the theoretical amount). When dried in a vacuum desiccator for a long time, ferrocenedisulfonic acid readily loses the solvated dioxane molecule.

   (ii) Ferrocene Sulfonation with Sulfuric Acid in Acetic Anhydride[1] (Based on Weinmayr's Procedure[2]). A 10-ml (0.188 mole) volume of concentrated sulfuric acid is gradually added at 0–5° to 9.3 g (0.05 mole) of ferrocene dissolved in 150 ml of acetic anhydride. The mixture is left for 12 hr at 0°. Precipitated ferrocenedisulfonic acid is filtered off, washed with a small amount of acetic anhydride, and carefully washed with benzene. The yield is 10.8 g (51% of the theoretical amount); m.p. 80–90°. Attempts at recrystallization failed.

   Ferrocenedisulfonic acid obtained in this manner contains four molecules of solvated water, as shown by elemental analysis and the potentiometric determination of molecular weight. Purer ferrocenedisulfonic acid can be obtained if the above compound is extracted in a Soxhlet apparatus for a long time with benzene. Partial removal of the benzene causes precipitation of gold-yellow crystals. They also contain four molecules of solvated water and yield the same methyl ester as above. The melting point is 123–125° in a sealed capillary.

References

1. A. N. Nesmeyanov, E. G. Perevalova, and S. S. Churanov, *Dokl. Akad. Nauk SSSR*, **114**, 335 (1957).
2. V. Weinmayr, *J. Amer. Chem. Soc.*, **77**, 3009 (1955).

3. G. R. Knox and P. L. Pauson, *J. Chem. Soc.*, **1958**, 692.
4. A. N. Nesmeyanov, E. G. Perevalova, S. S. Churanov, and O. A. Nesmeyanova, *Dokl. Akad. Nauk SSSR*, **119**, 949 (1958).
5. E. G. Perevalova, O. A. Nesmeyanova, and I. G. Lukyanova, *Dokl. Akad. Nauk SSSR*, **132**, 853 (1960).
6. N. A. Nesmeyanov and B. N. Strunin, *Dokl. Akad. Nauk SSSR*, **137**, 106 (1961).
7. N. A. Nesmeyanov and O. A. Reutov, *Izv. Akad. Nauk SSSR, Otd. Khim. Nauk*, **1959**, 926.
8. A. N. Nesmeyanov, E. G. Perevalova, S. P. Gubin, T. V. Nikitina, A. A. Ponomarenko, and L. S. Shilovtseva, *Dokl. Akad. Nauk SSSR*, **129**, 888 (1961).
9. A. N. Nesmeyanov, D. N. Kursanov, V. D. Vil'chevskaya, N. S. Kochetkova, V. N. Setkina, and Yu. N. Novikov, *Dokl. Akad. Nauk SSSR*, **160**, 1090 (1965).

F. Dialkylaminomethylation

1. Ferrocene Dialkylaminomethylation

Ferrocene reacts with formaldehyde and amines in the same manner as phenols. Ferrocene dialkylaminomethylation was performed in 1956 by Hauser and Lindsay.[1,2] *N,N*-Dimethylaminomethylferrocene was obtained in a yield greater than 50%. The reaction proceeds when ferrocene is heated together with formaldehyde and dimethylamine or tetramethyldiaminomethane in acetic acid. The yield of *N,N*-dimethylaminomethylferrocene (**45**) becomes much larger in the presence of phosphoric acid.[3]* Dimethylamine, piperidine,[3] and diethylamine[5] are also used as the amino components. Pauson and co-workers[6] found that prolonged heating (20 hr at 110–115°) gave 1,1'-bis(*N,N*-dimethylaminomethyl)ferrocene (**46**) in 13% yield together with the monosubstituted compound (77%). Earlier attempts to introduce the second dimethylaminomethyl via aminomethylation were unsuccessful.[5,7]

$$(41)$$

(**45**)　　　　　　　　(**46**)

Dimethylaminomethylferrocene methiodide is of great synthetic value. This is due both to its high reactivity and of the absence of other available ferrocene derivatives that permit easy ferrocenylmethylation. A review of the synthetic applications of trialkylferrocenylammonium salts has been presented by Rosenblum.[8] Soviet papers are also cited in a review by Nesmeyanov and Perevalova.[7]

---

* An experimental procedure of ferrocene dimethylaminoalkylation has been described by Lednicer and Hauser.[4]

2. Dialkylaminomethylation of Ferrocene Derivatives

Dialkylaminomethylation of ferrocene derivatives was studied by Nesmeyanov et al.[5,9–12] and Pauson et al.[13–17]

Methylferrocene[10,13,18,22] and ethylferrocene,[9] when dimethyl aminomethylated in the presence of phosphoric acid, give a mixture of isomeric mono- [compounds (47), (48), and (49)] and di(N,N-dimethylaminomethyl)-alkyl ferrocenes [compounds (50) and (51)].

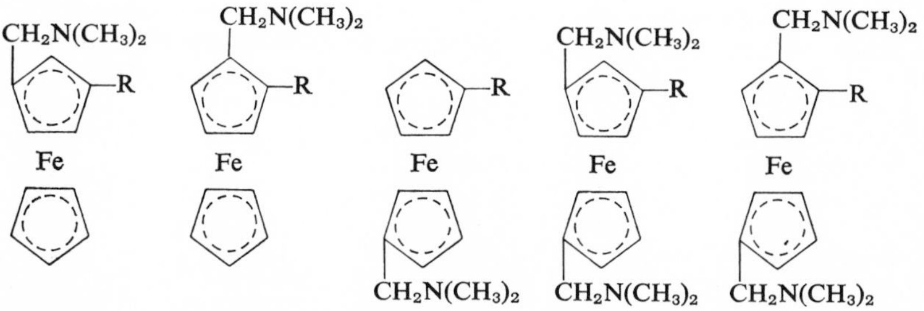

The yield of the diamines (50) and (51) is 7–15%. Monoaminomethylated alkyl ferrocenes (47), (48), and (49) are obtained in 70–80% yield. The amount of homoannular isomers (47) and (48) is three to four times as great as that of the heteroannular compound (50), and the amount of the 1,3-isomer (47) is two to three times as great as that of the 1,2-isomer (48). Hence aminomethylation takes place chiefly at position 3. The structures were assigned to products on the basis of infrared[9,10] and proton-magnetic-resonance spectra and in some cases by independent synthesis.[13,18]

Pauson et al. have carried out the aminomethylation of methylthio,[15] 1,1'-bis(methylthio)[15] methoxy,[16] and dimethoxy[16] ferrocenes. The significantly enhanced preference for homoannular over heteroannular attack found in alkyl ferrocenes is also observed in the case of monomethylthio and monomethoxy ferrocenes, but the relative reactivities of the 2- and 3-positions are reversed. The preferred location of aminomethylation of 1,1'-bis(methylthio)[15] and dimethoxy[16] ferrocenes is at the 2-position.[17]

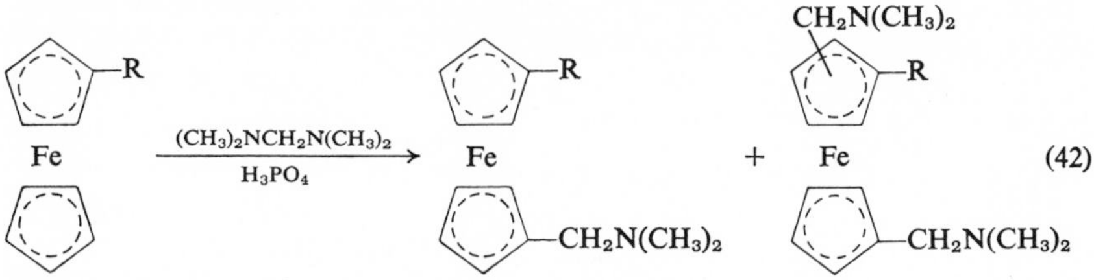

$(R = C_6H_5, p\text{-}CH_3C_6H_4, Cl)$

In the case of ferrocene derivatives with weak electron-withdrawing substituents, such as phenyl, p-tolyl, and chloro,[12] the free five-membered ring is predominantly aminomethylated.

The ratio of heteroannular to homoannular isomers is about 5:1. Two homoannular isomers were isolated with phenylferrocene.[12]

Pauson, Sandhu, and Watts[6] obtained 1,1'-bis(N,N-dimethylamino-methyl)ferrocene (46) in 23% yield by prolonged heating of N,N-dimethyl-aminomethylferrocene (45) together with tetramethyldiaminomethane in the presence of phosphoric acid.

Both β-ferrocenylethylamine and methyl (β-ferrocenylethyl)amine[19-21] (52) react with formaldehyde and formic acid to produce N-methyltetra-hydropyridoferrocene (53).

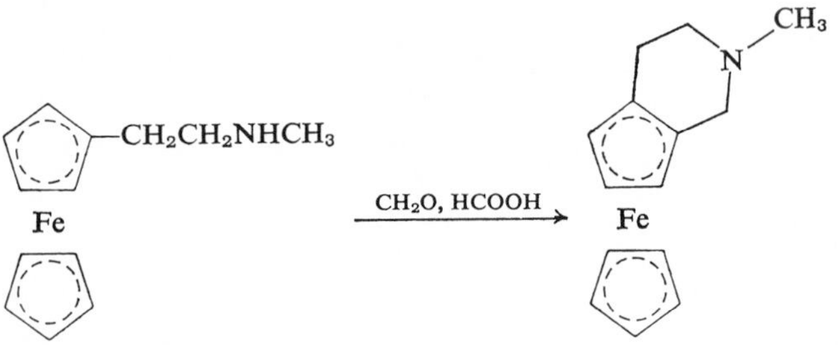

$$\text{(52)} \xrightarrow{\text{CH}_2\text{O, HCOOH}} \text{(53)} \tag{43}$$

This reaction may be an example of an intramolecular aminomethylation.

REFERENCES

1. C. R. Hauser and J. K. Lindsay, J. Org. Chem., 21, 382 (1956).
2. J. K. Lindsay and C. R. Hauser, J. Org. Chem., 22, 355 (1957).
3. J. M. Osgerby and P. L. Pauson, J. Chem. Soc., 1958, 656.
4. D. Lednicer and C. R. Hauser, Organic Syntheses, 40, 31 (1960).
5. A. N. Nesmeyanov, E. G. Perevalova, L. S. Shilovtseva, and Yu. A. Ustynjuk, Dokl. Akad. Nauk SSSR, 124, 331 (1959).
6. P. L. Pauson, M. A. Sandhu, and W. E. Watts, J. Chem. Soc., 1966, 251.
7. A. N. Nesmeyanov and E. G. Perevalova, Ann. N.Y. Acad. Sci., 125, 67 (1965).
8. M. Rosenblum, Chemistry of the Iron Group Metallocenes: Ferrocene, Ruthenocene, Osmocene, Part 1, Wiley, New York, 1965.
9. L. S. Shilovtseva, E. G. Perevalova, V. A. Nefedov, and A. N. Nesmeyanov, Izv. Akad. Nauk SSSR, Ser. Khim., 1966, 2239.
10. A. N. Nesmeyanov, E. G. Perevalova, L. S. Shilovtseva, and A. A. Ponomarenko, Izv. Akad. Nauk SSSR, Ser. Khim., 1967, 171.
11. A. N. Nesmeyanov, E. G. Perevalova, A. P. Gubin, T. V. Nikitina, A. A. Ponomar-enko, and L. S. Shilovtseva, Dokl. Akad. Nauk SSSR, 139, 888 (1961).
12. A. N. Nesmeyanov, E. G. Perevalova, and L. S. Shilovtseva, Izv. Akad. Nauk SSSR, Otd. Khim. Nauk, 1962, 1767.

13. P. L. Pauson, M. A. Sandhu, W. E. Watts, R. C. Haley, and G. R. Knox, *J. Chem. Soc.*, **1967C**, 1851.
14. G. R. Knox, P. L. Pauson, and G. V. D. Tiers, *Chem. Ind.* (*London*), **1959**, 1046.
15. G. R. Knox, I. G. Morrison, and P. L. Pauson, *J. Chem. Soc.*, **1967C**, 1842.
16. S. McVey, I. G. Morrison, and P. L. Pauson, *J. Chem. Soc.*, **1967C**, 1847.
17. G. R. Knox, I. G. Morrison, P. L. Pauson, M. A. Sandhu, and W. E. Watts, *J. Chem. Soc.*, **1967C**, 1853.
18. R. Dabard and P. Dixneuf, *Compt. Rend.*, **265C**, 324 (1967).
19. J. M. Osgerby and P. L. Pauson, *Chem. Ind.* (*London*), **1958**, 1144.
20. J. M. Osgerby and P. L. Pauson, *Chem. Ind.* (*London*), **1958**, 196.
21. D. Lednicer, J. K. Lindsay, and C. R. Hauser, *J. Org. Chem.*, **23**, 653 (1958).
22. H. Falk, G. Haller, and K. Schlögl, *Monatsh.*, **98**, 592 (1967).

G. Metalation

Ferrocene metalation with mercury(II) acetate and *n*-butyllithium was one of the first hydrogen-substitution reactions performed. Recently a number of substituted ferrocenes have been metalated.

At present mercury, sodium, and especially lithium derivatives of ferrocene are widely used to synthesize various substituted ferrocenes (see Chapter 2). Mercurated organic compounds have also been used to study the mechanism of electrophilic substitution in the ferrocene series.

1. Ferrocene Metalation

Ferrocene is easily metalated under very mild conditions. Ferrocene metalations with mercury(II) acetate,[1,2] organolithium,[1,3–5] and organosodium compounds[6,7] have been studied.

Ferrocene was mercurated first by Nesmeyanov and co-workers.[1] The reaction proceeds at room temperature. Even with a large excess of ferrocene over mercury(II) acetate both monomercurated and dimercurated ferrocenes invariably form.[2]

$$(C_5H_5)_2Fe \xrightarrow[\text{2. KCl}]{\text{1. Hg(OCOCH}_3)_2} FeC_{10}H_9HgCl + Fe(C_5H_4HgCl)_2 \qquad (44)$$

At equimolar ratios of reagents approximately equimolar amounts of ferrocenylmercury(II) chloride and ferrocenylene bis[mercury(II) chloride] are formed. The total yield with respect to mercury(II) acetate is almost quantitative, and about 30% of ferrocene remains unreacted (see mercuration technique in subsection 3-*a*). This ratio of the reaction products proves that if a hydrogen atom of ferrocene is replaced by mercury, further mercuration is facilitated. Only heteroannular ferrocenylene bis[mercury(II) chloride] has been isolated (the structure was established spectroscopically). This fact is very interesting from the point of view of the substituent effect on the reactivity of various positions in the ferrocene nucleus, but it cannot be discussed until it has been proved that the homoannular isomer does not form and the mechanism of the mercuration reaction has been established.

Ferrocene is metalated with organolithium and organosodium compounds. When ferrocene interacts with n-butyllithium, a mixture of monolithium-ferrocene and 1,1-dilithiumferrocene is formed.[1-5,8]

$$(C_5H_5)_2Fe \xrightarrow{n\text{-}C_4H_9Li} FeC_{10}H_9Li + Fe(C_5H_4Li)_2 \xrightarrow{CO_2} FeC_{10}H_9COOH + Fe(C_5H_4COOH)_2 \quad (45)$$

The total yield of monolithiumferrocene and dilithiumferrocene is about 30% [1,2,5] when ether is used as solvent, whereas in a mixture of ether and tetrahydrofuran (1:1) it is $70-78\%$,[3,4] as determined by the yield of acids after carboxylation. The ratio of monolithiumferrocene and dilithiumferrocene is approximately equimolar if there is a fourfold to sixfold excess of n-butyllithium.[3,4] The ratio changes with the amount of metalating agent, duration of reaction, and reaction temperature.

Goldberg and co-workers[9] have suggested a technique of ferrocene metalation with an equimolar amount of n-butyllithium in ether and a small amount of hexane. They assert that only monolithiumferrocene is formed (25% yield). Schlögl and Fried[10] attempted to isolate crystalline ferrocenyllithium.

Ferrocene interaction with organosodium compounds (phenylsodium[6] and n-amylsodium[7,9]) yields chiefly 1,1'-disodiumferrocene (see subsection

$$(C_5H_5)_2Fe \xrightarrow[n\text{-}C_5H_{11}Na]{C_6H_5Na \text{ or}} Fe(C_5H_4Na)_2 \xrightarrow{CO_2} Fe(C_5H_4COOH)_2 \quad (46)$$

3-b). Under the given reaction conditions no substantial destruction of ferrocene by organosodium compounds takes place. Ferrocene is not metalated by lithium or sodium in di-(n-butyl) ether. It is in fact partially decomposed by metallic sodium.[2]

2. Metalation of Ferrocene Derivatives

The mercuration of ferrocene derivatives has not been well studied. There has been only a short report from Nesmeyanov and co-workers[11] that the reaction of p-nitrophenylferrocene with mercury(II) acetate produces dimercurated derivatives in low yield. They also report that 1,1'-diacetyl-ferrocene could not be mercurated.

There are, however, numerous examples of the metalation of ferrocene derivatives by organolithium, organosodium, and organopotassium compounds.

In contrast to alkyl benzenes, alkyl ferrocenes are metalated only on the cyclopentadienyl rings by organolithium, organosodium, and organopotassium compounds.[7,8] The reaction is more difficult than it is with ferrocene. Thus 1,1'-dimethylferrocene is not metalated by n-butyllithium in ether.[7]

In the competitive metalation of ferrocene and methyl, ethyl, and propyl ferrocenes (the ratio of ferrocene, alkyl ferrocene, and n-butyllithium being 1:1:2.8) only the esters of the ferrocenecarboxylic acids were isolated after carboxylation and esterification with diazomethane.[12] Interaction of alkyl ferrocenes with n-amylsodium gives a mixture of monometalated and dimetalated derivatives even when the ratio of the reagents is equimolar.[12]

Benkeser and Bach[8] believe that there is an equilibrium between the monoanion and the dianion and that it is shifted to the right by the greater thermodynamic stability of the dianion.

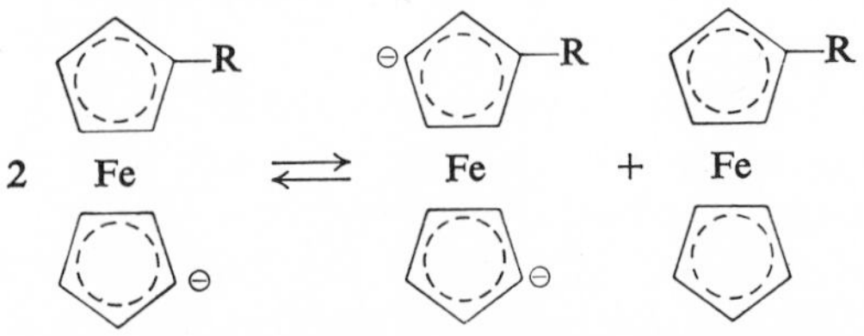

$$2 \quad \text{Fe} \quad \rightleftarrows \quad \text{Fe} \quad + \quad \text{Fe} \tag{47}$$

Benkeser and Bach[8] found that monometalation of alkyl ferrocenes with n-amylsodium proceeds in the 1'- and 3-positions.* The ratio of 1,1'- and 1,3-isomers averages 2.6:1, which is close to the statistical average (2.5:1— five 1'-positions and two 3-positions). Evidently the effect of electronic factors in metalation is equal for the 1'- and 3-positions.† Dimetalation gives chiefly 1,1',3-isomers, whereas in the case of a large $tert$-butyl group substitution takes place almost entirely in 1',3-positions. Table X shows the ratios of isomers that form during the metalation of alkyl ferrocenes with n-amylsodium in decane at equimolar amounts of the reagents.[8]

When isopropylferrocene was metalated with n-butyllithium in ether, the results were the same as those obtained with n-amylsodium. Metalated

TABLE X

Ratios of Isomers Formed in the Metalation of Alkyl Ferrocenes with
n-Amylsodium in Decane

	Isomer			
R	(A)	(B)	(C)	(D)
CH_3	2.4	1	6.6	0.8
C_2H_5	2.3	1	9	0.7
i-C_3H_7	2.7	1	8	0.25
$tert$-C_4H_9	3	1	10.8	0.11

* Only in the case of ethylferrocene were traces of the 1,2-isomer found.[8]

† This agrees with data on chemical shifts of protons in the substituted and free rings.[8,13]

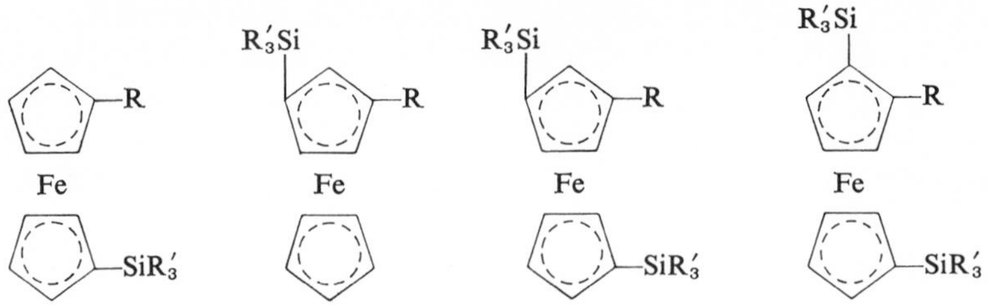

$$\text{(A)} \qquad \text{(B)} \qquad \text{(C)} \qquad \text{(D)}$$

alkyl ferrocenes were carboxylated or reacted with trialkylhalosilanes. The resulting trialkylsilyl derivatives were separated by gas–liquid chromatography. Acids were separated as methyl esters or reduced to alkyl ferrocenes and then separated on a chromatograph. The results obtained by the various methods coincided. The structures were established by the NMR technique. In addition, it has been shown that 3-ethyl-1,1'-dimethylferrocene, synthesized from the appropriate alkyl cyclopentadienes, is identical with the substance obtained on reducing 3-ethyl-1,1'-dicarbomethoxyferrocene.[8]

Oxygen-, chlorine-, and nitrogen-containing ferrocene derivatives (diphenylferrocenylcarbinol,[14] methoxyferrocene,[15] chloroferrocene,[16,17] and N,N-dimethylaminomethylferrocene[18,19]) are metalated in the 2-position by

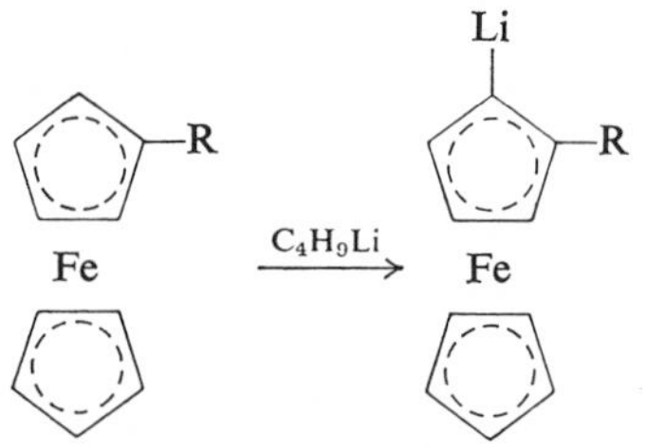

$$[R = C(C_6H_5)_2OH, \ OCH_3, \ Cl, \ CH_2N(CH_3)_2] \tag{48}$$

n-butyllithium. This can probably be explained by the fact that lithium initially forms a coordination bond with the heteroatom of the R-group.

Metalation of N,N-dimethylaminomethylferrocene (**45**) is easier than it is with ferrocene.[18,19] The yield of the monolithium derivative is more than 70% [established by the yield of carbinol (**54**) after reaction with benzophenone].

Dimetalation of N,N-dimethylaminomethylferrocene (**45**) with n-butyllithium proceeds under somewhat more drastic conditions and leads to the 1,2,1'-isomer (**55**). Derivatives that have been monometalated either in position 2 (**54**) or in position 1' (**56**) are also obtained.

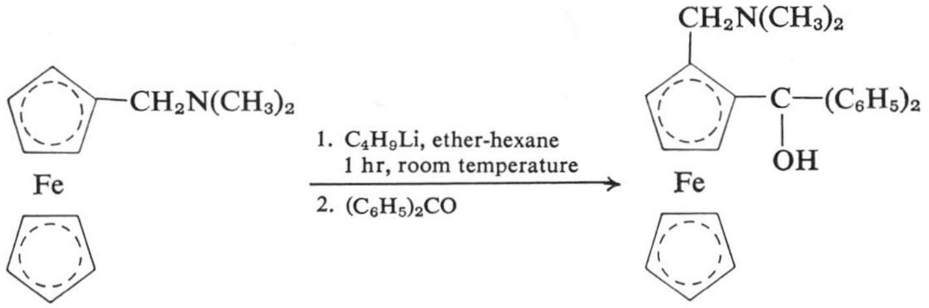

(49)

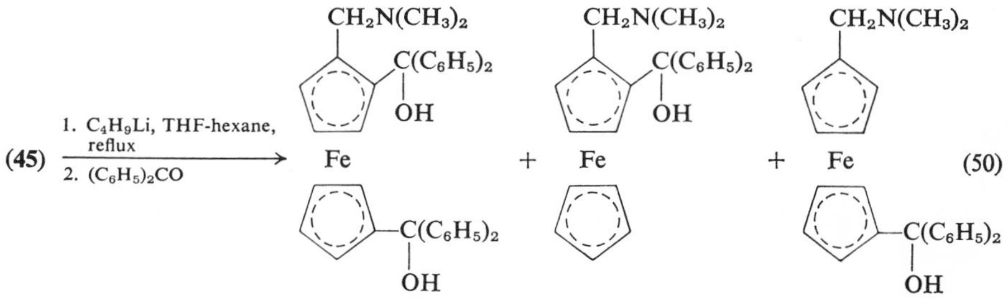

(50)

45%
(55)

13%
(54)

10%
(56)

The structures of the compounds that form were established by infrared and NMR spectra as well as by cyclization of the methiodide **(57)** to the ether **(58)**.[19]

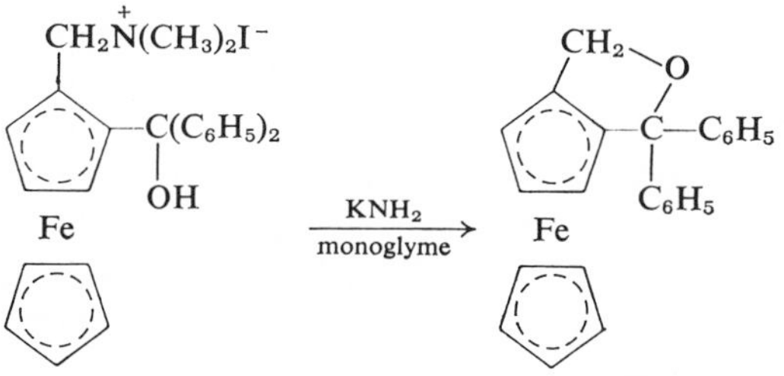

(51)

Metalation of methoxyferrocene with n-butyllithium and subsequent carboxylation yields 1,2-methoxyferrocenecarboxylic acid.[15]

Huffman and co-workers[16] have investigated the reaction of chloroferrocene with n-butyllithium in a tetrahydrofuran–hexane mixture. They found that after water treatment a multicomponent mixture is formed, composed of ferrocene, chloroferrocene, n-butylferrocene, diferrocenyl, and other compounds. After carboxylation of the reaction mixture, a small yield of 1,2-chloroferrocenylcarboxylic acid was obtained. Huffman and co-workers[16] believe that the reaction of chloroferrocene with *n*-butyllithium gives dehydroferrocene (ferrocyne), the ferrocene analog of dehydrobenzene, as an intermediate product.

Recently Nesmeyanov and co-workers[17] metalated chloroferrocene with *n*-butyllithium in ether and then reacted the organolithium substance with tri-(*n*-butyl) borate to obtain a high yield of 1,2-chloroferroceneboric acid (the technique is described in subsection 3-*c*).

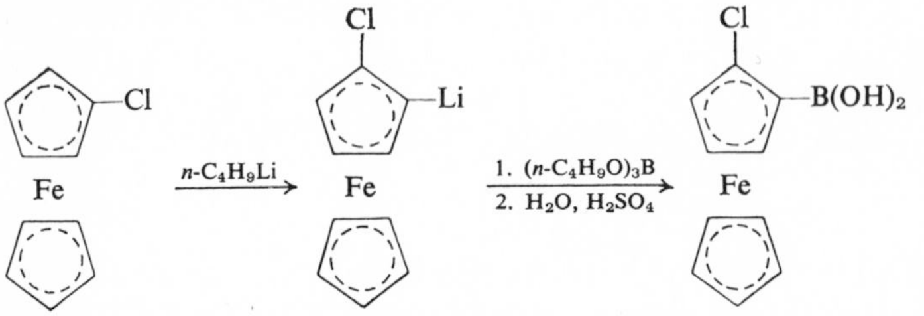

$$\text{(52)}$$

Research into the metalation of ferrocene derivatives has made available numerous homoannular disubstituted ferrocenes, particularly those of the 1,2-variety.

3. Examples of Syntheses

a. Ferrocene Mercuration.[1]*   To a stirred solution of 46 g (0.25 mole) of ferrocene in 230 ml of benzene in a 2-liter flask a solution of 80 g (0.25 mole) of mercury(II) acetate in 900 ml of methanol is added gradually over the course of 1 hr. The stirring is continued for 30 min more; then a solution of 18 g potassium chloride in 60 ml of water is added, and stirring is continued for 15 min. The precipitate is filtered on a Buchner funnel and extracted with dichloroethane in a Soxhlet apparatus, dissolving the ferrocenylmercury(II) chloride and the ferrocene. In 30–35 min the solution is poured out and replaced by fresh dichloroethane [after long heating ferrocenylmercury(II) chloride decomposes]. Extraction with fresh portions of dichloroethane is repeated eight times until extracts become pale yellow. The extraction time is gradually increased to 40–50 min. Almost pure heteroannular ferrocenylene bis[mercury(II) chloride] remains in the Soxhlet apparatus. A 46 g quantity of ferrocenylene bis[mercury(II) chloride] is formed (30% yield based on ferrocene).

The dichloroethane is removed under vacuum. The solvent is also separated from the filtrate under vacuum. The combined residues are extracted in a Soxhlet apparatus with a low-boiling-point petroleum ether for 5–6 hr (to almost colorless extracts). The ferrocenylmercury(II) chloride that remains

* Technique improved by A. G. Kozlovskii.

in the bulb contains some ferrocenylene bis[mercury(II) chloride]. It is recrystallized from boiling xylene (it can also be recrystallized from *n*-butanol). The solvent is first heated to boiling. The yield of ferrocenylmercury(II) chloride is 40 g (30% of the theoretical amount); m.p. 194–196° (decomposition).

b. Ferrocene Metalation with Phenylsodium.[6]* Into a four-necked 750-ml flask fitted with a stirrer, reflux condenser, stopcock to feed pure dry nitrogen, and dropping funnel is added 400 ml of dry benzene† as well as 23 g of sodium wire, 0.3–0.5 mm in diameter,‡ and 43 ml of dry chlorobenzene.§ In 30–60 min black regions of phenylsodium appear on the silvery surface of the wire and the mixture begins to evolve heat. The dropping funnel is replaced with a thermometer submerged in the liquid, and the flask is cooled so that the temperature of the mixture does not exceed 25–30°.‖ In 1.5–2 hr the wire is almost completely decomposed and black phenylsodium powder is formed. The reaction mixture is stirred at room temperature for 30 min more, the thermometer is removed, and while continuing the stirring 25 g of dry ferrocene is added through the open neck of the flask. The neck is then fitted with a cork, with a thermometer submerged into the liquid. The stirring is continued, and the flask is heated at 55–65° for 15–20 hr.¶ Then, without stopping the stirring, the dark-brown solution is cooled to room temperature, and, under nitrogen, the reaction mixture is poured into an evaporating dish containing 200–300 g of powdered solid carbon dioxide. The last portions of the reaction mixture are transferred to the evaporating dish with dry benzene. After 2 or 3 hr 25 ml of methanol is added to the liquid reaction mixture to destroy any unreacted, finely dispersed sodium. Gradually, in small portions, 500 ml of water is added, with stirring. When hydrogen bubbles cease to appear,** the water layer is removed in a separatory funnel. The benzene layer is then washed with a 5% aqueous solution of sodium

---

* Technique improved by S. S. Churanov.

† The purity of benzene greatly affects the rate of phenylsodium formation as well as the yield of ferrocenedicarboxylic acid. The best results are obtained with cryoscopy-grade benzene that has been distilled twice from lithium aluminum hydride.

‡ Sodium wire up to 1 mm in diameter can be used, but in this case the formation of phenylsodium takes more time.

§ Chlorobenzene is first dried and then distilled over phosphorus pentoxide.

‖ A temperature increase of over 35° leads to the formation of large amounts of diphenyl and a decrease in the yield of ferrocenedicarboxylic acid.

¶ The maximum yield was obtained after 18 hr of heating at 60–62°; if the reaction is carried out in boiling benzene, the yield of ferrocenecarboxylic acid decreases considerably.

** The evaporating dish should be covered with an asbestos sheet when water is added. If the remnants of sodium are not completely decomposed, the mixture can ignite when transferred to the separatory funnel.

hydroxide, and the water layers are combined.* The resultant solution contains sodium salts of benzoic, ferrocenemonocarboxylic, and ferrocenedicarboxylic acids. It is cooled to 0°, and, with stirring, a 10% solution of hydrochloric acid is added so that the medium is strongly acid to Congo Red test paper. The mixture of acids that precipitates is filtered on a Buchner funnel and washed with water on the filter. After drying in air, 25–30 g of a mixture of ferrocenedicarboxylic, ferrocenemonocarboxylic, and benzoic acids is obtained.†

To isolate pure ferrocenedicarboxylic acid the mixture of acids is placed into the extraction bulb of a Soxhlet apparatus and extracted with benzene until the solvent flux from the extractor ceases to be yellow orange. The paper thimble containing the ferrocenedicarboxylic acid is removed from the extractor and dried in air.

Between 16 and 21 g of light-brown, powdered ferrocenedicarboxylic acid, decomposition point above 230°, is obtained. After recrystallization from hot methanol, the decomposition point exceeds 250°. The yield of ferrocenedicarboxylic acid is 44–57% based on the ferrocene used in the reaction (65–75% based on the amount reacted).

c. Metalation of Chloroferrocene; 1,2-Chloroferroceneboric acid.[17] The reaction is carried out under nitrogen. To an ether solution of 5 g of chloro-ferrocene an ether solution of 1.45 g of n-butyllithium is added. The mixture is heated for 5 hr and left overnight. The organolithium derivative of chloro-ferrocene thus obtained is added (at −70°) to an ether solution of 30 g of tri(n-butyl) borate. The reaction mixture is stirred until it reaches room temperature and is left overnight. Then the mixture is decomposed by a 1% sulfuric acid solution. The ether solution is treated several times with 10 ml of 10% potassium hydroxide. [A total of 0.68 g (13%) of unreacted chloro-ferrocene was separated from the ether solution.] The alkaline extracts are washed with a small amount of ether, and carbon dioxide is passed through the alkaline solution. The precipitate of 1,2-chloroferroceneboric acid is filtered, washed with water, and dried over 65% sulfuric acid. The amount of 1,2-chloroferroceneboric acid obtained is 3.7 g (62% of the theoretical amount, based on the amount of chloroferrocene used in the reaction). The acid is a yellow crystalline substance that turns green in air and is soluble in benzene, ether, acetone, alcohol, and water. When heated, it is

---

* Between 8 and 11 g of the ferrocene–diphenyl mixture can be obtained from the benzene layer (dried with calcium chloride). After recrystallization, 6–8 g of ferrocene is obtained.

† A considerable amount of benzoic acid can be separated from the mixture by washing with hot water. After drying, a mixture of 20–25 g of ferrocenemonocarboxylic and ferrocenedicarboxylic acids, containing a small amount of benzoic acid, is obtained.

easily converted to the anhydride. It crystallizes from hexane as an anhydride, $C_{10}H_8ClBFeO$.

Chloroferrocenediboric acid is formed along with 1,2-chloroferroceneboric acid.

References

1. A. N. Nesmeyanov, E. G. Perevalova, R. V. Golovnya, and O. A. Nesmeyanova, *Dokl. Akad. Nauk SSSR*, **97**, 459 (1954).
2. M. Rausch, M. Vogel, and H. Rosenberg, *J. Org. Chem.*, **22**, 900 (1957).
3. D. W. Mayo, P. D. Shaw, and M. Rausch, *Chem. Ind.* (*London*), **1957**, 1388.
4. R. L. Schaaf and C. T. Lenk, *J. Chem. Eng. Data*, **9**, 103 (1964).
5. R. A. Benkeser, D. Goggin, and G. Schroll, *J. Amer. Chem. Soc.*, **76**, 4025 (1954).
6. A. N. Nesmeyanov, E. G. Perevalova, and Z. A. Beynoravichute, *Dokl. Akad. Nauk SSSR*, **112**, 459 (1957).
7. A. N. Nesmeyanov, E. G. Perevalova, Z. A. Beynoravichute, and L. L. Malygina, *Dokl. Akad. Nauk SSSR*, **120**, 1263 (1958).
8. R. A. Benkeser and J. H. Bach, *J. Amer. Chem. Soc.*, **86**, 890 (1964).
9. S. L. Goldberg, L. H. Keith, and T. S. Prokorov, *J. Org. Chem.*, **28**, 850 (1963).
10. K. Schlögl and M. Fried, *Monatsh.*, **94**, 537 (1963).
11. A. N. Nesmeyanov, E. G. Perevalova, R. V. Golovnya, N. A. Simukova, and O. V. Starovskii, *Izv. Akad. Nauk SSSR, Otd. Khim. Nauk*, **1957**, 638.
12. A. N. Nesmeyanov, E. G. Perevalova, V. D. Tiurin, and S. P. Gubin, *Izv. Akad. Nauk SSSR, Ser. Khim.* **1966**, 1938.
13. R. A. Benkeser, Y. Nagai, and J. Hooz, *Bull. Chem. Soc. Japan*, **36**, 482 (1963).
14. R. A. Benkeser, W. P. Fitzgerald, and M. S. Metzer, *J. Org. Chem.*, **26**, 2569 (1961).
15. A. N. Nesmeyanov, T. V. Baukova, and K. I. Grandberg, *Izv. Akad. Nauk SSSR, Ser. Khim.* **1967**, 1867.
16. I. W. Huffman, L. H. Keith, and R. L. Asbury, *J. Org. Chem.*, **30**, 1600 (1965).
17. A. N. Nesmeyanov, V. A. Sazonova, and N. S. Sazonova, *Dokl. Akad. Nauk SSSR*, **176**, 598 (1967).
18. D. W. Slocum, B. W. Rockett, and C. R. Hauser, *Chem. Ind.* (*London*), **1964**, 1831.
19. D. W. Slocum, B. W. Rockett, and C. R. Hauser, *J. Amer. Chem. Soc.*, **87**, 1241 (1965).

H. Reactions with Free Radicals

Only ferricinium salts react with free radicals, whereas ferrocene itself does not exhibit such reactions.

The free-radical reaction that is of the greatest synthetic importance in the ferrocene series consists of the arylation of ferrocene with diazonium salts. The first step of the process is an oxidation–reduction reaction in which ferrocene is oxidized with a diazonium cation to produce a ferricinium cation. The cation then reacts with aryl radicals formed from the decomposition of the aryldiazo salt.

Ferrocene derivatives, except for monoaryl ferrocenes, are arylated in very low yields. Heteroannular disubstituted ferrocenes with two electron-withdrawing substituents are destroyed by diazonium salts (see Chapter 3).

1. Arylation of Ferrocene

Ferrocene reacts with diazonium salts to form aryl ferrocenes. Monoannular or heteroannular diaryl ferrocenes are produced in preparative yields, depending on the conditions of the reaction (see Table XI).

TABLE XI
Ferrocene Arylation

Aryl in Aryldiazonium	Aryl in arylated ferrocene	Yield,[a] %	Ref.[b]
C_6H_5[c]	C_6H_5	66[d]	4, 1, 12, 18
	$1,1'-(C_6H_5)_2$	20	12, 4, 1, 18
	$1,2-(C_6H_5)_2$	—	1
	$1,3-(C_6H_5)_2$	—	1
	$?-(C_6H_5)_5$	42	3
$o\text{-}FC_6H_4$	$o\text{-}C_6H_4F$	32	10
$o\text{-}ClC_6H_4$	$o\text{-}C_6H_4Cl$	22	10
$m\text{-}ClC_6H_4$	$m\text{-}C_6H_4Cl$	34	4
	$1,1'-(m\text{-}C_6H_4Cl)_2$	0.4	4
$p\text{-}ClC_6H_4$	$p\text{-}C_6H_4Cl$	—	12
	$1,1'-(p\text{-}C_6H_4Cl)_2$	—	12
$o\text{-}BrC_6H_4$	$o\text{-}C_6H_4Br$	22	10
$m\text{-}BrC_6H_4$	$m\text{-}C_6H_4Br$	—	19
$p\text{-}BrC_6H_4$	$p\text{-}C_6H_4Br$	—	19
	$1,1'-(p\text{-}C_6H_4Br)_2$	17	17, 20
$o\text{-}IC_6H_4$	$o\text{-}C_6H_4I$	33	10
$o\text{-}O_2NC_6H_4$	$o\text{-}C_6H_4NO_2$	5	4, 13
$m\text{-}O_2NC_6H_4$	$m\text{-}C_6H_4NO_2$	56	6
$p\text{-}O_2NC_6H_4$[c]	$p\text{-}C_6H_4NO_2$	64	3, 12, 4, 7
	$1,1'-(p\text{-}C_6H_4NO_2)_2$	67	17, 3, 7, 12
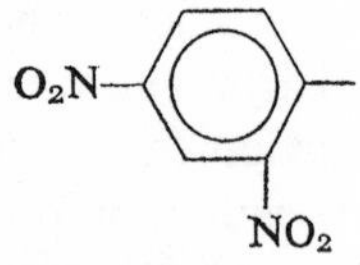 O_2N-⟨ring⟩-, NO_2	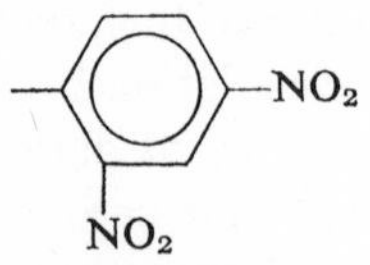 -⟨ring⟩-NO_2, NO_2	—	4
$o\text{-}CH_3C_6H_4$	$o\text{-}C_6H_4CH_3$	43	4, 10
$p\text{-}CH_3C_6H_4$	$p\text{-}C_6H_4CH_3$	62	21, 3, 22
$m\text{-}F_3CC_6H_4$	$m\text{-}C_6H_4CF_3$	—	10

(continued)

TABLE XI (*continued*)

Aryl in Aryldiazonium	Aryl in arylated ferrocene	Yield,[a] %	Ref.[b]
(2-methyl-6-nitrophenyl: CH₃ ortho, NO₂ ortho)	(2-methyl-6-nitrophenyl)	11	10
(2-methyl-4-nitrophenyl: CH₃, NO₂)	(2-methyl-4-nitrophenyl)	42	10
(3-methyl-4-nitrophenyl: CH₃, O₂N–)	(–NO₂, CH₃)	90	10
(2,6-dimethyl-4-nitrophenyl: CH₃, O₂N–, CH₃)	(–NO₂ dimethyl)	39	10
(H₃C–, CH₃, NO₂ trimethylnitrophenyl)	(–CH₃, CH₃, NO₂)	—	10
o-C₆H₅C₆H₄	o-C₆H₄C₆H₅	28	10, 23
p-C₆H₅C₆H₄	p-C₆H₄C₆H₅	41	23
	1,1′,X-(p-C₆H₄C₆H₅)₃	50	12
α-C₁₀H₇	α-C₁₀H₇	—	9, 7
	1,1′-(α-C₁₀H₇)₂	—	7
m-BF₄N₂C₆H₄N₂BF₄	C₆H₅	7	9
	m-C₆H₄C₅H₄FeC₅H₅	62	9
p-BF₄N₂C₆H₄C₆H₄N₂BF₄	p-C₆H₄C₆H₅	13	9
	p-C₆H₄C₆H₄C₅H₄FeC₅H₅	7	

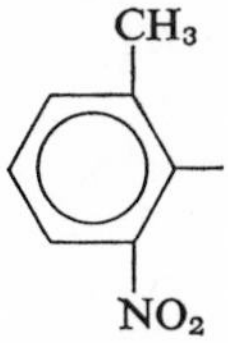

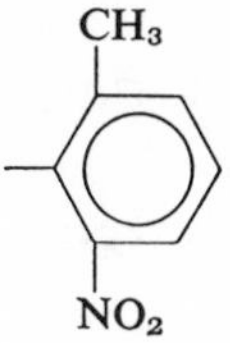

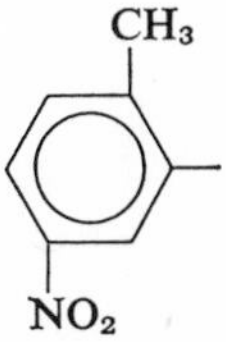

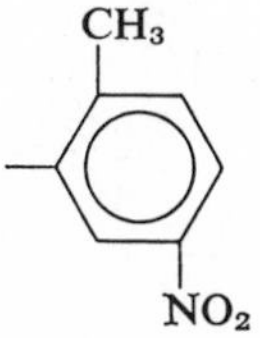

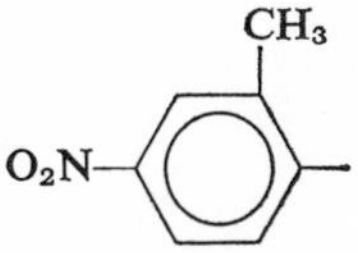

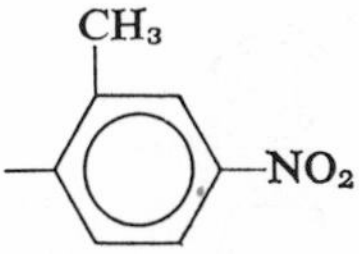

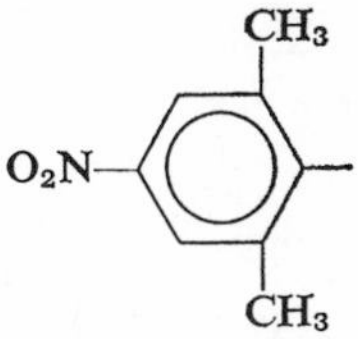

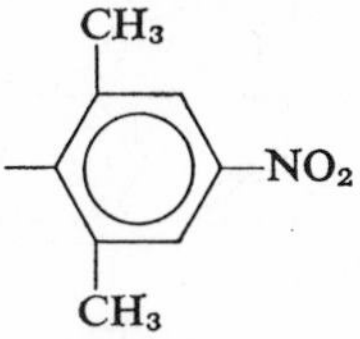

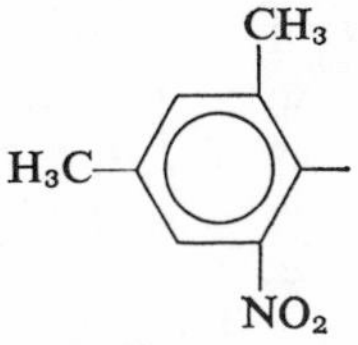

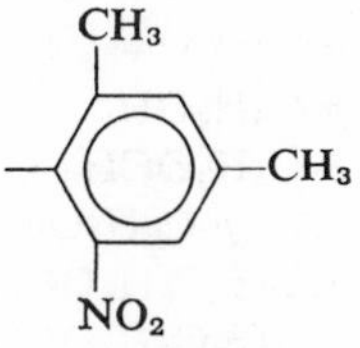

(*continued*)

TABLE XI (*continued*)

Aryl in Aryldiazonium	Aryl in arylated ferrocene	Yield,[a] %	Ref.[b]
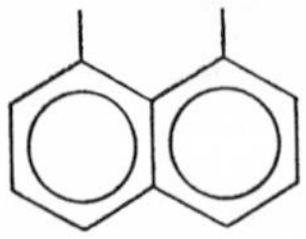	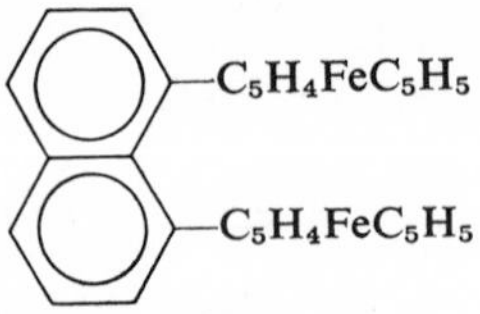	—	9
	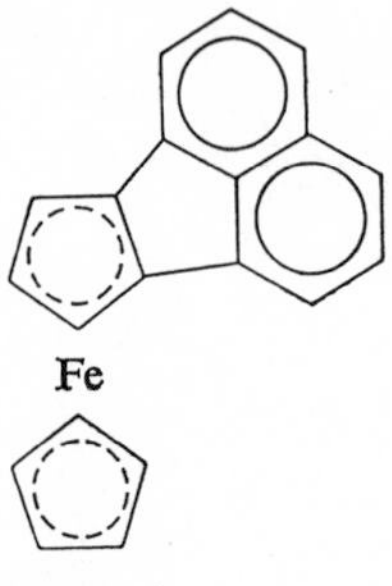	—	9
	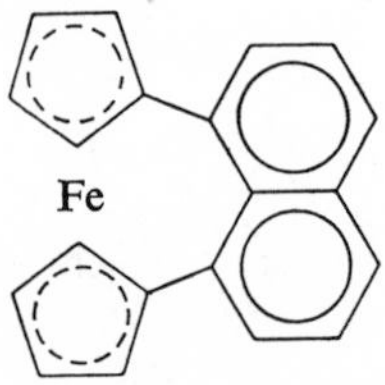	—	9
o-$CH_3OC_6H_4$	o-$C_6H_4OCH_3$	13	10
o-$C_2H_5OC_6H_4$	o-$C_6H_4OC_2H_5$	4	10
p-HOC_6H_4	p-C_6H_4OH	60	12, 6, 4
p-$CH_3OC_6H_4$	p-$C_6H_4OCH_3$	43	1, 3, 4, 7
	$1,1'$-$(p$-$C_6H_4OCH_3)_2$	7	4,1,7
	$1,2$-$(p$-$C_6H_4OCH_3)_2$	—	1
	$1,3$-$(p$-$C_6H_4OCH_3)_2$	—	1
p-$C_6H_5OC_6H_4$	p-$C_6H_4OC_6H_5$	31	24
p-$CH_3COC_6H_4$	p-$C_6H_4COCH_3$	—	1, 18
	$1,1$-$(p$-$C_6H_4COCH_3)_2$	—	1,18
	$1,2$-$(p$-$C_6H_4COCH_3)_2$	—	1
	$1,3$-$(p$-$C_6H_4COCH_3)_2$	—	1
o-$HOOCC_6H_4$	o-C_6H_4COOH	7	4, 25, 26
	$1,1'$-$(o$-$C_6H_4COOH)_2$	15	12
	$?$-$(o$-$C_6H_4COOH)_3$	—	12
	$?$-$(o$-$C_6H_4COOH)_4$	—	12

(*continued*)

TABLE XI (*continued*)

Aryl in Aryldiazonium	Aryl in arylated ferrocene	Yield,[a] %	Ref.[b]
	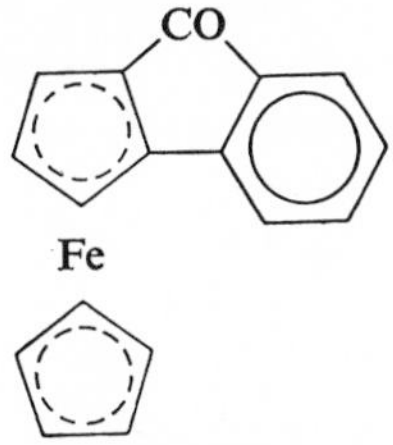	7	25
o-CH$_3$OOCC$_6$H$_4$	o-C$_6$H$_4$COOCH$_3$	45	10, 22, 27
	o-C$_6$H$_4$COOH	35	22, 27
m-CH$_3$OOCC$_6$H$_4$	m-C$_6$H$_4$COOCH$_3$	15	10
m-C$_2$H$_5$OOCC$_6$H$_4$	m-C$_6$H$_4$COOC$_2$H$_5$	20	10
p-C$_2$H$_5$OOCC$_6$H$_4$	p-C$_6$H$_4$COOC$_2$H$_5$	32	22, 27
	p-C$_6$H$_4$COOH	38	22, 27
p-NCC$_6$H$_4$	p-C$_6$H$_4$CN	10	10
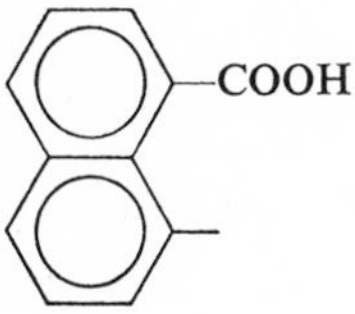	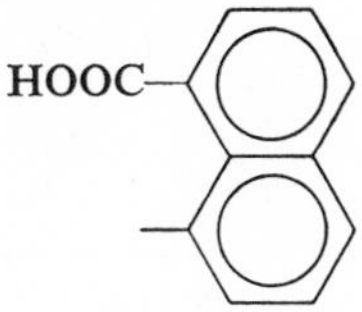	6	12
	1,1′,X- 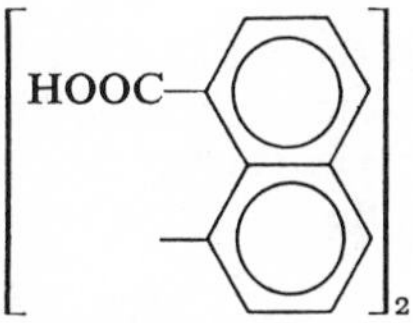	30	12
p-HO$_3$SC$_6$H$_4$	p-C$_6$H$_4$SO$_3$Ba$_{1/2}$	—	4
p-(C$_2$H$_5$OOC)$_2$CCH$_2$C$_6$H$_4$ | NHCHO	p-C$_6$H$_4$CH$_2$C(COOC$_2$H$_5$)$_2$ | NHCHO	64	28
p-C$_6$H$_5$N=NC$_6$H$_4$	p-C$_6$H$_4$N=NC$_6$H$_5$	21	13
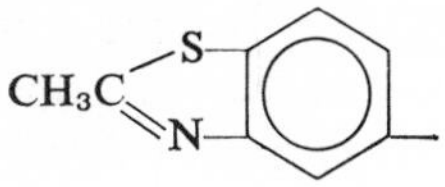	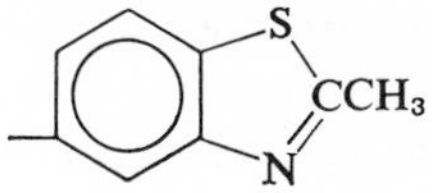	27	29
	1,1′- 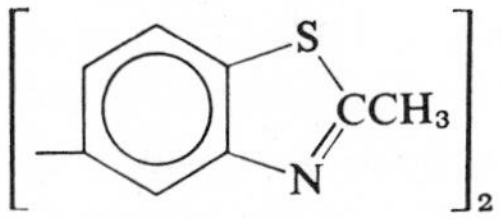	0.8	29

(*continued*)

TABLE XI (*continued*)

Aryl in Aryldiazonium	Aryl in arylated ferrocene	Yield,[a] %	Ref.[b]
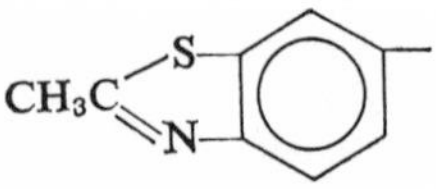	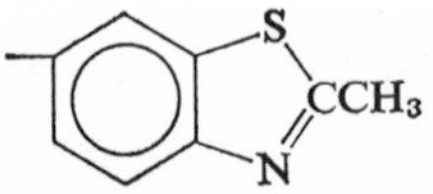	21	29
	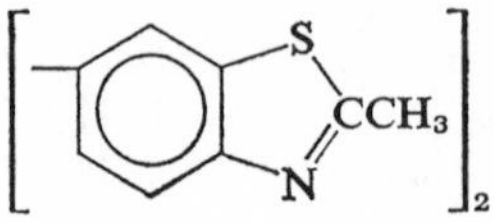	0.3	29
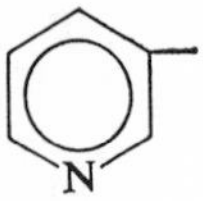	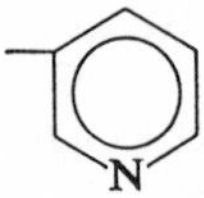	27	11
	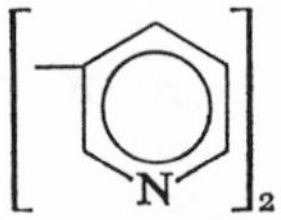	26	11

[a] Unless otherwise indicated, the yield refers to the amount of ferrocene taken for reaction.

[b] This table presents the best of all yields cited in the papers under review, with the reference corresponding to the best yield placed first.

[c] The procedure for obtaining the product is described in Section II-H-4.

[d] The yield refers to the amount of ferrocene reacted.

In addition, insignificant amounts of ferrocenyl biphenyls and homoannular 1,2- and 1,3-diaryl ferrocenes are formed. They were isolated in only a few instances by chromatography on alumina.[1]

Aryl diazoacetates[2,3] or N-nitrosoacetanilide[4,5] react in a manner similar to that of diazonium salts.

Arylation of ferrocene with diazo compounds may be a convenient route to the synthesis of aryl ferrocenes. Arylation of ferrocene was first performed by Nesmeyanov, Perevalova, and Golovnya[2,3] and independently by Broadhead and Pauson.[4] The reaction is usually carried out in acetic acid, but diazonium arylation in a water–ether medium,[2,3] in aqueous acetone,[1,4,7] and in halogenated hydrocarbons[8-10] has also been described.*

Yields of aryl ferrocenes vary widely (10–20 to 60–80%), depending on the nature of the substituent in the benzene ring (see Table XI). The best results

* As discussed subsequently, the ferrocene reaction with a number of *ortho*-substituted benzenediazonium salts proceeds irregularly in a halogenated hydrocarbon medium.

are obtained with phenyl, *p*-nitro, or *p*-methylbenzene diazonium salts, the total yield of monoaryl and diaryl ferrocenes being more than 70%.

Ferrocene reaction with bis(diazonium) salts has been described[9] and gives 1,3-diferrocenylbenzene (59) in good yield.

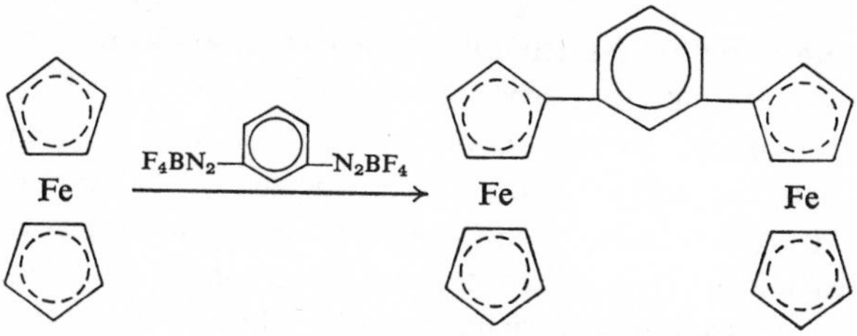

Ferrocene reacts with diazotized 1,8-diaminonaphthalene to give the ferrocenylene acenaphthene derivative (60).[9] Diazotized β-aminopyridine reacts with ferrocene in the same manner as benzenediazonium salts to produce compounds (61) and (62).

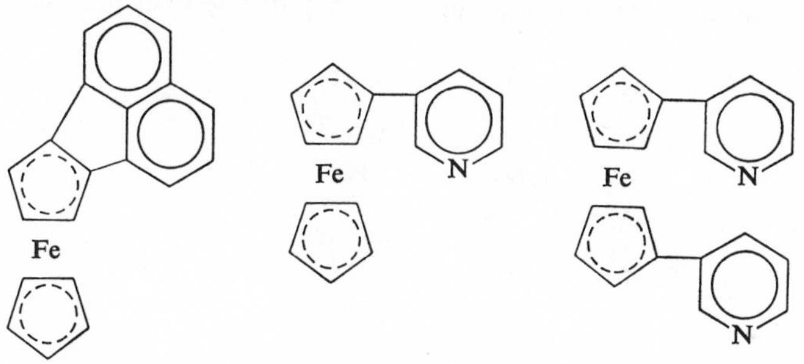

As a rule monoaryl ferrocenes are obtained in higher yields than diaryl ferrocenes. The ratio of monoaryl to diaryl ferrocenes depends both on the amount of diazonium salt used in the reaction and on the nature of the aryl group. The differences in the oxidation–reduction potentials of ferrocene, the ferricinium cation, and the diazonium cation significantly influence the ratio (see below for the mechanism of arylation). A great number of mono-aryl ferrocenes containing various substituents in the aryl group were synthesized in order to study their oxidation at the iron atom and to implement the Hammett–Taft analysis of the substituent effect (see Chapter 4).

When ferrocene is reacted with several *ortho*-substituted benzenedia-zonium salts in halogenated hydrocarbons (dichloromethane, chloroform, bromotrichloromethane, or 1,1-dichloroethane), the solvent is involved in the reaction and significant amounts of carbonyl-containing compounds are formed (ferrocene aldehyde, acetylferrocene, ferrocenecarboxylic acid).[8] In this system the aryl group may react with the solvent, forming a halogen-containing alkyl radical, which then reacts with a ferricinium ion (for details see below). Diazonium salts obtained from o-methyl, o-ethyl, 2,6-dimethyl, and 2,4,6-trimethyl anilines produce only carbonyl-containing ferrocenes, whereas diazotized o-iodoaniline, o-aminobiphenyl, 2,6-dimethyl-4-nitroaniline, and 2,4-dimethyl-6-nitroaniline yield the arylation products, together with small amounts of carbonyl-containing ferrocenes.[8]

A ferricinium-cation mixture containing traces of ferrocene is easily arylated by diazonium salts, but no reaction occurs in the complete absence of ferrocene.[12] It must be noted that the arylation of ferrocene or the ferricinium cation always leads to products containing ferrocene and aryl ferrocenes as well as the corresponding ferricinium salts. This means that arylation is always accompanied by an oxidation–reduction process.

No extensive study of the mechanism of the diazonium arylation of ferrocene has been carried out. Little and co-workers,[8,13] Beckwith and Leydon,[5,7,14,15] and Rosenblum[16] think that ferrocene is oxidized by a diazo cation to a radical cation, the ferricinium ion (63), which then reacts with an aryl radical formed from a diazonium salt. The intermediate state is

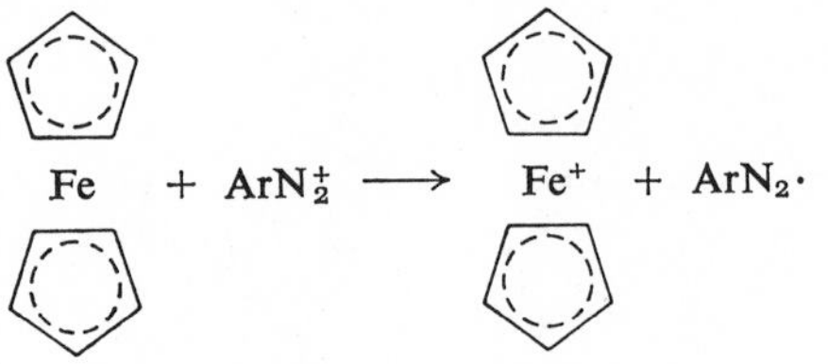

$$\text{Fe} + \text{ArN}_2^+ \longrightarrow \text{Fe}^+ + \text{ArN}_2\cdot \qquad (54)$$

$$(63)$$

$$\text{ArN}_2\cdot \longrightarrow \text{Ar}\cdot + \text{N}_2 \qquad (55)$$

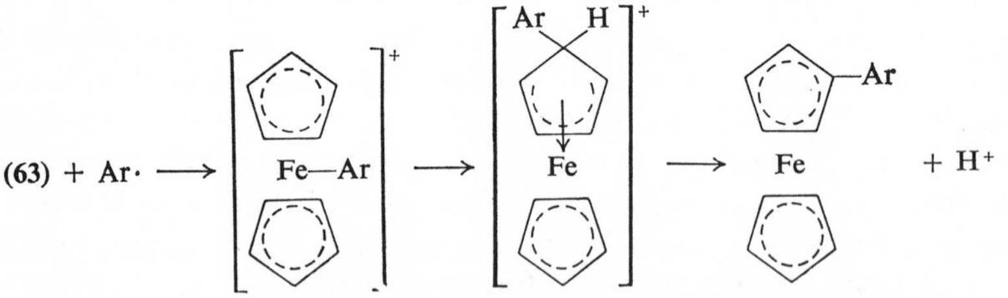

$$(63) + \text{Ar}\cdot \longrightarrow [\text{Fe}{-}\text{Ar}]^+ \longrightarrow \left[\begin{array}{c}\text{Ar} \quad \text{H}\\ \text{Fe}\end{array}\right]^+ \longrightarrow \text{Fe}{-}\text{Ar} + \text{H}^+ \qquad (56)$$

$$(64) \qquad\qquad (65)$$

thought to have structure (64) or (65) similar to the structures proposed for the electrophilic substitution of ferrocene. This mechanistic scheme is confirmed by the following evidence. Ferrocene does not react with the free radicals formed from phenylazotriphenylmethane, azobis(isobutyronitrile), or other compounds,[4,15] whereas the ferricinium cation does (see subsection 3). The reaction mixture obtained during the diazonium arylation of ferrocene must contain free radicals since their typical reaction products have been isolated (biaryls,[1] deaminated arenes,[1,4,9] and azo compounds[1,3]). On the other hand, the arylation products have already been noted to contain ferricinium and substituted ferricinium salts. Ferrocene derivatives, which are harder to oxidize than ferrocene, are usually arylated in low yields (see subsection 2).*

It must be noted, however, that one cannot exclude the hypothesis proposed by Pauson[4] and by Rosenblum and co-workers[1] (i.e., the formation of a ferrocene–diazo cation charge-transfer complex during the first step of the reaction).

2. Arylation of Ferrocene Derivatives with Diazonium Salts

The arylation of monosubstituted ferrocenes with diazonium salts takes place mainly in the unsubstituted ring. The arylation of alkyl, aryl, carbomethoxy, or acyl ferrocenes has been described (see Table XII). The yields are low (5–20%).

Arylation of methyl and ethyl ferrocenes produces monoarylated products along with biarylated and polyarylated derivatives. Ferrocenes that contain electron-withdrawing substituents and are harder to oxidize than ferrocene itself give only monoarylated derivatives in low yields.[21] This agrees with the mechanistic scheme for the arylation of ferrocene discussed in the preceding section.

Heteroannular diacyl ferrocenes, when arylated under the conditions of ferrocene arylation, react with diazonium salts. They undergo decomposition of the ferrocene nucleus and form fulvene azo derivatives.[17,21] The reaction mechanism is so far unknown. A scheme may be written involving the decomposition of a metal–ring bond (see Chapter 3 for details).

Diacyl ferrocenes are not decomposed at the pH values of the above reaction, provided no diazo compounds are present in the reaction mixture. Again, there is no reason to believe that a diacylferrocene enters an azo coupling, followed by the rupture of a metal–ring bond, because diacyl ferrocenes are not known to undergo electrophilic substitution reactions.

When reacted with a p-nitrobenzenediazonium salt, 1,1'-dicarbomethoxy-ferrocene gives p-nitrophenyl-1,1'-dicarbomethoxyferrocene in very low yield. In addition, products arising from the decomposition of the ferrocene nucleus are also formed.[21]

---

* However, 1,1'-di(p-nitrophenyl)ferrocene has been reported to result from the reaction of ferrocene with p-nitrobenzenediazonium chloride in a somewhat unexpected yield of about 70%.[17]

TABLE XII

Arylation of Ferrocene Derivatives

R in ferrocene derivative	Aryl in aryldiazonium	Reaction products[a]	Yield,[b] %	Ref.[c]
CH_3	C_6H_5	$1'\text{-}C_6H_5$; $?\text{-}(C_6H_5)_n$	5 —	21
C_2H_5	C_6H_5	$1'\text{-}C_6H_5$; $?\text{-}(C_6H_5)_n$	20 —	21
C_6H_5	C_6H_5	$1'\text{-}C_6H_5$; $1',X\text{-}(C_6H_5)_2$	52[d] 10[d]	4
$p\text{-}C_6H_4CH_3$	$p\text{-}CH_3C_6H_4$	$p\text{-}1'\text{-}C_6H_4CH_3$	9	21
$p\text{-}C_6H_4OCH_3$	$p\text{-}O_2NC_6H_4$	$p\text{-}1'\text{-}C_6H_4NO_2$; $p\text{-}2\text{-}C_6H_4NO_2$; $p\text{-}3\text{-}C_6H_4NO_2$;	— — —	30
		$p\text{-}C_6H_4NO_2$	—	
		$p\text{-}C_6H_4NO_2$		
$COCH_3$	$p\text{-}O_2NC_6H_4$	$p\text{-}1'\text{-}C_6H_4NO_2$; $p\text{-}X\text{-}C_6H_4NO_2$[e]	5	21
$COOCH_3$	$p\text{-}O_2NC_6H_4$	$p\text{-}1'\text{-}C_6H_4NO_2$	7	21
$1,1'\text{-}(COCH_3)_2$	C_6H_5	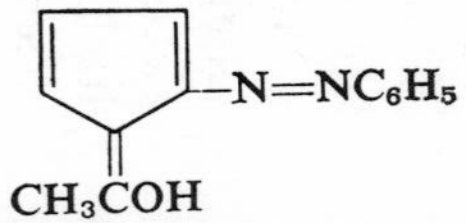	40	17, 31, 32

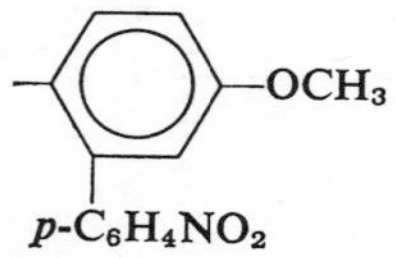

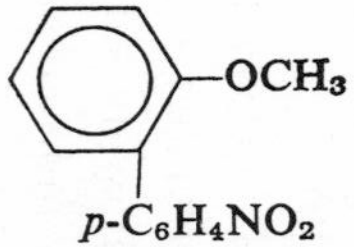

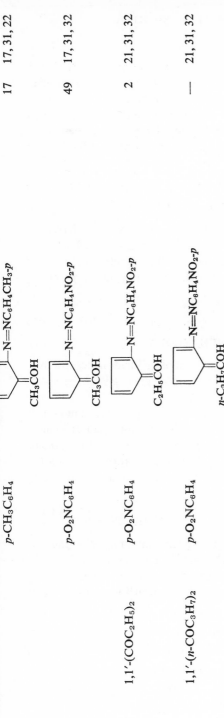

Entering group[a]	Ferrocene derivative	Structure	Yield (%)[b,c]	References
p-CH₃C₆H₄		=NC₆H₄CH₃-p, CH₃COH	17	17, 31, 22
p-O₂NC₆H₄		=NC₆H₄NO₂-p, CH₃COH	49	17, 31, 32
p-O₂NC₆H₄	1,1'-(COC₂H₅)₂	=NC₆H₄NO₂-p, C₂H₅COH	2	21, 31, 32
p-O₂NC₆H₄	1,1'-(n-COC₃H₇)₂	=NC₆H₄NO₂-p, n-C₃H₇COH	—	21, 31, 32
p-O₂NC₆H₄	1,1'-(COC₆H₅)₂	=NC₆H₄NO₂-p, C₆H₅COH	3	21, 31, 32
p-O₂NC₆H₄	1,1'-(COOCH₃)₂	=NC₆H₄NO₂-p, CH₃OCOH, ?-p-C₆H₄NO₂[f]	—	21, 31, 32
			1.5	21

[a] Only the entering group and its position are shown.
[b] Unless otherwise indicated, the yield is based on the amount of ferrocene derivative taken for reaction.
[c] This table lists the best of all yields cited in the papers under review, with the reference corresponding to the best yield placed first.
[d] Yield based on the amount of ferrocene derivative reacted.
[e] Homoannular.
[f] Structure not strictly proved.

255

3. Ferricinium-Cation Reactions with Free Radicals

Ferrocene does not interact with free radicals if formation of a ferricinium cation is impossible.[1,4,5,14,15] Ferricinium salts, however, being themselves cation radicals, react with aryl as well as with alkyl radicals.

Beckwith and Leydon[7,14] have shown that ferricinium salts are arylated with aryl radicals formed during the oxidation of aryl hydrazines. Thus ferrocene and phenylferrocene are formed after the interaction of ferricinium tetrafluoroborate with phenylhydrazine.

$$3[(C_5H_5)_2Fe^+BF_4^-] + PhNHNH_2 \longrightarrow Ph\cdot + N_2 + 3(C_5H_5)_2Fe + 3HBF_4 \quad (57)$$

$$(C_5H_5)_2Fe^+BF_4^- + Ph\cdot \longrightarrow C_5H_5FeC_5H_4Ph + HBF_4 \quad (58)$$

A good yield of aryl ferrocenes can be obtained if a mixture of ferrocene and arylhydrazine is treated with silver oxide in an acidic medium. Ferrocene is oxidized to a ferricinium cation and then further reacts with an aryl radical. The reaction is carried out with phenyl, p-methoxyphenyl, p-chloro-

$$2(C_5H_5)_2Fe + Ag_2O + 2H^+ \longrightarrow 2(C_5H_5)_2Fe^+ + 2Ag + H_2O \quad (59)$$

$$2ArNHNH_2 + 3Ag_2O \longrightarrow 2Ar\cdot + 2N_2 + 6Ag + 3H_2O \quad (60)$$

$$(C_5H_5)_2Fe^+ + Ar\cdot \longrightarrow C_5H_5FeC_5H_4Ar + H^+ \quad (61)$$

phenyl, p-nitrophenyl, 2,4-dinitrophenyl, and α-naphthyl hydrazines. Methyl, benzyl, and benzoyl hydrazines react in the same manner, giving the corresponding ferrocene derivatives.[7]

The interaction of phenylazotriphenylmethane with a ferricinium salt produces phenylferrocene, tritylferrocene, triphenylcarbinol, and ferrocene.[14]

The high reactivity of the ferricinium cation in reactions with free radicals is demonstrated by its interaction with the alkyl radical formed during the decomposition of azobis(isobutyronitrile). In this reaction 2-cyano-2-ferrocenylpropane is formed.[15]

$$(C_5H_5)_2Fe^+ + (CH_3)_2\dot{C}CN \longrightarrow C_5H_5FeC_5H_4C(CH_3)_2CN + H^+ \quad (62)$$

The reaction of ferricinium cations with halogen-containing alkyl radicals accounts for the formation of carbonyl-containing ferrocenes. The ferricinium cations and the alkyl radicals are formed after the arylation of ferrocene with diazonium salts in a halogenated hydrocarbon medium[8] (see subsection 1).

$$(C_5H_5)_2Fe + ArN_2^+ \longrightarrow (C_5H_5)_2Fe^+ + Ar\cdot + N_2 \quad (63)$$

$$Ar\cdot + CH_2Cl_2 \longrightarrow ArH + \cdot CHCl_2 \quad (64)$$

$$(C_5H_5)_2Fe^+ + \cdot CHCl_2 \longrightarrow C_5H_5FeC_5H_4CHCl_2 + H^+$$

$$\downarrow H_2O \quad (65)$$

$$C_5H_5FeC_5H_4CHO$$

The ferrocene–ferricinium oxidation may also be involved in the interaction of ferrocene with the trichloromethyl radicals formed during the thermolysis of trichloroacetic acid in the presence of copper(II) chloride, as described by N. A. Nesmeyanov and Reutov.[33] Hydrolysis of trichloromethylferrocene gives ferrocenecarboxylic acid (yield about 6%).

Beckwith and Leydon[5,15] and Pausacker[34] have described ferrocene reactions that also go via the intermediate ferricinium cation (e.g., interactions with free-radical agents like benzoyl peroxide or *tert*-butyl perbenzoate).

The reaction with *tert*-butyl perbenzoate in toluene gives benzylferrocene. The scheme of the reaction can be written as follows:[15]

$$(C_5H_5)_2Fe + PhCO_2OC(CH_3)_3 \longrightarrow (C_5H_5)_2Fe^+ + PhCO_2^- + (CH_3)_3CO \cdot \quad (66)$$

$$PhCH_3 + (CH_3)_3CO \cdot \longrightarrow PhCH_2 \cdot + (CH_3)_3COH \quad (67)$$

$$(C_5H_5)_2Fe^+ + PhCH_2 \cdot \longrightarrow C_5H_5FeC_5H_4CH_2Ph + H^+ \quad (68)$$

The interaction with benzoyl peroxide or *tert*-butyl perbenzoate in benzene leads to the formation of iron benzoate.[5,34] Only insignificant amounts of carbon dioxide are evolved during the above reactions. This proves the ferricinium cation to be very sensitive to free-radical attack, since it reacts with benzoate radicals more quickly than they are decarboxylated.[5]

Ferrocene interaction with maleic anhydride (in tetrahydrofuran in the presence of hydrogen peroxide) is a free-radical process. A ferrocene derivative (**66**) was isolated from the reaction mixture. The conditions of the reaction may allow an intermediate formation of a ferricinium cation.[35]

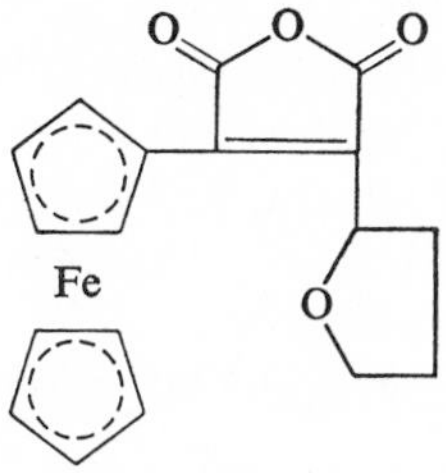

(**66**)

4. Examples of Syntheses

a. Phenylferrocene and 1,1′-Diphenylferrocene.[4,18] A solution of diazotized aniline prepared from 7.5 g of aniline (0.08 mole), 5.8 g of sodium nitrite (0.09 mole), 5 ml of concentrated sulfuric acid, and a minimum amount of water is added rapidly to a stirred solution of 10 g of ferrocene (0.05 mole) in 400 ml of acetic acid at room temperature. After allowing the reaction to proceed overnight at room temperature, the resulting dark-brown solution is poured into approximately 1 liter of water and treated with bisulfite to reduce ferricinium and phenylferricinium salts. The aqueous solution is extracted several times with ether, and the combined ether extracts are washed several times with water, with carbonate solution, and finally again with water. The solvent is removed, leaving 13 g of dark-brown, partly crystalline oil. Steam distillation of the crude product gives 1.4 g of unreacted ferrocene. The residue is dissolved in ether, and the solution is dried over magnesium sulfate. After removal of the solvent, the crude mixture is dissolved in Skellysolve B and chromatographed on 600 g of Merck alumina. Elution is carried out with Skellysolve B. In this manner 5.35 g of phenylferrocene, m.p. 90–100°, and 0.80 g of 1,1′-diphenylferrocene, m.p. 156–157°, are obtained. Recrystallization of the crude phenylferrocene from the ether–Skellysolve B solution gives 5.0 g, m.p. 114–115°.

The disubstituted substance can be made the major product of the reaction by employing a twofold excess of the diazonium salt and by carrying out the reaction at 0°.

b. *p-Nitrophenylferrocene.*[3] In hot hydrochloric acid (125 ml of concentrated hydrochloric acid and 125 ml of water) is dissolved 60 g (0.435 mole) of *p*-nitroaniline, and 400 g of ice is added to the solution. Sodium nitrite (34.5 g, 0.5 mole) dissolved in 80 ml of water is added to the mixture with vigorous stirring. After 10 min, excess nitrous acid is removed with urea, and the solution is neutralized with sodium acetate and filtered. It is then added with vigorous stirring to a cold (−10°) solution of ferrocene (20 g, 0.107 mole) in 600 ml of ether. The addition rate is maintained so that the reaction mixture does not rise above −2°. After stirring for 2 hr, the precipitate is filtered, combined with the material obtained after evaporation of the filtrate, dried in air, and extracted with a petroleum ether–benzene (2:1) mixture in a Soxhlet apparatus. Removal of the solvent gives 21 g (64% of the theoretical amount) of *p*-nitrophenylferrocene, dark-red plates, m.p. 166.5–167.5° (from petroleum ether). When purified by chromatography on alumina, the compound melts at 173° (from hexane).[7]

References

1. M. Rosenblum, W. G. Howells, A. K. Banerjee and C. Bennett, *J. Am. Chem. Soc.,* **84,** 2726 (1962).
2. A. N. Nesmeyanov, E. G. Perevalova, R. V. Golovnya, and O. A. Nesmeyanova, *Dokl. Akad. Nauk SSSR,* **97,** 459 (1954).
3. A. N. Nesmeyanov, E. G. Perevalova, and R. V. Golovnya, *Dokl. Akad. Nauk SSSR,* **99,** 539 (1954).
4. G. D. Broadhead and P. L. Pauson, *J. Chem. Soc.,* **1955,** 367.
5. A. L. J. Beckwith and R. J. Leydon, *Tetrahedron,* **20,** 791 (1964).
6. A. N. Nesmeyanov, E. G. Perevalova, R. V. Golovnya, and L. S. Shilovtseva, *Dokl. Akad. Nauk SSSR,* **102,** 535 (1955).

7. A. L. J. Beckwith and R. J. Leydon, *Australian J. Chem.*, **19**, 1381 (1966).
8. W. F. Little, K. N. Lynn, and R. Williams, *J. Amer. Chem. Soc.*, **85**, 3055 (1963).
9. W. F. Little, B. Nielsen, and R. Williams, *Chem. Ind. (London)*, **1964**, 195.
10. W. F. Little, C. N. Reilley, J. D. Johnson, K. N. Lynn, and A. P. Sanders, *J. Am. Chem. Soc.*, **86**, 1376 (1964).
11. K. Schlögl and M. Fried, *Monatsh.*, **94**, 537 (1963).
12. V. Weinmayr, *J. Amer. Chem. Soc.*, **77**, 3012 (1955).
13. W. F. Little and A. K. Clark, *J. Org. Chem.*, **25**, 1979 (1960).
14. A. L. J. Beckwith and R. J. Leydon, *J. Amer. Chem. Soc.*, **86**, 952 (1964).
15. A. L. J. Beckwith and R. J. Leydon, *Tetrahedron Letters*, **1963**, No. 6, 385.
16. M. Rosenblum, *Chemistry of the Iron Group Metallocenes*, Part 1, Wiley, New York, 1965, p. 201.
17. A. N. Nesmeyanov, E. G. Perevalova, R. V. Golovnya, N. Y. Simukova, and O. V. Starovskii, *Izv. Akad. Nauk SSSR, Otd. Khim. Nauk*, **1957**, 638.
18. M. Rosenblum, *J. Amer. Chem. Soc.*, **81**, 4530 (1959).
19. W. F. Little, A. K. Clark, G. Benner, and C. Nol, *J. Org. Chem.*, **29**, 713 (1964).
20. J. G. Mason and M. Rosenblum, *J. Amer. Chem. Soc.*, **82**, 4206 (1960).
21. E. G. Perevalova, N. A. Simukova, T. V. Nikitina, P. D. Reshetov, and A. N. Nesmeyanov, *Izv. Akad. Nauk SSSR, Otd. Khim. Nauk*, **1961**, 77.
22. A. N. Nesmeyanov, *Proc. Roy. Soc. (London)*, **246A**, 495 (1958).
23. M. D. Rausch, *Inorg. Chem.*, **1**, 414 (1962).
24. S. I. Goldberg, *J. Org. Chem.*, **25**, 482 (1960).
25. D. E. Bublitz, W. E. McEwen, and J. Kleinberg, *J. Amer. Chem. Soc.*, **84**, 1845 (1962).
26. M. Cais, A. Modiano, and A. Raveh, *J. Amer. Chem. Soc.*, **87**, 5607 (1965).
27. A. N. Nesmeyanov, *Referatenband XIV Internationaler Kongress für Reine und Angewandte Chemie, Zürich, 1955*, p. 193.
28. K. Schlögl, *Monatsh.*, **88**, 601 (1957).
29. I. K. Ushenko, K. D. Zhykhareva, and F. Z. Rodova, *Zh. Obshch. Khim.*, **33**, 798 (1963).
30. M. Rosenblum, J. O. Santer, and W. G. Howells, *J. Amer. Chem. Soc.*, **85**, 1450 (1963).
31. R. E. Bozak and K. L. Rinehart, *J. Amer. Chem. Soc.*, **84**, 1589 (1962).
32. A. N. Nesmeyanov, E. G. Perevalova, N. A. Simukova, Yu. N. Sheinker, and M. D. Reshetova, *Dokl. Akad. Nauk SSSR*, **133**, 851 (1960).
33. N. A. Nesmeyanov and O. A. Reutov, *Dokl. Akad. Nauk SSSR*, **120**, 1267 (1958).
34. K. H. Pausacker, *Australian J. Chem.*, **11**, 509 (1958).
35. R. E. Bozak, *J. Org. Chem.*, **31**, 610 (1966).

I. Cyanation

1. Substitution on the Ferricinium Cation

In 1960 Nesmeyanov and co-workers[1,2] tried to carry out a nucleophilic hydrogen substitution on the ferricinium cation. They found that when ferricinium ferribromide was dissoved in water and treated with potassium cyanide, the nitrile of ferrocenecarboxylic acid was formed in low yield (3%).

$$(C_5H_5)_2Fe^+FeBr_4^- \xrightarrow[H_2O]{KCN} C_5H_5FeC_5H_4CN \qquad (69)$$

When the reaction was carried out in an acidic medium, the yield increased somewhat (up to 6%) but remained too low to be of synthetic value. The yield of ferrocenecarboxylic acid nitrile increased sharply and surpassed 50% when a solution of liquid hydrogen cyanide in dry tetrahydrofuran was used.

$$(C_5H_5)_2Fe^+FeCl_4^- \xrightarrow[\text{THF}]{\text{HCN (liq)}} C_5H_5FeC_5H_4CN \qquad (70)$$

It was further established that the nitrile yield could be increased to 80–85% if the ferricinium salt was replaced by a mixture of ferrocene and an excess of anhydrous iron(III) chloride (4 moles to 1 mole of ferrocene).

$$(C_5H_5)_2Fe \xrightarrow[\text{THF}]{\text{FeCl}_3, \text{ HCN (liq)}} C_5H_5FeC_5H_4CN \qquad (71)$$

It should be noted that in all cases the nitrile of ferrocenecarboxylic acid was isolated from the reaction mixture in the reduced, instead of the cationic, state.

2. Cyanation of Ferrocene Derivatives

The reaction procedure was also used for the cyanation of ferrocene derivatives and has proved to be a good synthetic method, not only for ferrocene-carboxylic acid nitriles but also for substituted ferrocenecarboxylic acid nitriles as well.[1-3] The reaction of ferrocene with increased amounts of hydrogen cyanide and iron(III) chloride (10 moles of $FeCl_3$) yields a dinitrile of 1,1'-ferrocenedicarboxylic acid in a good yield (68%).[3]

$$(C_5H_5)_2Fe \xrightarrow[\text{THF}]{\text{FeCl}_3, \text{ HCN}} Fe(C_5H_4CN)_2 \qquad (72)$$

Nesmeyanov and co-workers[4,5] have also used the nitriles of ferrocene-carboxylic acids to synthetize other ferrocene derivatives.

For cyanation to be successful iron(III) chloride is required in greater amounts than in the ferrocene oxidation to the cation. If ferricinium fluo-borate (in the absence of $FeCl_3$) is introduced into the reaction, cyanation involves only 45% of the initial cation; the remaining ferricinium cation is reduced to ferrocene.[3] Therefore the ferricinium cation acts as an oxidant in this case.

The effect on cyanation of substituents on the ferrocene rings is of the same nature as it is in electrophilic substitution (the sole exception being the phenyl group). Electron-withdrawing substituents (chlorine, bromine, cyan-ide, p-nitrophenyl, phenylsulfonyl, carbomethoxy, and especially acetyl and nitro groups) make the cyanation reaction difficult and favor the formation of predominantly or exclusively heteroannular isomers.[1,3]

Cyanation of ferrocene derivatives with electron-donating substituents (methyl and ethyl) yields a mixture of isomeric nitriles of alkylferrocene-

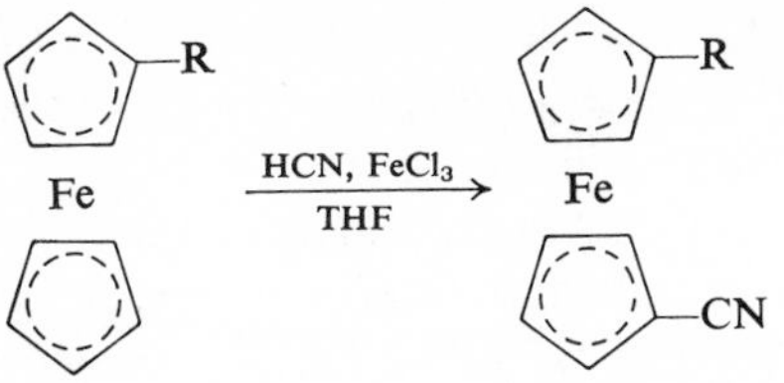

$$(73)$$

(R = COCH$_3$, NO$_2$, Cl, Br, p-C$_6$H$_4$NO$_2$, SO$_2$C$_6$H$_5$, CN)

carboxylic acids [compounds **(67)**, **(68)**, and **(69)**] in which homoannular isomers prevail.[1,4,6]

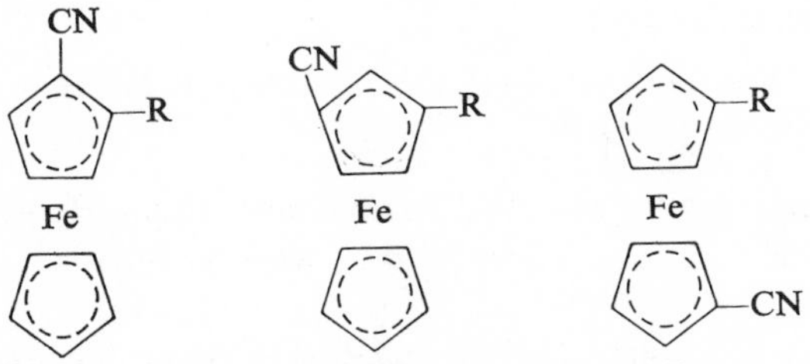

(R = CH$_3$, C$_2$H$_5$, C$_6$H$_5$)

In the process of phenylferrocene cyanation the cyanide group reacts chiefly with the substituted ring. Therefore in this case, unlike in the case of electrophilic substitution (acylation and deuteration) or oxidation to the ferricinium cation (see Chapter 4), the phenyl group displays electron-donating properties.[3,7,8]

The ratio of isomeric nitriles formed in the cyanation of methyl, ethyl, and phenyl ferrocenes was established by gas–liquid chromatography.[9] The results are presented in Table XIII.

TABLE XIII

Ratio of Isomers in a Mixture of Nitriles Obtained in the
Cyanation of C$_5$H$_5$FeC$_5$H$_4$—R

R	Number of moles FeCl$_3$	Ratio of isomers 1,2:1,3:1,1′	Relative reactivity of positions 2:3 :1′
CH$_3$	2.5	1.8:1.7:1.0	4.5:4.3:1.0
C$_2$H$_5$	2.5	2.1:1.0:1.1	4.6:2.1:1.0
C$_6$H$_5$	2.6	2.6:1.0:2.5	2.6:1.0:1.0

The structures of the isomers were established on the basis of infrared, ultraviolet; and NMR spectra; values of oxidation–reduction potentials; and comparative adsorption on alumina.[10,11]

Table XIII shows position 2 of the substituted ring to be the most reactive in all cases. Acylation of alkyl ferrocenes produces significant amounts of 1,3-disubstituted ferrocenes (cf. Section C). The difference may be due to the small size of the cyano group causing steric effects to be significantly less important in cyanation than in acylation. The effect of substituents on cyanation shows that this is not an S_N2 substitution of hydrogen atoms on a ferricinium cation

3. Mechanism of Reaction

In examining the mechanism of this uncommon reaction the following features should be remembered:

1. The reaction begins with the ferricinium cation. However, the final product, the nitrile of ferrocenecarboxylic acid, is isolated in the reduced form.

2. An oxidant is required for the reaction to occur. The oxidant used is either iron(III) chloride or the ferricinium cation.

3. The reaction is affected by substituents exactly as in electrophilic substitution, except that the phenyl substituent in cyanation displays electron-donating properties.

4. In the reaction mixture a cyanide anion is bonded to a ferricinium cation. This results in the liberation of a proton from a molecule of hydrogen cyanide. This fact is expressed by a decrease in the medium pH (by 0.5–0.8 unit) when solutions of hydrogen cyanide and ferricinium fluoborate are mixed together.

$$(C_5H_5)_2Fe^+ + HCN \rightleftharpoons (C_5H_5)_2FeCN + H^+ \qquad (74)$$

On the other hand, addition of hydrochloric acid to the reaction mixture reduces the yield of ferrocenecarboxylic acid nitrile.[12]

5. No kinetically independent group CN, either as a cation or as a radical, could be found in the reaction mixture.* For example, thiophene, which is somewhat more active than ferrocene in electrophilic substitution reactions,[14] is not cyanated when added to the reaction mixture, either in the presence or in the absence of ferrocene. This fact justifies rejection of all schemes, including that of Rosenblum,[15] that involve attack by a kinetically independent radical or CN cation.

The above characteristics of cyanation lead to the following overall mechanism: first the cyanide anion is coordinated by an iron atom and then the CN-group migrates intramolecularly to the five-membered ring.

* It has been shown that the CN radical is an electrophilic particle.[13]

$$Fe^+ + CN^- \longrightarrow \left[Fe\text{—}CN \right] \xrightarrow{FeCl_3} Fe\text{—}CN + H^+ \qquad (75)$$

Nesmeyanov has termed this type of reaction in which an initial attack on the metal atom is followed by the shifting of the attacking particle to a ligand a "ricochet" reaction.[6]

To conclude, it should be emphasized that cyanation is a unique reaction, with respect to both ferrocene and hydrogen cyanide. Unsuccessful attempts have been made to extend the reaction to other π-complexes of the transition metals: π-cyclopentadienyl manganese tricarbonyl, nickelocene, dibenzene-chromium, titanium bis(cyclopentadienyl) derivatives, and benzenecyclo-pentadienyliron. Attempts have also been made at causing the cyanide group covalently bonded with an iron atom in cyclopentadienyliron dicar-bonyl cyanide to migrate to the five-membered ring. Agents other than hydrogen cyanide have also been sought for this purpose. Only ruthenocinium-salt cyanation has been effected, and even that in low (3%) yield.[16]

4. Example of Syntheses: Nitrile of Ferrocenylcarboxylic Acid[1,2]

Ferrocene (3.72 g, 0.02 mole) is dissolved in 50 ml of tetrahydrofuran; anhydrous iron(III) chloride (13 g, 0.08 mole) and then liquid hydrogen cyanide (25 ml) are added. The mixture is refluxed for 3–4 hr in an apparatus connected with an absorber filled with potassium permanganate solution and left overnight. A 10% solution of sodium hydroxide is added until the blue ferricinium color disappeared. The mixture is extracted with ether, which is then removed, and the residue is dissolved in petroleum ether and chromato-graphed on alumina. Ferrocene is eluted with petroleum ether, and the nitrile is eluted with a petroleum ether–benzene (1:1) mixture to yield 3.6 g (86% of the theoretical amount) of the nitrile of ferrocenylcarboxylic acid, m.p. 107–108° (from petroleum ether).

References

1. E. G. Perevalova, L. P. Yur'eva, and Yu. I. Baukov, *Dokl. Akad. Nauk SSSR*, **135**, 1402 (1960).
2. A. N. Nesmeyanov, E. G. Perevalova, and L. P. Yur'eva, and *Ber.*, **93**, 2729 (1960).
3. A. N. Nesmeyanov, E. G. Perevalova, L. P. Yur'eva, and K. I. Grandberg, *Izv. Akad. Nauk SSSR, Otd. Khim. Nauk*, **1962**, 1773.
4. A. N. Nesmeyanov, E. G. Perevalova, L. P. Yur'eva, and K. I. Grandberg, *Izv. Akad. Nauk SSSR, Otd. Khim. Nauk*, **1963**, 1377.
5. A. N. Nesmeyanov, E. G. Perevalova, L. P. Yur'eva, and L. I. Denisovich, *Izv. Akad. Nauk SSSR, Otd. Khim. Nauk*, **1962**, 2241.

6. A. N. Nesmeyanov, E. G. Perevalova, L. P. Yur'eva, and L. N. Kakurina, *Izv. Akad. SSSR, Ser. Khim. Nauk*, **1964**, 1897.
7. A. N. Nesmeyanov, E. G. Perevalova, and L. P. Yur'eva, *Izv. Akad. Nauk SSSR, Ser. Khim. Nauk*, **1965**, 907.
8. A. N. Nesmeyanov, E. G. Perevalova, L. P. Yur'eva, and G. N. Gosteeva, *Izv. Akad. Nauk SSSR, Ser. Khim.*, **1966**, 1467.
9. A. N. Nesmeyanov, L. P. Yur'eva, and E. G. Perevalova, *Izv. Akad. Nauk SSSR, Ser. Khim.*, **1967**, 578.
10. G. G. Dvoryantseva, Yu, N. Sheinker, L. P. Yur'eva, and A. N. Nesmeyanov, *Dokl. Akad. Nauk SSSR*, **156**, 873 (1964).
11. A. N. Nesmeyanov, E. G. Perevalova, L. P. Yur'eva, and S. P. Gubin, *Izv. Akad. Nauk SSSR, Otd. Khim. Nauk*, **1965**, 909.
12. A. N. Nesmeyanov, E. G. Perevalova, and L. P. Yur'eva, unpublished results.
13. K. Koyama, T. Susuki, and Sh. Tsutsumi, *Tetrahedron Letters*, **1965**, 627.
14. K. Schlögl and H. Pelousek, *Ann.*, **651**, 1 (1962).
15. M. Rosenblum, *Chemistry of the Iron Group Metallocenes: Ferrocene, Ruthenocene, Osmocene*, Part 1, Wiley, New York, 1965, p. 207.
16. A. N. Nesmeyanov, A. A. Lubovich, L. P. Yur'eva, S. P. Gubin, and E. G. Perevalova, *Izv. Akad. Nauk SSSR, Ser. Khim.*, **1967**, 935.

J. Condensation

In this section we describe the condensation of ferrocene with aldehydes and ketones as well as ferrocene polycondensation in the presence of *tert*-butyl peroxide. Certain ferrocene condensations (i.e., Friedel–Crafts and aminomethylation) have been discussed in preceding sections.

1. Ferrocene Condensation with Aldehydes

The interaction of ferrocene with aldehydes, exemplified by the reaction with formaldehyde or benzaldehyde in the presence of anhydrous hydrogen fluoride, was first described by Weinmayr.[1,2] Later Nesmeyanov and Kritskaya[3] and then Riemschneider and Helm[4] independently demonstrated that ferrocene reacts with formaldehyde in the presence of concentrated sulfuric acid. The condensation products are 1,2-diferrocenylethane (**41**) and 1,2-diferrocenyl-1,2-diphenylethane (**70**), respectively.[5,6]

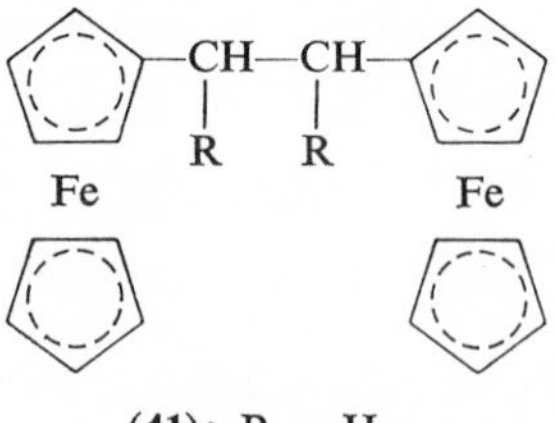

(**41**): R = H
(**70**): R = C$_6$H$_5$

The structure of 1,2-diferrocenylethane (**41**) has been confirmed by several syntheses. Rinehart and co-workers[5] prepared it from ferrocenylacetic acid according to the following scheme:

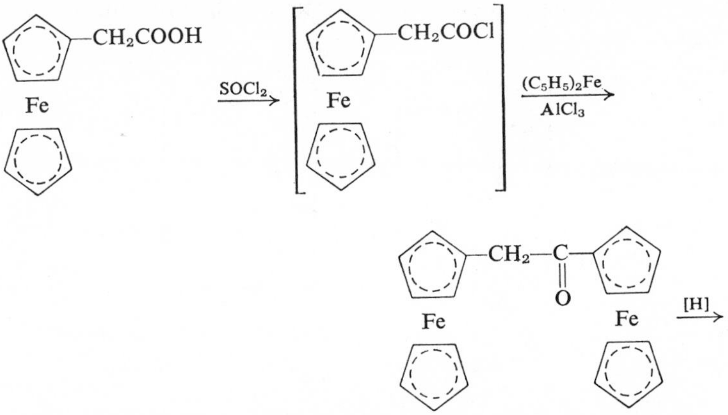

Originally the condensation product was erroneously described as 1,1'-bis(ferrocenylmethane) (71)[2,3] or 1,2-bis(ferrocenylmethane) (72).[7]

Nesmeyanov and co-workers[6,8] obtained 1,2-diferrocenylethane by reacting iron(III) chloride with ferrocenylmethyllithium.

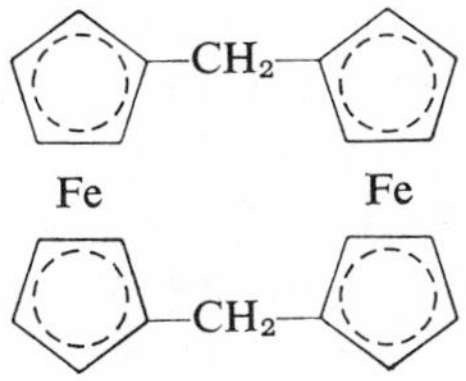

Ferrocene condensation with aldehydes is accompanied by ferrocene oxidation involving the iron atom. The resulting compounds are present *in situ* as salts of the ferricinium cation and are isolated after being reduced by tin(II) chloride[3,5] or zinc dust.[1,2]

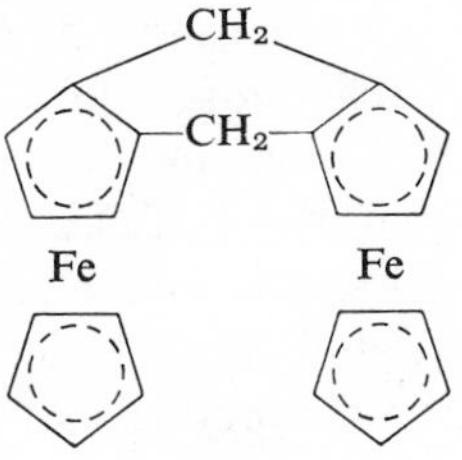

$$(C_5H_5)_2Fe + R-CHO \xrightarrow{H_2SO_4} C_5H_5Fe^+C_5H_4-\underset{\underset{R}{|}}{CH}-\underset{\underset{R}{|}}{CH}-C_5H_4Fe^+C_5H_5 \xrightarrow{SnCl_2}$$

$$C_5H_5FeC_5H_4-\underset{\underset{R}{|}}{CH}-\underset{\underset{R}{|}}{CH}-C_5H_4FeC_5H_5 \qquad (77)$$

$$(R = H, C_6H_5)$$

There is no analog in the benzene series with this ferrocene condensation with aldehydes. Rinehart, Michejda, and Kittle[5] assumed that in this reaction the ferrocenylmethyl cation (73) is formed as an intermediate product, which then dimerizes to give an oxidized form (75) of 1,2-diferrocenylethane (41).

The formation of compound (75) probably proceeds via the prior formation of a cation radical (74).

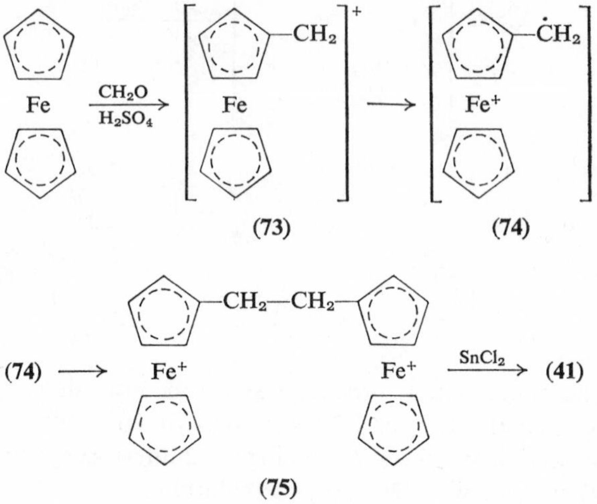

(78)

However, Cais and Eisenstadt[9] doubt that there is either an intermolecular or intramolecular oxidation–reduction reaction involving the iron. They tried in vain to find carbonium-ion isomerization to the cation radical as exemplified by ferrocenyl(phenyl)carbonium ion salt.

Ferrocene condensation with aldehydes does not always lead to dimer products. Thus, if paraformaldehyde takes part in the reaction, diferrocenyl-methane (76) is the main product and just a small amount of 1,2-diferrocenyl-ethane[10] is obtained.

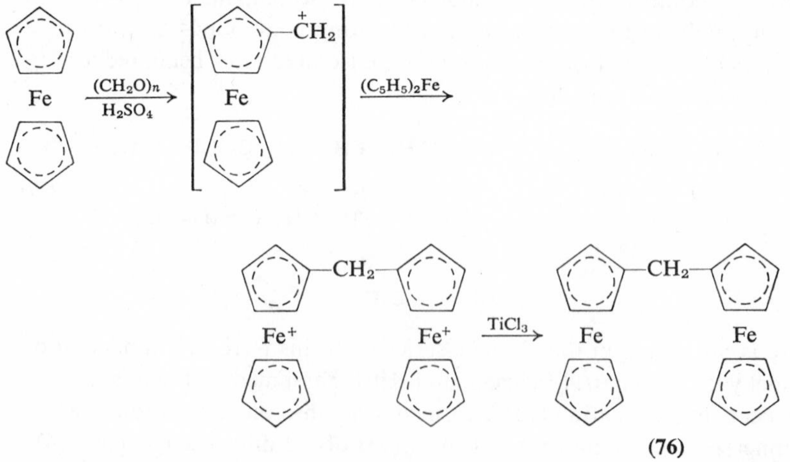

(79)

Ferrocene interaction with benzaldehyde in the presence of boron trifluoride leads to ferrocenyl(phenyl)carbinol (77) in low yield.[11]

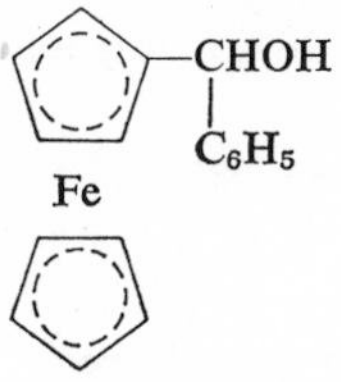

(77)

Ferrocene reaction with ferrocene aldehyde (or formic acid) in the presence of phosphorus oxychloride gives the diferrocenylmethyl cation as the perchlorate[12] $(C_5H_5FeC_5H_4)_2\overset{+}{C}HClO_4^-$.

Ferrocene interaction with p-dimethylaminobenzaldehyde has also been described.[7]

Ferrocene interaction with pyrrolaldehyde derivatives has been used to synthesize ferrocenylmethine dyes.[13] Dye (78) has been isolated as the perchlorate from the intractable mixture of reaction products.

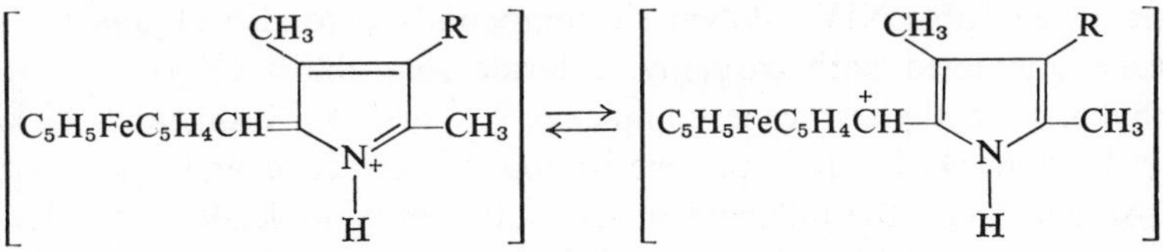

(80)

(78)

(R = H, C_2H_5, $COOC_2H_5$)

2. Ferrocene Condensation with Ketones

Ferrocene condensation with acetone and acetylacetone has already been described.[11] The reaction with acetone was carried out in the presence of boron trifluoride at room temperature or in the presence of concentrated hydrochloric acid in an autoclave at 145°. Both 2,2-diferrocenylpropane (79) and 2-methyl-2-ferrocenylpentanone-4 (80) were obtained in low yields.

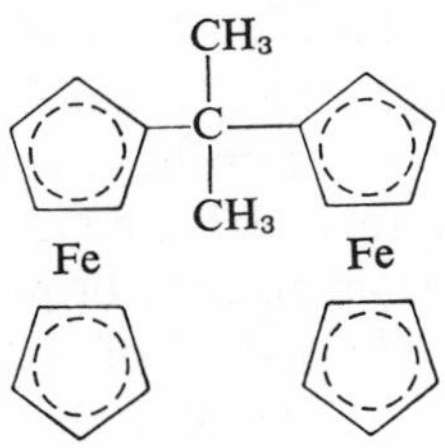

(79) 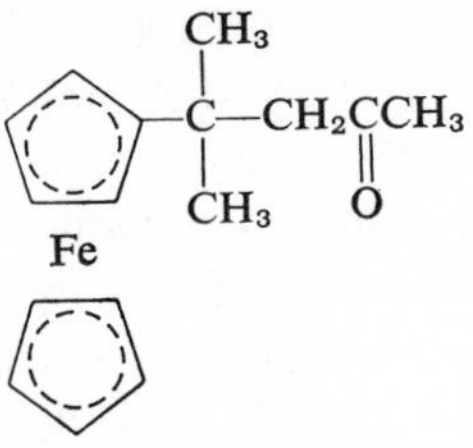   (80)

Also when ferrocene reacts with acetylacetone in the presence of hydro-chloric acid, 2,2-diferrocenylpropane (**79**) is formed.[11] Pauson and Watts[10] have shown that in moist benzene ferrocene reacts, if sodium amalgam is present, with benzoylferrocene (**81**) giving a low yield of diferrocenyl(phenyl)-

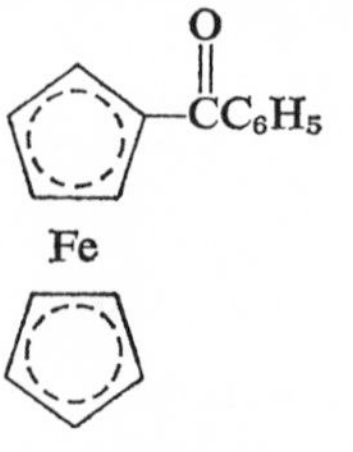

(**81**) 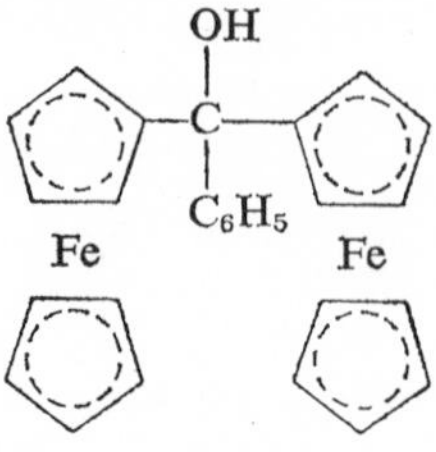   (**82**)

carbinol (**82**). All attempts at a similar condensation between ferrocene and benzophenone, acetophenone, or acetylferrocene have failed.[10]

3. Ferrocene Polycondensation

Recently ferrocene condensation with carbonyl compounds in the presence of Lewis acids at 120–200° has been used to obtain ferrocenyl-containing polymers (see Table XIV). Polymeric compounds were also obtained when ferrocene interacted with carbamyl chloride–zinc chloride[14] or the N,N-dimethylaminomethylferrocene complex.[15,16] Korshak, Sosin, and Alexeeva[17-19] have worked out a polymerization of ferrocene and alkyl ferro-cenes, which, under the influence of *tert*-butyl peroxide, leads to a polymer with molecular weights of up to 7000. Nesmeyanov, Korshak, and co-workers[20] believe that the tertiary butoxy and methyl radicals that result from peroxide decomposition remove hydrogen from ferrocene. The resulting radicals then combine to form polyferrocenylene. The polymer thus obtained has a complex structure that includes polyferrocenylene segments as well as methylene and aliphatic ether groups.[21]

A number of papers dealing with the synthesis of ferrocene-containing polymers have been covered in a recent review.[22]

4. Example of Syntheses: 1,2-Diferrocenylethane[3,6]

After cooling to −15°, 100 ml of 96% sulfuric acid is rapidly added to a stirred mixture of 14.4 g (0.08 mole) of ferrocene and 13.2 ml of 30% aqueous formaldehyde (0.08 mole) also cooled to −15°. Stirring is continued for 15 min at −15°, for 30 min at room temperature, and 75 min at 65–75°.

The solution, having gradually turned from reddish brown to green, is cooled to room temperature and poured into 500 ml of water. The black precipitate is filtered off, and 70 ml of hydrochloric acid is added to the solution. Small portions of crystalline tin(II) chloride are then added to the

TABLE XIV

Polymers Obtained by Ferrocene Condensation with Carbonyl Compounds

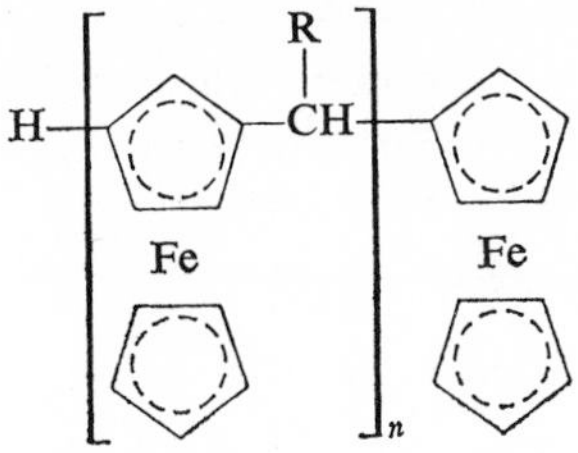

Carbonyl compound	R in Reaction product	Molecular weight	Yield, %	Ref.
HCHO	H	<2500	70	23
CH_3CHO	CH_3	<2500	70	23
$CH_3CH{=}CHCHO$	$CH{=}CHCH_3$	—	20–30	23
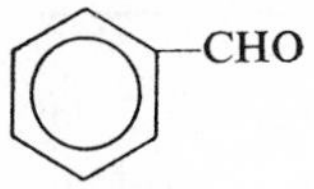	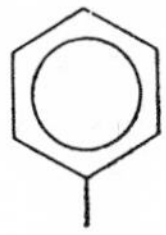	—	—	24
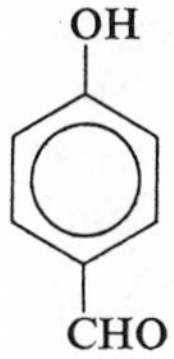	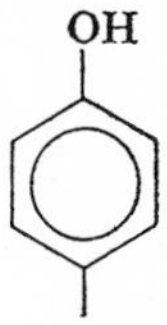	—	—	23
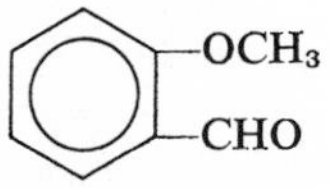	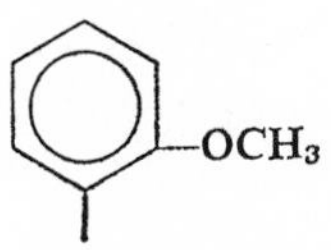	4000	60–70	25
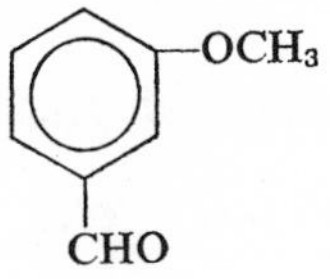	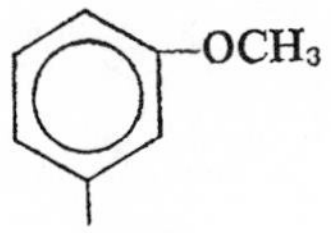	<5000	—	23
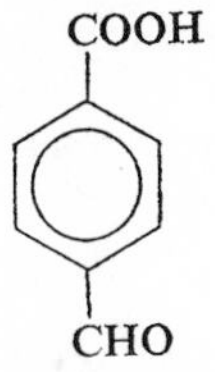		<5000	—	23

(continued)

TABLE XIV (*continued*)

Carbonyl compound	R in Reaction product	Molecular weight	Yield, %	Ref.
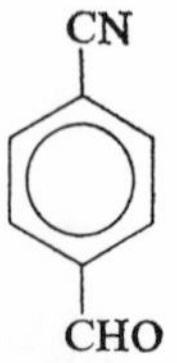 CN / CHO	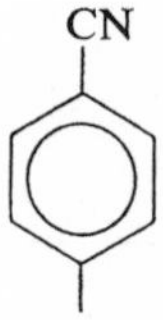 CN	< 5000	—	23
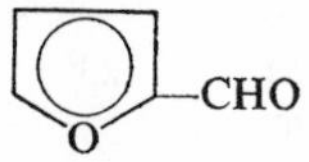 CHO, O	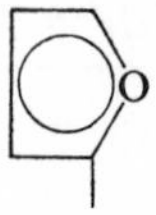 O	< 5000	75	23, 26
CH_3COCH_3	—	2500–3200	54	27

filtrate until the green color of the solution disappears. The mixture is left for 2 hr at room temperature. The precipitate is filtered, dried, and chromatographed on alumina of the first degree of activity. Petroleum ether is used to elute ferrocene (1.4 g, 9.8% of the original amount), and benzene is used to elute 1,2-diferrocenylethane, m.p. 195–196° (recrystallized from dioxane). The yield of 1,2-diferrocenylethane is 9.1 g (64% of the theoretical amount).

References

1. V. Weinmayr, U.S. Patent 2,694,721 (1954); *Chem. Abstr.*, **49**, 15955 (1955).
2. V. Weinmayr. *J. Amer. Chem. Soc.*, **77**, 3009 (1955).
3. A. N. Nesmeyanov and I. I. Kritskaya, *Izv. Akad. Nauk SSSR, Otd. Khim. Nauk*, **1956**, 253.
4. R. Riemschneider and D. Helm, *Chem. Ber.*, **89**, 155 (1956).
5. K. L. Rinehart, C. J. Michejda, and P. A. Kittle, *J. Amer. Chem. Soc.*, **81**, 3162 (1959).
6. A. N. Nesmeyanov and I. I. Kritskaya, *Izv. Akad. Nauk SSSR, Otd. Khim. Nauk*, **1962**, 352.
7. A. N. Nesmeyanov, L. A. Kazitsyna, B. V. Lokshin, and I. I. Kritskaya, *Dokl. Akad. Nauk SSSR*, **117**, 433 (1957).
8. A. N. Nesmeyanov, E. G. Perevalova, and Yu. A. Ustynyuk, *Dokl. Akad. Nauk SSSR*, **133**, 1105 (1960).
9. M. Cais and A. Eisenstadt, *J. Org. Chem.*, **30**, 1148 (1965).
10. P. L. Pauson and W. E. Watts, *J. Chem. Soc.*, **1962**, 3880.
11. A. N. Nesmeyanov, L. P. Yur'eva, and O. T. Nikitin, *Izv. Akad. Nauk SSSR, Ser. Khim*, **1969**, 1096.
12. C. Jutz, *Tetrahedron Letters*, **1959**, 1.
13. A. Treibs and R. Zimmer-Galler, *Chem. Ber.*, **93**, 2539 (1960).

14. T. P. Vishnyakova, I. A. Golubeva, and Ya. M. Paushkin, *Vysokomol. Soyedin.*, **8**, 181 (1966).
15. E. W. Neuse, E. Quo, and W. G. Howells, *J. Org. Chem.*, **30**, 4071 (1965).
16. E. W. Neuse and E. Quo, *Nature*, **204**, 494 (1965).
17. V. V. Korshak, S. L. Sosin, and V. P. Alekseeva, *Dokl. Akad. Nauk SSSR*, **132**, 360 (1960).
18. V V. Korshak, S. L. Sosin, and V. P. Alekseeva, *Vysokomol. Soyedin.*, **3**, 1332 (1961).
19. S. L. Sosin, V. V. Korshak, and V. P. Alekseeva, *Dokl. Akad. Nauk SSSR*, **149**, 327 (1963).
20. A. N. Nesmeyanov, V. V. Korshak, V. V. Voyevodsky, N. S. Kochetkova, S. L. Sosin, R. B. Materikova, T. N. Bolotnikova, V. M. Chibrikin, and N. M. Bazhin, *Dokl. Akad. Nauk SSSR*, **137**, 1370 (1961).
21. H. Rosenberg and E. W. Neuse, *J. Organometal. Chem.*, **6**, 76 (1966).
22. T. P. Vishnyakova, I. A. Golubeva, and T. A. Sokolinskaya, *Usp. Khim*, **36**, 2136 (1967).
23. E. W. Neuse, *Nature*, **204**, 179 (1964).
24. E. W. Neuse, *Abstracts of Papers Presented at the 148th National Meeting of the American Chemical Society, September 1964*, p. 59.
25. E. W. Neuse and K. Koda, *J. Organometal. Chem.*, **4**, 475 (1965).
26. E. W. Neuse, K. Koda, and E. Carter, *Makromol. Chem.*, **84**, 213 (1965).
27. Ya. M. Paushkin, T. P. Vishnyakova, I. I. Patalak, T. A. Sokolinskaya, and F. F. Machus, *Dokl. Akad. Nauk SSSR*, **149**, 856 (1965).

III. HYDROGEN-SUBSTITUTION REACTIONS OF THE CYCLOPENTADIENYL RINGS OF OSMOCENE AND RUTHENOCENE. COMPARISON OF THE REACTIVITY OF THE METALLOCENES AND OTHER AROMATIC SYSTEMS

A. General

The cyclopentadienyl rings of ferrocene undergo a large variety of hydrogen-substitution reactions (see Section II). Similar reactions of ruthenocene and osmocene are much less numerous, although more numerous than those of the bis(cyclopentadienyl) derivatives of other metals.

Metalation and Friedel–Crafts acylation of ruthenocene and osmocene have been investigated. The reaction of osmocene with a diazonium salt has been reported,[1-4] and Nesmeyanov and co-workers have performed the cyanation of a ruthenocinium salt.[5]

In electrophilic substitutions bis(cyclopentadienyl) compounds of ruthenium and osmium are much less active than ferrocene.

B. Acylation of Ruthenocene and Osmocene. Reactivity of Metallocenes Compared with that of Other Aromatic Systems

It is worthy of note that osmocene and ruthenocene have different reactivities in Friedel–Crafts acylation reactions.

When acylated by acyl halides in the presence of aluminum chloride, osmocene yields a monoacylated osmocene (**83**) even if excess acylating agent is used (the molar ratio of the reactants being $1:3:3$).[2,4]

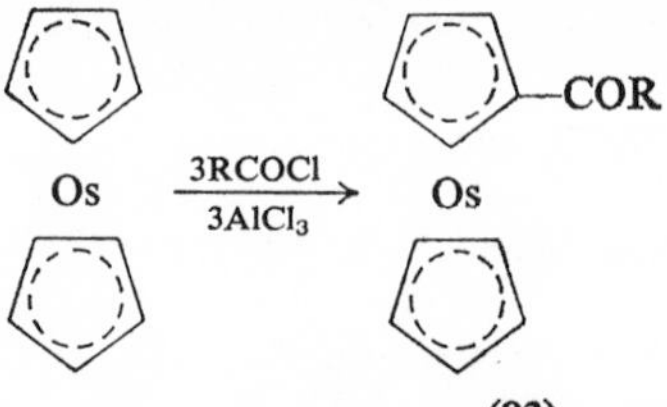

$$\text{Os} \xrightarrow[\text{3AlCl}_3]{\text{3RCOCl}} \text{Os} \quad\quad (81)$$

(**83**)

$$(R = C_6H_5, CH_3)$$

1,1'-Diacetylosmocene[6] is obtained in a small yield (0.1%) when osmocene is acylated by a large excess of acetic anhydride in the presence of phosphoric acid. This reaction gives monoacetylosmocene in yields as high as 91%.

When acylated by acyl halides in the presence of aluminum chloride, ruthenocene gives, with excess acylating agent, a mixture of monoannular and heteroannular diacylated ruthenocenes (**84**) and (**85**) (the molar ratio of the reactants being $1:3:3$).[1,2]

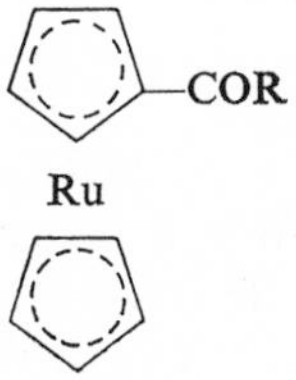

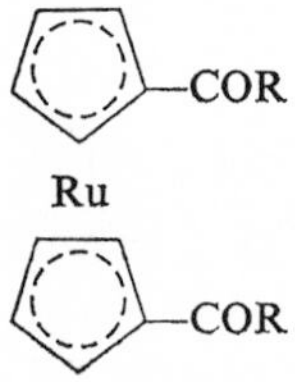

Ru   Ru

(**84**)   (**85**)

$$(R = C_6H_5, CH_3)$$

Benzoylation of ruthenocene also produces a small amount of homoannular dibenzoylruthenocene.[3,7,8] The NMR spectrum shows the homoannular ruthenocene to be a 1,2-isomer.[6] Hence monobenzoylruthenocene is substituted in position 2 more easily than in position 3. It thus resembles the ferrocenes that possess electron-withdrawing substituents (see Section II-C-6).

Interaction of ruthenocene with ferrocenoyl chloride yields ferrocenyl ruthenocenyl ketone (**86**)[2]

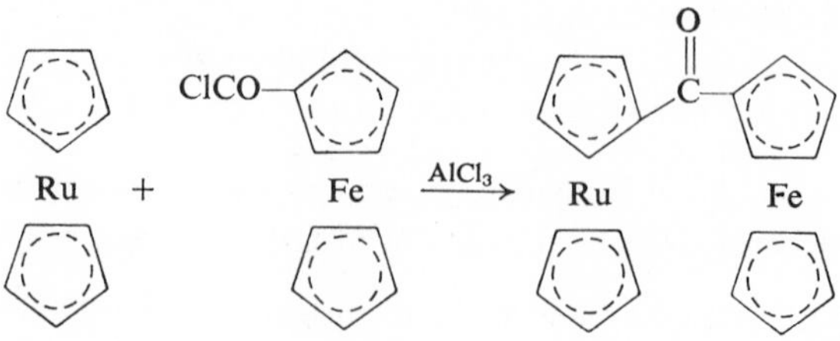

$$\text{Ru} \quad + \quad \text{ClCO—} \quad \text{Fe} \xrightarrow{\text{AlCl}_3} \text{Ru} \quad \text{Fe} \quad\quad (82)$$

(**86**)

Ruthenocene is like a benzenoid aromatic system in that it reacts, in the presence of aluminum chloride, with phenylisocyanate, yielding ruthenocene-carboxylic acid anilide.[9]

$$(C_5H_5)_2Ru + C_6H_5N{=}C{=}O \xrightarrow{AlCl_3} RuC_{10}H_9CONHC_6H_5 \qquad (83)$$

Attempts to formylate ruthenocene or osmocene have been unsuccessful.[2]

The reactivity of osmocene, ruthenocene, and ferrocene toward electrophilic substitution, such as Friedel–Crafts acylation, varies along with ease of oxidation to the cation. This is similar to the changes in reactivity caused by the introduction of electron-withdrawing substituents into the ferrocene nucleus. Thus ferrocene derivatives with electron-withdrawing substituents are inactive in electrophilic substitutions and stable to oxidation (see Chapter 4).

Recently Fischer and co-workers[10] studied a competing Friedel–Crafts acylation of ferrocene, ruthenocene, and osmocene; they found the ratio of acetylferrocene, acetylruthenocene, and acetylosmocene to be 8:1:0, respectively. Competing acylation of each of the three metallocenes and benzene gave the following order of reactivity in Friedel–Crafts acylation:

$$Fe(C_5H_5)_2 > C_6H_5OCH_3 > Ru(C_5H_5)_2 > Os(C_5H_5)_2 > C_6H_6$$

Ferrocene is much more reactive and reacts under milder conditions, in electrophilic substitutions, than benzene. Ferrocene also undergoes reactions benzene does not—e.g., acylation in the presence of tin(IV) chloride, formylation in the presence of phosphorus oxychloride, and sulfonation with the pyridine–sulfur trioxide complex. (For a description of these reactions see Sections II-C and II-E.)

Ferrocene is acetylated in the presence of aluminum chloride more quickly than benzene, phenol, and anisole, as shown by Broadhead, Osgerby, and Pauson[11] in their work with competing acylation of the corresponding mixtures. Gubin, Shepilov, and Nesmeyanov[12] determined the rate of ferrocene acetylation with the complex of $2CH_3COOH \cdot BF_3$ in glacial acetic acid under pseudo-first-order conditions. The results are shown in Table XV.

The reaction rate is increased if the amount of the catalyst is increased.

The data show that under these conditions ferrocene is acetylated 200–300 times as fast as anisole.

TABLE XV

Rate of Ferrocene Acetylation with the Complex $2CH_3COOH \cdot BF_3$

[ferrocene] $= 6.22 \times 10^{-3} M$; [BF$_3$] $= 2.66\ M$			
Temperature, °C	40	45	50	55
$K_1 \times 10^{-6}$ sec^{-1}	0.8	1.9	3.8	7.5

Rosenblum and co-workers[13] determined the relative rates of the Friedel–Crafts acylation of ferrocene, acetylferrocene, benzene, and alkylated benzenes. The authors found the acylation rate to increase in the following order:

benzene < acetylferrocene < mesitylene < pentamethylbenzene < ferrocene
  1.0 1.9×10^2 2.9×10^3 1.3×10^4 3.3×10^6

Thiophene is somewhat more active than ferrocene in Friedel–Crafts reactions. Ferrocene derivatives containing one or more thienyl groups [compound (87) or (88)] are first acetylated in the free α-position of the thienyl in low yield.[14]

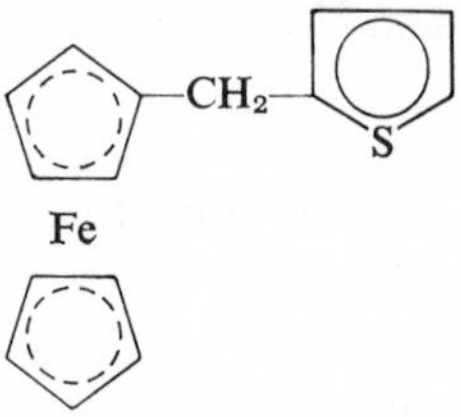

(87) 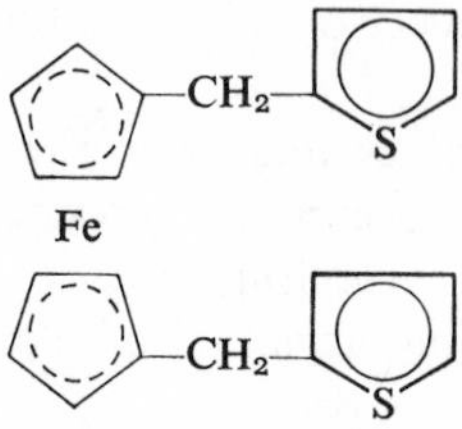   (88)

The comparative reactivity of ferrocene, its derivatives, and a similar benzene compound has also been demonstrated by deuteration. The results are discussed in Section II-B.

C. Metalation

Ruthenocene and osmocene are easily metalated with *n*-butyllithium.[1,2] Carboxylation of metalated ruthenocene or osmocene yields a mixture of metallocenecarboxylic acids whose composition has been determined only in the case of ruthenocene.

Ruthenocene is more active toward metalating agents than ferrocene. When it is metalated with *n*-butyllithium in ether, carboxylation yields ruthenocenemonocarboxylic (89) and ruthenocenedicarboxylic (90) acids, each in a yield of 24%.

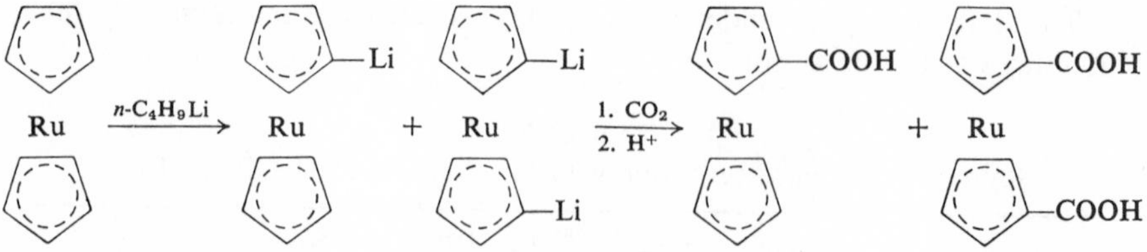

(89)   (90)

However, from ferrocene, under the same conditions, ferrocenemonocarboxylic and ferrocenedicarboxylic acids are obtained in 24 and 9% yield, respectively. When the reaction is carried out in tetrahydrofuran, ruthenocene gives the diacid in 86% yield and the monoacid in only 1% yield. Also in tetrahydrofuran ferrocene gives the monoacid and the diacid in 35 and 39% yields, respectively.[1,2]

Ruthenocene as well as ferrocene reacts with mercury(II) acetate; however, attempts to isolate a mercurated ruthenocene were unsuccessful.[2]

D. Other Reactions

Ruthenocene undergoes condensation with aldehydes in the presence of zinc(II) chloride, forming polymeric products.[15] The reaction demands more drastic conditions than that of ferrocene.

Osmocene is arylated by benzenediazonium salts, but the reaction goes much more slowly than that with ferrocene and the yields are small.[2]

References

1. M. D. Rausch, E. O. Fischer, and H. Grubert, *Chem. Ind. (London)*, **1958**, 756.
2. M. D. Rausch, E. O. Fischer, and H. Grubert, *J. Amer. Chem. Soc.*, **82**, 76 (1960).
3. D. E. Bublitz, I. Kleinberg, and W. E. McEwen, *Chem. Ind. (London)*, **1960**, 936.
4. R. Riemschneider, *Monatsh.*, **90**, 658 (1959).
5. A. N. Nesmeyanov, A. A. Lubovich, L. P. Yur'eva, S. P. Gubin, and E. G. Pereval-ova, *Izv. Akad. Nauk SSSR, Ser. Khim.*, **1967**, 935.
6. M. D. Rausch and V. Mark, *J. Org. Chem.*, **28**, 3225 (1963).
7. D. E. Bublitz, W. E. McEwen, and I. Kleinberg, *J. Amer. Chem. Soc.*, **84**, 1845 (1962).
8. D. E. Bublitz, I. Kleinberg, and W. E. McEwen, *Chem. Ind. (London)*, **1960**, 936.
9. R. A. Hill and J. H. Richards, *J. Amer. Chem. Soc.*, **83**, 3840 (1961).
10. E. O. Fischer, M. von Foester, C. G. Kreiter, and K. E. Schwarzhaus, *J. Organometal. Chem.*, **7**, 113 (1967).
11. G. D. Broadhead, J. M. Osgerby, and P. L. Pauson, *J. Chem. Soc.*, **1958**, 650.
12. S. P. Gubin, L. P. Shepilov, and A. N. Nesmeyanov, *Izv. Akad. Nauk SSSR, Ser. Khim.*, **1966**, 384.
13. M. Rosenblum, J. O. Santer, and W. G. Howells, *J. Amer. Chem. Soc.*, **85**, 1450 (1963).
14. K. Schlögl and M. Pelousek, *Ann.*, **651**, 1 (1962).
15. E. W. Neuse, *J. Organometal. Chem.*, **6**, 92 (1966).

IV. HYDROGEN-SUBSTITUTION REACTIONS IN BIS(CYCLOPENTADIENYL) ZIRCONIUM DERIVATIVES

The salts of bis(cyclopentadienyl) compounds of the transition metals have not been reported to undergo electrophilic substitution. Attempts at performing electrophilic substitution with ferricinium[1] or cobaltocinium[1-3] cations or with bis(cyclopentadienyl)titanium dichloride[4,5] were unsuccessful.*

* Earlier reports[6,7] of Friedel–Crafts alkylation of $(C_5H_5)_2TiCl_2$ have proved to be erroneous.[5]

The only example of such a reaction is the sulfonation of bis(cyclopentadienyl)zirconium dichloride.[8,9]

Reaction of $(C_5H_5)_2ZrCl_2$ with a mixture of sulfuric acid and acetic anhydride produces a sulfonated derivative of bis(cyclopentadienyl) bis-(bisulfato)zirconium. The derivative contains one or two molecules of acetic anhydride and is thought to have structure (91).

$$(C_5H_5)_2ZrCl_2 \xrightarrow[\text{(CH}_3\text{CO)}_2\text{O}]{\text{H}_2\text{SO}_4} [(C_5H_5)(C_5H_4SO_3H)Zr(OSO_3H)_2] \cdot n(CH_3CO)_2O(n = 1, 2)$$

$$\downarrow C_2H_5OH \quad (91)$$

$$[(C_5H_5)(C_5H_4SO_3H)Zr(OSO_3H)_2] \cdot C_2H_5OH$$
$$(92)$$

$$(85)$$

Acetic anhydride is replaced by ethanol to give the analogous compound (92).

Acetic anhydride has also been replaced by dimethylformamide. The bisulfate groups could not be replaced by chloride ions under the influence of hydrogen chloride. Compounds (91) and (92) contain unsubstituted cyclopentadienyl rings, as proved by the isolation of a thallium derivative, C_5H_5Tl. When acted on by acetylacetone, compound (91) exchanges the unsubstituted C_5H_5-ring and a bisulfate group for an acetylacetonate group to form compound (93).

$$[(C_5H_5)(C_5H_4SO_3H)Zr(OSO_3H)_2] \cdot (CH_3CO)_2O \xrightarrow{C_5H_8O_2}$$
$$[(C_5H_7O_2)_2(C_5H_4SO_3H)Zr(OSO_3H)] \cdot nC_5H_8O_2 \quad (86)$$
$$(93)$$
$$(n = 1, 2)$$

References

1. A. N. Nesmeyanov and E. G. Perevalova, *Usp. Khim.*, **27**, 11, 42 (1958).
2. E. O. Fisher and R. Jira, *Z. Naturforsch.*, **8b**, 1 (1953).
3. G. Wilkinson, *J. Amer. Chem. Soc.*, **74**, 6148 (1952).
4. G. Wilkinson and J. Birmingham, *J. Amer. Chem. Soc.*, **76**, 4281 (1954).
5. A. N. Nesmeyanov, O. V. Nogina, T. P. Surikova, and V. A. Dubovitskii, *Izv. Akad Nauk SSSR, Otd. Khim. Nauk*, **1963**, 1699.
6. A. N. Nesmeyanov, O. V. Nogina, T. P. Surikova, *Izv. Akad. Nauk SSSR, Otd. Khim. Nauk*, **1962**, 1314.
7. A. N. Nesmeyanov, O. V. Nogina, and V. A. Dubovitskii, *Izv. Akad. Nauk SSSR, Otd. Khim. Nauk*, **1962**, 2254.
8. E. M. Brainina, M. Kh. Minacheva and R. Kh. Freidlina, *Izv. Akad. Nauk SSSR, Otd. Khim. Nauk*, **1961**, 1716.
9. R. Kh. Freidlina, E. M. Brainina, M. Kh. Minacheva, and A. N. Nesmeyanov, *Izv. Akad. Nauk SSSR, Otd. Khim. Nauk*, **1964**, 1417.

Chapter 2

Substituent-Exchange Reactions in the Cyclopentadienyl Ring, C_5H_4X (X ≠ H)

I. GENERAL

This chapter describes the reactions of lithiated or mercurated ferrocene derivatives as well as ferrocenylboric acids and halogenated ferrocenes. These reactions are extensively used for the synthesis of other ferrocene derivatives.

Lithiated or mercurated ferrocene derivatives play an extremely important role as initial compounds in the synthesis of other ferrocene derivatives. This is the result of the ready availability and high reactivity of these compounds as well as the absence of other intermediates. Furthermore, unlike similar benzene derivatives, nitrated or halogenated ferrocenes cannot be obtained by direct substitution in ferrocene compounds. Magnesium ferrocene derivatives are difficult to obtain, and ferrocenesulfonic acids, though readily obtainable, do not exchange their sulfonate groups.

II. LITHIUM AND SODIUM EXCHANGE

A. Lithium Exchange

Readily available lithiated ferrocene compounds play an important role in the synthesis of ferrocene derivatives.

A series of monosubstituted or disubstituted ferrocenes have been obtained, starting from monolithiated or dilithiated ferrocenes. (see Table I). The most important ones, ferrocenecarboxylic and ferrocenylboric acids, have been used further in synthetic applications.[1,2]*

The lithium derivatives also provide a synthetic route to such ferrocene derivatives as ferrocenylamine,[3,4] nitroferrocene,[5,6] azoferrocene,[7,8]† and ferrocenylazide.[9] A route to diferrocenyl[10] has also been found in the reaction of cobalt(II) chloride with ferrocenyllithium.

Recently monosubstituted, monometalated ferrocenes have been widely used to synthesize both heteroannular and homoannular disubstituted ferrocenes (see Table II).

Lithiated alkyl ferrocenes have been converted to alkylferrocenecarboxylic acids or alkyl nitro ferrocenes.[11,12] This technique has permitted the conversion of chloroferrocene to 1-(2-chloroferrocenyl)boric acid,[13] after which the $B(OH)_2$-group was further exchanged with other groups (see Section V).

---

* For a complete description of the syntheses see the end of this section.
† A complete description of the experimental procedure is given in Ref. 7.

TABLE I

Reactions of Monolithiated and Dilithiated Ferrocenes[a]

Reactant	Reaction products[b]	Yield[c]	Ref.[d]
H_2O	—$C_5H_4FeC_5H_5$	0.4	10
CO_2	—COOH	40	8, 18
	—COOH; 1,1'-(—COOH)$_2$	43	19–23
	1,1'-(—COOH)$_2$	35	24, 25
$CO_2(CH_2N_2)$	—CO_2CH_3;	98	
	1,1'-(—CO_2CH_3)$_2$	28	11, 26
$(C_6H_5)_2CO$	1,1'-[—$C(C_6H_5)_2OH$]$_2$	8	24, 27
		80	
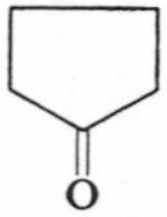 (cyclopentanone)	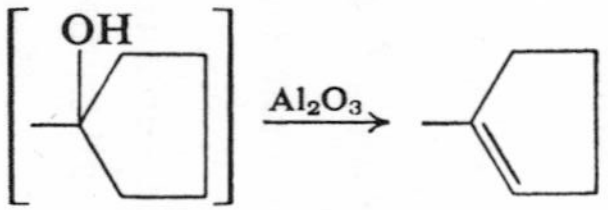 [—OH carbinol] $\xrightarrow{Al_2O_3}$ (1-methylcyclopentene)	—	28
$(C_5H_5FeC_5H_4)_2CO$	—$C(C_5H_4FeC_5H_5)_2OH$	60[e]	29
	—$C(C_5H_4FeC_5H_5)_2OH$;	53	30
	—$C((C_5H_4FeC_5H_5)(C_4H_9)OH$	7	
$C_6H_5N{=}C{=}O$	—$CONHC_6H_5$	9.7	31
$C_5H_5FeC_5H_4CN$	—$COC_5H_4FeC_5H_5$	59	29
CH_3ONH_2	—NH_2	8	4
$C_6H_5CH_2ONH_2$	—NH_2	<1	3
$C_3H_7ONO_2$	—NO_2	—	6
N_2O_4	—NO_2	—	5
N_2O	—$N{=}NC_5H_4FeC_5H_5$	25	8
$p\text{-}MeC_6H_4SO_2N_3$	—N_3;	28	32
	1,1'-(—N_3)$_2$	6	

Reagent	Product		
MeCOCH=CHNMe₂	—CH=CHCOCH₃;	9	33
	$C_{32}H_{34}O_5Fe_2 \cdot H_2O$	—	33
$n\text{-}C_3H_7COCH=CHNMe_2$	—CH=CHCOC₃H₇;	17	33
	1,1'-(—CH=CHCOC₃H₇)₂	4	33
$C_6H_5COCH=CHNMe_2$	—CH=CHC₆H₅;	21	34
	1,1'-(—CH=CHC₆H₅)₂	7	
$CH_2\!-\!CHCH_2Cl$ (epoxide)	—CH₂CH——CH₂ (epoxide)	13	
	1,1'-[—CH₂CH—CH₂]₂ (epoxide)	0.3	
$C_6H_5CH_2Cl$	H—(C₅H₄FeC₅H₄)ₙ—H	42	35
C_2H_5Br	—C₂H₅; 1,1'-(—C₂H₅)₂;	18ᶠ	35
	—C₅H₄FeC₅H₅;	2	
	—C₅H₄FeC₅H₄C₂H₅—?	5	
C_2H_5I	—C₂H₅;	15	
	1,1'-(—C₂H₅)₂;	12	
	—C₅H₄FeC₅H₅;	4	
	—C₅H₄FeC₅H₄C₂H₅—?;	9.5	
	(C₅H₄FeC₅H₄C₂H₅)₂	—	
(pyridine)	(pyridine substituent)	32	36, 37
	1,1'-[pyridine]₂	3	

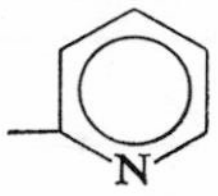

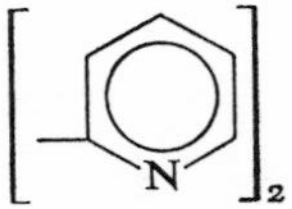

279

(continued)

TABLE I (*continued*)

Reactant	Reaction products[b]	Yield,[c]	Ref.[d]
	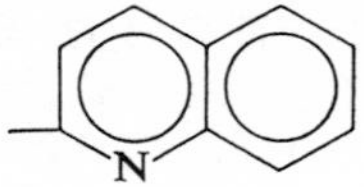	21.6	38, 36
	1,1'- 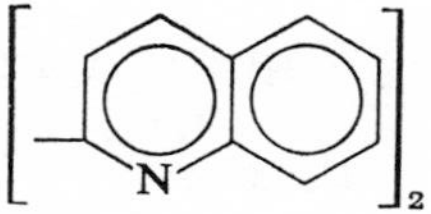	6.7	
B(OC$_4$H$_9$)$_3$	—B(OH)$_2$;	44	2, 1
	1,1'-[—B(OH)$_2$]$_2$	18	
C$_6$H$_5$N$_3$	—N=NNHC$_6$H$_5$;	57	32
	1,1'-(—N=NNHC$_6$H$_5$)$_2$	24	
C$_5$H$_5$FeC$_5$H$_4$N$_3$	—N=NNHC$_5$H$_4$FeC$_5$H$_5$	—	32
Me$_3$SiCl	—SiMe$_3$;	19	22, 26
	1,1'-(—SiMe$_3$)$_2$	27	
Me$_2$Si(Cl)CH$_2$SiMe$_3$	—SiMe$_2$CH$_2$SiMe$_3$;	23	39
	1,1'-(—SiMe$_2$CH$_2$SiMe$_3$)$_2$;	9	
	1,1'-(—SiMe$_2$CH$_2$SiMe$_2$—);	8	
	1,1'-(—SiMe$_2$CH$_2$SiMe$_2$CH$_2$SiMe$_2$—);	—	
	1-SiMe$_3$-1'-SiMe$_2$CH$_2$SiMe$_3$;	4	

$(C_6H_5)_3SiCl$	$1,1'-(-SiMe_2CH_2CH_2SiMe_2-)$	14	
	$-Si(C_6H_5)_3$;	49	21
	$1,1'-[-Si(C_6H_5)_3]_2$	12	
$(n-C_6H_{13})_3SiBr$	$-Si(C_6H_{13})_3$;	32	25
	$1,1'-[-Si(C_6H_{13})_3]_2$	35	
$CoCl_2$	$-C_5H_4FeC_5H_5$;	11	10
	$-C_5H_4FeC_5H_4C_5H_4FeC_5H_5$;	5	
	$-C_5H_4FeC_5H_4C_4H_9$	6.5	
	$H-(C_5H_4FeC_5H_4)_n-H$	74.6	35
$CoCl_2, C_6H_5CH_2Cl$	$-COOH; 1,1'-(-COOH)_2$;	—	35
	$-CO-[-(C_{10}H_8Fe)-CO]_n-C_5H_4FeC_5H_5$	—	

---

[a] Monolithiated or dilithiated ferrocenes are obtained by the metalation of ferrocene with n-butyllithium.

[b] Only the entering group and its position are shown.

[c] Unless otherwise indicated, the yield refers to the amount of ferrocene taken for reaction.

[d] This table presents the best of all yields cited in the papers under review, with the reference corresponding to the best yield placed first.

[e] The yield refers to the amount of ferrocene reacted.

[f] The yield refers to the mixture of both compounds, with no individual product isolated.

TABLE II

Reactions of Ferrocene Derivatives Lithiated with n-Butyllithium

Substituent in ferrocene derivative	Reactant	Reaction products[a]	Yield,[b] %	Ref.
Me	CO_2, CH_2N_2	$1'$-CO_2Me;	14	11
		$1',?$-$(-CO_2Me)_2$	6	11
	$C_3H_7ONO_2$	$1'$-NO_2	7	11
	Pyridine	2-$(\alpha$-Pyridyl$)$;	2	36
		3-$(\alpha$-Pyridyl$)$;	28	
		$1'$-$(\alpha$-Pyridyl$)$	—	
C_2H_5	CO_2, CH_2N_2	$1'$-CO_2Me;	13	11
		$?,1'$-$(-CO_2Me)_2$	5	
n-C_3H_7	$C_3H_7ONO_2$	$1'$-NO_2	18[c]	11
	CO_2, CH_2N_2	$1'$-CO_2Me;	23[d]	11
		$?,1'$-$(-CO_2Me)_2$		
i-C_3H_7	$C_3H_7ONO_2$	$1'$-NO_2	8	11
	Me_3SiCl	3-$SiMe_3$;	—	26
		$1'$-$SiMe_3$;		
		$2,1'$-$(-SiMe_3)_2$;	—	
		$3,1'$-$(-SiMe_3)_2$	—	
—OMe	CO_2	2-$COOH$	70	40
	CO_2, CH_2N_2	2-CO_2Me	—	40
—CPh_2OH	CO_2	2-$COOH$	73	41
	MeI	2-Me	69	41
Cl	$B(OC_4H_9)_3$	2-$B(OH)_2$	62	13
—CH_2NMe_2	D_2O	2-D; 3-D; $1,1'$-D_2	—	14
		2-D	—	14

$(CH_2O)_n$	2-CH_2OH	75	17, 15
Me_2CO	2-CMe_2OH	14	14
Ph_2CO	2-CPh_2OH;	13	14
	1'-CPh_2OH;	10	
	2,1'-($-CPh_2OH)_2$	45	
	2-CPh_2OH	71	14
	2-$C(Me)(FeC_{10}H_9)OH$	30	17
$FeC_{10}H_9COMe$			

2-

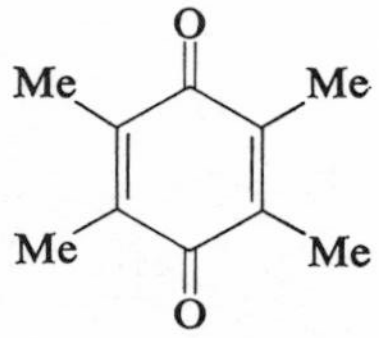

42°   42

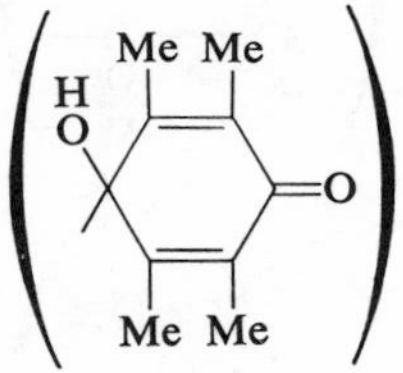

2-

64°   42

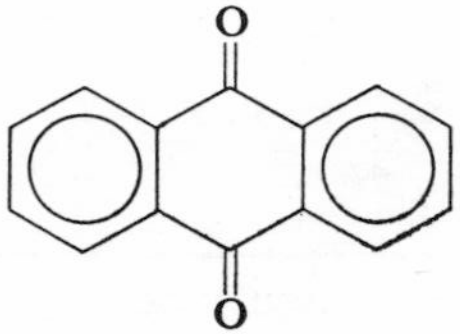

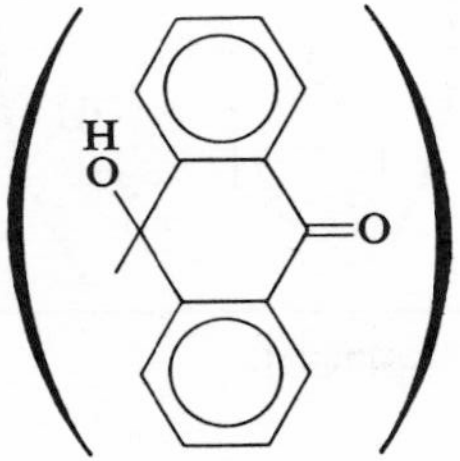

(continued)

283

TABLE II (continued)

Substituent in ferrocene derivative	Reactant	Reaction products[a]	Yield,[b] %	Ref.
	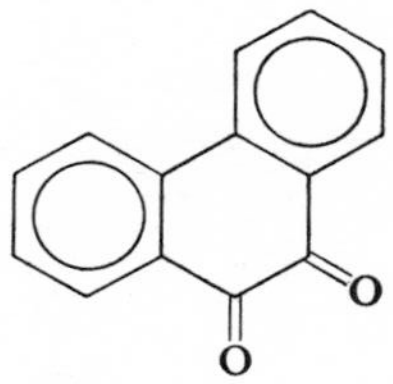	2- 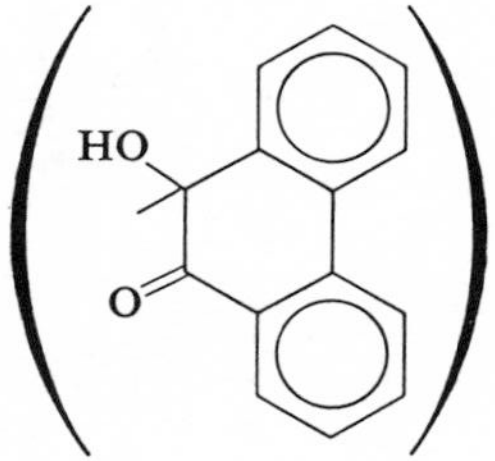	21[c]	42
	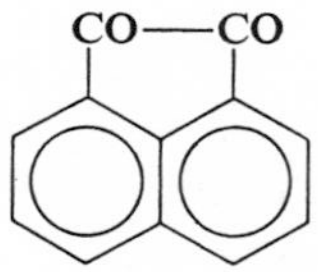	2- 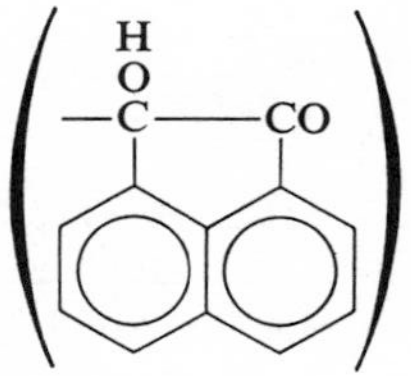	10[c]	42
	C_2Cl_6	2-Cl	60	43
	$PhN{=}C{=}O$	2-CONHPh	31	14
	PhCN	2-COPh	58	14
	$B(OC_4H_9)_3$	2-B(OH)$_2$	92	16
	Me_3SiCl	2-SiMe$_3$	79	44

Reagent	Product		
Me_2SiCl_2	2-SiMe$_2$ / Fe (CH$_2$NMe$_2$)	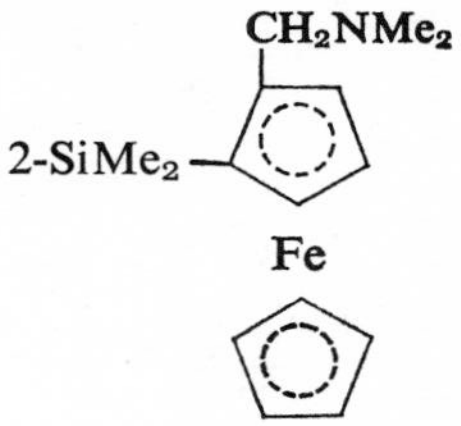 55	44
H_2O	(C$_4$H$_9$, 2-methylpyridine)	30	45
Ph_2CO	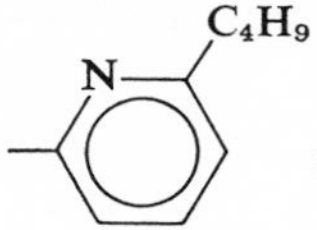 (C$_4$H$_9$, 2-methylpyridine) ;	9	45
	1- -2-CPh$_2$OH;	41	

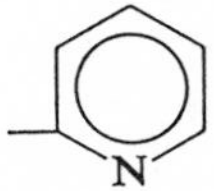

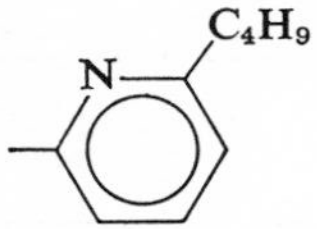

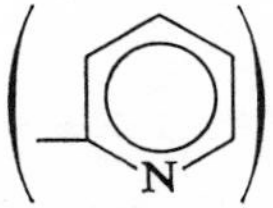

(continued)

285

TABLE II (*continued*)

Substituent in ferrocene derivative	Reactant	Reaction products[a]	Yield,[b] %	Ref.
		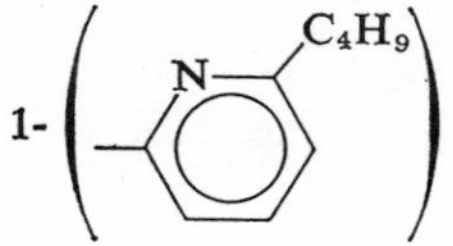 1-(C$_4$H$_9$-pyridyl)-2-CPh$_2$OH;	20	
		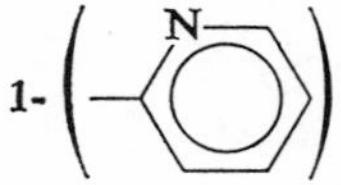 1-(pyridyl)-2,1'-(—CPh$_2$OH)$_2$;	16	
		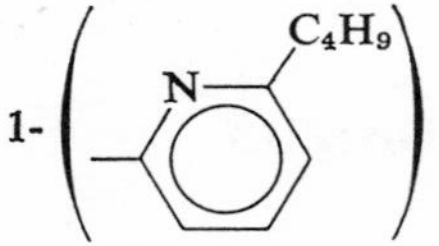 1-(C$_4$H$_9$-pyridyl)-2,1'-(—CPh$_2$OH)$_2$	5	

| 1-CH₂NMe₂-2-CPh₂OH | Ph₂CO | 1'-CPh₂OH | 33 | 14 |

$1-CH_2NMe_2-2-CPh_2OH$ Ph_2CO $1'-CPh_2OH$ 33   14

$\xrightarrow[\text{2. H}_2\text{O}]{\text{1. C}_6\text{H}_5\text{Li}}$

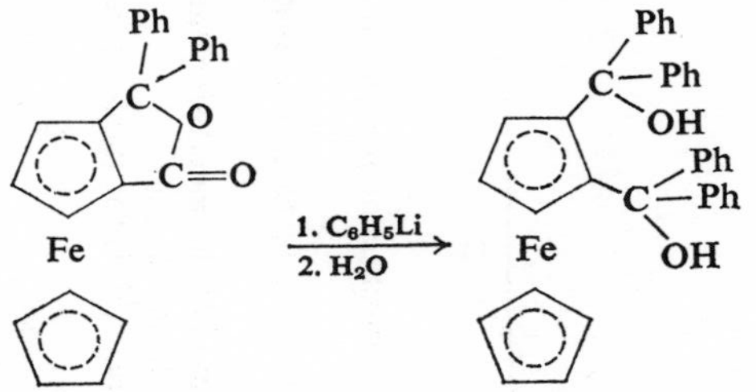

1,2-CPh₂OCO[e]	1. PhLi; 2. H₂O	1,2-(—CPh₂OH)₂	97	41
1,1'-(—OMe)₂	CO₂	2-COOH	70	40
	CO₂, CH₂N₂	2-CO₂Me	—	40

[a] Only the entering group and its position are shown. Except for the α-pyridyl derivatives, a substituent originally present in a ferrocene derivative is not rementioned.

[b] Unless otherwise indicated, the yield refers to the amount of ferrocene derivative taken for reaction.

[c] The yield refers to the amount of ferrocene derivative reacted.

[d] The yield is for the mixture of compounds, with no individual products isolated.

[e] Reaction with C_6H_5Li.

TABLE III
Reactions of Metalated Ferrocene Derivatives[a,b]

Substituent in ferrocene derivative	Reactant	Reaction products[c]	Yield,[d] %
Me	CO_2, CH_2N_2	1'-CO_2Me;[e] 3-CO_2Me;[e] 2,1'-(—CO_2Me)$_2$;[e] 3,1'-(—CO_2Me)$_2$[e]	90[f]
	MeSiCl	2,1'-(—SiMe$_3$)$_2$; 3,1'-(—SiMe$_3$)$_2$	— —
	Et$_3$SiBr	1'-SiEt$_3$; 3-SiEt$_3$; 2,1'-(—SiEt$_3$)$_2$; 3,1'-(—SiEt$_3$)$_2$	— — —
C_2H_5	CO_2, CH_2N_2	1'-CO_2Me; 2,1'-(—CO_2Me)$_2$	— —
	Me$_3$SiCl	2,1'(—SiMe$_3$)$_2$; 3,1'-(—SiMe$_3$)$_2$	— —
	Et$_3$SiBr	1'-SiEt$_3$; 2,1'-(—SiEt$_3$)$_2$; 3,1'-(—SiEt$_3$)$_2$	— —
i-C_3H_7	CO_2, CH_2N_2	2,1'-(—CO_2Me)$_2$; 3,1'-(—CO_2Me)$_2$	— —
	Me$_3$SiCl	3-SiMe$_3$; 1'-SiMe$_3$; 2,1'-(—SiMe$_3$)$_2$; 3,1'-(SiMe$_3$)$_2$	— — — —
—CMe$_3$	CO_2, CH_2N_2	2,1'-(—CO_2Me)$_2$; 3,1'-(—CO_2Me)$_2$	— —
	Me$_3$SiCl	1'-SiMe$_3$; 3-SiMe$_3$; 2,1'-(—SiMe$_3$)$_2$; 3,1'-(—SiMe$_3$)$_2$	— — — —
1,1'-Me$_2$	CO_2	?, ?-(—COOH)$_2$[g]	52
	CO_2, CH_2N_2	?, ?-(—CO_2Me)$_2$[g]	—

[a] The metalating agent was n-C_5H_{11}Na.

[b] Data from Ref. 26 unless otherwise indicated.

[c] Only the entering group and its position are shown; a substituent present in the ferrocene derivative is not rementioned.

[d] Unless otherwise indicated, the yield refers to the amount of ferrocene derivative taken for reaction.

[e] The same products were obtained when n-C_5H_{11}K was used as the metalating agent. The yield for the mixture was 19%, with no individual products isolated.

[f] The yield, based on the amount of ferrocene derivative reacted, is for the mixture of compounds, with no individual products isolated.

[g] Data from Ref. 12.

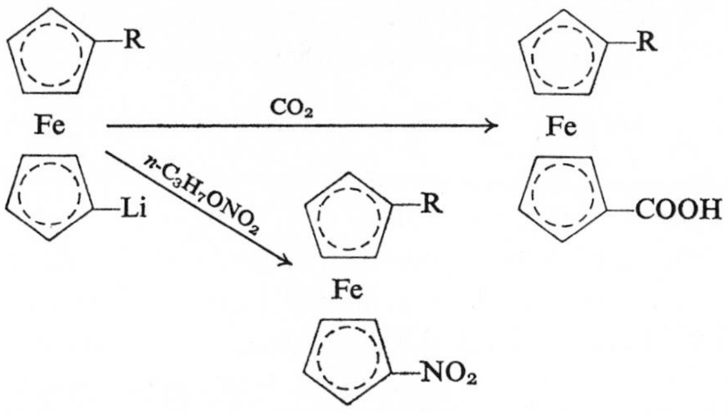

$$(1)$$

A series of 1,2-disubstituted ferrocenes have been obtained, starting with metalated dimethylaminomethylferrocene.[14–17]

B. Sodium Exchange

Sodium and potassium ferrocene derivatives are of less interest in synthesis. (see Table III). The reactions of monosodium and disodium ferrocenes are shown in Table IV.

TABLE IV
Reactions of Monosodium and Disodium Ferrocenes[a]

Reactant	Reaction products[b]	Yield,[c] %	Ref.
CO_2	—COOH;	5	46
	$1,1'$-(—COOH)$_2$	54.5	
	$1,1'$-(—COOH)$_2$	68	12
	$1,1'$-(—COOH)$_2$[d]	42	27
CO_2, CH_2N_2	—COOCH$_3$;	—	26
	$1,1'$-(—COOCH$_3$)$_2$	—	
$(CH_3)_3SiCl$	—Si(CH$_3$)$_3$;	10	46
	$1,1'$-[Si(CH$_3$)$_3$]$_2$	23	
$(C_6H_5)_3SiCl$	—Si(C$_6$H$_5$)$_3$;	10	46
	$1,1'$-[—Si(C$_6$H$_5$)$_3$]$_2$	23	
$(n\text{-}C_6H_{13})_3SiBr$	—Si(C$_6$H$_{13}$)$_3$;	0.5	25
	$1,1'$-[—Si(C$_6$H$_{13}$)$_3$]$_2$[d]	8	
$(C_6H_5)_3GeBr$	—Ge(C$_6$H$_5$)$_3$;	3.5	46
	$1,1'$-[—Ge(C$_6$H$_5$)$_3$]$_2$	12	

[a] Unless otherwise indicated, the metalating agent was n-C$_5$H$_{11}$Na.
[b] Only the entering group and its position are shown.
[c] The yield refers to the amount of ferrocene taken for reaction.
[d] The metalating agent was C$_6$H$_5$Na.

C. Example of Syntheses: Ferrocenylboric and
1,1'-Ferrocenylenediboric Acids*

* Proposed by Nesmeyanov, Sazonova, and Drozd;[1] modified by Schechter and Helling[2].

Ferrocenyllithium, dissolved in a 1:1 (v/v) mixture of tetrahydrofuran and ether (220 ml), is obtained from n-butyllithium (0.25 mole) and ferrocene (16.7 g, 0.09 mole). The solution is filtered through glass wool and added dropwise to butyl borate (72.5 g, 0.315 mole) in ethyl ether for 2 hr at $-70°$. A solid forms. The mixture is warmed to room temperature (1.5 hr), decomposed with 10% aqueous sodium hydroxide (100 ml), and filtered. The ether solution is extracted nine times with 10% aqueous sodium hydroxide (total volume 400 ml). Acidification of the alkaline solution with 10% sulfuric acid at 0° gives a yellow precipitate, which is then washed with water. The precipitate is extracted with alcohol for 4 days in a Soxhlet apparatus. Removal of the solvent gives ferrocenylboric acid (9.02 g, 0.03 mole, 44%), a yellow powder, m.p. 136–140°. The insoluble yellow residue is 1,1'-ferrocenylenediboric acid (4.42 g, 0.016 mole, 18%), which decomposes at 200°. The ether solution is washed with alkali and concentrated. Filtration and vacuum sublimation of the residue yield a crude ferrocene (4.93 g, 29%).

References

1. A. N. Nesmeyanov, V. A. Sazonova, and V. N. Drozd, *Dokl. Akad. Nauk SSSR*, **126**, 1004 (1959); *Ber.*, **93**, 2717 (1960).
2. H. Schechter and J. F. Helling, *J. Org. Chem.*, **26**, 1034 (1961).
3. A. N. Nesmeyanov, E. G. Perevalova, R. V. Golovnya, and L. S. Shilovtseva, *Dokl. Akad. Nauk SSSR*, **102**, 535 (1955).
4. E. M. Acton and R. M. Silverstein, *J. Org. Chem.*, **24**, 1487 (1959).
5. J. F. Helling and H. Schechter, *Chem. Ind. (London)*, **1959**, 1157.
6. G. Grubert and K. L. Rinehart, Jr., *Tetrahedron Letters*, **1959**, 16.
7. R. B. King, *Organometallic Syntheses*, Vol. 1, Academic Press, New York, 1965.
8. A. N. Nesmeyanov, E. G. Perevalova, and T. V. Nikitina, *Tetrahedron Letters*, **1960**, 1,
9. A. N. Nesmeyanov, V. N. Drozd, and V. A. Sazonova, *Dokl. Akad. Nauk SSSR*, **150**, 321 (1963).
10. K. Hata, J. Motoyama, and H. Watanabe, *Bull. Chem. Soc. Japan*, **37**, 1719 (1964).
11. A. N. Nesmeyanov, E. G. Perevalova, V. D. Tiurin, and S. P. Gubin, *Izv. Akad. Nauk SSSR, Ser. Khim.* **1966**, 1938.
12. A. N. Nesmeyanov, E. G. Perevalova, Z. A. Beynoravichute, and L. L. Malygina *Dokl. Akad. Nauk SSSR*, **120**, 1263 (1958).
13. A. N. Nesmeyanov, V. A. Sazonova, and N. S. Sazonova, *Dokl. Akad. Nauk SSSR*, **176**, 598 (1967).
14. D. W. Slocum, B. W. Rockett, and C. R. Hauser, *J. Amer. Chem. Soc.*, **87**, 1241 (1965).
15. J. Tirouflet and C. Moisek, *Compt. Rend.*, **262C**, 1889 (1966).
16. G. Marr, R. E. Moore, and B. W. Rockett, *J. Organometal. Chem.*, **7**, P11 (1967).

17. G. Marr, J. H. Peet, B. W. Rockett, and A. Rushworth, *J. Organmetal. Chem.*, **8**, P17 (1967).
18. S. L. Goldberg, L. H. Keith, and T. S. Prokopov, *J. Org. Chem.*, **28**, 850 (1963).
19. D. W. Mayo, P. D. Shaw, and M. Rausch, *Chem. Ind. (London)*, **1957**, 1388.
20. A. N. Nesmeyanov, E. G. Perevalova, R. V. Golovnya, and O. A. Nesmeyanova, *Dokl. Akad. Nauk SSSR*, **97**, 459 (1954).
21. R. A. Benkeser, D. Goggin, and G. Schroll, *J. Amer. Chem. Soc.*, **76**, 4025 (1954).
22. M. Rausch, M. Vogel, and H. Rosenberg, *J. Org. Chem.*, **92**, 900 (1957).
23. R. L. Shaaf and C. T. Lenk, *J. Chem. Eng. Data*, **9**, 103 (1964).
24. M. D. Rausch and D. J. Ciappenelli, *J. Organometal. Chem.*, **10**, 127 (1967).
25. S. L. Goldberg, D. W. Mayo, M. Vogel, H. Rosenberg, and M. Rausch, *J. Org. Chem.*, **24**, 824 (1959).
26. R. A. Benkeser and J. L. Bach, *J. Amer. Chem. Soc.*, **86**, 890 (1964).
27. A. N. Nesmeyanov, E. G. Perevalova and Z. A. Beynoravichute, *Dokl. Akad. Nauk SSSR*, **112**, 439 (1957).
28. A. N. Nesmeyanov, N. S. Kochetkova, P. V. Petrovskii, and E. L. Fedin, *Dokl. Akad. Nauk SSSR*, **152**, 875 (1963).
29. A. N. Nesmeyanov, E. G. Perevalova, L. P. Yur'eva, and L. I. Denisovich, *Izv. Akad. Nauk SSSR, Otd. Khim. Nauk*, **1962**, 2241.
30. P. L. Pauson and W. E. Watts, *J. Chem. Soc.*, **1962**, 3880.
31. P. Shaw, D. Mayo, and A. M. Lovelace, *J. Org. Chem.*, **23**, 505 (1958).
32. A. N. Nesmeyanov, V. N. Drozd, and V. A. Sazonova, *Dokl. Akad. Nauk SSSR*, **150**, 321 (1963).
33. A. N. Nesmeyanov and M. I. Rybinskaya, *Izv. Akad. Nauk SSSR, Ser. Khim.* **1967**, 2642.
34. K. Hata, J. Motoyama, and H. Watanabe, *Bull. Chem. Soc. Japan*, **36**, 1698 (1963).
35. J. J. Spilness and J. P. Pollegrini, Jr., *J. Org. Chem.*, **30**, 3800 (1965).
36. K. Schlögl and M. Fried, *Monatsh.*, **94**, 537 (1963).
37. A. N. Nesmeyanov, V. A. Sazonova, and A. V. Gerasimenko, *Dokl. Akad. Nauk SSSR*, **147**, 634 (1962).
38. A. N. Nesmeyanov, V. A. Sazonova, V. I. Romanenko, N. A. Rodionova, and G. P. Zolnikova, *Dokl. Akad. Nauk SSSR*, **155**, 1130 (1964).
39. M. Kumada, H. Tsunemi, and S. Imasaki, *J. Organometal. Chem.*, **10**, 111 (1967).
40. A. N. Nesmeyanov, T. V. Baukova, and K. I. Grandberg, *Izv. Akad. Nauk SSSR, Ser. Khim.*, **1967**, 1867.
41. R. A. Benkeser, W. P. Fitzgerald, and M. S. Melzer, *J. Org. Chem.*, **26**, 2569 (1961).
42. R. E. Moore, B. W. Rockett, and D. G. Brown, *J. Organometal. Chem.*, **9**, 141 (1967).
43. R. L. Gay, T. F. Crimmins, and C. R. Hauser, *Chem. Ind. (London)*, **1966**, 1635.
44. G. Marr, *J. Organometal. Chem.*, **9**, 147 (1967).
45. D. J. Booth and B. W. Rockett, *Tetrahedron Letters*, **1967**, 1483.
46. D. Seyferth, H. P. Hofmann, R. Burton, and J. F. Helling, *Inorg. Chem.*, **1**, 227 (1962).

III. MERCURY EXCHANGE

A. General Survey

Nesmeyanov and co-workers[1-3] have shown that in the presence of various electrophiles the mercury atom in mercurated ferrocene derivatives is readily exchanged for other groups.

TABLE V
Reactions of Ferrocenylmercury(II) Chloride

Reactant	Reaction products[a]	Yield, %	Ref.
NaI	—HgC$_5$H$_4$FeC$_5$H$_5$	99	9
Na$_2$S$_2$O$_3$	—HgC$_5$H$_4$FeC$_5$H$_5$	100	10
Na$_2$SnO$_3$	—HgC$_5$H$_4$FeC$_5$H$_5$	70	9
HCl	H	100	10, 6
Na, C$_2$H$_5$OH	H	99	9
Br$_2$	Br	—	4
I$_2$	I	70	11, 4
CuCl$_2$	Cl	58	12
$Cu\left(-N\overset{CO}{\underset{CO}{\diagup\diagdown}}C_6H_4\right)_2$	$-N\overset{CO}{\underset{CO}{\diagup\diagdown}}C_6H_4$	4	12
$\begin{array}{l}CH_2CO\\ \quad\diagdown NBr\\CH_2CO\diagup\end{array}$	Br	57	13
	Br;	50	13
	H;	8	
	—HgC$_5$H$_4$FeC$_5$H$_5$;	18	
	HgBr	4	
CH$_3$CONHBr	Br;	48	13
	H	5	
(C$_5$H$_5$NH)$^+$Br$_3^-$	Br;	58	13
	H	42	
$\begin{array}{l}CH_2CO\\ \quad\diagdown NI\\CH_2CO\diagup\end{array}$	I;	85	13
	—HgI	—	
CH$_3$COCl	H; (C$_5$H$_5$)$_2$Fe$^+$	—	9
(CH$_3$)$_3$SiCl	H; (C$_5$H$_5$)$_2$Fe$^+$	—	9
C$_2$H$_5$Li, H$_2$O	H	82	14
C$_2$H$_5$Li, CO$_2$	—COOH	64	15, 14
C$_4$H$_9$Li, CO$_2$	—COOH;	50	15
	H	25	
C$_6$H$_5$Li, CO$_2$	—COOH	58	15
C$_2$H$_5$Li, (C$_6$H$_5$)$_2$CO	—C(C$_6$H$_5$)$_2$OH;	65	15, 14
	H	4	
C$_2$H$_5$Li, (CH$_3$)$_3$SiCl	—Si(CH$_3$)$_3$	54	15
C$_2$H$_5$Li, (C$_6$H$_5$)$_3$SiCl	—Si(C$_6$H$_5$)$_3$	66	14, 15

[a] Only the entering group is shown.

TABLE VI
Reactions of Diferrocenylmercury

Reactant	Reaction products[a]	Yield, %	Ref.
HCl	H	100	6
CCl_4	H;	22	3
	—HgCl	57	
$(C_6H_5)_3CCl$	—$C(C_6H_5)_3$	18	1
CH_3COCl	—$COCH_3$;	1.1	1
	H	94	
$C_6H_5SO_2I$	—$SO_2C_6H_5$;	22	1
	H	—	
$C_5H_5FeC_5H_4SO_2I$	—$SO_2C_5H_4FeC_5H_5$;	27	3, 1
	H	23	
n-C_4H_9Li, CO_2	—COOH;	43	15
	H	19	
n-C_4H_9Li, CO_2	—COOH	73	16
$Hg(C_6H_5)_2$	C_6H_5;	45	16
	H	—	
	—$C_5H_4FeC_5H_5$;	—	
	$C_6H_5C_6H_5$	—	
$Hg(o$-$C_6H_4C_6H_5)_2$	o-$C_6H_4C_6H_5$;	6	16
	H	—	
	o-$C_6H_5C_6H_4C_6H_4C_6H_5$-o	—	
$Hg(m$-$C_6H_4C_6H_5)_2$	m-$C_6H_4C_6H_5$;	22	16
	H	—	
	m-$C_6H_5C_6H_4C_6H_4C_6H_5$-m	—	
$Hg(p$-$C_6H_4C_6H_5)_2$	p-$C_6H_4C_6H_5$;	20	16
	H	—	
	p-$C_6H_5C_6H_4C_6H_4C_6H_5$-p	—	
Na	H	10	3
Ag	H;	68	16
	—$C_5H_4FeC_5H_5$	61	
Pd	H;	6	2
	—$C_5H_4FeC_5H_5$;	3	
	—$(C_{10}H_8Fe)_n$—$C_5H_4FeC_5H_5$	—	
$CuCl_2$	H;	—	3
	Cl;	—	
	—HgCl	41	
$SnCl_2$	H	15.5	3
$(CNS)_2$	—SCN	23	17
$(CNS)_2$, $Na_2S_2O_3$	—$SSC_5H_4FeC_5H_5$;	15	1
	H	25	
$SeBr_4$, $Na_2S_2O_3$	—$SeC_5H_4FeC_5H_5$	21	1

[a] In most cases only the entering group is shown.

TABLE VII

Reactions of Various Mercurated Ferrocenes

Mercurated ferrocene	Reactant	Reaction products[a]	Yield, %	Ref.
$C_5H_5FeC_4H_4HgBr$	$CuBr_2$	Br	69	12
	$Cu(OCOCH_3)_2$	—$OCOCH_3$	2	12
$ClC_5H_4FeC_5H_4HgCl$	I_2	1-Cl-1'-I	64	18
	$Na_2S_2O_3$	$Hg(C_5H_4FeC_5H_4Cl)_2$	95	19
$BrC_5H_4FeC_5H_4HgBr$	I_2	1-Br-1'-I	76	18
	$Na_2S_2O_3$	$Hg(C_5H_4FeC_5H_4Br)_2$	94	19
$(ClC_5H_4FeC_5H_4)_2Hg$	I_2	1-Cl-1'-I	64	19
$(BrC_5H_4FeC_5H_4)_2Hg$	I_2	1-Br-1'-I	76	19
$Fe(C_5H_4HgCl)_2$	HCl	H	100	10
	Br_2	1,1'-$(Br)_2$	—	4
	I_2	1,1'-$(I)_2$	25	4
	$CuCl_2$	1,1'-$(Cl)_2$	17	12
	$Cu(SCN)_2$	1,1'-(—SCN)$_2$	6	12
	CH₂CO—NI / CH₂CO	1,1'-$(I)_2$	42	13
	C_2H_5Li, CO_2	1,1'-(—COOH)$_2$	44	15
	C_2H_5Li, Me_3SiCl	1,1'-(—$SiMe_3$)$_2$;	36	15
		—$SiMe_3$	8	
$Fe(C_5H_4HgBr)_2$	$CuBr_2$	1,1'-$(Br)_2$	36	12

[a] In most cases only the entering group is shown.

Mercurated ferrocene derivatives have been used in the synthesis of a number of substituted ferrocenes (see Tables V, VI, and VII). Ferrocenyl sulfones[1] and halogenated ferrocenes[4,5] were first obtained via the mercurated derivatives.*

The kinetics of the protolysis (exchange of a mercury atom for a proton) of both ferrocenylmercury(II) chloride and diferrocenylmercury by hydrochloric acid in a dioxane–water mixture (90%, v/v) have been studied at various temperatures.[6] The reaction rates always obey second-order kinetic equations. Protolysis of diferrocenylmercury is six times as fast as that of bis(p-anisyl)mercury under similar conditions and 130 times as fast as the protolysis of ferrocenylmercury(II) chloride.

The effects of substituents (methoxy, acetoxy, chlorine, and bromine) on the protolysis rate of both symmetrical and asymmetrical ferrocene derivatives, (1) and (2), have also been studied.[7]

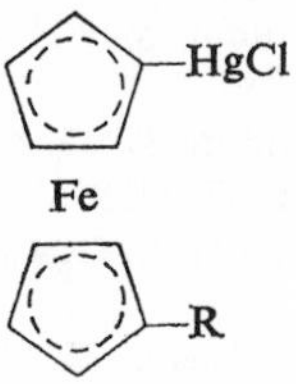

(1) 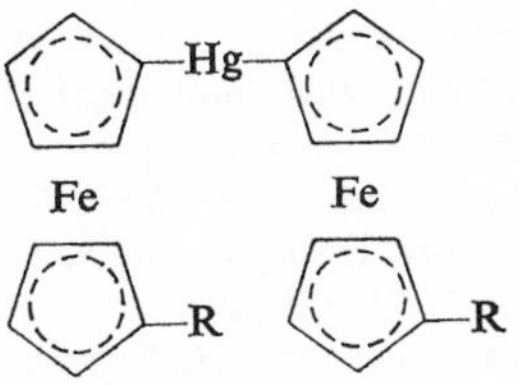   (2)

(R = OCH₃, OCOCH₃, Cl, Br)

(R = OCH_3, $OCOCH_3$, Cl, Br)

The methoxy group accelerates the rate of protolysis by a factor of about 2. Other substituents, such as acetoxy, chlorine, and bromine, slow down the reaction. The rate constants of the compounds studied correlate well with the σ_p^0 values of the substituents.

The effects of such factors as the water–dioxane ratio, anion of the acid, and addition of potassium chloride on the protolysis rates of diphenylmercury and diferrocenylmercury were found to be similar. Based on this, it seems likely that the mechanism of mercury removal in diferrocenylmercury is not very different from the mechanism in diphenylmercury. Thus there is no need to assume that the rate-determining step of the protolyses involves the metal atom.[8]

B. Examples of Syntheses: Iodoferrocene[20]

A solution of iodine (0.56 g, 2.2 mmole) in 83 ml of absolute CH_2Cl_2 cooled down to −30° is rapidly added to a stirred solution of ferrocenylmercury chloride (1.0 g, 2.4 mmole) in 20 ml. absolute CH_2Cl_2 also cooled down to −30°. A blue precipitate is formed, the solution becoming colorless.

* A complete description of iodoferrocene synthesis is given in subsection B.

The precipitate disappears after an hour of stirring at room temperature. The turbid yellow solution is filtered. After evaporating the filtrate *in vacuo*, the solid residue is chromatographed on alumina. Iodoferrocene is eluted with petroleum ether to give 0.51 g (75%) of product, m.p. 42–43°.

References

1. A. N. Nesmeyanov, E. G. Perevalova, and O. A. Nesmeyanova, *Dokl. Akad. Nauk SSSR*, **119**, 288 (1958).
2. O. A. Nesmeyanova and E. G. Perevalova, *Dokl. Akad. Nauk SSSR*, **126**, 1007 (1959).
3. A. N. Nesmeyanov, E. G. Perevalova, and O. A. Nesmeyanova, *Izv. Akad. Nauk SSSR, Otd. Khim. Nauk*, **1962**, 17.
4. A. N. Nesmeyanov, E. G. Perevalova, and O. A. Nesmeyanova, *Dokl. Akad. Nauk SSSR*, **100**, 1099 (1955).
5. E. G. Perevalova and O. A. Nesmeyanova, *Dokl. Akad. Nauk SSSR*, **132**, 1093 (1960).
6. A. N. Nesmeyanov, A. G. Kozlovskii, S. P. Gubin, and E. G. Perevalova, *Izv. Akad. Nauk SSSR, Otd. Khim. Nauk*, **1965**, 580.
7. A. N. Nesmeyanov, A. G. Kozlovskii, S. P. Gubin, L. G. Chernov, and E. G. Perevalova, *Izv. Akad. Nauk SSSR, Ser. Khim.*, **1967**, 1139.
8. A. N. Nesmeyanov, E. G. Perevalova, S. P. Gubin, and A. G. Kozlovskii, *J. Organometal. Chem.*, **11**, 577 (1968).
9. M. Rausch, M. Vogel, and H. Rosenberg, *J. Org. Chem.*, **22**, 900 (1957).
10. A. N. Nesmeyanov, E. G. Perevalova, R. V. Golovnya, and O. A. Nesmeyanova, *Dokl. Akad. Nauk SSSR*, **97**, 459 (1954).
11. H. Schechter and J. F. Helling, *J. Org. Chem.*, **26**, 1034 (1961).
12. V. A. Nefedov and M. N. Nefedova, *Zh. Obshch. Khim.*, **36**, 122 (1966).
13. M. Rosenblum and R. W. Fish, *J. Org. Chem.*, **30**, 1253 (1965).
14. D. Seyferth and J. F. Helling, *Chem. Ind. (London)*, **1961**, 1568.
15. D. Seyferth, H. P. Hofmann, R. Burton, and J. F. Helling, *Inorg. Chem.*, **1**, 227 (1962).
16. M. D. Rausch, *Inorg. Chem.*, **1**, 414 (1962).
17. G. R. Knox, I. G. Morrison, and P. L. Pauson, *J. Chem. Soc.*, **1967C**, 1842.
18. A. N. Nesmeyanov, V. A. Sazonova, and V. N. Drozd, *Ber.*, **93**, 2717 (1960).
19. A. N. Nesmeyanov, V. A. Sazonova, V. N. Drozd, and L. A. Nikonova, *Dokl. Akad. Nauk SSSR*, **131**, 1088 (1960).
20. A. N. Nesmeyanov, E. G. Perevalova, D. A. Lemonovski, V. P. Alekseev, and K. I. Grandberg, *Dokl. Akad. Nauk SSSR*, **198**, 1099 (1971).

IV. HALOGEN EXCHANGE

A. General Survey

Nesmeyanov, Sazonova, and Drozd have shown that the halogen of halogenated ferrocenes readily undergoes nucleophilic substitution in the presence of copper salts.[1-6] The halogen atom bonded to the ferrocene nucleus is exchanged for acetoxy,[1,3] phthalimido,[1] phenylacetylene,[4] thienyl,[4] azido,[5] or other groups (see Tables VIII and IX).

TABLE VIII
Substitution of Bromine in Bromoferrocene

Reactant	Reaction product[a]	Yield, %	Ref.
$NaN_3, CuBr_2$	N_3	98	5
$Cu_2(CN)_2$	$-CN$	84	1, 2
$Cu(OCOCH_3)_2$	$-OCOCH_3$	90	1–3
C_6H_5OK, Cu	$-OC_6H_5$	30	13
$CuC{\equiv}CC_6H_5$	$-C{\equiv}CC_6H_5$	48	4
		64	1, 2
$KB(C_6H_5)_4, Cu_2Br_2$	$-C_6H_5$	56	4
$CuB(C_6H_5)_4 \cdot C_5H_5N,$ Cu^{2+}	$-C_6H_5;$ H	57 —	4
$NaB(C_6H_4CH_3\text{-}p)_4,$ Cu_2Br_2	$-C_6H_4CH_3\text{-}p$	53	4
$C_6H_5N(Na)COCH_3,$ Cu_2Br_2	$-NHC_6H_5$	38	14
$(C_6H_5)_2NNa,$ Cu_2Br_2	$-N(C_6H_5)_2$	67	14
, Cu_2Br_2	; H, $-C_5H_4FeC_5H_5$	17 — —	4
, Cu_2Br_2		35	4
, Cu_2Br_2		81	4
$C_5H_5FeC_5H_4N(Na)COCH_3,$ Cu_2Br_2	H; $-C_5H_4FeC_5H_5;$ $-N{=}NC_5H_4FeC_5H_5;$ $-N(COCH_3)C_5H_4FeC_5H_5;$ $-NH(COCH_3)$	— — — — —	15

(*continued*)

TABLE VIII (*continued*)

Reactant	Reaction product[a]	Yield, %	Ref.
Mg, CO_2	—COOH; —$C_5H_4FeC_5H_5$	49 9	16
Mg, CH_3I, CO_2	—COOH	84	16
Mg, $C_2H_4Br_2$, $CoCl_2$	—$C_5H_4FeC_5H_5$	80	16
C_6H_5MgBr, Cu_2Br_2, Cu	—C_6H_5	75–81	6
$C_6H_{11}MgCl$, Cu_2Br_2, Cu	H; C_6H_{11}	80 —	6
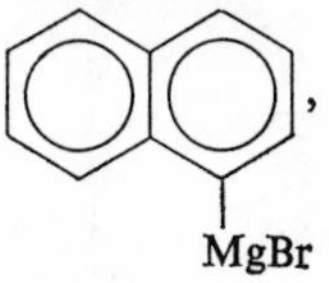 MgBr Cu_2Br_2, Cu	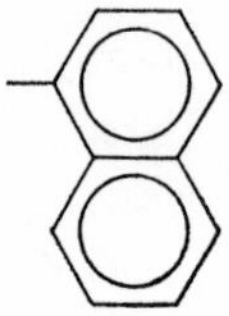	73	6
 —MgBr, Cu_2Br_2, Cu	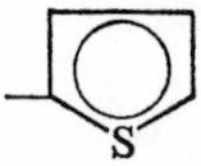	87	6
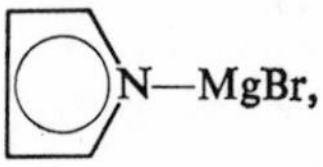 N—MgBr, Cu_2Br_2, Cu	  NH NH	15 11	6
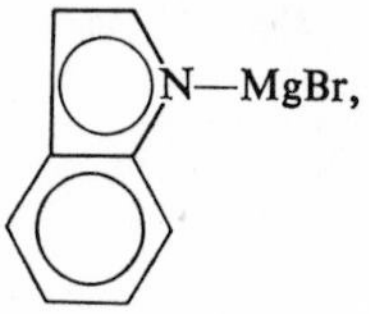 N—MgBr, Cu_2Br_2, Cu	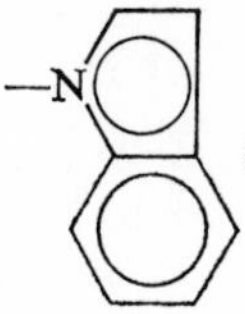 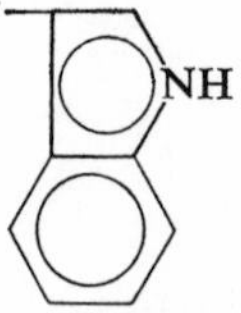 —N ; NH	14–16 11	6

[a] Only the substituent is shown.

298

The bromine of 1,1'-bromoethylferrocene exchanges[7] approximately as readily as the bromine of bromoferrocene. The exchange proceeds more slowly in 1,1'-bromoacetylferrocene[7] than in bromoferrocene. However, unlike other electron-withdrawing substituents, the carboxy group facilitates a nucleophilic substitution of the halogen; therefore 1,1'-bromoferrocene-carboxylic acid reacts[8] approximately as readily as bromoferrocene. Nesmeyanov, Sazonova, and Drozd think that the copper salt of 1'-bromoferrocene-1-carboxylic acid, as initially formed, contains a coordinate $Cu \cdots Br$ bond. This would favor polarization of the C—Br bond and hence more rapid exchange. It should be noted that the halogen of halogenated ferrocenes does not undergo nucleophilic exchange in the absence of copper salts.[9]

When heated with copper, iodoferrocene yields diferrocenyl.[10] Substituted haloferrocenes, in similar fashion, yield substituted diferrocenyl derivatives when heated with copper.[11]

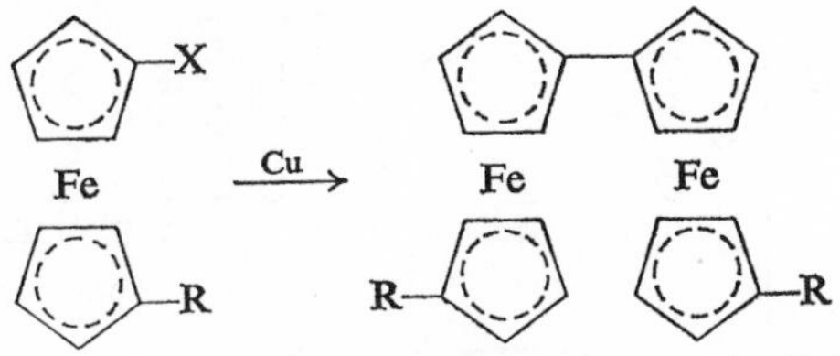

$$(R = H, Cl, COCH_3, COOCH_3, C_2H_5; \quad X = I, Br) \tag{2}$$

Bromoferrocene and 1,1'-dibromoferrocene form 1,1'-polyferrocenylenes under similar conditions. However, when iodoferrocene is heated with copper or magnesium *in the presence of alcohol or ether*, it produces ferrocene.[10] These reactions are of a homolytic nature.[12]

Electrophilic replacement of a halogen by a proton in halogenated ferrocenes has been discussed in detail in Section II-B of Chapter 1.

B. Examples of Syntheses

1. α-Thienylferrocene[4]

A mixture of bromoferrocene (0.40 g, 1.5 millimoles), potassium tetra-(α-thienyl)boronate (0.15 g, 1.7 millimoles), and copper(I) bromide (0.25 g) wetted with absolute pyridine (0.6 ml) is placed in a tube fitted with a nitrogen inlet and a reflux condenser. The air is forced out by nitrogen, and the reaction mixture is heated at 125–130° for 30 min. The α-thienyl chloride is extracted from the cooled reaction mixture with ether. The ether layer is washed with water, dried over anhydrous magnesium sulfate, and evaporated. The residue is dissolved in a minimum amount of heptane and chromatographed on a 30 × 0.5-cm alumina column (III–IV degree of activity).

TABLE IX
Substitution of Halogen in Halogenated Ferrocenes

Halogenated ferrocene	Reactant	Reaction products[a]	Yield, %	Ref.
$C_5H_5FeC_5H_4Cl$	$Cu_2(CN)_2$	—CN	42	1, 2
	$Cu(OCOCH_3)_2$	—$OCOCH_3$	84	1, 2
	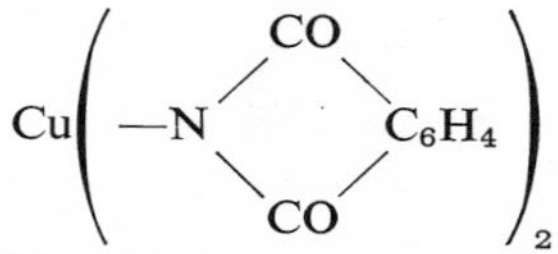 $\left(Cu{-}N\dfrac{CO}{CO}C_6H_4 \right)_2$	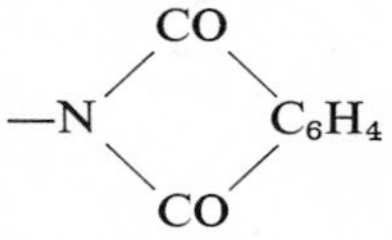 $-N\dfrac{CO}{CO}C_6H_4$	53	1, 2
$C_5H_5FeC_5H_4I$	Mg, CH_3I, CO_2	—COOH	15	16
	$CuC{\equiv}CC_6H_5$	—$C{\equiv}CC_6H_5$	84	17
	$CuC{\equiv}CC_5H_4FeC_5H_5$	—$C{\equiv}CC_5H_4FeC_5H_5$	84	17
	$Cu(OCOCH_3)_2$	—$OCOCH_3$	67	18
	Cu	—$C_5H_4FeC_5H_5$	79	10
	Cu, CH_3OH	H	—	10
	Mg, CH_3I, CO_2	—COOH	65	16
	$Mg, C_2H_4Br_2, CO_2$	H;	62	16
		—$C_5H_4FeC_5H_5$	34	
	$n\text{-}C_4H_9Li, CO_2$	H;	60	16
		—$C_5H_4FeC_5H_5$;	20	
		—COOH	17	
$C_5H_5FeC_5H_3(Cl)$-$B(OH)_2$-1,2	$Cu(OCOCH_3)_2$	1,2-(—$OCOCH_3)_2$	34	19

Starting material	Reagents	Product	Yield (%)	Ref.
$C_2H_5C_5H_4FeC_5H_4Br$	$Cu_2(CN)_2$	$1\text{-}CN\text{-}1'\text{-}C_2H_5$	80	7
	$Cu(OCOCH_3)_2$, KOH, C_6H_5COCl	$1\text{-}OCOC_6H_5\text{-}1'\text{-}C_2H_5$	71	7
	$\left[Cu\!\!-\!\!N\!\!\diamond\!\!\begin{smallmatrix}CO\\CO\end{smallmatrix}\!\!C_6H_4 \right]_2$	$1\text{-}N\!\diamond\!\begin{smallmatrix}CO\\CO\end{smallmatrix}\!C_6H_4\text{-}1'\text{-}C_2H_5$	72	7
$CH_3COC_5H_4FeC_5H_4Br$	Cu	$(C_5H_4FeC_5H_4C_2H_5)_2$	100	11
	$Cu(OCOCH_3)_2$, H_2O	$1\text{-}OH\text{-}1'\text{-}COCH_3$	26	7
	Cu	$(C_5H_4FeC_5H_4COCH_3)_2$	54	11
$CH_3COOC_5H_4FeC_5H_4Br$	Cu	$(C_5H_4FeC_5H_4OCOCH_3)_2$	71.5	11
$Fe(C_5H_4Br)_2$	NaN_3, $CuBr_2$	$1,1'\text{-}(-N_3)_2$	31	5
	$Cu(OCOCH_3)_2$	$1,1'\text{-}(-OCOCH_3)_2$	65	2
	C_6H_5OK, Cu	$1,1'\text{-}(-OC_6H_5)_2$	20	13
	Mg, CH_3I, CO_2	$-COOH;$ $1,1'\text{-}(-COOH)_2;$	16 59	16
	$C_5H_5FeC_5H_4Br$, Cu	$-C_5H_4FeC_5H_5;$ $1,1'\text{-}(-C_5H_4FeC_5H_5)_2;$ $-(C_{10}H_8Fe)_nC_5H_4FeC_5H_5$	57 14 —	11
$Fe(C_5H_4I)_2$	$CuC\!\equiv\!CC_6H_5$	$1,1'\text{-}(-C\!\equiv\!CC_6H_5)_2$	57	17
$ClC_5H_4FeC_5H_4I$	Cu	$(C_5H_4FeC_5H_4Cl)_2$	88	11

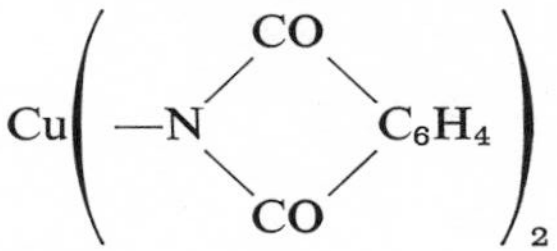

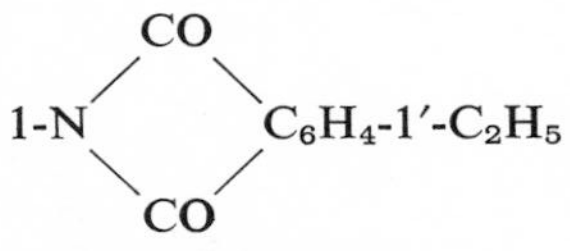

[a] In most cases only the substituent is shown.

The first fraction is a bright-green band consisting of a mixture of ferrocene* and unreacted bromoferrocene. After this an orange band of α-thienylferrocene is eluted. The heptane is evaporated, and the α-thienylferrocene is recrystallized from ethanol to give 0.30 g (74% yield) of the compound, m.p. 116.5–117.5°.

2. Ferrocenyl Acetate[1]

Bromoferrocene (0.30 g) is refluxed in 50% ethanol (30 ml) with copper(II) acetate (1 g) for 15 min. The mixture is diluted with water and then extracted with ether. The ether is washed with water, 5% alkali, again with water, and finally evaporated to yield ferrocenyl acetate (0.25 g, 90% of the theoretical amount), m.p. 60–62°. Beilstein's test should show the absence of halogen. After recrystallization from ethanol, the ferrocenyl acetate (m.p. 64.5–66.5°) is hydrolyzed to produce oxyferrocene, which, after Schotten–Baumann benzoylation, gives ferrocenyl benzoate, m.p. 108.5–109.5°. Similarly ferrocenyl acetate (0.28 g, 84% of the theoretical amount) is obtained from chloroferrocene (0.30 g) and copper(II) acetate (1 g) in 30 ml of 50% ethanol.

3. N-Ferrocenyl Phthalimide[1]

A mixture of bromoferrocene (0.60 g) and copper(II) phthalimide (15 g) is heated at 135–140° (oil bath) for 2 hr, and the mixture is then repeatedly washed with ether. After being washed with water, 10% potassium hydroxide, and water again, the red ether solution is evaporated to give N-ferrocenyl phthalimide (0.48 g, 64% of the theoretical amount), m.p. 150–153°. After recrystallization from ethanol it melted at 156–157°. N-Ferrocenyl phthalimide is a red crystalline compound, soluble in ether, acetone, chloroform, and benzene. It is less soluble in ethanol. N-Ferrocenyl phthalimide (0.24 g, 53% of the theoretical amount) is similarly prepared from chloroferrocene (0.30 g) and copper(II) phthalimide (1.5 g).

4. Ferrocenyl Azide[5]

To a solution of bromoferrocene (2.0 g) in dimethylformamide (60 ml) are added solutions of sodium azide (4 g) in water (10 ml) and copper(II) bromide (0.70 g) in water (3 ml). The reaction mixture is left at room temperature in the absence of light for 48 hr and then extracted with ether. The ether solution is washed with water, dried over $MgSO_4$, and evaporated to give ferrocenyl azide (1.68 g, 98% of the theoretical amount), m.p. 53–54° (from hexane after cooling with Dry Ice–acetone).

References

1. A. N. Nesmeyanov, V. A. Sazonova, and V. N. Drozd, *Ber.*, **93**, 2717 (1960).
2. A. N. Nesmeyanov, V. A. Sazonova, and V. N. Drozd, *Dokl. Akad. Nauk SSSR*, **130**, 1030 (1960).

* Ferrocene is a side product formed as a result of the bromoferrocene reduction.

3. A. N. Nesmeyanov, V. A. Sazonova, and V. N. Drozd, *Dokl. Akad. Nauk SSSR*, **129**, 1060 (1959); *Tetrahedron Letters*, **1959**, 13.
4. A. N. Nesmeyanov, V. A. Sazonova, and V. N. Drozd, *Dokl. Akad. Nauk SSSR*, **154**, 158 (1964).
5. A. N. Nesmeyanov, V. A. Sazonova, and V. N. Drozd, *Dokl. Akad. Nauk SSSR*, **150**, 321 (1963).
6. A. N. Nesmeyanov, V. A. Sazonova, and V. N. Drozd, *Dokl. Akad. Nauk SSSR*, **165**, 575 (1965).
7. A. N. Nesmeyanov, V. A. Sazonova, and V. N. Drozd, *Dokl. Akad. Nauk SSSR*, **137**, 102 (1961).
8. A. N. Nesmeyanov, V. A. Sazonova, and V. N. Drozd, *Izv. Akad. Nauk SSSR*, *Otd. Khim. Nauk*, **1962**, 45.
9. A. N. Nesmeyanov, E. G. Perevalova, and O. A. Nesmeyanova, *Dokl. Akad. Nauk SSSR*, **100**, 1099 (1955).
10. E. G. Perevalova and O. A. Nesmeyanova, *Dokl. Akad. Nauk SSSR*, **132**, 1093 (1960).
11. A. N. Nesmeyanov, V. N. Drozd, V. A. Sazonova, V. I. Romanenko, A. K. Prokof'ev, and L. A. Nikonova, *Izv. Akad. Nauk SSSR, Otd. Khim. Nauk*, **1963**, 667.
12. A. N. Nesmeyanov, E. G. Perevalova, and O. A. Nesmeyanova, *Izv. Akad. Nauk SSSR, Otd. Khim. Nauk*, **1962**, 47.
13. V. A. Nefedov and M. N. Nefedova, *Zh. Obshch. Khim.*, **36**, 122 (1966).
14. A. N. Nesmeyanov, V. A. Sazonova, and V. I. Romanenko, *Dokl. Akad. Nauk SSSR*, **157**, 922 (1964).
15. A. N. Nesmeyanov, V. A. Sazonova, and V. I. Romanenko, *Dokl. Akad. Nauk SSSR*, **161**, 1085 (1965).
16. H. Schechter and J. F. Helling, *J. Org. Chem.*, **26**, 1034 (1961).
17. M. D. Rausch, A. Siefel, and L. P. Klemann, *J. Org. Chem.*, **31**, 2703 (1966).
18. S. McVey, I. G. Morrison, and P. L. Pauson, *J. Chem. Soc.*, **1967C**, 1847.
19. A. N. Nesmeyanov, V. A. Sazonova, and N. S. Sazonova, *Dokl. Akad. Nauk SSSR*, **176**, 598 (1967).

V. B(OH)$_2$-GROUP EXCHANGE

A. General Survey

The properties of ferrocenylboric or ferrocenylenediboric acids resemble those of arylboric acids. The B(OH)$_2$-group of monoboric and diboric acids is readily exchanged for other groups.[1-6] Monoacetoxy or diacetoxy ferrocenes,[3,6] as well as chloroferrocene and 1,1'-dichloroferrocene,[2,3] have been obtained in this manner. The B(OH)$_2$-group has also been exchanged for bromine, mercury, and a propoxy group (see Table X).

Copper salts initially react with 1,1'-ferrocenylenediboric acid to cause the exchange of only one B(OH)$_2$-group.[3,4] In this manner a series of ferrocene derivatives with two different substituents has been obtained:

Ferrocenylboric acid, when reacted with an ammonia solution of silver oxide, produces ferrocene and diferrocenyl.[2,3] Chloroferrocenylboric acid under these conditions gives bis(1'-chloroferrocenyl) (3).[1]

TABLE X
Substitution of the $B(OH)_2$-Group in Ferrocenylboric Acids

Ferrocenylboric acid	Reactant	Reaction products[a]	Yield, %	Ref.[b]
$C_5H_5FeC_5H_4B(OH)_2$	$CuCl_2$	Cl	84	2, 3
	$CuBr_2$	Br	80	2
	$Cu(OCOCH_3)_2$	$—OCOCH_3$;	59	6, 3
		$—C_5H_4FeC_5H_5$	21	
	$Cu(OCOCH_2CH_3)_2$	$—OCOCH_2CH_3$;	53	1, 6
		$—C_5H_4FeC_5H_5$	20	
	$Cu\left(—N\begin{matrix}CO\\CO\end{matrix}C_6H_4\right)_2$	$—N\begin{matrix}CO\\CO\end{matrix}C_6H_4$	47	5
	$HgCl_2$	HgCl	76	2, 3
	Ag_2O, NH_4OH	$C_5H_4FeC_5H_5$;	52	2
		H	31	
$C_5H_5FeC_5H_3[CH_2N(CH_3)_2]B(OH)_2$-1,2	$ZnCl_2, H_2O$	H	82	2
	$CuCl_2$	$1\text{-}CH_2N(CH_3)_2\text{-}2\text{-}Cl$	88	8
	$CuBr_2$	$1\text{-}CH_2N(CH_3)_2\text{-}2\text{-}Br$	95	8
$C_5H_5FeC_5H_3(Cl)B(OH)_2$-1,2	$CuCl_2$	$1,2\text{-}(\text{-}Cl)_2$	57	7
	$Cu(OCOCH_3)_2$	$1,2\text{-}(\text{-}OCOCH_3)_2$	34	7
	$HgCl_2$	$1\text{-}Cl\text{-}2\text{-}HgCl$	58	7
	$ZnCl_2, H_2O$	Cl	71	7
	Ag_2O, NH_4OH	Cl;	30	7
		$1\text{-}Cl\text{-}2\text{-}Ag$	37	
$ClC_5H_4FeC_5H_4B(OH)_2$	$Cu(OCOCH_3)_2$	$1,1'\text{-}(—OCOCH_3)_2$	70	9, 3
	$HgCl_2$	$1\text{-}Cl\text{-}1'\text{-}HgCl$	88	3, 4

Starting material	Reagent	Substituent[a]	Yield	Ref
$BrC_5H_4FeC_5H_4B(OH)_2$	$ZnCl_2$, H_2O	Cl	79	4
	$AgNO_3$, NH_4OH	Cl;	22	1
		$(—C_5H_4FeC_5H_4Cl)_2$	26	3
	$CuCl_2$	1,1'-(Cl)$_2$	—	3
	$Cu(OCOCH_3)_2$	1,1'-(—$OCOCH_3$)$_2$	83	3, 9
	$HgBr_2$	1-Br-1'-HgBr	84	4, 3
$Fe[C_5H_4B(OH)_2]_2$	$ZnCl_2$, H_2O	Br	88	4
	$CuCl_2$	1,1'-(Cl)$_2$	75	2, 3
		1-Cl-1'-B(OH)$_2$	52	3, 4
	$CuBr_2$	1,1'-(Br)$_2$	76	2, 3
		1-Br-1'-B(OH)$_2$	65	3, 4
	$Cu(OCOCH_3)_2$	1,1'-(—$OCOCH_3$)$_2$	41	3, 9
	$\mathrm{Cu}{\left(\!\!\begin{array}{c}\mathrm{CO}\\ N\quad C_6H_4\\ \mathrm{CO}\end{array}\!\!\right)}_2$	$1,1'\text{-}{\left(\!\!\begin{array}{c}\mathrm{CO}\\ N\quad C_6H_4\\ \mathrm{CO}\end{array}\!\!\right)}_2$	29	5
	$\bigcirc\!\!N$, $ZnCl_2$, H_2O	H	—	2
	$\bigcirc\!\!N$, $CuCO_3$	H	—	10

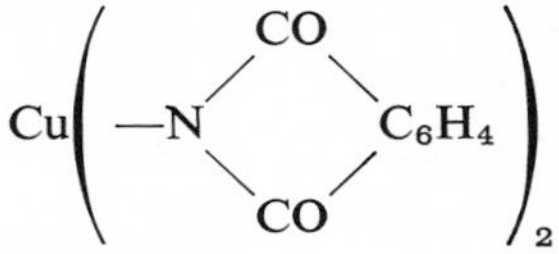

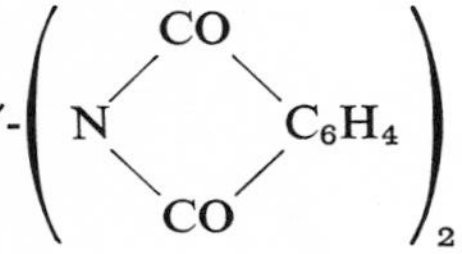

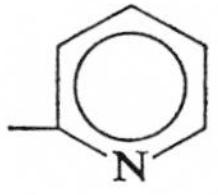

[a] Only the substituent and its position are shown.

[b] This table lists the best yields cited in the papers under review, with the reference corresponding to the best yield placed first.

$$(HO)_2BC_5H_4FeC_5H_4B(OH)_2 \xrightarrow{\ CuX_2\ } X-C_5H_4FeC_5H_4B(OH)_2$$

$$\downarrow HgX_2$$

$$Hg(C_5H_4FeC_5H_4-X)_2 \xleftarrow{\ Na_2S_2O_3\ } X-C_5H_4FeC_5H_4Hg-X \qquad (3)$$

$$\downarrow I_2$$

$$IC_5H_4FeC_5H_4-X$$

$$(X = Cl, Br)$$

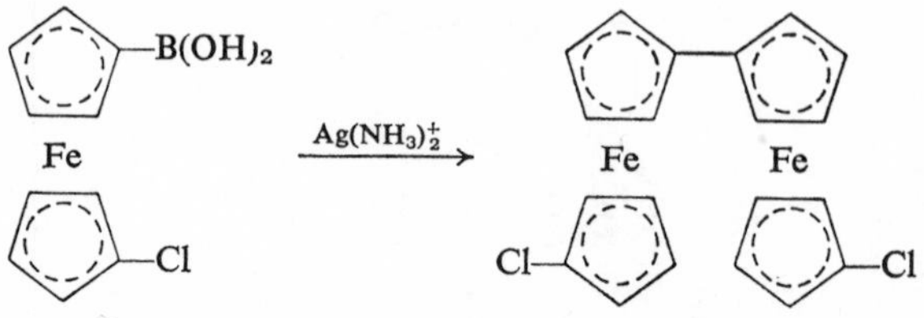

(4)

Nesmeyanov, Sazonova, and Drozd[7] performed the exchange of a B(OH)$_2$-group with a silver atom and, for the first time, obtained compound (4), a stable ferrocene derivative of silver.

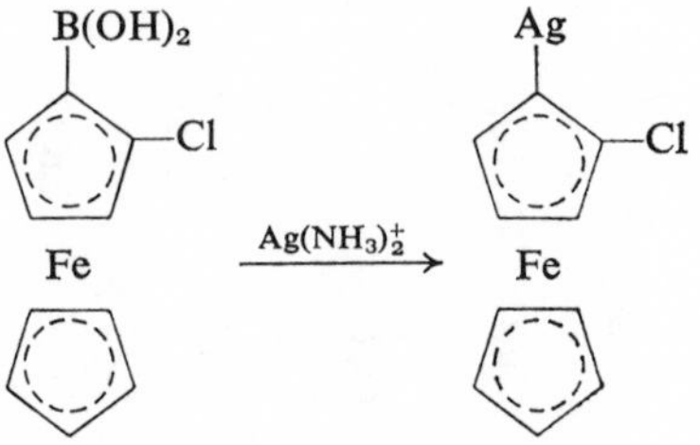

(5)

B. Examples of Syntheses

1. Chloroferrocene[2]

A solution of copper(II) chloride dihydrate (0.30 g) in water (5 ml) is added to ferrocenylboric acid (0.25 g) dissolved in water (50 ml), poured into a round-bottom flask, and steam distilled. The chloroferrocene is then extracted from the distillate with ether, which is evaporated to give 0.20 g (84% of the theoretical amount) of chloroferrocene, m.p. 53–55°. After recrystallization from ethanol, it melts at 59–60°.

2. Bromoferrocene, 1,1′-Dichloroferrocene, and 1,1′-Dibromoferrocene[2,3]

Bromoferrocene, 1,1′-dichloroferrocene, and 1,1′-dibromoferrocene are prepared in the same manner.

Bromoferrocene (0.15 g, 80% of the theoretical amount) is obtained from ferrocenylboric acid (0.16 g) in water (35 ml) and copper(II) bromide (0.50 g) in water (5 ml), m.p. 28–30°. After recrystallization from ethanol, it melts at 32–33°.

1,1'-Dichloroferrocene (0.35 g, 75% of the theoretical amount) is obtained from ferrocenyldiboric acid (0.50 g) in water (175 ml) and copper(II) chloride (3 g); m.p. 69–71°. After recrystallization from water–ethanol, it melts at 75–77°.

1,1'-Dibromoferrocene (0.95 g, 75% of the theoretical amount) is obtained from 1,1'-ferrocenylenediboric acid (1 g) and copper(II) bromide (5 g); m.p. 42–44°. After recrystallization from ethanol, it melts at 50–51°.

References

1. A. N. Nesmeyanov, V. N. Drozd, V. A. Sazonova, V. I. Romanenko, A. K. Prokof'ev, and L. A. Nikonova, *Izv. Akad. Nauk SSSR, Otd. Khim. Nauk*, **1963**, 663.
2. A. N. Nesmeyanov, V. A. Sazonova, and V. N. Drozd, *Dokl. Akad. Nauk SSSR*, **126**, 1004 (1959).
3. A. N. Nesmeyanov, V. A. Sazonova, and V. N. Drozd, *Ber.*, **93**, 2717 (1960).
4. A. N. Nesmeyanov, V. A. Sazonova, V. N. Drozd, and L. A. Nikonova, *Dokl. Akad. Nauk SSSR*, **131**, 1088 (1960).
5. A. N. Nesmeyanov, V. A. Sazonova, A. V. Gerasimenko, and V. G. Medvedeva, *Izv. Akad. Nauk SSSR, Otd. Khim. Nauk*, **1962**, 2073.
6. A. N. Nesmeyanov, V. A. Sazonova, and V. N. Drozd, *Dokl. Akad. Nauk SSSR*, **129**, 1060 (1959); *Tetrahedron Letters*, **1959**, No. 17, 13.
7. A. N. Nesmeyanov, V. A. Sazonova, and V. N. Drozd, *Dokl. Akad. Nauk SSSR*, **176**, 598 (1967).
8. G. Marr, R. E. Moore, and B. W. Rockett, *J. Organometal. Chem.*, **7**, P11 (1967).
9. A. N. Nesmeyanov, V. A. Sazonova, V. N. Drozd, and L. A. Nikonova, *Dokl. Akad. Nauk SSSR*, **133**, 126 (1960).
10. A. N. Nesmeyanov, V. A. Sazonova, and A. V. Gerasimenko, *Dokl. Akad. Nauk SSSR*, **147**, 634 (1962).

VI. EXCHANGE OF OTHER GROUPS

The reactions discussed in the preceding sections—the exchange of lithium, mercury, halogen, and the $B(OH)_2$-group—are of synthetic value. Similar reactions are also known for other groups, i.e., the exchange of methoxy or methylthio groups or iodine for a proton or an acetyl group. This type of substitution is performed in the presence of aluminum chloride (cf. Section II-C-6 of Chapter 1).

Exchange of a halogen for deuterium is described in detail in Section II-B of Chapter 1.

When 1,1'-diacetylferrocene is sulfonated with sulfur trioxide in dichloroethane, the acetyls are exchanged for sulfonic groups (cf. Section II-E of Chapter 1).

Substitution of trimethylsilyl by a proton was studied with trimethyl-silylferrocene in the presence of hydrochloric acid.[1] The reaction rate is approximately equal to that of anisyltrimethylsilane protodesilation.

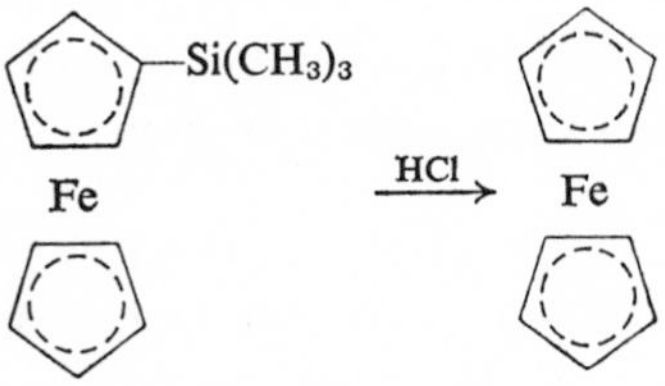

$$\text{(6)}$$

The effects of alkyl substituents (methyl, isopropyl, *tert*-butyl) on the replacement rate of this silyl group have been studied.[2] It was found that the

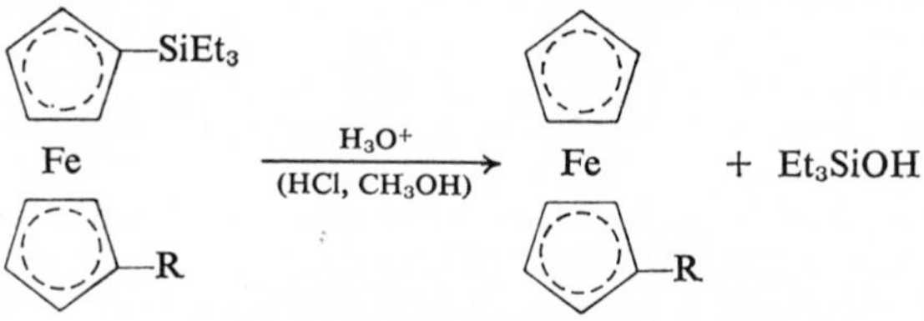

$$\text{(7)}$$

$$[R = H, CH_3, CH(CH_3)_2, C(CH_3)_3]$$

methyl and isopropyl groups increase, whereas the *tert*-butyl decreases, this rate.

Two possible mechanisms describing the silyl-group replacement in ferrocene derivatives have been discussed.[2] The first of them assumes that a hydroxonium ion initially attacks the iron atom, forming complex (5),

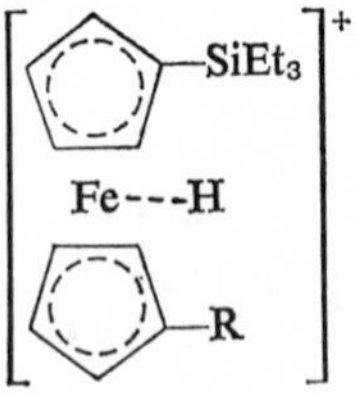

(5)

whereas the second involves the formation of the σ-complex (6). The experimental data, however, do not allow an unambiguous conclusion to be made.

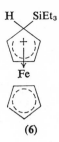

(6)

References

1. G. Marr and D. E. Webster, *J. Organometal. Chem.*, **2**, 99 (1964).
2. R. A. Benkeser, Y. Nagai, and S. Hooz, *J. Amer. Chem. Soc.*, **86**, 3742 (1964).

Chapter 3

Reactions Involving the Metal–Ring Bond

Reactions involving the metal–cyclopentadienyl ring bond may be of two types: (a) exchange of cyclopentadienyl rings for other ligands or atoms and (b) addition to the cyclopentadienyl rings involving the transformation of the nature of the metal–ring bond.

I. EXCHANGE OF CYCLOPENTADIENYL RINGS

The only two metallocenes that are not known to exchange their cyclopentadienyl groups are osmocene and ruthenocene. The exchange reaction is more or less characteristic of the cyclopentadienyl compounds of other transition metals. This ring exchange is the most important reaction of certain metallocenes and determines the main features of their reactivity. Various exchange reactions have been described for the cyclopentadienyl compounds of chromium and nickel, not to mention ionic bis(cyclopentadienyl)manganese or tris(cyclopentadienyl) compounds of scandium, yttrium, and the lanthanides.

The more ionic the C_5H_5—M bond, the easier, as a rule, the exchange of cyclopentadienyl rings for other ligands. However, other features of the electronic structure may also play an important role, as, for example, in nickelocene.

A. Reactions with Water, Acids, or Alkalies

The action of water leading to the rupture of a C_5H_5—M bond in transition-metal cyclopentadienyl compounds has not been studied systematically. Usually it is just mentioned that the compounds are "stable" or "unstable" in the presence of aqueous solutions of acids or bases. The products have been isolated only occasionally.

However, although very incomplete, the published data may help to construct a more or less general idea of the stability of the C_5H_5—M bond toward hydrolysis as a function of the location of the metal in the periodic system. For example, the group VIII elements can be said to be the most stable. Also, neutral compounds are usually less reactive than the corresponding cations.

The information below is classified according to group in the periodic system. In addition, subsection 2 describes the destruction of ferrocene derivatives illuminated in aqueous solutions.

1. Reactions of Metallocenes and Their Cations

a. Group III. Ionic tris(cyclopentadienyl) compounds of scandium, yttrium, and the lanthanides are vigorously decomposed by water, forming cyclopentadiene.[1,2] However, the metal–ring bond of at least one uranium cyclopentadienyl compound is quite stable in water.[3]

Hydrolysis of tetrakis(cyclopentadienyl)thorium seems to result in the abstraction of two cyclopentadienyls, with a bis(cyclopentadienyl)thorium compound being formed.[3]

b. Group IV. The cyclopentadienyl–titanium bond of titanium bis-(cyclopentadienyl) compounds is relatively stable. Bis(cyclopentadienyl) titanium dibromide, for example, is decomposed by water to the oxygen-bridged compound (1);* the metal–cyclopentadienyl bond remains intact.[5,6]

$$(C_5H_5)_2TiBr_2 \xrightarrow{H_2O} (C_5H_5)_2Ti\underset{\underset{Br}{|}}{\text{—}}O\text{—}\underset{\underset{Br}{|}}{Ti}(C_5H_5)_2 \tag{1}$$

(1)

Bis(cyclopentadienyl)titanium dichloride is difficult to hydrolyze, the reaction demanding prolonged refluxing in water. Titanium dioxide is produced (determined by infrared spectroscopy), and more than 50% of the initial amount of bis(cyclopentadienyl)titanium dichloride remains unreacted.[7]

The C_5H_5—Ti bond of bis(cyclopentadienyl)titanium diacetate is less stable. Hydrolysis results in the elimination of a cyclopentadienyl ring and the formation of an oxygen-bridged structure.[8]

$$(C_5H_5)_2Ti(OCOCH_3)_2 \xrightarrow{H_2O} [C_5H_5Ti(OCOCH_3)_2]_2O \tag{2}$$

In the presence of mineral acids in water or hydrogen chloride or bromide in organic solvents $(C_5H_5)_2Ti$† or $(C_5H_5)_2TiCl_2$ undergoes either oxidation–reduction reactions or halogen exchange rather than the rupture of the C_5H_5—Ti bond.[4,10–12]

The C_5H_5—Ti bond of bis(cyclopentadienyl)titanium dichloride or dibenzoate is quite stable toward alcoholysis. However, if the two benzoate groups are substituted by acetoxy or propoxy groups, the metal–cyclopentadienyl bonds become significantly weakened, so that ethanol decomposes the two compounds to cyclopentadiene.[13]

$$(C_5H_5)_2Ti(OCOR)_2 \xrightarrow{C_2H_5OH} [C_5H_6] \xrightarrow{TlOH} C_5H_5Tl \tag{3}$$
$$(R = CH_3, C_2H_5)$$

The C_5H_5—Ti bond is readily destroyed under alkaline conditions.[14,15] When refluxed with potassium ethoxide, $(C_5H_5)_2TiCl_2$ loses its two rings to produce cyclopentadiene in more than 98% yield.[14]

---

* The hydrolysis product was thought to be $(C_6H_5)_2Ti(OH)Br \cdot H_2O$.[4]

† One must note that Watt and Bayet[9] were not able to repeat the synthesis of titanocene described by Fischer and Wilkinson.[10]

The C_5H_5—Zr bond, however, is stable in ethanol or mineral acid. This is exemplified by the bis(cyclopentadienyl) compounds of zirconium(IV), $(C_5H_5)_2ZrX_2$ (X = Cl, Br, OAlk), as well as oxygen-bridged derivatives,[5,16,17] such as $[(C_5H_5)_2ClZr]_2O$.

The metal–ring bond is not destroyed when bis(cyclopentadienyl)zirconium dichloride is sulfonated by concentrated sulfuric acid,[18,19] nor is it destroyed by CF_3COOH.[20] Organic acids, however, as well as β-diketones or 8-oxyquinoline, replace one of the rings at elevated temperatures.[17,20,21]

$$(C_5H_5)_2ZrCl_2 + RH \longrightarrow C_5H_5(R)_2ZrCl \qquad (4)$$

$$\left(RH = R'COOH,\ R'COCH_2COR',\ \underset{OH}{\underset{N}{\bigcirc\bigcirc}} \right)$$

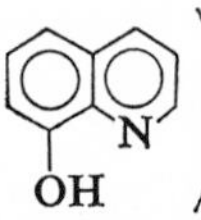

The ease of this reaction can be explained by the extremely stable zirconium compounds obtained. The compounds are thought to have two chelate rings and the octahedral structure (2).[21]

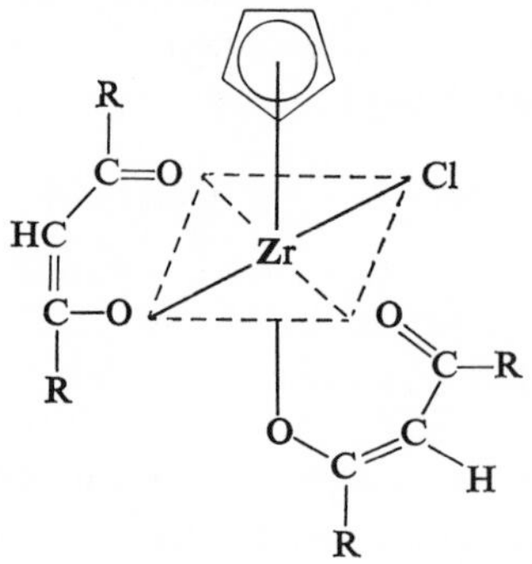

(2)

Similar reactions are described[22,23] for the hafnium compounds $(C_5H_5)_2HfCl_2$ and $[(C_5H_5)_2ClHf]_2$.

Tetrakis(cyclopentadienyl)zirconium,* when boiled with water or ethanol, is totally decomposed to cyclopentadiene, isolated in the first case as C_5H_5Tl.[25]

$$(C_5H_5)_4Zr- \begin{cases} \xrightarrow{\text{H}_2\text{O, }100°} ZrO_2 + [C_5H_6] \xrightarrow{\text{TlOH}} C_5H_5Tl \\ \xrightarrow{\text{C}_2\text{H}_5\text{OH, }95°} Zr(OC_2H_5)_4 \end{cases} \qquad (5)$$

* The structures of $(C_5H_5)_4Zr$ and $(C_5H_5)_4Hf$ have not been determined. The NMR spectrum of $(C_5H_5)_4Zr$ (at $+20$ to $-50°$) shows only one peak, that of C_5H_5-ring protons, whereas the infrared spectrum shows the absence of dienic ligands.[22-24]

Nitric or hydrochloric acid causes loss of only two cyclopentadienyl rings, whereas organic acids (acetic, benzoic, etc.) induce replacement of three rings and the formation of monocyclopentadienyl oxygen-bridged zirconium compounds.[25] Three rings are readily replaced by chelating anions (8-oxyquinoline, acetylacetone, benzoylacetone, or dibenzoylmethane).[26]

$$(C_5H_5)_4Zr \xrightarrow{\text{HX}} (C_5H_5)_2ZrX_2 \qquad (6)$$
$$(X = Cl, NO_3)$$

$$(C_5H_5)_4Zr \xrightarrow{\text{RCOOH}} [C_5H_5(RCOO)_2Zr]_2O \qquad (7)$$
$$(R = CH_3, C_6H_5)$$

$$(C_5H_5)_4Zr \xrightarrow{\text{RH}} C_5H_5ZrR_3 \qquad (8)$$

$$\left(RH = \underset{\text{OH}}{\overset{\text{N}}{\text{[structure]}}} , \begin{array}{l} CH_3COCH_2COCH_3, \\ C_6H_5COCH_2COCH_3, \\ C_6H_5COCH_2COC_6H_5 \end{array} \right),$$

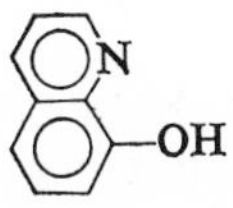

Tetrakis(cyclopentadienyl)hafnium decomposes completely when boiled with 10% potassium hydroxide solution, whereas nitric or hydrochloric acid produces the bis(cyclopentadienyl) compound (3). Three rings of $(C_5H_5)_4Hf$ are replaced by 8-oxyquinoline.[22]

$$(C_5H_5)_4Hf \begin{cases} \xrightarrow{\text{10\% KOH, 100°}} [C_5H_6] \xrightarrow{\text{TlOH}} C_5H_5Tl \\ \\ \xrightarrow{\text{HX}} (C_5H_5)_2HfX_2 \quad (X = Cl, NO_3) \qquad (9) \\ \phantom{\xrightarrow{\text{HX}}} \quad (3) \\ \\ \xrightarrow{\text{8-oxyquinoline}} C_5H_5Hf(OC_9H_6N)_3 \end{cases}$$

c. Group V. Bis(cyclopentadienyl)vanadium dichloride is stable in water or in organic solvents when they are absolutely airfree. Oxygen causes loss of the cyclopentadienyl rings to form $VOCl_2$.[27] Bis(cyclopentadienyl)vanadium dichloride dissolved in water–acid mixtures is stable for only several hours in the presence of air. The compound is decomposed immediately by an alkaline solution.[4,28] In contrast, bis(cyclopentadienyl)vanadium, $(C_5H_5)_2V$, is fairly stable toward water or mineral acids.[29,30]

d. Group VI. Bis(cyclopentadienyl)chromium is stable in water but reacts with dilute mineral acids.[31] The deep-blue solutions formed on interaction between $(C_5H_5)_2Cr$ and hydrochloric acid or hydrogen bromide contain the anions $(C_5H_5CrX_3)^-$ ($X = Cl^-$, Br^-). These have been isolated as the NH_4^+-salts.[32]

e. Group VII. Ionic bis(cyclopentadienyl)manganese reacts vigorously with water, forming cyclopentadiene.[30,33] In contrast, the bis(cyclopentadienyl)technetium dimer $[(C_5H_5)_2Tc]_2$ is quite stable toward hydrolysis.[34] The C_5H_5—M bond in bis(cyclopentadienyl)rhenium hydride is also stable.[35]

f. Group VIII. Nickelocene is stable in water or hydrochloric acid. Nitric acid oxidizes it to a cation, $(C_5H_5)_2Ni^+$, which decomposes in aqueous solution rather rapidly, especially in the presence of base.[12,36]

Cobaltocene is oxidized[30] by water to an extremely stable cobalticinium cation, $(C_5H_5)_2Co^+$, which is isoelectronic with ferrocene. Cobalticinium salts are not decomposed by concentrated sulfuric or nitric acid.[37,38] The cations arising from rhodium or iridium bis(cyclopentadienyl) compounds resemble cobalticinium.[39]

The most stable transition-metal cyclopentadienyl compounds are ferrocene, osmocene, and ruthenocene.[40,41] For example, ferrocene does not react with 10% sodium hydroxide solution or with boiling concentrated hydrochloric acid.[41]

Ferrocene derivatives with electron-withdrawing substituents are hydrolyzed in acidic media. When heated for 7 hr with 10% hydrochloric acid at 100°, phenylferrocene, benzoylferrocene, 1,1′-ferrocenyldicarboxylic acid, 1,1′-dibenzoylferrocene, acetylferrocene, ferrocene aldehyde, and 1,1′-diacetylferrocene are decomposed. The percentage of decomposition, determined from the amount of an iron salt formed, was 8, 11, 14, 21, 24, 34, and 62%, respectively. Under these conditions the degree of decomposition of alkyl ferrocenes is 5–8%, and ferrocene is not decomposed at all.[42]

The C_5H_5—M bond is less stable in a ferricinium cation than in ferrocene.[43] The ferricinium cation is relatively stable in acid solutions but partially decomposes in water, forming small amounts of ferrocene, the decomposition being accompanied by a decrease in the pH value of the solution.[44] If acidic, aqueous solutions of ferrocene are made alkaline, the characteristic ferricinium color rapidly disappears, and ferrocene is precipitated. However, the amount does not exceed 60–65%, and ferric hydroxide is invariably formed.[45] (For a more detailed description of the reaction, see Chapter 4, Section II-A-2.)

2. Reactions of Irradicated Ferrocene Derivatives

Nesmeyanov and Sazonova have found that ferrocene derivatives in which an α-atom attached to a five-membered ring carries some positive charge readily undergo destruction of an iron–ring bond. The derivatives formed include ferrocenedisulfonic and ferrocenedicarboxylic acids, acetylferrocene, ferrocenylamine salts, α-pyridylferrocene salts, and α-quinolylferrocene salts.

The compounds react when irradiated in acid or alkaline solutions at room temperature.

When irradiated in water for several hours, 1,1′-ferrocenedisulfonic acid produces an iron(II) salt of a dimer of cyclopentadienesulfonic acid, with the iron(II) salt of ferrocenedisulfonic acid being formed as an intermediate.[46]

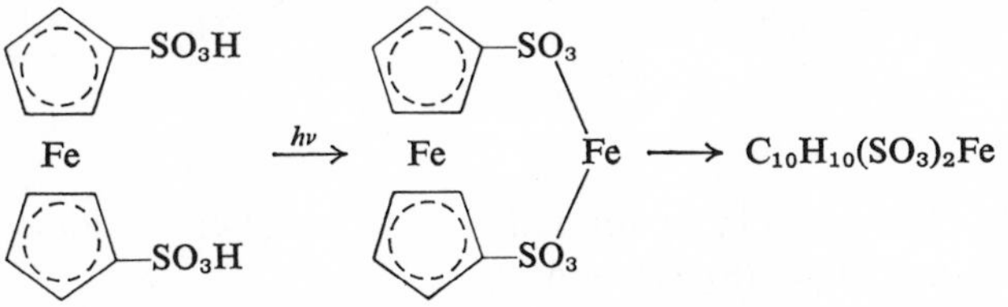

SO₃H
Fe
SO₃H
hν
SO₃
Fe
Fe
SO₃
C₁₀H₁₀(SO₃)₂Fe

(10)

Ferrocenedicarboxylic acid also decomposes readily when irradiated in alkaline solution.[47]

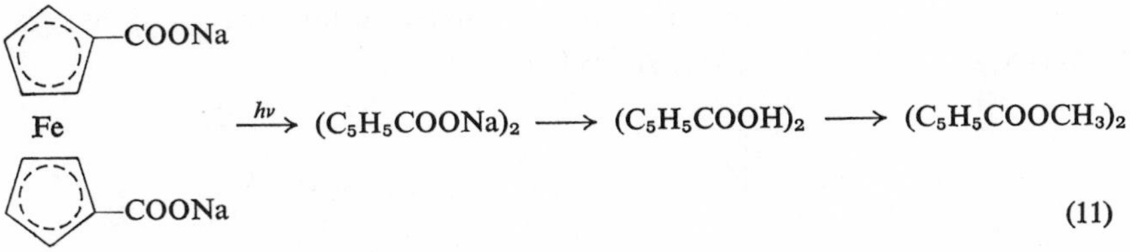

COONa
Fe
COONa
hν
(C₅H₅COONa)₂
(C₅H₅COOH)₂
(C₅H₅COOCH₃)₂

(11)

Irradiation very readily causes the decomposition of *N*-methyl-2-ferrocenylpyridinium hydroxide (**4**),[48]

N+
Fe
CH₃
hν
+ Fe²⁺ +
TlOH
C₅H₅Tl
N
CH₃
N+
CH₃

(12)

(**4**) (**5**)

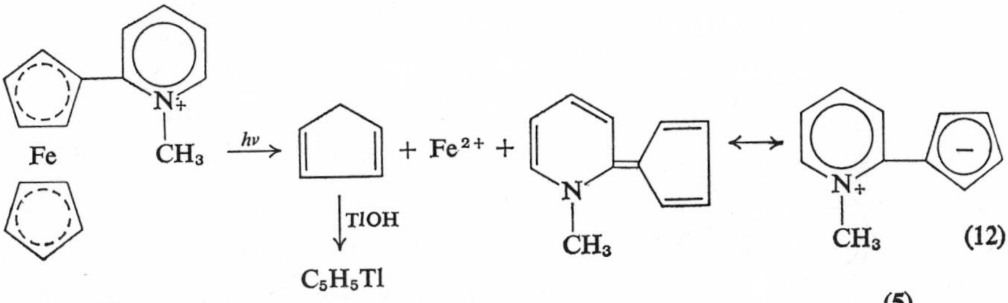

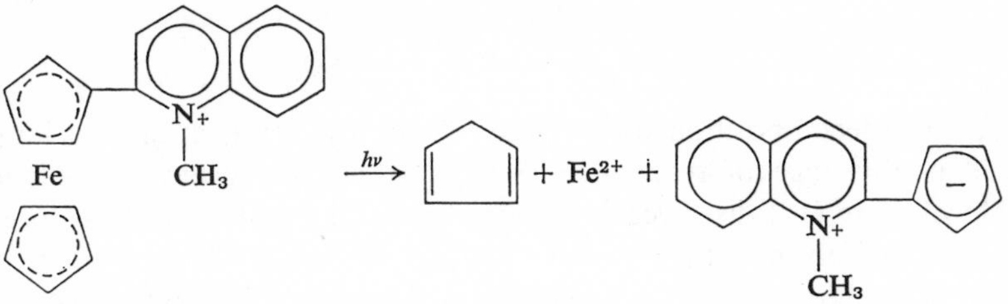

or *N*-methyl-3-ferrocenylquinolinium hydroxide (**6**),[46]

N+
Fe
CH₃
hν
+ Fe²⁺ +
N+
CH₃

(13)

(**6**) (**7**)

or trialkylferrocenylammonium hydroxide (8).[46,49,50]

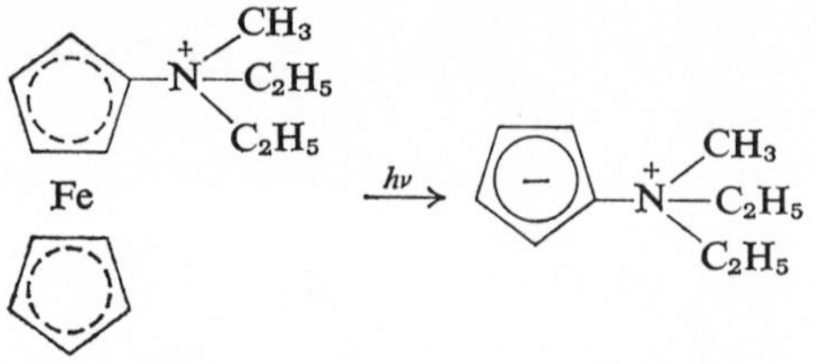

(14)

(8)   (9)

All the reactions result in the formation of cyclopentadiene, ionic iron, and the corresponding ylides (5), (7), and (9).

Ferrocene derivatives whose positively charged substituent is separated from the ring by a double C=C bond or by a benzene ring are also unstable toward irradiation. Thus 1-ferrocenyl-2-(α-pyridyl)ethene (10) or p-dimethyl-aminoferrocene (12) methiodides, when irradiated in alkaline solutions, are converted to the corresponding ylides (11) and (13).[49]

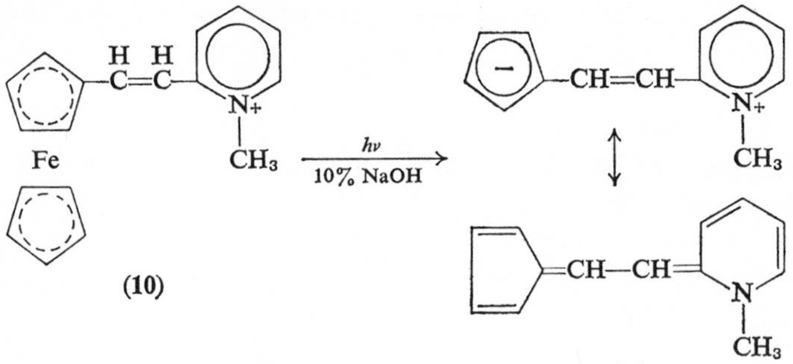

(15)

(10)

(11)

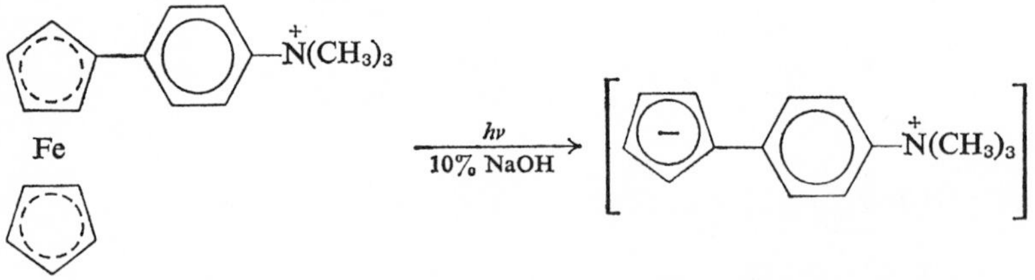

(16)

(12)   (13)

The easiest decomposition occurs when ferrocenyl (aryl)carbonium ions are used in this type of reaction.[51-54] Thus diphenylferrocenylcarbonium tetrachloroferrate (14) dissolved in acetone is decomposed by hydrochloric acid to diphenylfulvene (15).[53,54]

When hydrochloric acid is added to a solution of diphenylferrocenyl-carbinol or 1,1'-bis(diphenyloxymethyl)ferrocene (16) in acetic acid, diphenyl-

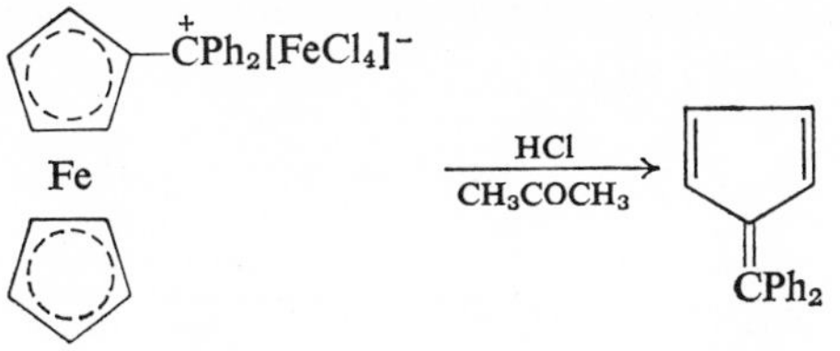

$$\text{(14)} \xrightarrow[\text{CH}_3\text{COCH}_3]{\text{HCl}} \text{(15)} \tag{17}$$

fulvene is formed very rapidly. The reaction may proceed via the formation of the corresponding carbonium salts (17).[53]

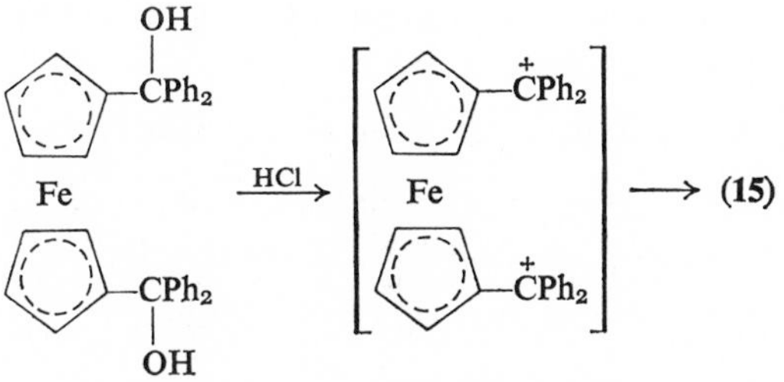

$$\text{(16)} \xrightarrow{\text{HCl}} \text{(17)} \longrightarrow \text{(15)} \tag{18}$$

Triferrocenylchloromethane hydrochloride, when dissolved in a water–methanol mixture at room temperature, gives diferrocenylfulvene (18) after several minutes, even in the absence of any irradiation. The fulvene is isolated as an adduct with acetylenedicarboxylic acid dimethyl ester (19) or reduced to cyclopentyldiferrocenylmethane (20).[55]

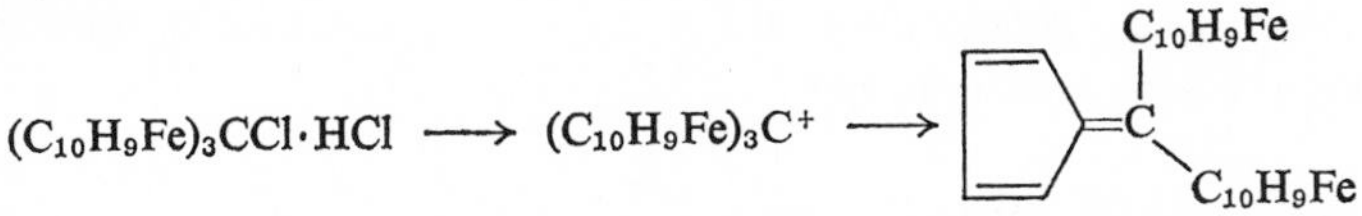

$$(\text{C}_{10}\text{H}_9\text{Fe})_3\text{CCl}\cdot\text{HCl} \longrightarrow (\text{C}_{10}\text{H}_9\text{Fe})_3\text{C}^+ \longrightarrow \text{(18)} \tag{19}$$

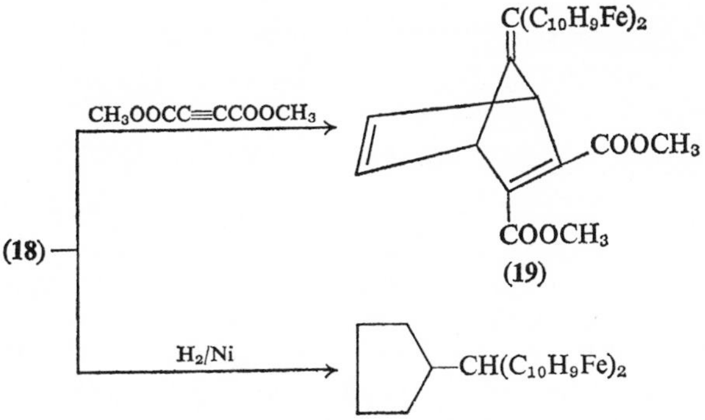

$$\text{(18)} \begin{cases} \xrightarrow{\text{CH}_3\text{OOCC}\equiv\text{CCOOCH}_3} \text{(19)} \\[2em] \xrightarrow{\text{H}_2/\text{Ni}} \text{(20)} \end{cases} \tag{20}$$

The mechanisms of these reactions have not been studied. They are very likely to be hydrolytic in all cases.

B. Reactions with Halogens or Halides

In considering metallocene reactions with halogens or halides the stability of a C_5H_5—M bond shows the same dependence on the metal as in the hydrolysis reactions described above. One must note, however, that the problem has not been studied systematically.

Only group IV bis(cyclopentadienyl) compounds are reported to exchange a C_5H_5-ring for a halogen. Bis(cyclopentadienyl)titanium, when reacted with chlorine, exchanges a cyclopentadienyl ring for the halogen atom and forms a monocyclopentadienyl derivative:[56–58]

$$(C_5H_5)_2TiCl_2 + 3Cl_2 \longrightarrow C_5H_5TiCl_3 + C_5H_5Cl_5 \tag{21}$$

The prolonged action of chlorine results in the loss of the other ring as well. Bromine reacts with $(C_5H_5)_2TiCl_2$ similarly to chlorine:[56]

$$(C_5H_5)_2TiCl_2 + 3Br_2 \longrightarrow C_5H_5TiCl_2Br + C_5H_5Br_5 \tag{22}$$

Substitution of a C_5H_5-ring by a halogen atom also occurs when titanium (IV) chloride reacts with $(C_5H_5)_2TiCl_2$.[56,57*]

$$(C_5H_5)_2TiCl_2 + TiCl_4 \xrightarrow{\Delta} 2C_5H_5TiCl_3 \tag{23}$$

Bis(cyclopentadienyl) metal dichlorides, $(C_5H_5)_2MCl_2$ (M = Zr, Hf, V), are also reported to lose a cyclopentadienyl ring under the influence of halogens (chlorine, bromine, fluorine).[59] Only a σ-bonded phenyl ring is substituted by a chlorine atom when chlorine acts on μ-oxo-bis[di(cyclopentadienyl)phenylzirconium].[60]

$$[(C_5H_5)_2ZrC_6H_5]_2O \xrightarrow[C_6H_6]{Cl_2} [(C_5H_5)_2ZrCl]_2O \tag{24}$$

Bis(cyclopentadienyl)zirconium dihalide readily reacts with zirconium tetrakis(acetylacetonate).[61]

$$(C_5H_5)_2ZrX_2 + (C_5H_7O_2)_4Zr \longrightarrow C_5H_5(C_5H_7O_2)_2ZrX \tag{25}$$
$$(X = Cl, Br)$$

Tetrakis(cyclopentadienyl) zirconium is reported to react with zirconium(IV) chloride with the exchange of two cyclopentadienyl rings.[25]

$$(C_5H_5)_4Zr + ZrCl_4 \longrightarrow (C_5H_5)_2ZrCl_2 \tag{26}$$

The interaction of ferrocene with halogens has been studied in more detail. Neither iodine nor potassium hypoiodite decomposes the ferrocene nucleus.[62–64] Depending on the conditions of the reaction, bromine and

---

* Complete description of the reaction is given in Ref. 58.

chlorine decompose ferrocene partially or totally.[64-69] Ferrocene dissolved in an organic solvent reacts with bromine at $-20°$ or with chlorine at $-40°$ to yield ferricinium ferrihalides as the main products.[64,68*] The reaction with bromine converts a cyclopentadienyl ring to tribromocyclopentene.[63,64]

$$(C_5H_5)_2Fe \xrightarrow{Br_2} [(C_5H_5)_2Fe]^+ [FeBr_4]^- + C_5H_5Br_3 \qquad (27)$$

If the reaction is carried out at elevated temperature with a great excess of the halogen, pentahalogenated cyclopentane is formed together with the iron(III) salt.

$$2(C_2H_5)_2Fe + 13X_2 \longrightarrow 4C_5H_5X_5 + 2FeX_3 \qquad (X = Br, Cl) \qquad (28)$$

Potassium hypobromite destroys ferrocene, yielding an iron(III) salt, pentabromocyclopentadiene, and perbromocyclopentadiene.[63]

Monosubstituted ferrocenes (ferrocenecarboxylic acid, ethylferrocene, and o-carboxybenzoylferrocene), when mixed with bromine, produce pentabromocyclopentane and its corresponding derivatives (the derivatives were not isolated as individual compounds).[67,70] The formation of pentahalogenated cyclopentanes from substituted ferrocenes decomposed by halogens is an excellent qualitative reaction demonstrating the presence of an unsubstituted cyclopentadienyl ring.

The action of cyanogen and thiocyanogen on ferrocene has been studied.[71,72] Cyanogen does not react with ferrocene, whereas thiocyanogen oxidizes ferrocene and partially decomposes it to ferricinium ferrithiocyanate, $[(C_5H_5)_2Fe]_3^+[Fe(SCN)_6]^{3-}$, which is insoluble in the reaction medium. The structure of the salt has been definitely proved by Mössbauer spectroscopy.[73]

Halides like Cl^- and Br^- destroy the ferricinium cation, forming a complex anion $[FeX_4]^-$, which in turn precipitates the ferricinium cation as a poorly soluble salt $[C_5H_5)_2Fe]^+[FeX_4]^-$, thus removing the cation from the reaction.[71] The thiocyanate anion acts similarly. (For the action of a CN^- anion on ferricinium, see Chapter 1, Section II-I.)

Reactions of transition-metal cyclopentadienyl compounds with iron(II) chloride are to be discussed separately.† Ionic bis(cyclopentadienyl)manganese[30] as well as the tris(cyclopentadienyl) compounds of scandium, yttrium, and the lanthanides[1,2] instantly form ferrocene when reacted with

---

* Kaufmann[65] has isolated the species $C_5H_5MX_2$ after a reaction of ferrocene, nickelocene, or cobaltocene dissolved in CCl_4 with halogens (chlorine and bromine). The author believes them to be the products arising from a cyclopentadienyl substitution by two halogen atoms, but there is no evidence to confirm this. Ferrocene reacts with hexachlorocyclopentadiene to produce $[C_5H_5FeCl_2]_2$.[66]

† The reaction may be considered as a qualitative one and is characteristic of cyclopentadienyl compounds with an ionic or covalent σ-bond.

iron(II) chloride in tetrahydrofuran.

$$2(C_5H_5)_3M + 3FeCl_2 \longrightarrow 3(C_5H_5)_2Fe + 2MCl_3 \qquad (29)$$

If π-bonded to metal, cyclopentadienyl rings are not substituted by a chlorine atom in the presence of iron(II) chloride. Thus no formation of ferrocene can be detected in the reaction of iron(II) chloride with ruthenium, osmium, cobalt,* and nickel cyclopentadienyl compounds,[30] with bis(cyclopentadienyl)rhenium hydride,[35,74] or with bis(cyclopentadienyl)titanium.[10]

Wilkinson, Cotton, and Birmingham[30] investigated the interaction of ferrocene with an isotopic iron salt and found that exchange does not take place.

Tetrakis(cyclopentadienyl)zirconium exchanges only two C_5H_5-rings, the reaction proceeding with difficulty and in low yield.[25]

$$(C_5H_5)_4Zr + FeCl_2 \longrightarrow (C_5H_5)_2ZrCl_2 + (C_5H_5)_2Fe \qquad (30)$$

Bis(cyclopentadienyl)vanadium produces only traces of ferrocene.[30] Tris(cyclopentadienyl)uranium chloride does not react with iron(II) chloride at room temperature. However, with prolonged heating—8 days at 100°—small amounts of ferrocene are formed.[75]

Bis(cyclopentadienyl)chromium, when reacted with iron(II) chloride, produces ferrocene in high yield (70% of the theoretical amount), thus behaving similarly to ionic metal cyclopentadienyls.[30]

The titanium–ring bond in $(C_5H_5)_2TiCl_2$, $(C_5H_5)_2Ti(OCOCF_3)_2$, and $(C_5H_5)_2Ti(OCOC_6H_5)_2$ is stable enough not to be broken by iron(II) chloride. If the chlorine atoms of $(C_5H_5)_2TiCl_2$ are replaced by acetoxy groups, however, the resulting bis(cyclopentadienyl)titanium diacetate readily reacts with iron(II) and ferrocene is formed.[76-78]

$$(C_5H_5)_2Ti(OCOCH_3)_2 \xrightarrow{\text{FeCl}_2} \underset{46\%}{(C_5H_5)_2Fe} \qquad (31)$$

It is also interesting to see how metallocenes behave in the presence of aluminum chloride. Aluminum chloride does not destroy metallocenes under Friedel–Crafts conditions, but serves as a catalyst. However, if ferrocene is heated with aluminum chloride in organic solvents for long periods, it undergoes partial destruction of the nucleus.[79-82] Alkyl ferrocenes give a mixture of ferrocene and 1,1'-dialkyl ferrocenes under the influence of aluminum chloride. The reaction proceeds as a ligand exchange rather than transalkylation. (For details on these two reactions, see Chapter 1, Section II-D.)

The exchange of a ferrocene cyclopentadienyl ring for an arene under the influence of aluminum chloride is described in Section F-3.

---

* Cobaltocene reacts with $FeCl_2$ to produce cobalticinium chloride and iron.[30]

C. Reactions with Carbon Monoxide or Metal Carbonyls

Exchange of C_5H_5-rings for CO-groups, the reaction that is the inverse of metallocene synthesis, is performed with metallocenes whose ring hydrogens are not known to undergo electrophilic substitution. Osmocene, for example, will not react with carbon monoxide.[83] However, chromium, vanadium, cobalt, and manganese bis(cyclopentadienyl) compounds as well as a titanium tris(cyclopentadienyl) compound have been reported to exchange their C_5H_5-rings for CO.

When heated with compressed carbon monoxide, bis(cyclopentadienyl)-chromium forms a cyclopentadienylchromium carbonyl or chromium hexacarbonyl, depending on the reaction temperature.[84,85]

$$(C_5H_5)_2Cr + CO \longrightarrow \begin{array}{l} \xrightarrow[\text{100 atm}]{\text{100–110°}} (C_5H_5)_3Cr_2(CO)_3 \\ \qquad\qquad\quad \textbf{(21)} \\ \xrightarrow{\text{150–170°}} [(C_5H_5)Cr(CO)_3]_2 \\ \qquad\qquad\quad \textbf{(22)} \\ \xrightarrow{\text{250°}} Cr(CO)_6 \end{array} \qquad (32)$$

Fischer and co-workers[84,86] think that bis(cyclopentadienyl)chromium first reacts with carbon monoxide to exchange its C_5H_5-ring for three CO-groups. The resulting radical, $C_5H_5Cr(CO)_3$, reacts with the unreacted $(C_5H_5)_2Cr$, forming compound (21). On the basis of its infrared spectrum and its paramagnetism, this compound is thought to be $[(C_5H_5)_2Cr]^+$ $[C_5H_5Cr(CO)_3]^-$. Higher temperatures give rise to dimerization of the radical $C_5H_5Cr(CO)_3$, producing compound (22). If the reaction is carried out in the presence of hydrogen, cyclopentadienylchromium tricarbonyl hydride (23) is formed[84–86] together with small amounts of bis(cyclopenta-diene)chromium(IV) dicarbonyl (24).[87]

$$(C_5H_5)_2Cr \xrightarrow{CO\ +\ H_2} C_5H_5Cr(CO)_3H + (C_5H_6)_2Cr(CO)_2 \qquad (33)$$
$$\qquad\qquad\qquad\qquad \textbf{(23)} \qquad\qquad\quad \textbf{(24)}$$

Thus an exchange of a cyclopentadienyl ring for CO-groups occurs at the same time as an addition of hydrogen to the rings and with transformation of the metal–ring bond.

Carbon monoxide reacts with bis(cyclopentadienyl)vanadium to give cyclopentadienylvanadium tetracarbonyl.[88,89]*

$$(C_5H_5)_2V \xrightarrow{CO} C_5H_5V(CO)_4 \qquad (34)$$

Bis(cyclopentadienyl)cobalt, when heated with compressed carbon monoxide, forms cyclopentadienylcobalt dicarbonyl.[90,91]*

$$(C_5H_5)_2CO \xrightarrow{CO} C_5H_5Co(CO)_2 \xrightarrow{CO} Co_2(CO)_8 \qquad (35)$$

* A complete description of the synthesis is given in Ref. 58.

Titanium bis(cyclopentadienyl) compounds, $(C_5H_5)_2TiCl_2$ or $(C_5H_5)_2Ti$-$(C_6H_5)_2$, do not produce carbonyls when reacted with carbon monoxide.[92] Tris(cyclopentadienyl)titanium is transformed by carbon monoxide into bis(cyclopentadienyl)titanium dicarbonyl.[93]

$$(C_5H_5)_3Ti \xrightarrow[80°, 150\ atm]{CO} (C_5H_5)_2Ti(CO)_2 \qquad (36)$$

Nickelocene, when heated with carbon monoxide, exchanges the two cyclopentadienyl rings to produce nickel tetracarbonyl.[94] Only one C_5H_5-ring is exchanged for CO if nickelocene reacts with nickel tetracarbonyl.* The reaction results in the formation of the diamagnetic cyclopentadienyl-nickel carbonyl dimer (25) and the paramagnetic, trinuclear tris(cyclopentadienyl)-tri-nickel dicarbonyl (26).

$$(C_5H_5)_2Ni \xrightarrow{Ni(CO)_4} (C_5H_5NiCO)_2 + (C_5H_5)_3Ni_3(CO)_2 + CO \qquad (37)$$
$$\qquad\qquad\qquad (25) \qquad\qquad (26)$$

Compound (25) has been found to have structure (27),

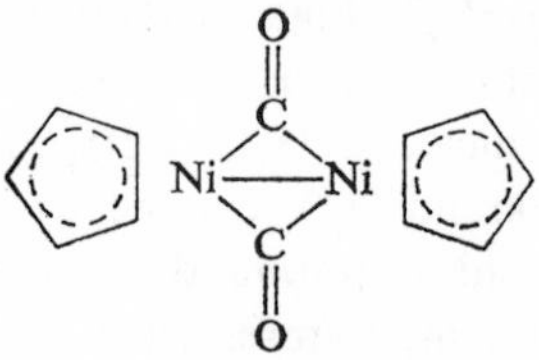

(27)

whereas for the trinuclear compound (26) the alternative structures (28) or (29) have been proposed.

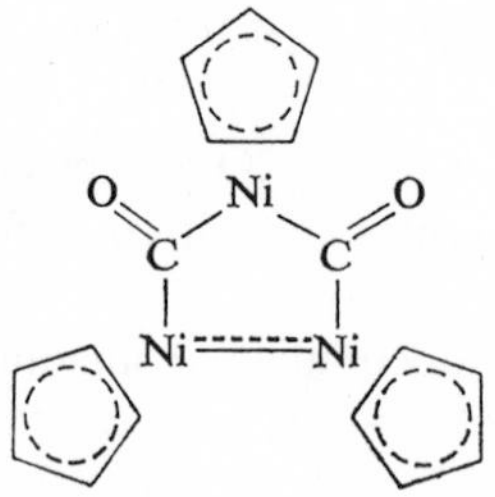

(28) 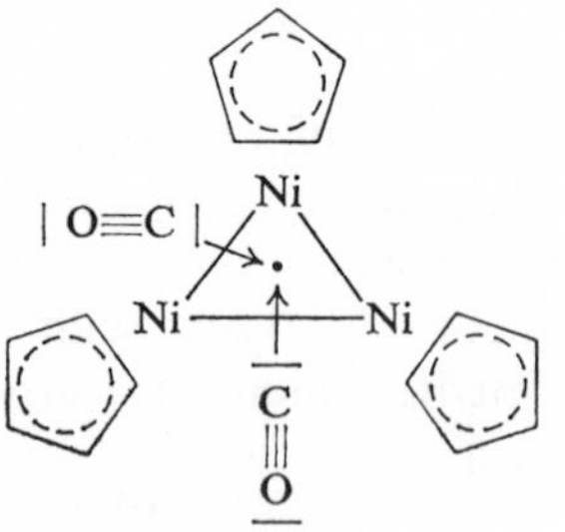   (29)

Nickelocene reacts with iron pentacarbonyl, leading to a mixture of compounds (30), (31), and (25).[95]

---

* A complete description of the synthesis is given in Ref. 58.

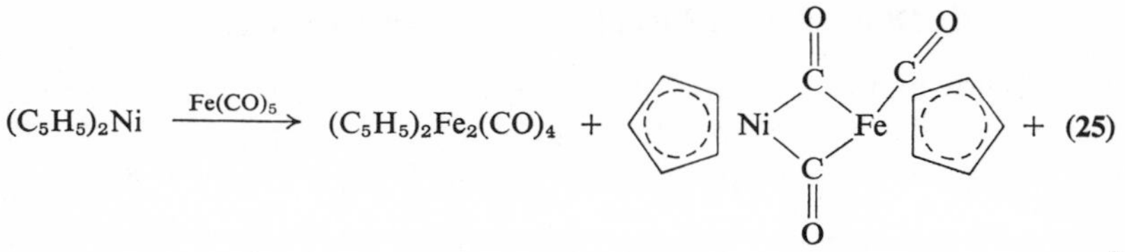

$$(C_5H_5)_2Ni \xrightarrow{Fe(CO)_5} (C_5H_5)_2Fe_2(CO)_4 + \text{[structure]} + (25)$$

(30)   (31)   (38)

Cobaltocene reacts with iron pentacarbonyl, forming dicobaltocinium tridecacarbonyl ferrate, (32).[96]

$$(C_5H_5)_2Co \xrightarrow{Fe(CO)_5} [(C_5H_5)_2Co]_2Fe_4(CO)_{13} + CO \qquad (39)$$
$$(32)$$

D. Reactions with Nitric Oxide

An exchange of the C_5H_5-ring for NO-groups occurs with nickel, chromium, and manganese bis(cyclopentadienyl) compounds.

Nickelocene reacts at 0° with nitric oxide in petroleum ether or without solvent to form cyclopentadienylnickel nitrosyl.[88,97,98]* The molecule has C_{5v} symmetry.[99]

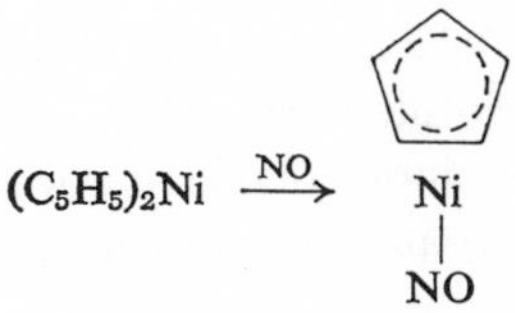

$$(C_5H_5)_2Ni \xrightarrow{NO} \underset{\underset{NO}{|}}{Ni} \qquad (40)$$

A cyclopentadienyl nitrosyl derivative of chromium, $C_5H_5Cr(NO)_2Cl$, is obtained by the reaction of nitric oxide with a product [the product, not identified, is perhaps $(C_5H_5)_2CrCl$] formed during the reaction of sodium cyclopentadienyl with chromium(III) chloride in tetrahydrofuran.[97,100]

Bis(cyclopentadienyl)manganese reacts with nitric oxide to give compound (33) whose structure is thought to be as follows:[97,100]

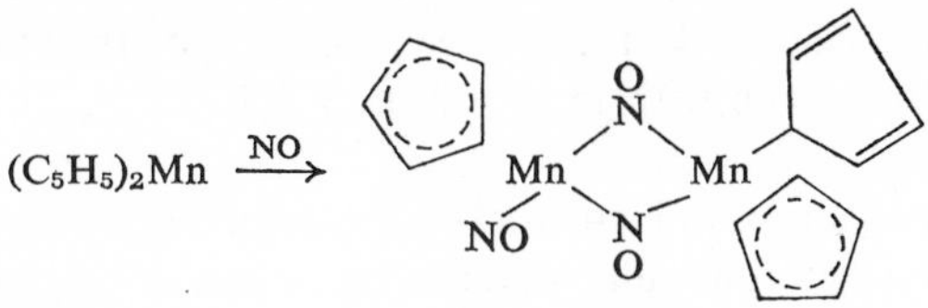

$$(C_5H_5)_2Mn \xrightarrow{NO} \text{[structure]} \qquad (41)$$

(33)

* A complete description of the synthesis is given in Ref. 58.

E. Destruction of Metallocenes by Reducing Agents

Nesmeyanov and co-workers[67] have shown that ferrocene, when subjected to hydrogen under high temperature and pressure in the presence of Raney nickel, decomposes to cyclopentane and metallic iron.

$$(C_5H_5)_2Fe + 5H_2 \xrightarrow[300°, 250\ atm]{Ni} 2C_5H_{10} + Fe \tag{42}$$

Ferrocene derivatives [1,1'-ferrocenedicarboxylic acid, 1,1'-di-(p-nitrophenyl)ferrocene, 1,1'-diacetoxyferrocene,[67] and a mixture of acetylated 1,1'-dimethyl ferrocenes[101] when hydrogenated, are transformed into the corresponding cyclopentane derivatives.

Unlike catalytic hydrogenation, proceeding only under drastic conditions, the cleavage of ferrocene readily takes place with alkali metals dissolved in amines or liquid ammonia, as described by Trifan and Nichols.[102] The optimum conditions for the reaction are brought about with lithium in ethylamine. As a result metallic iron is formed together with cyclopentadiene (isolated as an adduct with maleic anhydride).

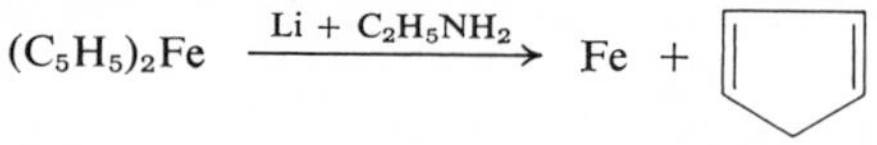

$$(C_5H_5)_2Fe \xrightarrow{Li + C_2H_5NH_2} Fe + \boxed{} \tag{43}$$

Pauson and co-workers[103] have used this reaction to obtain cyclopentadiene derivatives from substituted ferrocenes. Thus lithium in ethylamine decomposes N,N-dimethylaminomethylferrocene to lithium N,N-dimethylaminomethylcyclopentadienyl and lithium cyclopentadienyl. The N,N-dime-

$$\tag{44}$$

thylaminomethylcyclopentadiene was not isolated. The reaction mixture was treated with iron(II) chloride to give a mixture of the initial N,N-dimethylaminomethylferrocene with ferrocene and 1,1'-bis(N,N-dimethylaminomethyl)ferrocene.

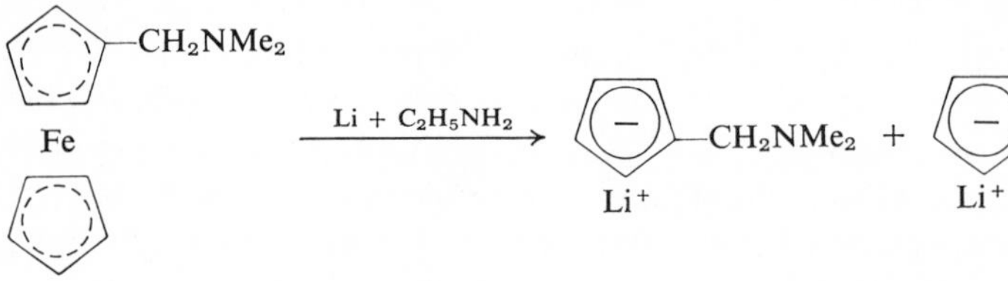

Similarly Nesmeyanov and co-workers[104] obtained dialkylcobalticinium salts starting from heteroannular dialkyl ferrocenes. The yield of the salts was 6–18%.

Ruthenocene, when heated in hydrogen to 595°, produces very pure films of metallic ruthenium.[105]

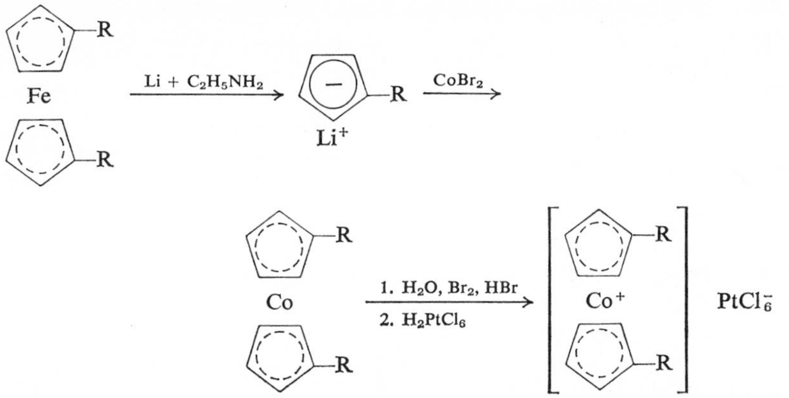

Fe $\xrightarrow{\text{Li} + \text{C}_2\text{H}_5\text{NH}_2}$ [$\odot$—R]$^-$ Li$^+$ $\xrightarrow{\text{CoBr}_2}$

Co $\xrightarrow[\text{2. H}_2\text{PtCl}_6]{\text{1. H}_2\text{O, Br}_2, \text{HBr}}$ [Co$^+$]$_2$ PtCl$_6^-$ (45)

$$(R = C_2H_5, n\text{-}C_3H_7)$$

Ferrocene,[9] nickelocene,[9,106] and chromocene[9] are destroyed by potassium dissolved in liquid ammonia, with the liberation of the corresponding metals. Ferrocene and nickelocene do not react with potassium amide dissolved in liquid ammonia, whereas chromocene forms CrN under these conditions.[9]

F. Other Reactions

This section deals with various reactions of ferrocene, nickelocene, and cobaltocene in which the metal–ring bond is involved. We discuss these compounds together, although this joint treatment is somewhat artificial. Actually ferrocene, as well as a number of its derivatives, undergoes a rupture of an iron–cyclopentadienyl bond under drastic conditions. This usually leads to the destruction of the molecule.* The only reaction known for ferrocene and its derivatives in which one cyclopentadienyl ring is exchanged is the reaction with aromatic compounds in the presence of aluminum chloride. On the other hand, the metal–cyclopentadienyl bond of nickelocene is much more labile. Reactions involving ring exchange or transformation of the nickel–ring bond character are characteristic of nickelocene derivatives possessing two unpaired electrons and not having an inert-gas electron configuration.

Zirconium and hafnium bis or tetrakis cyclopentadienyl compounds exchange their cyclopentadienyls for acetylacetonate or 8-oxyquinoline groups[17,20–24,26] (see Section I-A-1).

1. Destruction of the Ferrocene Nucleus by Oxidizing Agents

It has been demonstrated above that the destruction of the ferrocene nucleus by halogens proceeds by a ferrocene–ferricinium oxidation. The

* Mass spectrometry of ferrocene, nickelocene, or a mixture of these compounds has shown a rupture of a metal–cyclopentadienyl bond and formation of heavy particles. The particles include $(C_5H_5)_3M_2$, $(C_5H_5)_2M_3$ (M = Ni or Fe).[107]

destruction of ferrocene by organic peroxides has also been described.[108] Iron(III) benzoate is formed when ferrocene dissolved in benzene is boiled with benzoyl peroxide.

$$(C_5H_5)_2Fe \xrightarrow{(C_6H_5COO)_2} Fe(OCOC_6H_5)_3 \qquad (46)$$

The action of *tert*-butyl peroxide transforms ferrocene and its homologs to the polyferrocenylenes.[109–111]

Oxidation of 1,1'-dioxyferrocene by atmospheric oxygen produces the cyclopentadienone dimer.[112,113]

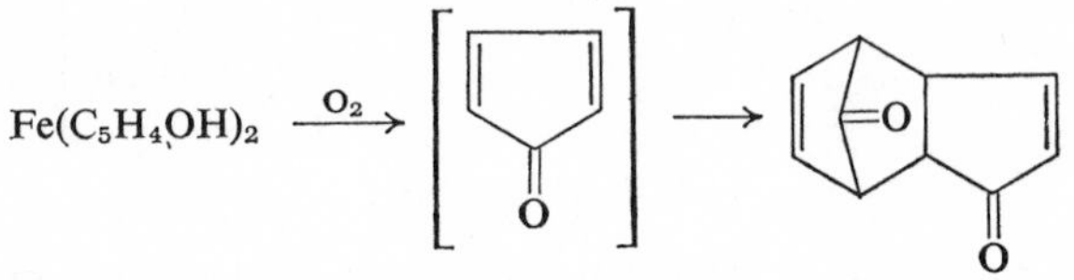

$$Fe(C_5H_4OH)_2 \xrightarrow{O_2} \qquad \longrightarrow \qquad (47)$$

2. Destruction of Ferrocene Derivatives by Diazonium Salts

Ferrocene derivatives containing two electron-withdrawing substituents are destroyed when treated with diazonium salts. It has been found that 1,1'-diacetylferrocene[114] interacts with a diazonium chloride in acetic acid to give a 40–50% yield of the iron–free cyclopentadiene derivative (34) plus ionic Fe^{3+}.

$$Fe(C_5H_4COCH_3)_2 \xrightarrow[CH_3COOH]{ArN_2Cl} CH_3COC_5H_4N_2Ar + Fe^{3+} \qquad (48)$$

$$(34)$$

$$(Ar = p\text{-}C_6H_4NO_2, C_6H_5, p\text{-}C_6H_4CH_3)$$

Neither ketone nor hydroxy groups can be detected in the cyclopentadiene compound (34) formed. Its qualitative reactions show the absence of enol, and the infrared-spectrum contains no bands due to C=O, C—OH, or N—H bonds. The compound forms a complex with cadmium chloride, thus behaving similarly to isoxazoles. On the basis of this evidence Nesmeyanov, Perevalova, and others[115] attributed to compound (34) the structure of 1,2,3-oxadiazine (35), with the location of double bonds being arbitrary. However, an NMR investigation carried out by Bozak and Rinehart[116] has shown that compound (34) has the enol structure (36).

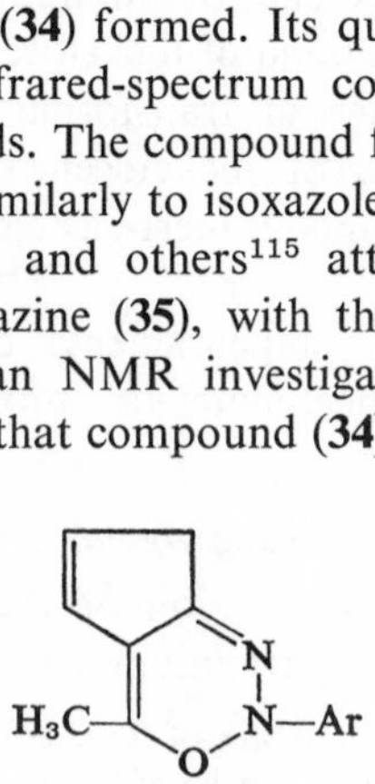

(35) 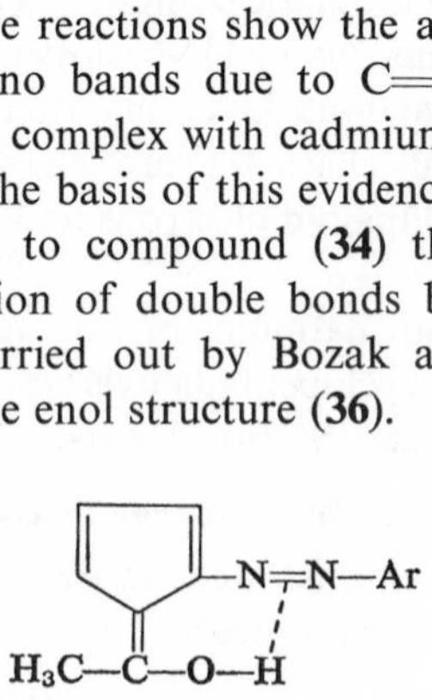   (36)

Heteroannular dipropionyl, dibutyryl, and dibenzoyl ferrocenes react with p-nitrobenzenediazonium chloride in the same manner as does 1,1'-diacetyl-ferrocene, but the yields of iron–free compounds are much lower (1–3%). The diacyl ferrocenes remain partially untransformed, and significant amounts of tar are formed. Also 1,1'-di(carbomethoxy)ferrocene undergoes a rupture of the iron-cyclopentadienyl bond when reacted with p-nitrobenzenediazonium chloride, but no cyclopentadiene derivatives of type (36) were isolated as pure compounds.[117]

3. Exchange of the Ferrocene C_5H_5-Ring with Arenes

In 1963 Nesmeyanov, Vol'kenau, and Bolesova showed[118,119] that when ferrocene reacts with benzene in the presence of aluminum chloride, one of the cyclopentadienyl rings is replaced by a benzene ring, forming the benzene cyclopentadienyliron cation.*

$$\text{Fe} + \text{C}_6\text{H}_6 \xrightarrow{\text{AlCl}_3} \left[\text{Fe}\right]^+ \quad [\text{AlCl}_4]^- + [\text{C}_5\text{H}_5]\text{X} \qquad (49)$$

An exchange of a cyclopentadienyl ring for an arene has been performed with a great number of ferrocene derivatives and with a number of aromatic compounds (see Tables I, II, and III). The cations obtained are isolated as stable salts with various anions, such as BPh_4^-, BF_4^-, PF_6^-, I^-, and I_3^-.

Electron-donating substituents in a ferrocene or arene facilitate exchange, whereas electron-withdrawing substituents (especially in benzene ring) hinder it.[119,121,122] For example, the substituted cyclopentadienyl ring is exchanged mainly for an arene when ethylferrocene reacts with benzene or mesitylene,[119,122] but only the unsubstituted ring is replaced during the reaction of acetylferrocene with mesitylene.[122]

An attempt to obtain bis(arene) iron via the exchange of the two ferrocene cyclopentadienyls was unsuccessful.[118]

Aluminum bromide can be used in this reaction instead of aluminum chloride, but other Lewis acids ($SnCl_4$, $TiCl_4$, BF_3) are ineffective.[121]

Since the ferricinium cation does not exchange its C_5H_5-ring for an arene, powdered aluminum must be added to the reaction mixture in order to

* The cation was earlier obtained from a reaction of benzene with cyclopentadienyliron dicarbonyl chloride in the presence of aluminum chloride.[120]

$$C_5H_5Fe(CO)_2Cl + C_6H_6 \xrightarrow{\text{AlCl}_3} [C_5H_5FeC_6H_6]^+X^-$$

A complete description of the synthesis is given in Ref. 58.

TABLE I

Exchange of a Cyclopentadienyl Ring of Ferrocene for Arenes Leading to $C_5H_5Fe^+[—\pi\text{-Arene}]$

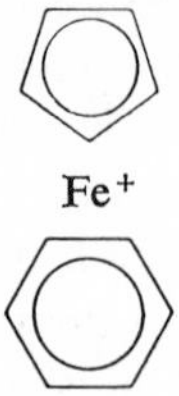

Arene exchanging	Temp., °C	Time hr	Yield, %	Ref.
Benzene	80	6	20	118, 119
Toluene	110	5	37	121
p-Xylene	135–140	3	—	121
Mesitylene	160–165	3	66	118
Diphenyl[a]	160–170	3	40	121
Naphthalene[a]	110–120	3.5	33	121
Tetralin[a]	160–165	3.5	48	118
Fluorene[a]	135–140	3.5	25	121
Chlorobenzene	130–135	3	25	121
Bromobenzene[b]	60–70	10	—	121
Acetanilide	115–125	5	23	121

[a] One aromatic ring takes part in replacing a cyclopentadienyl ring.
[b] Bromobenzene and benzene complexes are formed.

TABLE II

Arenes Exchanging for a Cyclopentadienyl Ring in Monosubstituted Ferrocenes[a] $R—C_5H_4FeC_5H_5$ To Form Reaction Products $R—C_5H_4Fe^+[—\pi\text{-Arene}] + C_5H_5Fe^+[—\pi\text{-Arene}]$

R in ferrocene derivative	Arene exchanging	Temp., °C	Time, hr	Yield, %	Ref.
—C_2H_5	Benzene	80	8	—	122
	Mesitylene	70–80	5	—	122
—C_6H_5	Benzene	80	15	—	122
—$COCH_3$	Mesitylene	90–100	4	—	122
—CN	Benzene	80	6	75[b]	122

[a] All ferrocene derivatives substituted in the 1-position.
[b] The yield is for a mixture of both products, $NCC_5H_4Fe^+C_6H_6 + C_5H_5Fe^+C_6H_6$.

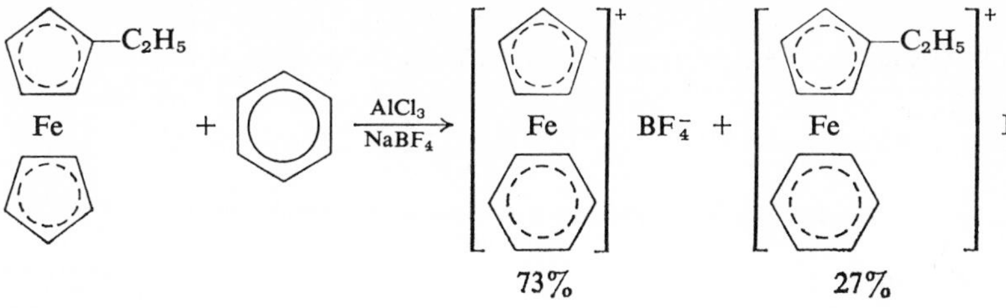

$$(50)$$

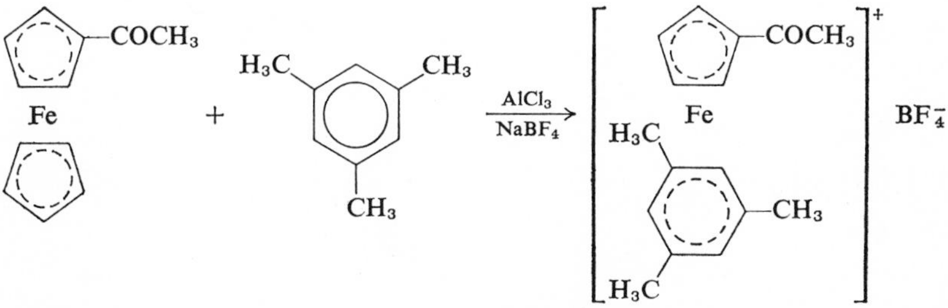

$$(51)$$

TABLE III

Arenes Exchanging for a Cyclopentadienyl Ring in Heteroannular Disubstituted Ferrocenes $R—C_5H_4FeC_5H_4—R$ To Form Reaction Product $R—C_5H_4Fe^+—\pi$-Arene

R in $R—C_5H_4FeC_5H_4—R$	Arene exchanging	Temp., °C	Time, hr	Yield, %	Ref.
—C_2H_5	Benzene	80	5	32	122
	Mesitylene	120–130	5	39	122
—C_6H_5	Benzene	80	5	—	122
Cl	Benzene	70–75	4	25	123
—$COCH_3$	Mesitylene	120–130	4.5	22	118, 122

suppress the ferrocene–ferricinium oxidation. Ferrocene derivatives with electron–withdrawing substituents ($COCH_3$, CN, Cl) are oxidized only slightly, and the addition of powdered aluminum is unnecessary. In obtaining halogen-substituted arenecyclopentadienyliron compounds,

$$[BrC_6H_5FeC_5H_5]^+X^- \quad or \quad [ClC_5H_4FeC_6H_6]^+X^-$$

powdered aluminum promotes dehalogenation and the formation of a by-product, $[C_6H_6FeC_5H_5]^+X^-$.[121]

4. Exchange of Nickelocene $C_5H_5^-$-Rings

Paramagnetic nickelocene, whose central atom possesses a 20-electron shell, very readily exchanges one or two of its cyclopentadienyl rings for various nucleophiles.

TABLE IV

Exchange of One Cyclopentadienyl Ring in Nickelocene

Reactant	Reaction product	Ref.
CH_2=$CHCH_2MgBr$	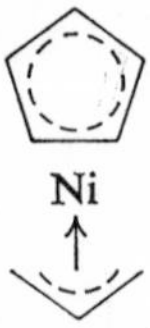	124
CH_2=$CHCH$=CH_2	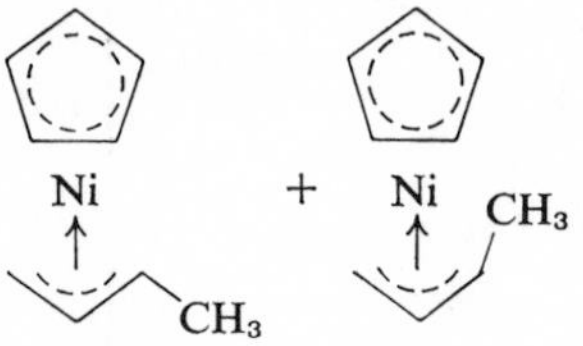	125
PPh_3 + CCl_4 (or HCl) or $(PPh_3)_2 \cdot NiCl_2$	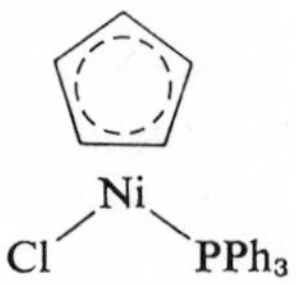	128
PPh_3 + I_2 (or HI)	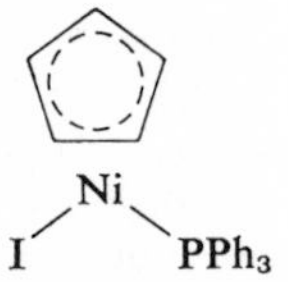	126, 127

(continued)

    a. Exchange of One C_5H_5-Ring. Nickelocene reacts with allylmagnesium bromide,[124] butadiene,[125] triphenylphosphine in carbon tetrachloride,[126] a mixture of triphenylphosphine and hydrogen halides or iodine,[126,127] a complex of triphenylphosphine–nickel(II) chloride,[128] and azobenzene.[129] In this process the substitution of one cyclopentadienyl ring occurs and the corresponding monocyclopentadienylnickel compounds are obtained (see Table IV).

    When nickelocene reacts with acetylene,[53] thiols,[130] nickel tetrakis(phenylisocyanide), or nickel tetrakis(cyclohexylisocyanide),[131–133] binuclear monocyclopentadienyl complexes are formed (see Table IV).

    Nickelocene reacts with allylmagnesium chloride[124] and with thiols[130] at 20–25°. The reaction of nickelocene with acetylene[134] or butadiene[125] is performed at elevated temperatures and in an autoclave. The interaction of diphenylacetylene with nickelocene in the presence of nickel tetracarbonyl produces compound (37).[135] The reaction may proceed via the formation of

TABLE IV (*continued*)

Reactant	Reaction product	Ref.
$C_6H_5N=NC_6H_5$	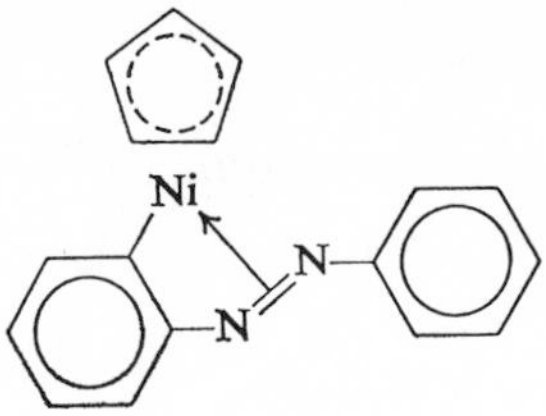	129
$CH\equiv CH$	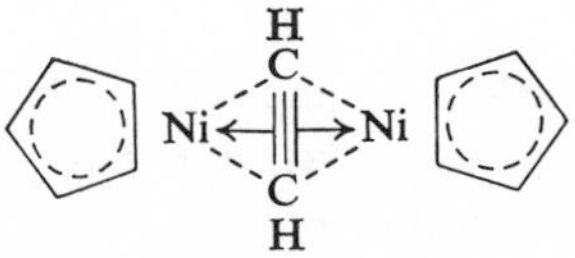	53
RSH	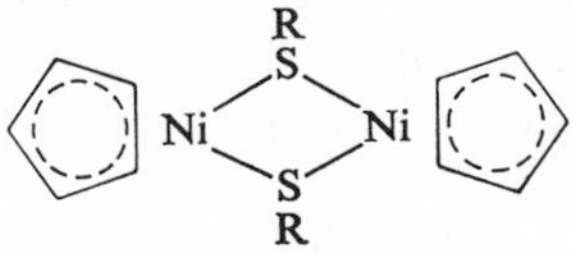	130
$Ni(:C=\ddot{N}C_6H_5)_4$ or $Ni(:C=\ddot{N}C_6H_{11})_4$	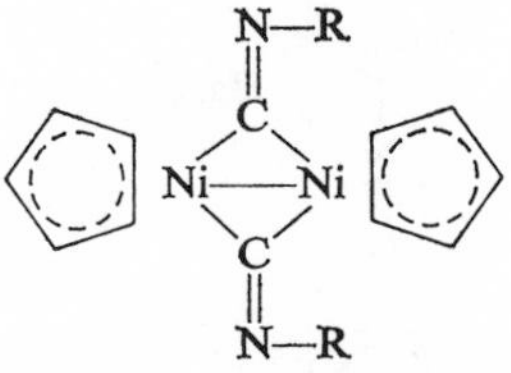 $(R = C_6H_5, C_6H_{11})$	131–133

cyclopentadienylnickel carbonyl [see the reaction of nickelocene with $Ni(CO)_4$ in Section I-C].

$$(C_5H_5)_2Ni + C_6H_5C\equiv CC_6H_5 \xrightarrow[\substack{\text{boiling } C_6H_6 \\ 6 \text{ hr}}]{Ni(CO)_4}$$

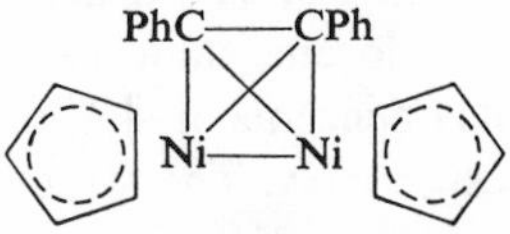

(52)

(37)

Kleiman and Dubeck[129] have demonstrated that nickelocene, when heated with azobenzene, produces a compound whose magnetic and spectroscopic properties indicate it to be cyclopentadienyl-[o-(phenylazo)phenyl]nickel (38). This compound possesses a π-bonded cyclopentadienyl ring, a σ-bond between nickel and an *ortho*-carbon of the phenyl nucleus, and a coordinated azo group.* The existence of nickel bonded to a phenyl nucleus has been

---

* The mode of coordination between an azo group and nickel is as yet unknown. The problem may be resolved only on the basis of X-ray investigations. Azobenzene palladium, platinum, and iron complexes are known where one of the azo-group nitrogens is thought to complex with the metal.[136,137]

confirmed by the formation of azobenzene containing 10% deuterium as a result of reaction with lithium aluminum deuteride.

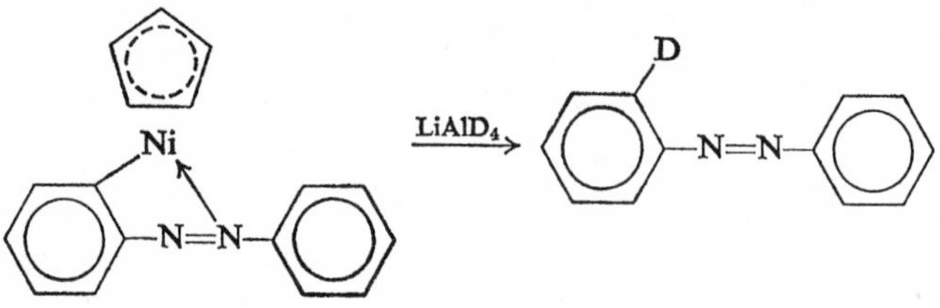

(53)

(38)

Ustynyuk and co-workers[138] have not only confirmed the presence of a Ni—C bond in compound **(38)** but have also established that it is attached to the phenyl group in the *ortho* position. Mercury salts [$HgCl_2$ or $Hg(OCOCH_3)_2$] destroy the Ni—C bond in compound **(38)** (a process typical of a carbon–metal σ-bond). Bromination of the resulting mercurated azobenzene then yields *o*-bromoazobenzene.

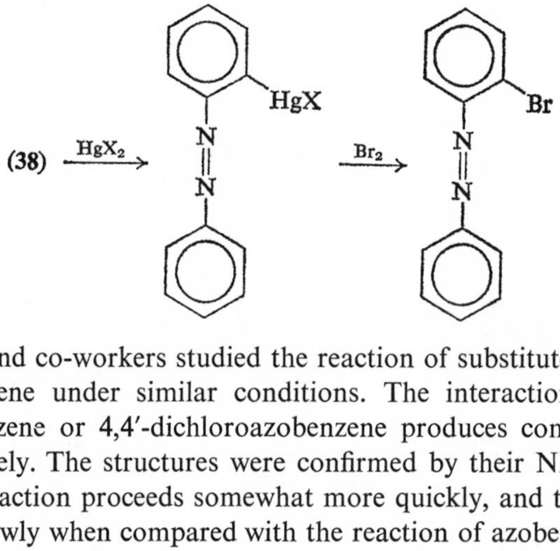

(54)

Ustynyuk and co-workers studied the reaction of substituted azobenzenes with nickelocene under similar conditions. The interaction with 4,4'-dimethylazobenzene or 4,4'-dichloroazobenzene produces complexes **(39)** or **(40)**, respectively. The structures were confirmed by their NMR spectra.[139] The former reaction proceeds somewhat more quickly, and the latter somewhat more slowly when compared with the reaction of azobenzene. When 4-

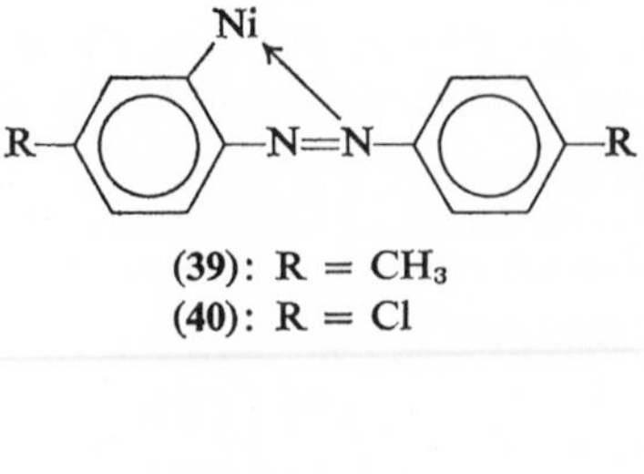

(39): R = CH_3
(40): R = Cl

methylazobenzene reacts with nickelocene, the two possible isomers (41) and (42) are formed; NMR gives their ratio as 1:1.[139] Similarly 4-carbomethoxy-azobenzene gives a mixture of isomers (43) and (44), with complex (43) predominating.[140]

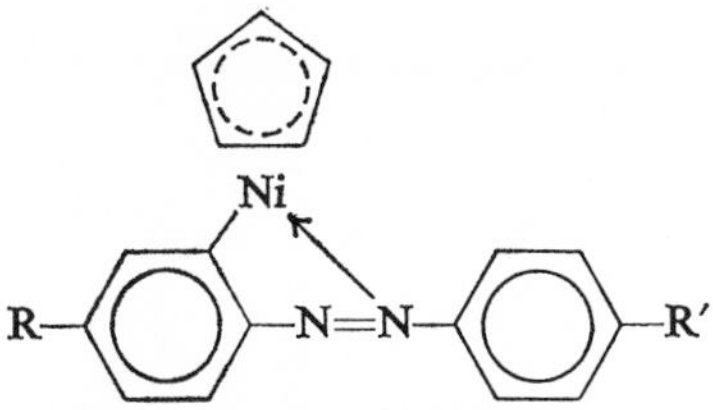

(41): R = H, R′ = CH₃
(42): R = CH₃, R′ = H
(43): R = COOCH₃, R′ = H
(44): R = H, R′ = COOCH₃

Only one isomer, (45), could be isolated from reaction with 4-chloro-azobenzene,[139] whereas interaction with 3,3′-dichloroazobenzene[139] resulted in a 5:1 ratio of the isomeric complexes (46) and (47).

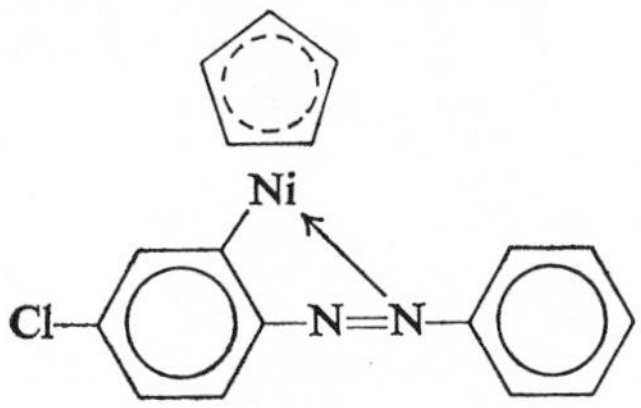

(45)

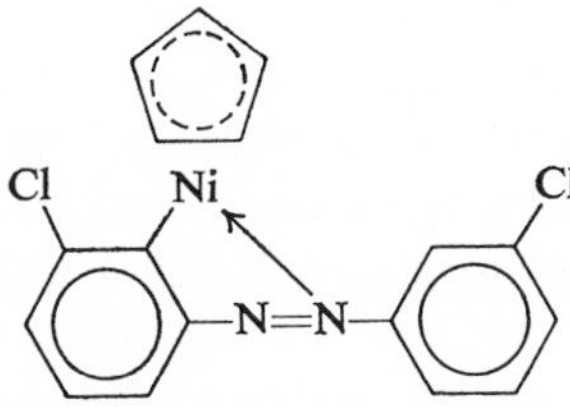

(46) 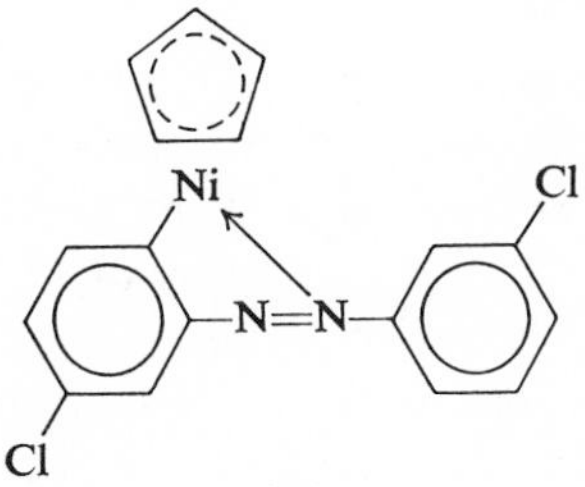   (47)

The reaction of 2-chloroazobenzene with nickelocene is somewhat different. Substitution occurs with the halogen, not the hydrogen, and the product is cyclopentadienyl-[o-(phenylazo)phenyl]nickel (38). The reaction proceeds much more quickly than that of azobenzene.[141]

Complex (38) also reacts with excess o-chloroazobenzene, and a new nonbenzenoid aromatic compound (48) is formed. This is a pseudoazulene, whose structure was determined by physical and chemical methods.[141]

Unlike *o*-chloroazobenzene, *o*-methoxyazobenzene reacts without elimination of the substituent and gives isomeric complexes (49) and (50), the ratio being 5:3.[140]

(38) $\xrightarrow{\quad}$ (55)

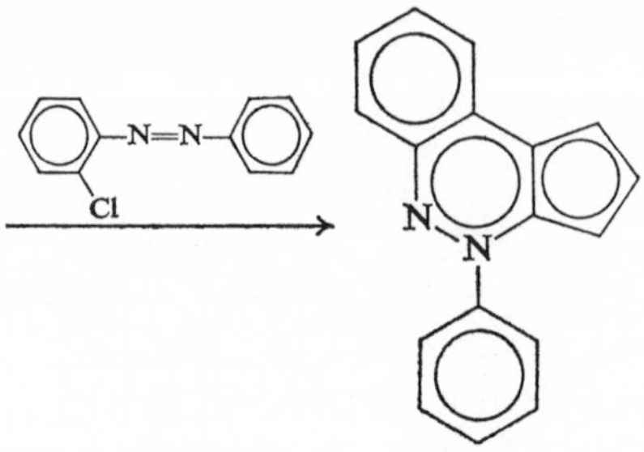

(48)

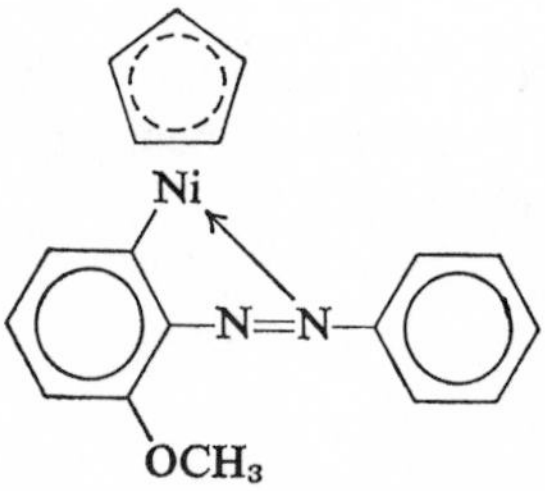

(49) 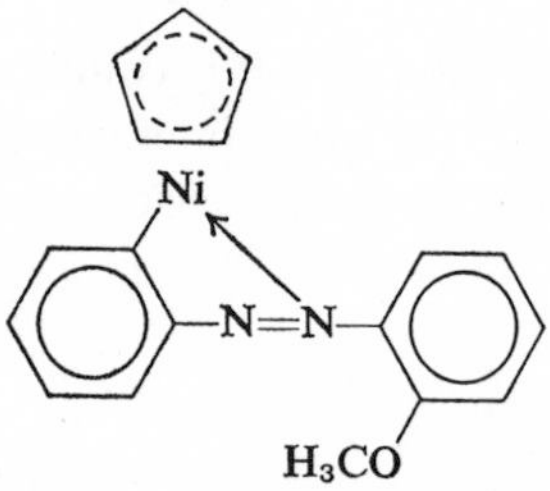   (50)

Azoxybenzene reacts with nickelocene to form cyclopentadienyl-[*o*-(phenylazo)phenyl] nickel (38) in low yield. The azoxybenzene–azobenzene reduction may be an early step in this reaction.[140]

b. Exchange of Two C_5H_5-*Rings.* Nickelocene reacts when heated with triphenylphosphine,[126] triphenylphosphite,[142] or phosphorus trifluoride,[143] or when reacted with phenylisonitrile,[131,144] *o*-phenanthroline,[144,145] 2,2'-dipyridyl,[144,145] 2,2',2''-tripyridyl,[144] 1,2-bis(diphenylphosphine)ethane, or 1,1,1-tris(diphenylphosphinomethyl)ethane.[144] This causes substitution of the two cyclopentadienyl rings, producing nickel(0) complexes (see Table V).

A cyclopentadienyl ligand of nickelocene can be directly exchanged for a substituted C_5H_5-ring. For example, when nickelocene was treated with excess lithium α-phenyldimethylaminomethylcyclopentadienyl, 1,1'-bis(α-phenyldimethylaminomethyl)nickelocene (51) was obtained.[140]

Nickelocene very readily exchanges its rings in the reaction with pyridine.[146] Even when dissolved in cold pyridine under argon, nickelocene gives a very air-sensitive nickel derivative (52). The structure of the latter was proved with the aid of NMR and chemical techniques. When pyridine hydrochloride was added to the reaction mixture, the chloride (53) was obtained in 85% yield.

TABLE V

Substitution of the Two Cyclopentadienyl Rings in Nickelocene

Reactant	Reaction product	Ref.
PPh_3	$Ni(PPh_3)_4$	126
$P(OPh)_3$	$Ni[P(OPh)_3]_4$	142
PF_3	$Ni(PF_3)_4$	143
$PhN=C$	$Ni(C=NPh)_4$	131, 144
o-Phenanthroline	$Ni(o$-phen$)_2$	144, 145
2,2'-Dipyridyl	$Ni(dipy)_2$	144, 145
2,2',2''-Tripyridyl	$Ni(tripy)_2$	144
$Ph_2PCH_2CH_2PPh_2$	$Ni(Ph_2PCH_2CH_2PPh_2)_2$	144
$CH_3C(CH_2PPh_2)_3$	$Ni[CH_3C(CH_2PPh_2)_3]_2$	144
KCN, NH_3	$K_2[Ni(CN)_4]$	144

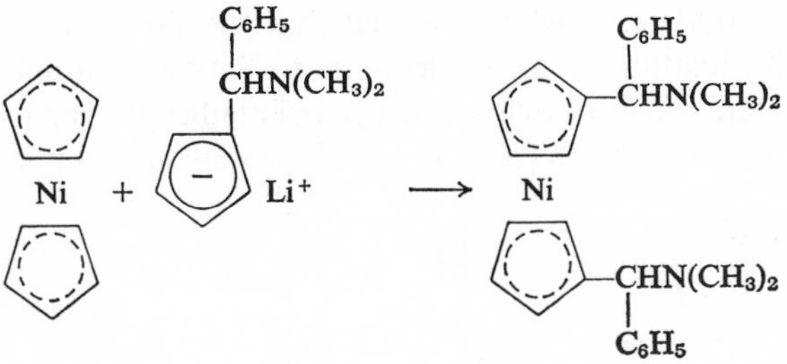

$$(56)$$

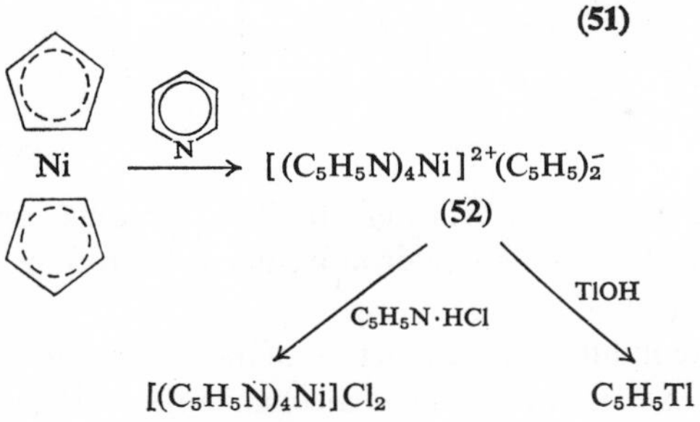

Hydrolysis of **(52)** followed by interaction with thallium(I) hydroxide produces cyclopentadienylthallium.

In a similar manner nickelocene reacts with potassium cyanide in liquid ammonia.[144] Under analogous conditions ammonia or aliphatic amines do not react with nickelocene, whereas potassium in liquid ammonia destroys it to metallic nickel.[147]

$$(C_5H_5)_2Ni + 4KCN \xrightarrow{NH_3(liq.)} K_2[Ni(CN)_4] + 2KC_5H_5 \qquad (58)$$

Nickelocene dissolved in ethanol at room temperature very readily reacts with dimethylglyoxime, quantitatively forming nickel dimethylglyoximate (54) and thus behaving similarly to nickel(II) ionic compounds.[145]

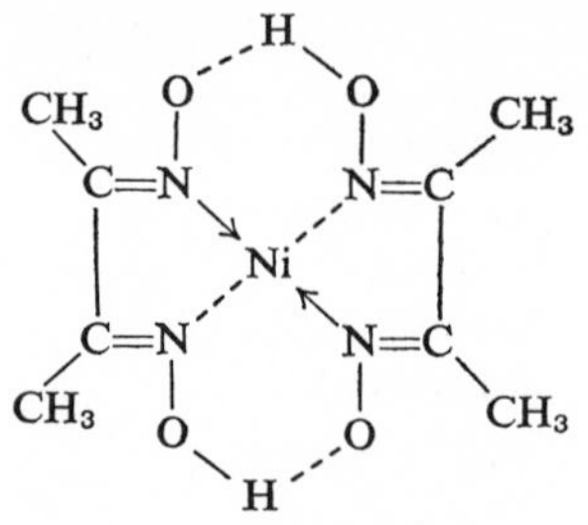

(54)

One should note that substitution reactions in nickelocene generally result in a final product with an 18-electron configuration.

Reaction types of nickelocene shown above were mechanistically interpretated by Ustynyuk,[126] who proposed that the first step of the reaction should be coordination of the nucleophile to the nickel atom accompanied by a π–σ rearrangement of one of the cyclopentadienyl ligands.*

This would lead to the 18-electron π-cyclopentadienyl compound (55). The

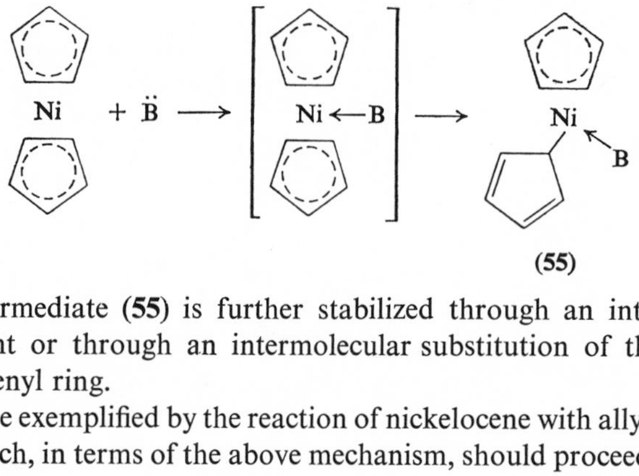

(55)

unstable intermediate (55) is further stabilized through an intramolecular rearrangement or through an intermolecular substitution of the σ-bonded cyclopentadienyl ring.

This may be exemplified by the reaction of nickelocene with allylmagnesium bromide, which, in terms of the above mechanism, should proceed as follows:

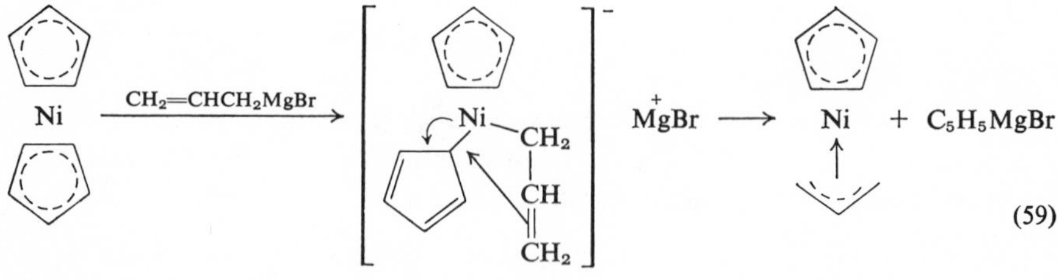

(59)

* Examples of similar π–σ rearrangements are known for palladium π-allyl complexes.[148,149]

Ustynyuk and co-workers[126] have proved that an intermediate σ-cyclopentadienyl compound (**56**) is actually formed during the reaction of nickelocene with triphenylphosphine.

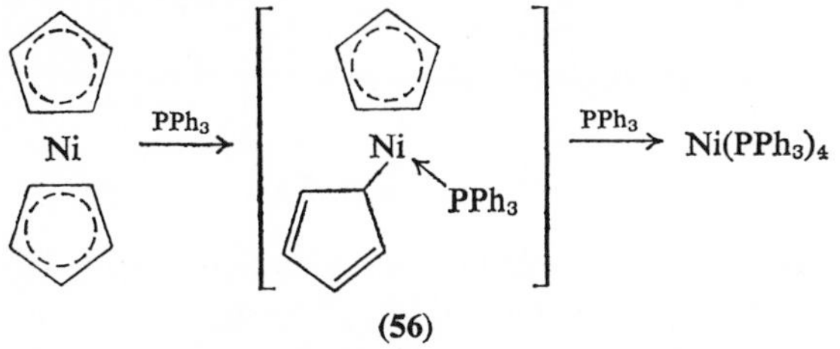

PPh3
Ni
PPh3
Ni
PPh3
Ni(PPh3)4
(56)

(60)

The interaction of equimolar amounts of nickelocene and triphenylphosphine was studied at 50° in benzene. A very unstable green complex was found among the products of the reaction, and all attempts to isolate the substance led to the initial nickelocene and triphenylphosphine. The complex is thought to have a cyclopentadienylnickel σ-bond based on its reactions with carbon tetrachloride and hydrogen chloride (in benzene). These are similar to the reactions of triphenylphosphine-π-cyclopentadienyl-(σ-methyl)nickel, (**57**), giving triphenylphosphine-(π-cyclopentadienyl)nickel halides (**58**) or (**59**).[126]

Ni
PPh3
[(56)]
CCl4
or HCl
Ni
Cl
PPh3
(58)
CCl4
Ni
CH3
PPh3
(57)
I2
Ni
I
PPh3
(59)

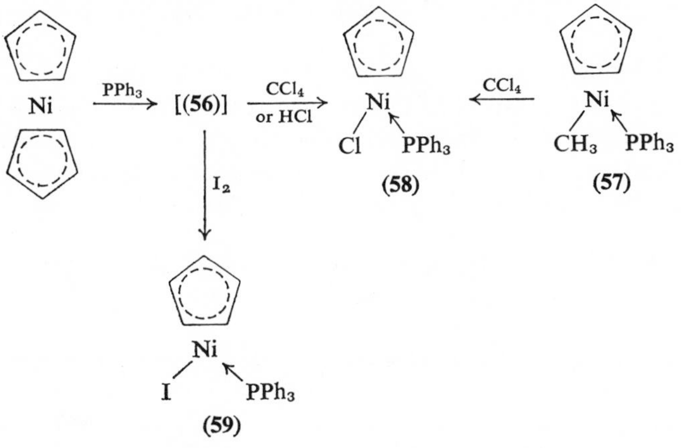

(61)

Triphenylphosphite, under more drastic conditions, behaves as triphenylphosphine, producing triphenylphosphite (π-cyclopentadienyl)nickel chloride after reaction with nickelocene in carbon tetrachloride.[146]

5. *Exchange of Cobaltocene* C_5H_5-*Rings*

Comparatively little has been reported on the ring exchange reactions of cobaltocene.

Cobaltocene reacts with tetraphenylcyclobutadienepalladium bromide to

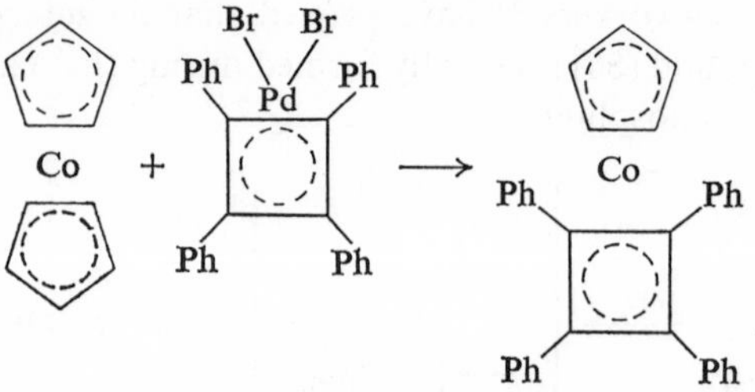

$$(62)$$

give π-cyclopentadienyl-(π-tetraphenylcyclobutadiene)cobalt.[150] Aryl acety-lenes bearing a variety of functional groups attached to the triple bond also react with cobaltocene to produce cyclobutadiene complexes.[151]

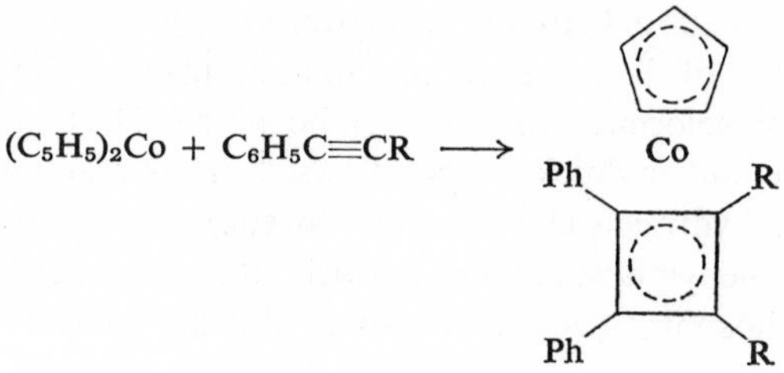

$$(C_5H_5)_2Co + C_6H_5C{\equiv}CR \longrightarrow \qquad (63)$$

$$[R = Si(CH_3)_3, CH_3, COCH_3, CF_3]$$

Recently Joh, Hagihara, and Murahashi[152] have shown that both cobalto-cene and cyclopentadienylcobalt dicarbonyl react with azobenzene to form complex (60). This gives o-aminodiphenylamine when reduced with hydrogen. Also N-phenylbenzimidazolone (61) and cyclopentadienylcobalt dicarbonyl are formed by reaction with carbon monoxide. Complex (60) was also

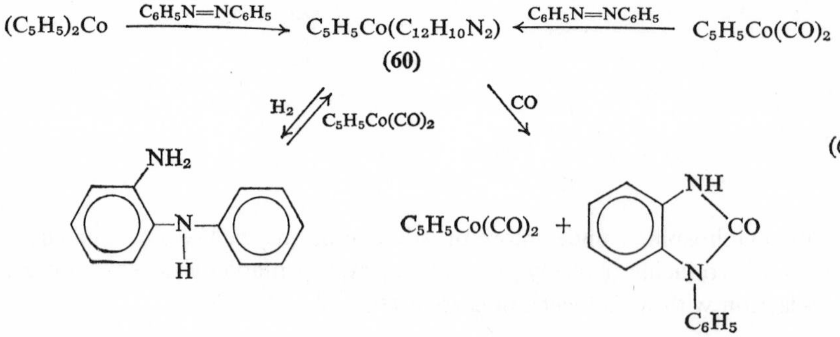

$$(C_5H_5)_2Co \xrightarrow{C_6H_5N{=}NC_6H_5} C_5H_5Co(C_{12}H_{10}N_2) \xleftarrow{C_6H_5N{=}NC_6H_5} C_5H_5Co(CO)_2$$

(60)

$$(64)$$

(61)

obtained from a reaction of o-aminodiphenylamine with $C_5H_5Co(CO)_2$. These results plus NMR spectra suggest that complex (60) has either or both of structures (62) and (63).

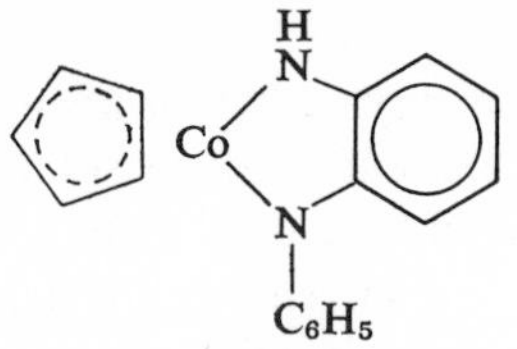

(62) 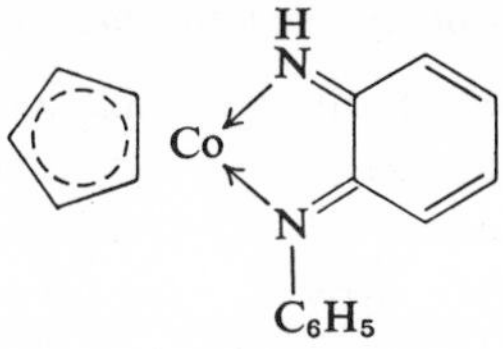   (63)

These structures indicate that coordination of azobenzene to the cobalt atom is, surprisingly, accompanied by migration of the phenyl group.

A reaction of cobaltocene with phosphorus trifluoride has also been reported.[153]

$$(C_5H_5)_2Co + 2PF_3 \longrightarrow C_5H_5Co(PF_3)_2 \qquad (65)$$

G. Examples of Syntheses

1. Photolysis of α-Pyridylferrocene Methiodide[48]

The reaction is carried out in a nitrogen atmosphere. The α-pyridylferrocene methiodide (1 g) is dissolved in water, and 20 ml of 16% sodium hydroxide is added to the solution. It is then irradiated for an hour by either a 300-watt lamp located 25 cm from the solution or by sunlight. The bright-green reaction mixture becomes orange, and a precipitate is formed. The mixture is extracted with ether, washed with a small portion of water, and then extracted with 10% sulfuric acid to remove the nitrogen base. Both the acid and the ether layers are decolorized during the extraction. The acid layer is made alkaline, forming an orange oil, which is extracted with benzene. Removal of the benzene in a flow of nitrogen gives 0.32 g of N-methyl-2-cyclopentadienylidene-1,2-dihydropyridine (84% of the theoretical amount), m.p. 73–74.5° (from a hexane-benzene mixture). Cyclopentadiene formed during the reaction is swept out of the reaction mixture with nitrogen into a thallium(I) hydroxide solution and isolated as C_5H_5Tl.

2. Reaction of Nickelocene with Azobenzene[129]

Bis(cyclopentadienyl)nickel (5 g) and azobenzene (20 g) are heated at 135° for 4 hr. After removal of excess azobenzene by sublimation under reduced pressure, the reaction residue is dissolved in low-boiling petroleum ether and chromatographed twice on alumina. (During the sublimation of the reaction mixtures a liquid was collected which was identified as aniline by comparison of its infrared spectrum with that of an authentic sample and by preparation of acetanilide.) The yield of the purple-blue crystalline cyclopentadienyl-[o-(phenylazo)phenyl]nickel, m.p. 115 118°, is 2.0 g. An analytical sample of the complex is prepared by several recrystallizations from petroleum ether followed by an additional chromatographic purification; m.p. 118–119°.

3. Reactions of Nickelocene with Thiols[130]

Equimolar amounts of nickelocene and methyl, ethyl, or phenyl mercaptan are dissolved in the necessary amount of benzene, and the solution is stirred for 15 hr at 25°. An immediate reaction is indicated by a color change from green to dark brown. After removal of the solvent, the residue is recrystallized from ether or hexane and dried *in vacuo* to give black crystals.

	$(C_5H_5NiSCH_3)_2$	$(C_5H_5NiSC_2H_5)_2$	$(C_5H_5NiSC_6H_5)_2$
Melting point, °C	118	78	125
Yield, %	67	96	95

References

1. G. Wilkinson and J. M. Birmingham, *J. Amer. Chem. Soc.*, **76**, 6210 (1954).
2. J. M. Birmingham and G. Wilkinson, *J. Amer. Chem. Soc.*, **78**, 42 (1956).
3. L. T. Reynolds and G. Wilkinson, *J. Inorg. Nucl. Chem.*, **2**, 246 (1956).
4. G. Wilkinson and J. M. Birmingham, *J. Amer. Chem. Soc.*, **76**, 4281 (1954).
5. E. Samuel, *Bull. Soc. Chim. France*, **1966**, 3548.
6. A. N. Nesmeyanov, O. V. Nogina, and V. A. Dubovitskii, *Izv. Akad. Nauk SSSR, Ser. Khim.*, **1968**, 527.
7. S. A. Giddings, *Inorg. Chem.*, **3**, 684 (1964).
8. A. N. Nesmeyanov, O. V. Nogina, A. M. Berlin, A. S. Girshovich, and T. V. Shatalov, *Izv. Akad. Nauk SSSR, Otd. Khim. Nauk*, **1961**, 2146.
9. G. W. Watt, and L. J. Bayet, *J. Inorg. Nucl. Chem.*, **26**, 2099 (1964).
10. A. K. Fischer and G. Wilkinson, *J. Inorg. Nucl. Chem.*, **2**, 146 (1956).
11. J. C. Brantley, U.S. Patent 2,983,741 (1961); *Chem. Abstr.*, **55**, 22339 (1961).
12. G. Wilkinson, P. L. Pauson, J. M. Birmingham, and F. A. Cotton, *J. Amer. Chem. Soc.*, **75**, 1011 (1953).
13. A. N. Nesmeyanov, O. V. Nogina, N. A. Lazareva, and V. A. Dubovitskii, *Izv. Akad. Nauk SSSR, Ser. Khim.*, **1967**, 808.
14. A. N. Nesmeyanov and O. V. Nogina, *Izv. Akad. Nauk SSSR, Otd. Khim. Nauk*, **1963**, 831.
15. A. Andrianov and T. V. Pichkhadze, *Vysokomol. Soyedin.*, **3**, 577 (1961).
16. E. M. Brainina, R. Kh. Freidlina, and A. N. Nesmeyanov, *Dokl. Akad. Nauk SSSR*, **154**, 1113 (1964).
17. R. Kh. Freidlina, E. M. Brainina, L. A. Petrashkevich, and M. Kh. Minacheva, *Izv. Akad. Nauk SSSR, Otd. Khim. Nauk*, **1966**, 1396.
18. E. M. Brainina, M. Kh. Minacheva, and R. Kh. Freidlina, *Izv. Akad. Nauk SSSR, Otd. Khim. Nauk*, **1961**, 1716.
19. R. Kh. Freidlina, E. M. Brainina, M. Kh. Minacheva, and A. N. Nesmeyanov, *Izv. Akad. Nauk SSSR, Otd. Khim. Nauk*, **1964**, 1417.
20. E. M. Brainina and R. Kh. Freidlina, *Izv. Akad. Nauk SSSR, Otd. Khim. Nauk*, **1963**, 835.
21. R. Kh. Freidlina, E. M. Brainina, and A. N. Nesmeyanov, *Dokl. Akad. Nauk SSSR*, **138**, 1369 (1961).
22. M. Kh. Minacheva, E. M. Brainina, and R. Kh. Freidlina, *Dokl. Akad. Nauk SSSR*, **173**, 581 (1967).

23. E. M. Brainina, M. Kh. Minacheva, and B. V. Lokshin, *Izv. Akad. Nauk SSSR, Otd. Khim. Nauk*, **1968**, 817.
24. E. M. Brainina and G. G. Dvoryantseva, *Izv. Akad. Nauk SSSR, Otd. Khim. Nauk*, **1967**, 442.
25. E. M. Brainina, M. Kh. Minacheva, and R. Kh. Freidlina, *Izv. Akad. Nauk SSSR, Otd. Khim. Nauk*, **1965**, 1877.
26. E. M. Brainina, Ye. I. Mortikova, L. A. Petrashkevich, and R. Kh. Freidlina, *Dokl. Akad. Nauk SSSR*, **169**, 335 (1966).
27. G. A. Abakumov, A. Ye. Shilov, and S. V. Shulyndin, *Kinetika i Kataliz*, **5**, 228 (1964).
28. G. Wilkinson, M. Rosenblum, M. C. Whiting, and R. B. Woodward, *J. Amer. Chem. Soc.*, **74**, 2125 (1952).
29. E. O. Fischer and U. Hafner, *Z. Naturforsch.*, **9b**, 503 (1954).
30. G. Wilkinson, F. A. Cotton, and J. M. Birmingham, *J. Inorg. Nucl. Chem.*, **2**, 95 (1956).
31. G. Wilkinson, *J. Amer. Chem. Soc.*, **76**, 209 (1954).
32. E. O. Fischer, K. Ulm, and P. Kuzel, *Z. Anorg. Allg. Chem.*, **319**, 253 (1963).
33. L. T. Reynolds and G. Wilkinson, *J. Inorg. Nucl. Chem.*, **9**, 86 (1959).
34. D. K. Higgins and H. D. Kaesz, *J. Amer. Chem. Soc.*, **83**, 4474 (1961).
35. G. Wilkinson and J. M. Birmingham, *J. Amer. Chem. Soc.*, **77**, 3421 (1955).
36. E. O. Fischer and R. Jira, *Z. Naturforsch.*, **8b**, 217 (1953).
37. E. O. Fischer and R. Jira, *Z. Naturforsch.*, **8b**, 1 (1953).
38. G. Wilkinson, *J. Amer. Chem. Soc.*, **74**, 6148 (1952).
39. F. A. Cotton, R. O. Whipple, and G. Wilkinson, *J. Amer. Chem. Soc.*, **74**, 3586 (1953).
40. E. O. Fischer and H. Grubert, *Chem. Ber.*, **92**, 2302 (1959).
41. T. J. Kealy and P. L. Pauson, *Nature*, **168**, 1039 (1951).
42. A. N. Nesmeyanov, E. G. Perevalova, and Z. A. Beynoravichute, unpublished data.
43. I. Pavlik and J. Klikorka, *Coll. Czech. Chem. Commun.*, **30**, 664 (1965).
44. V. Weinmayr, *J. Amer. Chem. Soc.*, **77**, 3009 (1955).
45. A. A. Pendin, M. S. Zakhar'evskii, and T. K. Leont'evskaya, *Kinetika i Kataliz*, **7**, 1074 (1966).
46. A. N. Nesmeyanov, V. A. Sazonova, V. I. Romanenko, N. A. Rodionova, and G. P. Zol'nikova, *Dokl. Akad. Nauk SSSR*, **155**, 1130 (1964).
47. A. N. Nesmeyanov, V. A. Sazonova, V. I. Romanenko, and G. P. Zol'nikova, *Izv. Akad. Nauk SSSR, Otd. Khim. Nauk*, **1965**, 1694.
48. A. N. Nesmeyanov, V. A. Sazonova, A. V. Gerasimenko, and N. S. Sazonova *Dokl. Akad. Nauk SSSR*, **149**, 1354 (1963).
49. A. N. Nesmeyanov, V. A. Sazonova, V. I. Romanenko, V. N. Postnov, G. P. Zol'nikova, V. A. Blinova, and R. M. Kalenova, *Dokl. Akad. Nauk SSSR*, **173**, 589 (1967).
50. A. N. Nesmeyanov, V. A. Sazonova, and V. I. Romanenko, *Dokl. Akad. Nauk SSSR*, **152**, 1358 (1963).
51. A. N. Nesmeyanov, V. A. Sazonova, V. N. Drozd, N. A. Rodionova, and G. I. Zudkova, *Izv. Akad. Nauk SSSR, Ser. Khim.*, **1965**, 2061.
52. A. N. Nesmeyanov, V. A. Sazonova, G. I. Zudkova, and L. S. Isaeva, *Izv. Akad. Nauk SSSR, Ser. Khim.*, **1966**, 2017.
53. A. N. Nesmeyanov, V. A. Sazonova, and V. N. Drozd, *Dokl. Akad. Nauk SSSR*, **154**, 1393 (1964).
54. A. N. Nesmeyanov, V. A. Sazonova, V. N. Drozd, and N. A. Rodionova, *Dokl. Akad. Nauk SSSR*, **160**, 355 (1965).

55. A. N. Nesmeyanov, E. G. Perevalova, L. I. Leont'eva, and Yu. A. Ustynyuk, *Izv. Akad. Nauk SSSR, Ser. Khim.*, **1966**, 556.
56. R. D. Gorsich, *J. Amer. Chem. Soc.*, **82**, 4211 (1960).
57. R. D. Gorsich, *J. Amer. Chem. Soc.*, **80**, 4744 (1958).
58. R. B. King, *Organometallic Syntheses, Vol.* 1, *Transition Metal Compounds*, Academic Press, New York, 1965.
59. R. D. Gorsich, U.S. Patent 3,080,305 (1963); *Chem. Abstr.*, **59**, 3957 (1963).
60. E. M. Brainina, G. G. Dvoryantseva, and R. Kh. Freidlina, *Dokl. Akad Nauk SSSR* **156**, 1375 (1964).
61. E. M. Brainina, R. Kh. Freidlina, *Izv. Akad. Nauk SSSR, Otd. Khim. Nauk*, **1964**, 1421.
62. A. N. Nesmeyanov, G. E. Perevalova, and O. A. Nesmeyanova, *Dokl. Akad. Nauk SSSR*, **100**, 1099 (1955).
63. A. N. Nesmeyanov, N. S. Kochetkova, and R. B. Materikova, *Dokl. Akad. Nauk SSSR*, **147**, 113 (1962).
64. A. N. Nesmeyanov, L. P. Yur'eva, R. B. Materikova, and B. N. Getnarskii, *Izv. Akad. Nauk SSSR, Ser. Khim.*, **1965**, 731.
65. D. Kaufman, U.S. Patent, 2,922,805 (1960); *Chem. Abstr.*, **54**, 11048 (1960).
66. H. P. Fritz and L. Schäfer, *Z. Naturforsch.*, **19b**, 169 (1964).
67. A. N. Nesmeyanov, E. G. Perevalova, R. V. Golovnya, T. V. Nikitina, and N. A. Simukova, *Izv. Akad. Nauk SSSR, Otd. Khim. Nauk*, **1956**, 739.
68. R. Riemschneider and D. Helm, *Chem. Ber.*, **89**, 155 (1956).
69. V. A. Nefedov, *Zh. Obshch. Khim.*, **36**, 1508 (1966).
70. A. N. Nesmeyanov, N. A. Vol'kenau, and V. D. Vil'chevskaya, *Dokl. Akad. Nauk SSSR*, **118**, 512 (1958).
71. A. N. Nesmeyanov, E. G. Perevalova, and L. P. Yur'eva, *Izv. Akad. Nauk SSSR, Otd. Khim. Nauk*, **1968**, 2406.
72. M. F. A. Dove and D. B. Sowerby, *Z. Naturforsch.*, **20b**, 394 (1965).
73. R. A. Stukan and L. P. Yur'eva, *Zh. Tekhn. i Eksper. Khim.*, **1967**, 544.
74. F. A. Cotton and G. Wilkinson, *Chem. Ind. (London)*, **1956**, 1305.
75. L. T. Reynolds and G. Wilkinson, *J. Inorg. Nucl. Chem.*, **2**, 246 (1956).
76. A. N. Nesmeyanov, O. V. Nogina, and V. A. Dubovitskii, *Izv. Akad. Nauk SSSR, O.d. Khim. Nauk*, **1962**, 1481.
77. A. N. Nesmeyanov, E. L. Fedin, P. V. Petrovskii, V. A. Dubovitskii, O. V. Nogina, and N. A. Lazareva, *Dokl. Akad. Nauk SSSR*, **163**, 659 (1965).
78. G. G. Dvoryantseva, Yu. N. Sheinker, A. N. Nesmeyanov, O. V. Nogina, N. A. Lazareva, and V. A. Dubovitskii, *Dokl. Akad. Nauk SSSR*, **161**, 603 (1965).
79. S. I. Goldberg, *J. Amer. Chem. Soc.*, **84**, 3022 (1962).
80. A. N. Nesmeyanov, N. S. Kochetkova, P. V. Petrovskii, and E. I. Fedin, *Dokl. Akad. Nauk SSSR*, **152**, 875 (1963).
81. A. N. Nesmeyanov and N. S. Kochetkova, *Dokl. Akad. Nauk SSSR*, **126**, 307 (1959).
82. A. N. Nesmeyanov, N. S. Kochetkova, and R. B. Materikova, *Dokl. Akad. Nauk SSSR*, **136**, 1096 (1961).
83. E. O. Fischer and H. Grubert, *Chem. Ber.*, **92**, 2302 (1959).
84. E. O. Fischer and W. Hafner, *Z. Naturforsch.*, **10b**, 140 (1955).
85. E. O. Fischer, W. Hafner, and H. O. Stahl, *Z. Anorg. Allg. Chem.*, **282**, 47 (1955).
86. E. O. Fischer and H. P. Kögler, *Angew. Chem.*, **68**, 462 (1956).
87. E. O. Fischer and K. Ulm, *Z. Naturforsch.*, **15b**, 59 (1960).
88. T. S. Piper, F. A. Cotton, and C. Wilkinson, *J. Inorg. Nucl. Chem.*, **1**, 165 (1955).
89. E. O. Fischer and W. Hafner, *Z. Naturforsch.*, **9b**, 503 (1954).

90. E. O. Fischer and R. Jira, *Z. Naturforsch.*, **9b**, 618 (1954).
91. E. O. Fischer and R. Jira, *Z. Naturforsch.*, **10b**, 355 (1955).
92. J. G. Murray, *J. Amer. Chem. Soc.*, **81**, 752 (1959).
93. E. O. Fischer and A. Löchner, *Z. Naturforsch.*, **15b**, 266 (1960).
94. E. O. Fischer and C. Palm, *Chem. Ber.*, **91**, 1725 (1958).
95. J. F. Tilney-Bassett, *Proc. Chem. Soc.*, **1960**, 419; *J. Chem. Soc.*, **1963**, 4784.
96. G. A. Razuvaev, G. G. Petukhov, and V. I. Yermolaev, *Zh. Obshch. Khim.*, **37**, 672 (1967).
97. T. S. Piper and G. Wilkinson, *J. Inorg. Nucl. Chem.*, **3**, 104 (1956).
98. E. O. Fischer, O. Beckert, W. Hafner, and H. O. Stahl, *Z. Naturforsch.*, **10b**, 598 (1955).
99. A. P. Cox, Z. P. Thomas, and J. Cheridan, *Nature*, **181**, 1157 (1958).
100. T. S. Piper and G. Wilkinson, *J. Inorg. Nucl. Chem.*, **2**, 38 (1956).
101. A. N. Nesmeyanov, E. G. Perevalova, Z. A. Beynoravichute, and I. L. Malygina, *Dokl. Akad. Nauk SSSR*, **120**, 1263 (1958).
102. D. S. Trifan and L. Nichols, *J. Amer. Chem. Soc.*, **79**, 2746 (1957).
103. P. L. Pauson, G. R. Knox, J. D. Munro, and J. M. Osgerby, *Angew. Chem.*, **72**, 37 (1960).
104. A. N. Nesmeyanov, R. B. Materikova, N. S. Kochetkova, and L. A. Zurgozen, *Dokl. Akad. Nauk SSSR*, **160**, 137 (1965).
105. D. E. Trent, B. Paris, and H. H. Krause, *Inorg. Chem.*, **7**, 1057 (1964).
106. L. J. Baye, *Dissert. Abstr.*, **14**, 3968 (1964).
107. E. Schumacher and R. Taubenest, *Helv. Chim. Acta*, **47**, 1525 (1964).
108. K. H. Pausacker, *Australian J. Chem.*, **11**, 509 (1958).
109. A. N. Nesmeyanov, V. V. Korshak, V. V. Voevodskii, N. S. Kochetkova, S. L. Sosin, R. B. Materikova, T. N. Bolotnikova, V. M. Chimbrikin, and N. M. Bazhyn, *Dokl. Akad. Nauk SSSR*, **137**, 370 (1961).
110. A. N. Nesmeyanov, A. M. Rubinstein, G. L. Slonimski, A. A. Slinkin, N. S. Kochetkova, and R. B. Materikova, *Dokl. Akad. Nauk SSSR*, **138**, 125 (1961).
111. Yu. S. Korimov and I. S. Shcheglov, *Dokl. Akad. Nauk SSSR*, **146**, 1370 (1962).
112. A. N. Nesmeyanov, V. A. Sazonova, V. N. Drozd, and L. A. Nikonova, *Dokl. Akad. Nauk SSSR*, **133**, 126 (1960).
113. A. N. Nesmeyanov, V. A. Sazonova, and V. N. Drozd, *Chem. Ber.*, **93**, 2717 (1960).
114. A. N. Nesmeyanov, E. G. Perevalova, R. V. Golovnya, N. A. Simukova, and O. V. Starovskii, *Izv. Akad. Nauk SSSR, Otd. Khim. Nauk*, **1957**, 638.
115. A. N. Nesmeyanov, E. G. Perevalova, N. A. Simukova, Yu. N. Sheinker, and M. L. Reshetova, *Dokl. Akad. Nauk SSSR*, **135**, 851 (1960).
116. R. E. Bozak and K. L. Rinehart, Jr., *J. Amer. Chem. Soc.*, **84**, 1589 (1962).
117. E. G. Perevalova, N. A. Simukova, T. V. Nikitina, P. D. Reshetov, and A. N. Nesmeyanov, *Izv. Akad. Nauk SSSR, Otd. Khim. Nauk*, **1961**, 77.
118. A. N. Nesmeyanov, N. A. Vol'kenau, and I. N. Bolesova, *Dokl. Akad. Nauk SSSR*, **149**, 615 (1963).
119. A. N. Nesmeyanov, N. A. Vol'kenau, and T. N. Bolesova, *Tetrahedron Letters*, **1963**, 1725.
120. T. H. Coffield, V. Sandel, and R. D. Clossen, *J. Amer. Chem. Soc.*, **79**, 5826 (1957).
121. A. N. Nesmeyanov, N. A. Vol'kenau, and I. N. Bolesova, *Dokl. Akad. Nauk SSSR*, **166**, 607 (1966).
122. A. N. Nesmeyanov, N. A. Vol'kenau, and L. S. Shilovtseva, *Dokl. Akad. Nauk SSSR*, **160**, 1327 (1965).
123. A. N. Nesmeyanov, N. A. Vol'kenau, and L. S. Isaeva, *Dokl. Akad. Nauk SSSR*, **176**, 106 (1967).

124. W. R. McClellan, H. H. Hoehn, H. N. Gripps, E. L. Muetterties, and B. W. Howk, *J. Amer. Chem. Soc.*, **83**, 1601 (1961).

125. D. W. McBride, E. Dudek, and F. G. A. Stone, *J. Chem. Soc.*, **1964**, 1752.

126. Yu. A. Ustynyuk, T. I. Voevodskaya, N. A. Zharikova, and N. A. Ustynyuk, *Dokl. Akad. Nauk SSSR*, **181**, 372 (1968).

127. M. Van den Akker and F. Jellinek, *Rec. Trav. Chim.*, **86**, 897 (1967).

128. G. E. Schroll, U.S. Patent 3,054,815; *Chem. Abstr.*, **58**, 1494c (1963).

129. J. P. Kleiman and M. Dubeck, *J. Amer. Chem. Soc.*, **85**, 1544 (1963).

130. W. K. Schropp, *J. Inorg. Nucl. Chem.*, **24**, 1688 (1962).

131. P. L. Pauson and W. H. Stubbs, *Angew. Chem., Intern. Ed.*, **1**, 333 (1962).

132. K. K. Joshi, O. S. Mills, P. L. Pauson, B. W. Shaw, and W. H. Stubbs, *Chem. Commun.*, **1966**, 181.

133. J. Yamoto and N. Hagihara, *Bull. Chem. Soc. Japan*, **39**, 1084 (1966).

134. M. Dubeck, *J. Amer. Chem. Soc.*, **82**, 502 (1960).

135. J. F. Tilney-Bassett, *J. Chem. Soc.*, **1961**, 577.

136. A. C. Cope and R. W. Siekman, *J. Amer. Chem. Soc.*, **87**, 3272 (1965).

137. M. N. Bagga, P. L. Pauson, F. J. Preston, and R. J. Reed, *Chem. Commun.*, **1965**, 543.

138. Yu. A. Ustynyuk, N. V. Barinov, and E. I. Sirotkina, *Dokl. Akad. Nauk SSSR*, **187**, 112 (1969).

139. Yu. A. Ustynyuk, N. V. Barinov, and E. I. Sirotkina, *Dokl. Akad. Nauk SSSR*, **187**, 115 (1969).

140. Yu. A. Ustynyuk and N. V. Barinov, unpublished data.

141. Yu. A. Ustynyuk and N. V. Barinov, *J. Organometal. Chem.*, **23**, 551 (1970).

142. J. R. Olechowski, C. G. McAlister, and R. F. Clark, *Inorg. Chem.*, **4**, 246 (1965).

143. J. F. Nixon, *Chem. Commun.*, **1966**, 34.

144. H. Behrens and K. Meyer, *Z. Naturforsch.*, **21b**, 489 (1966).

145. Yu. A. Ustynyuk, I. V. Barinov, T. I. Voevodskaya, ad N. A. Rodionova, *Progress in Organometallic Chemistry, Proceedings of the Fourth International Conference on Organometallic Chemistry, Bristol, U.K., 28 July–August 1, 1969*, M. J. Bruce and F. G. A. Stone, Eds., *Chemical Society Burlington House, London*.

146. Yu. A. Ustynyuk, T. I. Voevodskaya, N. A. Rodionova, I. M. Pribytkova, and N. A. Ustynyuk, unpublished data.

147. L. J. Baye, *Dissert. Abstr.*, **14**, 3968 (1964).

148. G. L. Statton and K. C. Ramey, *J. Amer. Chem. Soc.*, **88**, 1327 (1966).

149. J. Powell, S. D. Robinson, and B. L. Shaw, *Chem. Commun.*, **1965**, 78.

150. P. M. Maitlis and M. L. Games, *J. Amer. Chem. Soc.*, **85**, 1887 (1963).

151. J. F. Helling, S. C. Rennison, and A. Merijan, *J, Amer. Chem. Soc.*, **89**, 7140 (1967).

152. T. Joh, N. Hagihara, and Sh. Murahashi, *Bull. Chem. Soc. Japan*, **40**, 661 (1967).

153. Th. Kruck, W. Hieber, and W. Lang, *Angew. Chem.*, **78**, 208 (1966).

II. REACTIONS OF METALLOCENES IN WHICH THE NATURE OF THE METAL–RING BOND IS TRANSFORMED

The reactions dealt with in this section are characteristic of nickelocene and cobaltocene. Except for bis(cyclopentadienyl)chromium, other metallocenes are not yet known to undergo such reactions.

A. Addition to Nickelocene

Addition to a nickelocene cyclopentadienyl ring is as characteristic of this compound as are ligand-exchange reactions. Addition occurs at either the 1,2- or the 1,4-position.

Nickelocene, when reduced with sodium amalgam in ethanol, yields cyclopentadienyl(cyclopentenyl)nickel (64).[1] This same compound is formed in the reaction of nickelocene with ethene at 70° in n-pentane.[2]

Addition of tetrafluorethene to nickelocene occurs, giving complex (65) in low yield.[3] Chlorotrifluoroethene adds in the same way as tetrafluoroethene.[3] Nickelocene, when heated with hexafluorobutyne[2] or acetylenedicarboxylic ester,[4] forms norbornadienyl derivatives (66) or (67). A complete X-ray investigation of compound (67) has been performed.[5]

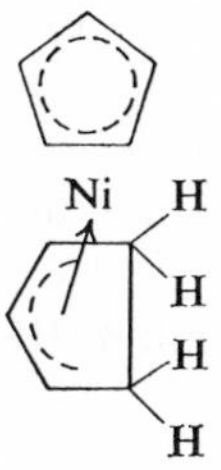

(64) 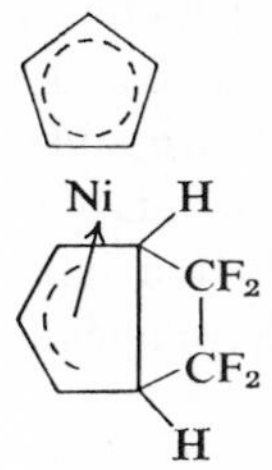   (65) 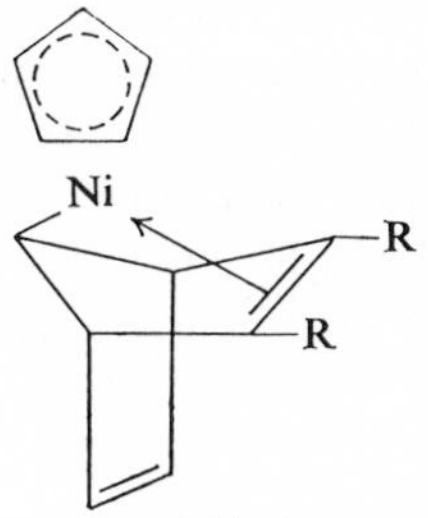   (66): R = CF_3
                            (67): R = $COOCH_3$

It should be noted that nickelocene addition reactions, like those of ligand exchange, lead to the formation of nickel compounds with the energetically favored 18-electron configuration.

Both addition and ring-substitution reactions of nickelocene can proceed via preliminary coordination of the attacking agent to the metal atom, followed by a π–σ rearrangement of one of the cyclopentadienyl rings.

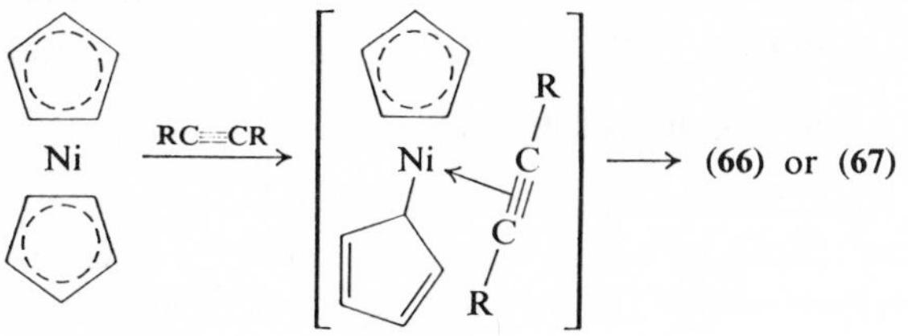

(68)

(R = CF_3, $COOCH_3$)

(66)

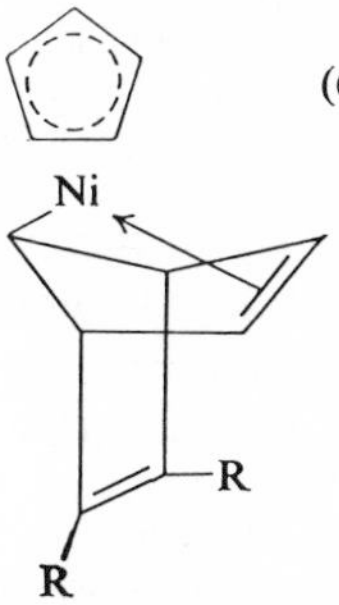

(69)

An excellent confirmation[6] of the preliminary coordination of the attacking agent to the metal atom can be obtained from the structure of norbornadienyl complexes, formed during the reaction of nickelocene with hexafluorobutyne or acetylenedicarboxylic ester. Such a transition state would be compound (68). This then undergoes an internal Diels–Alder reaction—without rupture of either of the two bonds holding the reacting groups to the metal. This explains why nickel becomes coordinated at the double bond located between the carbons carrying the two electronegative substituents. If the reaction involved no preliminary coordination, it would lead to the formation of the energetically more favorable isomer (69).

B. Addition to Bis(cyclopentadienyl)chromium

Fischer and Ulm[7,8] have shown that interaction of bis(cyclopentadienyl)-chromium with a mixture of carbon monoxide and hydrogen under pressure (see Section I-F-5) produces not only cyclopentadienylchromium tricarbonyl hydride, $C_5H_5Cr(CO)_3H$, but also small amounts of a yellow compound of the composition $CrC_{12}H_{12}O_2$.* According to the infrared and NMR spectra this compound may be cyclopentadienyl(cyclopentenyl)chromium(II) dicarbonyl (70).[8]

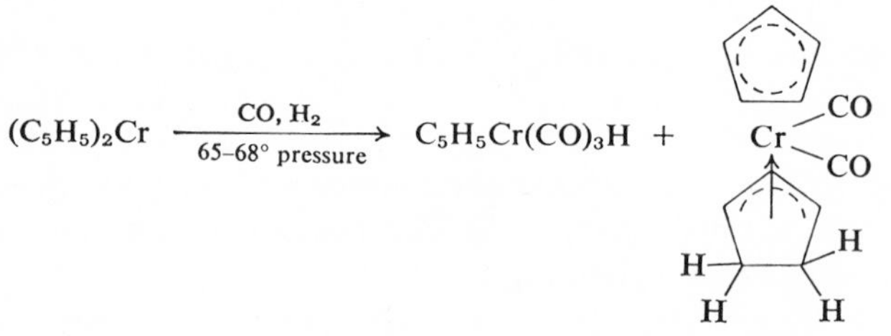

$$(C_5H_5)_2Cr \xrightarrow[\text{65-68° pressure}]{CO, H_2} C_5H_5Cr(CO)_3H \ + \qquad\qquad (67)$$

(70)

Thus under these conditions the exchange of a cyclopentadienyl-ring for a CO-group goes together with hydrogen addition, resulting in the transformation of a cyclopentadienyl ligand to a cyclopentenyl.

C. Addition to Cobaltocene

Paramagnetic, 19-electron cobaltocene is extremely reactive.

Halogen compounds (carbon tetrachloride,[9,10] methyl iodide,[10,11] benzoyl chloride,[12]* or trifluoromethyl iodide[10]) in an inert-gas medium undergo a peculiar reaction, resulting in the formation of equimolecular amounts of a

---

* The compound was first thought to have a bis(cyclopentadienyl)chromium(0) dicarbonyl structure.[7]

* Acetyl chloride gives only cobalticinium chloride.

cobalticinium salt and the neutral, stable cobalt π-cyclopentadienylcyclo-pentadienic complex (71).

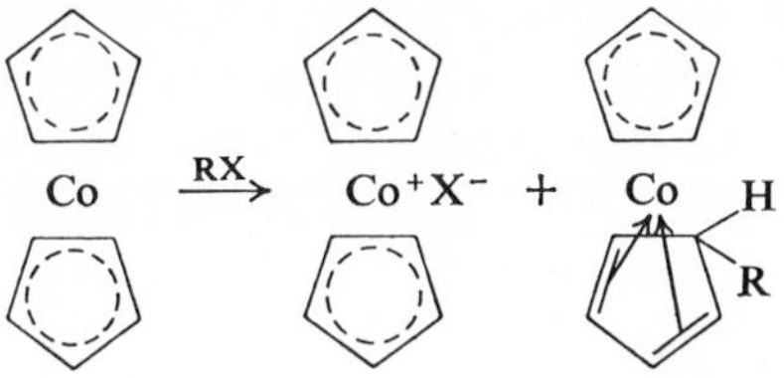

$$Co \xrightarrow{RX} Co^+X^- + Co \begin{matrix} H \\ R \end{matrix} \qquad (68)$$

(71)

(R = CCl₃, CH₃, COC₆H₅; X = Cl)
(R = CH₃, CF₃; X = I)

Tetrafluoroethene transforms cobaltocene to the binuclear compound (72).[11,12]

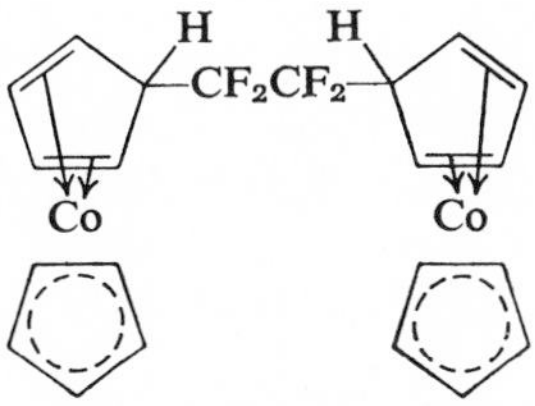

(72)

The reaction of cobaltocene with carbon tetrachloride is supposed[13] to proceed via the one-electron reduction of carbon tetrachloride by cobalto-cene, with cobalticinium chloride and the trichloromethyl radical being formed. The radical then adds to another molecule of cobaltocene and produces the π-cyclopentadienyl-1-trichloromethyl-2,4-dienic cobalt complex (73).

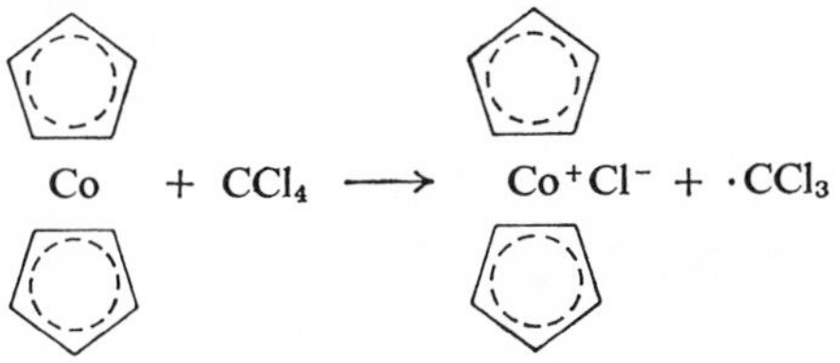

$$Co + CCl_4 \longrightarrow Co^+Cl^- + \cdot CCl_3 \qquad (69)$$

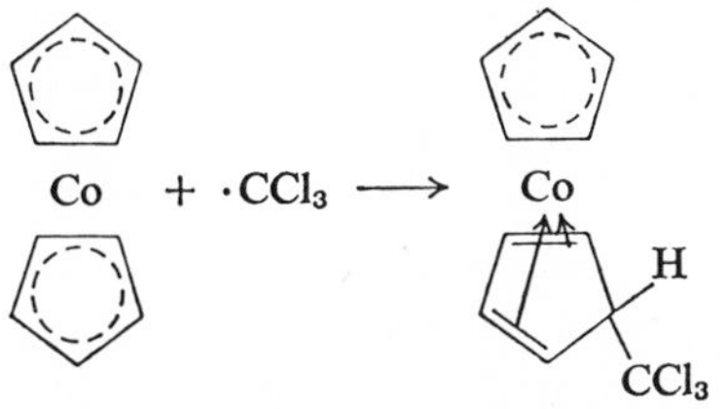

$$Co + \cdot CCl_3 \longrightarrow Co \begin{matrix} H \\ CCl_3 \end{matrix} \qquad (70)$$

(73)

Addition to its cyclopentadienyl rings is characteristic not only of cobalto-cene itself but also of a cobalticinium cation, which is transformed to the cyclopentadienylcyclopentadienic complex (71) by nucleophiles (LiAlH$_4$,[10] NaBH$_4$,[10] as well as organic lithium and sodium compounds).[14–16]

Similar reactions involving lithium aluminum hydride, sodium borohy-dride, phenyllithium, or cyclopentadienylsodium have been performed with a bis(cyclopentadienyl)rhodium cation.[10,17]

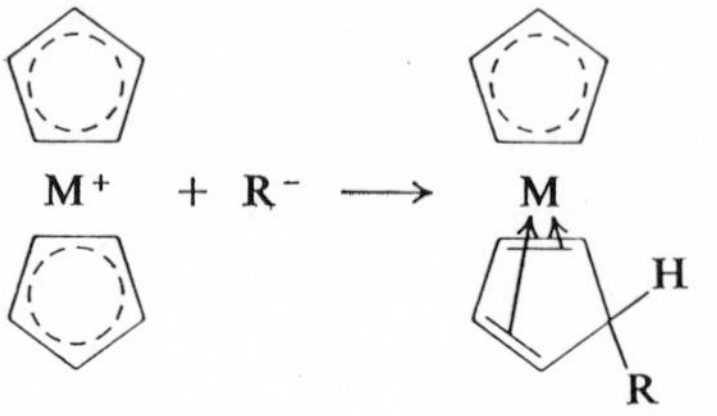

$$M^+ \ + \ R^- \ \longrightarrow \ M \hspace{2cm} (71)$$

$$\left(M = Co; \ R = H, \ D, \ CH_3, \ C_6H_5, \ \right)$$

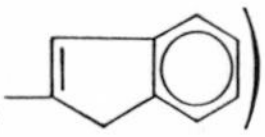

$$(M = Rh; \ R = H, \ C_6H_5, \ C_5H_5)$$

A π-methylcyclopentadienyl-π-methylcyclopentadienic complex of cobalt $CH_3C_5H_4CoC_5H_5CH_3$, is obtained from 1,1′-dimethylcobalticinium bromide and lithium aluminum hydride.[10] Monodeuterated cyclopentadienylcyclo-pentadienecobalt, $C_5H_5CoC_5H_5D$, is obtained from cobalticinium chloride and lithium aluminum deuteride.

A reaction of cyclopentadienyl sodium with the cobalticinium cation gives a compound of the composition $Co_2C_{25}H_{24}$,[16] which, according to X-ray,[18,19] infrared, and NMR[20] evidence, is 2,4-bis(π-cyclopentadienylcobaltcyclo-pentadien)-yl-cyclopentadiene-2,4, (74).

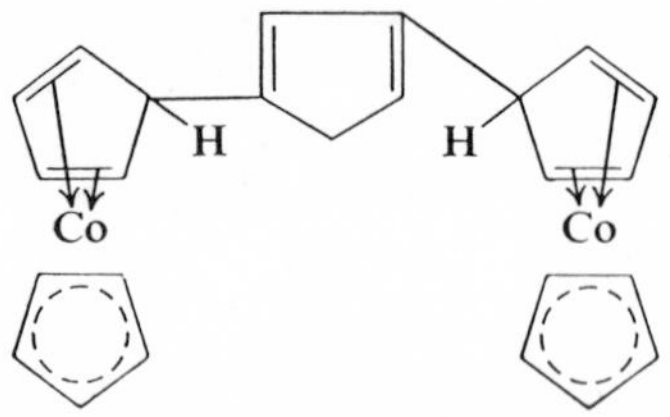

(74)

An X-ray investigation has shown the bonds between the bridge cyclo-pentadiene and the sandwiches to be *exo* oriented with respect to the sand-wiches—rather than *endo* oriented, as would appear from the infrared spectrum.

The cobalticinium cation reacts in a similar fashion with methylcyclopentadienylsodium.[16]

The mechanism of reaction beween cobalt and rhodium bis(cyclopentadienyl) compounds and nucleophiles has not been studied. It is, as yet, unknown whether the reaction proceeds as a direct attack on the cyclopentadienyl ring or as a ricochet substitution involving preliminary coordination of the nucleophile to the metal atom with subsequent migration to the ring. The first hypothesis should lead to *exo* orientation of an entering group and the second one to *endo* orientation.[13]

The bond nature and stereochemistry of cobalt and rhodium cyclopentadienylcyclopentadiene complexes have not been determined. Only cyclopentadienyl-1-phenylcyclopentadienecobalt has been studied by X-ray diffraction.[21] Churchill and Mason[21] have shown the phenyl group to be *exo* oriented with respect to the cobalt atom and the cyclopentadienyl ring to be nonplanar. The tetrahedral C(1) atom is deflected from the plane of the ring by 36° and the C(3)—C(4) bond is 1.38 Å in length, thus being shorter than other bonds. On the basis of all this evidence the authors thought the structure of the compound to be (75), in which a cyclopentadiene ring is bonded to a cobalt atom by means of one π- and two σ-bonds.

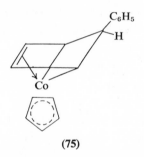

(75)

Churchill and Mason think that the cobalt atom of this compound has an octahedral configuration. A cyclopentadienyl-1-phenylcyclopentadienic complex of rhodium is known to be isomorphic with its cobalt analog.[17]

Earlier all complexes of the $C_5H_5CoC_5H_5R$ type (R = CCl_3, CH_3, CF_3, C_6H_5, etc.) were thought[10,14,15] to have structures with an *endo* orientation of the substituent group. This assumption was based on the fact that the infrared absorption band at 2750 cm^{-1}, found in a spectrum of unsubstituted cyclopentadienylcyclopentadienecobalt, was absent from the infrared spectra of the complexes. However, the X-ray data cited above have shown the assumption to be incorrect in the case of cyclopentadienyl-1-phenylcyclopentadienecobalt. The hydrogen of this compound is *endo* oriented with respect to the metal, but twisting of the cyclopentadienyl ring may result in the hydrogen–metal distance being too great for the interaction responsible for the absorption at 2750 cm^{-1}. This must also be taken into account with other cyclopentadienylcyclopentadienic complexes. Thus their structures cannot be determined solely from infrared spectra.

The cyclopentadienyl–cyclopentadienic ligand transformation described above is reversible. Cobalt, rhodium, or iridium cyclopentadienylcyclopentadienic complexes (76), when oxidized by oxygen or by hydrogen peroxide in acidic solutions or when reacted with hydrogenchloride or carbon tetrachloride, readily lose a hydride ion, producing the bis(cyclopentadienyl) cations (77) of cobalt, rhodium, or iridium.[10,22]

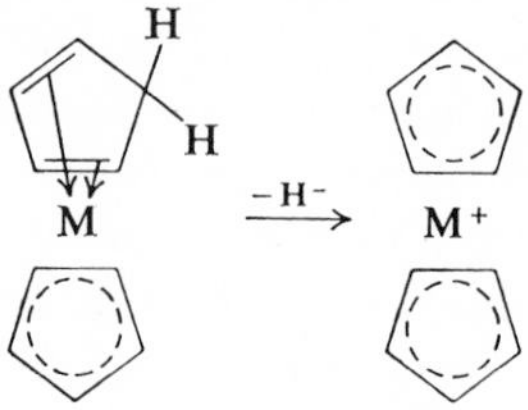

$$\xrightarrow{-\text{H}^-}$$ (72)

(76)   (77)

(M = Co, Rh, Ir)

Cyclopentadienyl-1-phenylcyclopentadienerhodium, when oxidized, gives the phenyl derivative of bis(cyclopentadienyl)rhodium cation, the yield being almost quantitative.[17]

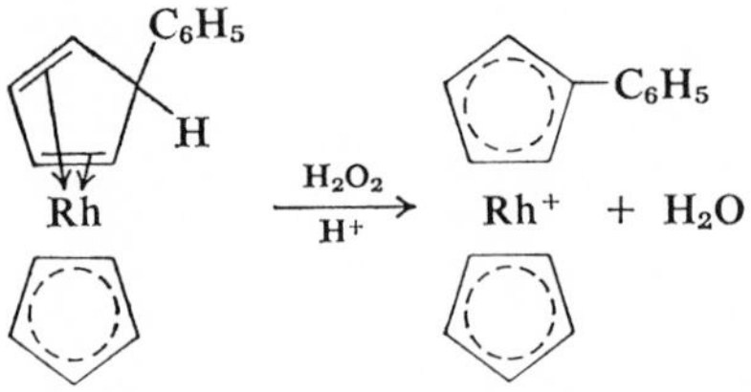

$$\xrightarrow[\text{H}^+]{\text{H}_2\text{O}_2}$$ Rh$^+$ + H$_2$O   (73)

However, attempts to obtain substituted cobaltocene cations via a similar route were unsuccessful. They led either to removal of a substituent followed by formation of cobalticinium or to complete destruction of the molecule.[9,14]

Fischer and Wawersik[23] have found an interesting new reaction, a reversible dimerization of rhodium or iridium cyclopentadienyl compounds, resulting in the formation of a bond between the two metallocene nuclei. The formation is accompanied by cyclopentadienyl–cyclopentadiene ligand transformation.

Fischer and Wawersik have shown that the metallocinium salts, when mixed with fused sodium in an inert gas and sublimed, give rather stable, crystalline, diamagnetic dimers (78). When condensed on a surface cooled with liquid nitrogen, however, these vapors produce extremely unstable, paramagnetic, monomeric bis(cyclopentadienyl) rhodium or iridium compounds (79). Elevation of the temperature causes fast dimerization of the compounds.

$$(77) \xrightarrow{\text{Na}} \qquad \text{M} \qquad \text{M} \rightleftarrows 2 \quad \text{M} \qquad (74)$$
$$(78) \qquad\qquad (79)$$

Sodium in liquid ammonia causes a bis(cyclopentadienyl)rhodium cation to react via another route, forming cyclopentadienylcyclopentadienerhodium [compound (76), M = Rh].

D. Example of Syntheses: Reaction of Cobaltocene with Carbon Tetrachloride[10]

Cobaltocene (3 g) is treated with carbon tetrachloride (5 ml). After 1 hr, the carbon tetrachloride is removed, and the residue is extracted with light (b.p. 40–60°) petroleum ether. After chromatography with light petroleum ether, the eluate is evaporated, and the product (45% yield based on cobaltocene) is recrystallized at low temperatures from isopentane.

References

1. M. Dubeck and A. H. Tilbey, *J. Amer. Chem. Soc.*, **83**, 1257 (1961).
2. D. W. McBride, E. Dudek, and F. G. A. Stone, *J. Chem. Soc.*, **1964**, 1752.
3. D. W. McBride, R. L. Pruetl, E. Pitcher, and F. G. A. Stone, *J. Amer. Chem. Soc.*, **84**, 497 (1962).
4. M. Dubeck, *J. Amer. Chem. Soc.*, **82**, 6193 (1960).
5. L. F. Dahe and C.-H. Wey, *Inorg. Chem.*, **2**, 713 (1963).
6. Yu. A. Ustynyuk, T. I. Voevodskaya, N. A. Zharikova, and N. A. Ustynyuk, *Dokl. Akad. Nauk SSSR*, **181**, 372 (1968).
7. E. O. Fischer and K. Ulm, *Z. Naturforsch.*, **15b**, 59 (1960).
8. E. O. Fischer and K. Ulm, *Chem. Ber.*, **94**, 2413 (1961).
9. S. Katz, J. F. Weiher, and A. F. Voigt, *J. Amer. Chem. Soc.*, **80**, 6459 (1958).
10. M. L. H. Green, L. Pratt, and G. Wilkinson, *J. Chem. Soc.*, **1959**, 3753.
11. H. H. Hoehn, L. Pratt, K. F. Watterson, and G. Wilkinson, *J. Chem. Soc.*, **1961**, 2738.
12. K. F. Watterson and G. Wilkinson, *Chem. Ind. (London)*, **1960**, 1358.
13. J. P. Collman, *Transition Metal Chemistry*, Vol. 2, R. L. Carlin, Ed., Marcel Dekker, New York, 1966, pp. 62, 63.
14. E. O. Fischer and G. E. Herberich, *Chem. Ber.*, **94**, 1517 (1961).
15. C. Furlani and J. Collamati, *Chem. Ber.*, **95**, 2928 (1962).
16. E. O. Fischer, W. Fellman, and G. E. Herberich, *Chem. Ber.*, **95**, 2254 (1962).
17. R. J. Angelici and E. O. Fisher, *J. Amer. Chem. Soc.*, **85**, 3733 (1963).

18. O. V. Starovskii and Yu. T. Struchkov, *Zh. Strukturn. Khim.*, **2**, 612 (1961).
19. O. V. Starovskii and Yu. T. Struchkov, *Zh. Strukturn. Khim.*, **6**, 248 (1965).
20. H. P. Fritz and H. J. Keller, *Chem. Ber.*, **95**, 2259 (1962).
21. M. R. Churchill and R. Mason, *Proc. Chem. Soc.*, **1963**, 112.
22. E. O. Fischer and U. Zahn, *Chem. Ber.*, **92**, 1624 (1959).
23. E. O. Fischer and H. Wawersik, *J. Organometal. Chem.*, **5**, 559 (1966).

Chapter 4

Oxidation–Reduction Reactions of the Metalocenes

I. GENERAL

This chapter covers the oxidation–reduction reactions of the metal atom in metallocenes. Metallocene oxidation to a metallocinium cation is a reaction characteristic of metallocenes

$$(C_5H_5)_2M \underset{\longleftarrow}{\overset{-e}{\longrightarrow}} (C_5H_5)_2M^+ \tag{1}$$

In most cases the reaction is reversible, and the bis(cyclopentadienyl) metal cation can be reduced to a neutral metallocene. In oxidation–reduction transformations, with the metal atom acting as the reaction center, metallocenes react more like inorganic complexes of transition metals. No systematic study of oxidation–reduction reactions in metallocene chemistry has been conducted to date.

Oxidation–reduction transformations have been studied most extensively in ferrocene and a large number of its derivatives. Analysis of oxidation reduction potentials and equilibrium constants shows that they have a definite correlation with the electronic effects of the substituents.

Quite a few papers have been published on the oxidation–reduction reactions of bis(cyclopentadienyl) compounds of titanium and vanadium. These compounds are used in polymerization catalysts for olefins. Research into their oxidation–reduction transformations is necessary to further elucidate the mechanism of this action.

II. OXIDATION–REDUCTION REACTIONS OF GROUP VIII METAL BIS(CYCLOPENTADIENYL) COMPOUNDS

A. Oxidation–Reduction Transformations of Ferrocene and Its Derivatives

1. Ferrocene Oxidation

Ferrocene is quite stable in air, both in the solid state and in organic solvents. However, ferrocene oxidation to the ferricinium cation proceeds easily in an acid medium in the presence of oxygen. Also used are organic and inorganic oxidants (including nitric[1-3] or sulfuric[1-4] acid, silver or ceric sulfate,[5] quinone,[5] anthraquinone,[6] and N-bromosuccinimide[7]) as well as electrochemical means.[5,8,9]

$$(C_5H_5)_2Fe \overset{-e^-}{\longrightarrow} (C_5H_5)_2Fe^+ \tag{2}$$

In organic solvents ferrocene is oxidized by halides: iron(III),[5,10,11] aluminum,[12*] and copper(II)[13] chlorides. The reaction of iron(III) chloride with ferrocene is a convenient method of obtaining ferricinium tetrachloroferrate,[10,11] one of the most stable ferricinium salts. This is also formed when ferrocene is heated to 90–120° in hexachlorocyclopentadiene.[14] The Mössbauer spectrum confirms the existence of separate ferricinium and tetrachloroferrate ions.[15]

$$(C_5H_5)_2Fe + 2FeCl_3 \longrightarrow [(C_5H_5)_2Fe]^+[FeCl_4]^- + FeCl_2 \qquad (3)$$

Ferricinium salts with other complex anions have also been obtained,[16] but ferricinium salts with simple anions could not be isolated from solution.

Halogens (chlorine or bromine) produce, depending on the conditions, either complete or partial decomposition plus oxidation to the ferricinium cation.[3,17,18] Iodine in organic solvents slowly oxidizes ferrocene to a cation. Syrkin and Savitskii[19-22] studied the kinetics of the process in alcohol and benzene. Ferrocene is oxidized by mercury(II) ions[23] and by the phenylmercury cation.[24]

$$2(C_5H_5)_2Fe + Hg^{2+} \longrightarrow 2(C_5H_5)_2Fe^+ + Hg \qquad (4)$$

$$(C_5H_5)_2Fe + C_6H_5Hg^+ \longrightarrow (C_5H_5)_2Fe^+ \qquad (5)$$

Oxidation by mercury(II) ions proceeds quantitively and is recommended for the analytical determination of ferrocene or mercury(II) ions.[23]

Hawthorne has proved that ferrocene is oxidized by the triphenylmethyl cation.[25] Beckwith and Leydon believe that the inverse reaction also takes place.[26]

$$(C_5H_5)_2Fe^+ + (C_6H_5)_3C\cdot \rightleftarrows [(C_5H_5)_2FeC(C_6H_5)_3]^+ \rightleftarrows$$
$$(C_5H_5)_2Fe + (C_6H_5)_3C^+ \qquad (6)$$

Due to a similar equilibrium, as well as the similarity in the stabilities of the ferrocenemethyl cation (1) and the triphenylmethyl cation,[27] the former could be expected to undergo an oxidation–reduction (intramolecular or intermolecular) reaction leading to the formation of the cation radical (2).

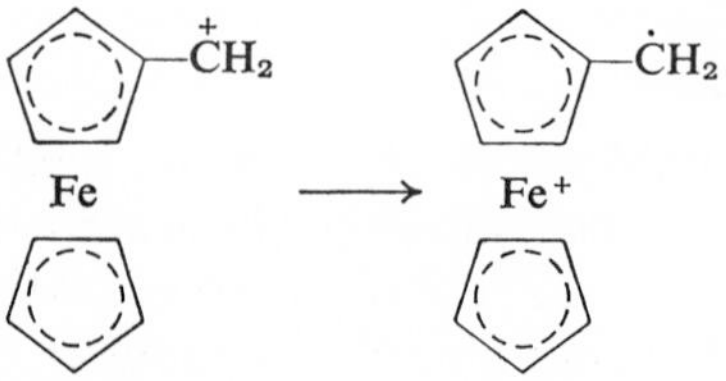

$$(7)$$

(1)   (2)

* There are no reliable data on ferrocene oxidation with aluminum chloride. The green compound obtained when $AlCl_3$ reacts with ferrocene is believed to be the complex $(C_5H_5)_2FeHAlCl_4$.

Rinehart and co-workers[28] gave precisely this explanation for the formation of diferrocenylethane dication (3) in the reaction of ferrocenylcarbinol with concentrated sulfuric acid. A similar explanation was later given[29] for the formation of diferrocenyldiphenylcarbinyl azide. Physical methods have, however, proved the existence of a cation radical[30,31] in only one case [structure (4)].

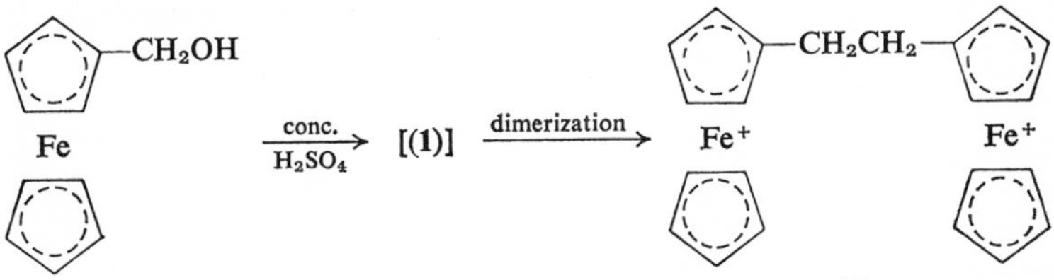

(3)

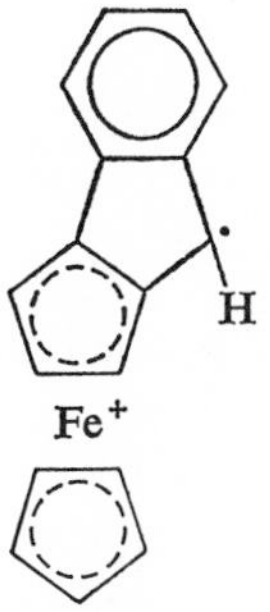

(4)

Ferrocene oxidation to the ferricinium cation takes place as a side reaction during electrophilic substitution of ferrocene hydrogens, e.g., in sulfonation, mercuration, and acylation reactions (see Chapter 1). Because ferrocene is easily oxidized, certain electrophilic hydrogen-substitution reactions have not been possible (nitration, halogenation, and azo coupling).

Nesmeyanov, Kursanov, Setkina, and co-workers[32,33] have found that isotopic exchange of ferrocene hydrogens (in a mixture of acetic and tri-fluoroacetic acids) is, to a greater or lesser extent, accompanied by ferrocene oxidation to the ferricinium cation.

Peroxide radicals oxidize ferrocene to the ferricinium cation.[34,35] Rate constants have been found for the reaction of ferrocene and its derivatives (ethyl, phenyl, and acetyl ferrocenes; ferrocenecarboxylic acid; and ferro-cenecarboxylic acid nitrile) with the peroxide radicals formed from an ethyl-benzene oxidation.[35]

Ferrocene does not react with alkyl or aryl free radicals.[36,37] For further information about ferricinium-cation interaction with free radicals see Chapter 1, Section II-H.

Ferrocene oxidation and the formation of ferricinium chloride occurs when ferrocene is subjected to radiolysis in carbon tetrachloride.[38]

$$(C_5H_5)_2Fe \xrightarrow{CCl_4} [(C_5H_5)_2Fe]^+Cl^- \tag{9}$$

The ease with which ferrocene oxidizes promoted its use in the reductive defluorination of perfluorinated amines.[39] This opened the path to a one-stage synthesis of perfluorinated imines, nitriles, and azomethines. Until recently these compounds were obtained by pyrolysis.

$$R_fCF_2NF_2 \xrightarrow{(C_5H_5)_2Fe} R_fCF{=}NF \tag{10}$$

$$R_f(CF_2NF_2)_2 \xrightarrow{(C_5H_5)_2Fe} R_f(CF{=}NF)_2 \tag{11}$$

$$C_2F_5NFCF_2CF_3 \xrightarrow{(C_5H_5)_2Fe} C_2F_5N{=}CFCF_3 \tag{12}$$

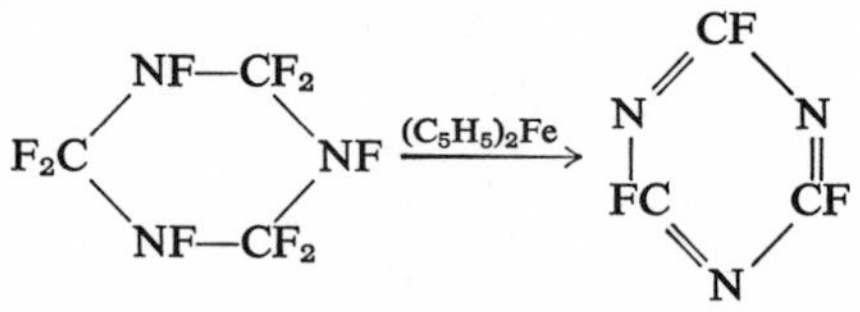

$$\tag{13}$$

Since these reactions proceed in high yield at room temperature, it is possible to use aprotic, halogen-containing solvents. The progress of the reaction can be conveniently followed by the decrease in the yellow-orange color of ferrocene and by the increase in the amount of the blue-green ferricinium salt precipitated. This may be a ferricinium fluoride not described earlier. There are no direct indications as to the composition of the ferricinium salt formed.

Ferrocene has been used in analytical chemistry to determine the iron(III) ion in the presence of other ions [manganese(II), cobalt(II), nickel(II), zinc(II), cadmium(II), etc.].[40] The method is called ferrocenometry.

$$(C_5H_5)_2Fe + Fe^{3+} \longrightarrow (C_5H_5)_2Fe^+ + Fe^{2+} \tag{14}$$

Oxidation–reduction resins have been prepared by using ferrocene as the basic starting material.[41]

2. Ferricinium-Cation Reduction

Ferrocene oxidation is chemically reversible. Ferricinium salts are easily reduced to ferrocene by a number of reducing agents, e.g., tin(II) chloride,[5] sodium sulfite or thiosulfate, ascorbic acid [4,6] and $Ti_2(SO_4)_3$.[42]

$$(C_5H_5)_2Fe^+ \longrightarrow (C_5H_5)_2Fe \tag{15}$$

When acted on by alkali, spontaneously, or when steam distilled, aqueous ferricinium solutions yield ferrocene.[43] Pendin, Zakhar'evskii, and Leont'-evskaya[44] have shown chemically that the first stage of ferricinium hydrolytic decomposition, which is especially rapid in an alkaline medium, is the formation of the unstable complex, $(C_5H_5)_2FeOH$. This then undergoes slow, first-order decomposition, with the abstraction of cyclopentadienyl rings and the formation of ionic iron. The organic residues then probably reduce the unreacted ferricinium cation to ferrocene.

Ferricinium-cation reduction by hydrogen in water solution has been studied and its thermodynamic characteristics have been determined.[45]

$$(C_5H_5)_2Fe^+ + \tfrac{1}{2}H_2 \rightleftarrows (C_5H_5)_2Fe + H^+ \tag{16}$$

The conversion of the ferricinium cation to ferrocene in high yield (80–90%) takes place with certain nucleophilic reactants, e.g., diethylamine and ethylmagnesium or phenylmagnesium bromide.[10] In the latter case diphenyl has been isolated as a product.

$$[(C_5H_5)_2Fe]^+[FeCl_4]^- + 2C_6H_5MgBr \longrightarrow$$
$$(C_5H_5)_2Fe + C_6H_5C_6H_5 + FeCl_2 + 2MgBrCl \tag{17}$$

Certain ferricinium-cation reactions with diazonium salts, free radicals, anhydrides of aliphatic acids,[46] and hydrocyanic acid are peculiar in that they lead to the formation of hydrogen-substitution products (by the corresponding groups) and simultaneous reduction of the ferricinium nucleus to the ferrocene nucleus. For a more detailed description of reactions with diazonium salts, free radicals, and hydrocyanic acid see Chapter 1.

3. Ferrocene $\rightleftarrows$ Ferricinium Cation System

Electrochemical (polarographic[47] and chronopotentiometric[48]) studies of the oxidation–reduction transformation of ferrocene $\rightleftarrows$ ferricinium cation has shown that ferrocene oxidation is a one-electron process and is electrochemically reversible.

$$(C_5H_5)_2Fe \rightleftarrows (C_5H_5)_2Fe^+ + e^- \tag{18}$$

The ferrocene $\rightleftarrows$ ferricinium cation system is characterized by the great ease of its reversible transformation compared with that of oxidation–reduction transfers of the typical iron(II) complexes.

Table I correlates standard ferrocene oxidation–reduction potentials and some iron complexes.

The position of ferrocene in Table I shows that it is oxidized somewhat more easily than iron(II) and less easily than the ferrocyanide ion.

The rate of electron exchange between ferrocene and the ferricinium cation has been found by several methods.[49–53] It appears to be larger than the electron-exchange rate of other typical iron complexes with a stable coordination sphere (see Table II).

The rapid exchange and high reversibility of the ferrocene $\rightleftarrows$ ferricinium cation system show that the type of metal–ligand bond does not change substantially in oxidation–reduction transfers. The infrared spectrum and

TABLE I

Standard Oxidation–Reduction Potentials of Some Iron-Containing Complexes

Reaction	E_0, volts[a]
$[Fe(CN)_6]^{4-} \rightleftharpoons [Fe(CN)_6]^{3-} + e^-$	-0.36
$(C_5H_5)_2Fe \rightleftharpoons (C_5H_5)_2Fe^+ + e^-$	-0.56
$[Fe(H_2O)_6]^{2+} \rightleftharpoons [Fe(H_2O)_6]^{3+} + e^-$	-0.711
$[Fe(dipy)_3]^{2+} \rightleftharpoons [Fe(dipy)_2]^{3+} + e^-$	-1.096
$[Fe(o\text{-phen})_3]^{2+} \rightleftharpoons [Fe(o\text{-phen})_3]^{3+} + e^-$	-1.14

[a] Versus the normal calomal electrode.

TABLE II

Electron-Exchange-Rate Constants in Bimolecular Reactions of Typical Iron and Ferrocene Complexes

Reaction	k
$[Fe(CN)_6]^{4-} \rightleftharpoons [Fe(CN)_6]^{3-} + e^-$	$\approx 10^2$
$[Fe(o\text{-phen})_3]^{2+} \rightleftharpoons [Fe(o\text{-phen})_3]^{3+} + e^-$	$\approx 1 \times 10^5$
$(C_5H_5)_2Fe \rightleftharpoons (C_5H_5)_2Fe^+ + e^-$	$\approx 9.0 \times 10^5$

other physicochemical studies of the ferricinium cation confirm this conclusion.[54]

The unique properties of the ferrocene $\rightleftharpoons$ ferricinium cation system—such as high reversibility, high electron-exchange rate, and practically complete insolubility of ferrocene in water—were successfully put to use by Nikol'skii and co-workers[55] in obtaining an electrode that is reversible with respect to the ferricinium cation. The electrode has also been used to study complex formation by the ferricinium cation, to find the concentration and activity indices of ferricinium salts, and to find the acid content of acetic acid–water solutions.

The polarographic reduction of the ferricinium cation in various solvents has been studied.[56] The ferrocene–ferricinium oxidation–reduction system has been considered as a reference electrode since its potential is but slightly dependent on the nature of the solvent.

4. Oxidation of Ferrocene Derivatives

Reversible oxidation at the iron atom in ferrocene and a number of its derivatives has been studied by these techniques: oxidative potentiometric titration. chronopotentiometry, and polarography. The oxidation,[57–60] chronopotentiometric,[61–64] and polarographic[65–68] potentials of many ferrocene derivatives have been found and have been shown to be dependent on the nature of substituents.

The variation in the oxidation potentials of ferrocene derivatives with substituents correlates well with the variation in activity toward electrophilic substitution reactions. A number of papers describe a correlation analysis of oxidation potentials and show that there is a rather satisfactory correlation with the Hammett σ_p-constant.[57,62–67]

The oxidation of ferrocene derivatives has been extensively studied by Nesmeyanov and co-workers.[68–72] The systematic correlational analysis of equilibrium constants calculated from the oxidation–reduction potentials of a large series of ferrocene derivatives with substituents varying in the nature of their influence showed that the best correlation is found between the quantities $\log k_x/k_H$ and again the Taft σ_p^0-constant.

The σ_p^0-constant is the parameter that characterizes the effect of a given substituent on the dissociation constants of *para*-substituted phenylacetic acids. Thus the substituted, five-membered aromatic ring, C_5H_4X, interacts with its reaction center (iron atom) in a way that resembles the interaction of the *para*-substituted benzyl group (p-$XC_6H_5CH_2$) with its reaction center (carboxyl). It should be noted that the separation of the carboxyl from the phenyl ring by a CH_2-group will effectively prevent conjugation. The transmission of the substituents' influence along the ring–metal bond can thus be said to be predominantly inductive in nature.

The reactivity of heteroannular, disubstituted ferrocenes in oxidation is described by the equation $\log k_H = \rho_0 \Sigma \sigma_p^0$, where $\Sigma \sigma_p^0$ is the sum of the substituents' constants. Therefore there is no substantial interaction between the two substituents on the different rings.

Analysis of the dissociation constants of ferrocenecarboxylic acids, X—$C_5H_4FeC_5H_4COOH$ (X = alkyl, H, OCH_3, Cl, Br, COR, $COOCH_3$, CN), as well as a study of absorption spectra of heteroannular, disubstituted ferrocenes, shows that the ferrocenyl nucleus inhibits conjugation between substituents in different rings.[72] Yet the inductive conductivities of the ferrocenyl ($\rho_i = 1.385$) and phenyl ($\rho_i = 1.469$) groups are very close in magnitude.

5. Ferrocene Complex Formation

Ferrocene, like aromatic hydrocarbons, forms charge-transfer complexes with compounds having electron-withdrawing properties, such as tetracyanoethylene, aromatic polynitro compounds, iodine, and benzoquinone.[73–81] In the case of electron acceptors with high oxidation–reduction potentials (e.g., 2,3-dichloro-5,6-dicyanoquinone) an electron is completely transferred from ferrocene, yielding a ferricinium salt.[82]

Aly and co-workers[83] isolated ferrocene adducts with some acids (Cl_3CCO_2H, F_3CCO_2H, Cl_2HCCO_2H, picric acid, and HBF_4) and have shown that they are best represented as charge-transfer salts, $[(C_5H_5)_2Fe]$ $[(HB)^-(HB)_{n-1}]^-$, where $(HB)_{n-1}$ are formally neutral acid molecules that can share in the process of electron holding.

Ferrocene complexes are as a rule low in stability, and most of them have been studied only in solutions.[75,79-81] Only the ferrocene complexes with iodine[81] and tetracyanoethylene are stable.[73,74]

Ferrocene forms with tetracyanoethylene a green complex (of 1:1 composition) that can be isolated as a solid.[73,74] Similar tetracyanoethylene complexes are formed with methyl,1,1'-dimethyl, and phenyl ferrocenes. On the other hand, ruthenocene and osmocene do not react with tetracyanoethylene under similar conditions.

Originally the ferrocene complex with tetracyanoethylene was described as a ferricinium salt because a strong signal of the tetracyanoethylene anion radical was found in the electron-spin-resonance spectrum (acetonitrile solution).[73] Later Rosenblum and co-workers,[74] who intensively studied the physical properties of the complex (infrared, visible, and ultraviolet spectra as well as magnetic properties), obtained convincing proof that the compound was a charge-transfer complex rather than a ferricinium salt. Collins and Pettit[84] confirmed the conclusion of Rosenblum et al. and suggested structure (5), which was soon proved by the X-ray studies of Adman, Rosenblum, Sullivan, and Margulis.[85]

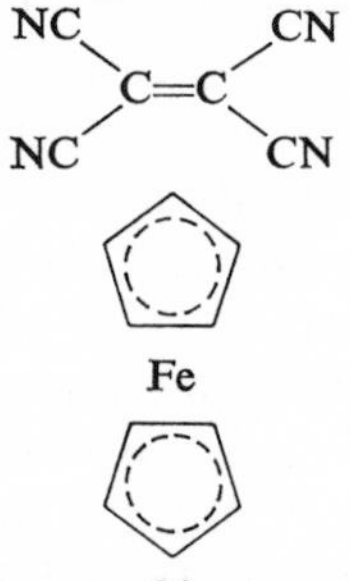

(5)

The structures of other complexes have not been established. Two possible structures, (6) and (7), are the subject of discussion.[79,81]

In the benzene series the equilibrium constants for charge-transfer-complex formation vary in the same direction as the activities in electrophilic substitution. This is in line with the idea that a charge-transfer complex between the aromatic system and the electrophile is the first stage in electrophilic substitution. No such dependence, however, has been observed for ferrocene.

In its ability to form complexes with tetracyanoethylene ferrocene is a cross between benzene on the one hand and naphthalene and pentamethyl-benzene on the other. Yet in acetylation the activity of ferrocene is known to be six orders of magnitude greater than that of benzene and two orders of magnitude greater than that of pentamethylbenzene (see Chapter 1, Section II-C).

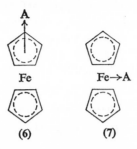

This difference may be due to the difference in the spatial arrangements of components between the charge-transfer complexes and the transition states of electrophilic substitution.

Further research into charge-transfer complexes may prove valuable in determining the nature of the transition state of electrophilic substitution in metallocenes.

6. Ferricinium-Cation Complex Formation

The iron atom in the ferricinium cation retains the ability to form additional bonds. This is seen in the formation of complexes with a number of anions.[86–88]

Smith[86] was the first to show spectrophotometrically that in acetone or alcohol the ferricinium cation forms with the thiocyanate anion a strongly colored complex (composition 1:1) that is destroyed by water. Peterson and Dune[87] used the same technique to study the formation of a complex between the ferricinium cation and the chloride anion and determined the complex-formation constant to be 3.

Nikol'skii and co-workers[88] employed the potentiometric technique to study the formation of complexes between the ferricinium cation and a number of anions. By using the ferrocene–ferricinium electrode, which they had developed earlier and whose potential was highly sensitive to ferricinium-cation concentration in solution, Nikol'skii et al. studied the formation of complexes between the ferricinium cation and the OH^-, Cl^-, CNS^-, and ClO_4^- anions, and found the stability constants. In the case of the chloride ion the constant obtained (2.2) is virtually identical with the one found by Peterson and Dune[87] spectrophotometrically. Nikol'skii and co-workers have also shown that there is no appreciable formation of complexes between the ferricinium cation and such typical iron-complexing agents as o-phenanthroline and ethylenediaminetetraacetic acid. This contradicts the data obtained by Smith[86] spectrophotometrically.

B. Oxidation–Reduction Transformations of Ruthenocene and Osmocene

Ferrocene analogs, such as ruthenocene and osmocene, differ from it appreciably in their oxidation–reduction properties.

A single-charged osmicinium cation, analogous to the ferricinium ion, has not been obtained. Mild oxidants, such as silver sulfate and p-quinone, are ineffective on osmocene.[89] However, both iodine in sulfuric acid and the iron(III) atom in $(NH_4)_2Fe(SO_4)_2 \cdot 12H_2O$ slowly oxidize osmocene to the doubly charged cation.[89]

$$(C_5H_5)_2Os + I_2 + H_2SO_4 \longrightarrow [(C_5H_5)_2OsI]^+ \tag{19}$$

$$(C_5H_5)_2Os + 2Fe^{3+} + H_2O \longrightarrow [(C_5H_5)_2OsOH]^+ + 2Fe^{2+} + H^+ \tag{20}$$

In the presence of reducing agents ($SnCl_2$ and H_2SO_3) the osmicinium dication is converted into neutral osmocene.[89]

In contrast to osmocene, ruthenocene is easily converted to the singly-charged ruthenocinium cation, $[(C_5H_5)_2Ru]^+$, by mild oxidants (iodine, bromine in water, and silver sulfate) in an acidic medium. It is also converted electrochemically under controlled potential in a mixture of 90% alcohol and perchloric acid.[90]

The kinetics of ruthenocene oxidation by iodine have been studied.[21,22] Dilute nitric acid and stronger oxidants cause destruction of ruthenocene, with the formation of red-colored solutions of ruthenium(III) and ruthenium(IV).[90]

Nesmeyanov and co-workers[91] oxidized ruthenocene with iron(III) chloride in ether and obtained a ruthenocinium salt of the composition $C_{10}H_{10}RuFeCl_5$. They proposed that this is the salt of the double-charged ruthenocinium cation, $[(C_5H_5)_2RuCl]^+[FeCl_4]^-$. The salt, when reduced by sodium sulfite, is converted into neutral ruthenocene.

The polarographic oxidation of osmocene at a dropping-mercury electrode in 0.5 N HCl in 50% ethanol is reversible and proceeds as a two-electron process.[67]

$$(C_5H_5)_2Os - 2e^- \; \underset{\longleftarrow}{\longrightarrow} \; (C_5H_5)_2Os^{2+} \tag{21}$$

The polarographic oxidation of ruthenocene at a dropping-mercury electrode in 90% ethanol ($E_{1/2} = 0.260$ V versus the normal calomel electrode) proceeds as a one-electron process. The polarographic reduction potential ($E_{1/2} = 0.22$ V) differs noticeably from the oxidation potential; therefore the process is electrochemically irreversible.[47]

$$(C_5H_5)Ru \xrightarrow{-e^-} (C_5H_5)_2 Ru^+ \tag{22}$$

The chronopotentiometric oxidation of ruthenocene in acetonitrile differs from polarographic oxidation in that it proceeds as a two-electron, one-stage process.[48,61] Under the same conditions osmocene is oxidized in two stages, each of which is a one-electron process.[48,61]

$$(C_5H_5)_2Ru \xrightarrow{-2e^-} (C_5H_5)_2Ru^{2+} \tag{23}$$

$$(C_5H_5)_2Os \xrightarrow{-e^-} (C_5H_5)_2Os^+ \xrightarrow{-e^-} (C_5H_5)_2Os^{2+} \tag{24}$$

C. Oxidation–Reduction Transformations of Cobalt, Rhodium, and Iridium Bis(cyclopentadienyl) Compounds

In the cobalt subgroup only the neutral bis(cyclopentadienyl)cobalt compound has been studied. Dark-violet bis(cyclopentadienyl)cobalt (cobaltocene), containing 19 electrons in the external shell, is highly sensitive to oxidants and is easily converted to the diamagnetic cobalticinium cation. This can then be quantitatively precipitated from aqueous solution as a salt by complex anions.[92]

Cobaltocene is a strong reducing agent and reduces iron(II) chloride to metallic iron.[2]

$$2(C_5H_5)_2Co + FeCl_2 \longrightarrow 2[(C_5H_5)_2Co]^+ Cl^- + Fe° \tag{25}$$

A similar reaction occurs with cobalt(II) chloride,[93] from which cobaltocene is thus difficult to obtain. Therefore, if a good yield of cobaltocene is to be obtained, the ammonia complex, $Co(NH_3)_6Cl_2$, is used because it is more difficult to reduce than cobalt(II) chloride.

Cobaltocene is easily oxidized by acids (e.g., 3 N HCl) in the absence of oxygen.[2] In an inert atmosphere cobaltocene is slowly oxidized by water containing no dissolved oxygen.[2,11]

With such electron acceptors as trinitrobenzene and p-chloranil, cobaltocene forms charge-transfer complexes that, in contrast to cobaltocene, are relatively stable in air and can be isolated from solutions.[81] In acetonitrile a cobaltocene complex with trinitrobenzene decomposes into the cobalticinium ion and the trinitrobenzene anion radical, whereas the complex with p-chloranil decomposes into the original components.

The action of alkyl halides on cobaltocene, which leads to the formation of cobalticinium halide salt and π-cyclopentadienyl-π-cyclopentadiene cobalt

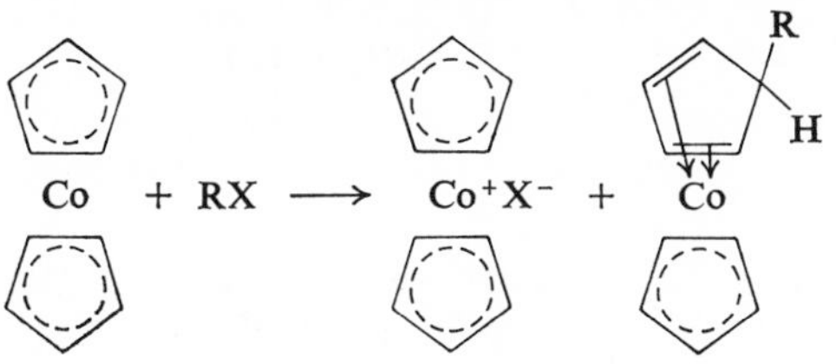

$$Co \quad + RX \longrightarrow \quad Co^+X^- \quad + \quad Co \tag{26}$$

complexes, has been discussed in chapter 3. This can be described as an oxidation–reduction reaction because in cobaltocene the metal atom is surrounded by a 19-electron shell, whereas in the reaction product it has an 18-electron shell.

Bis(cyclopentadienyl) rhodium and iridium salts are obtained by the action of cyclopentadienylmagnesium bromide on acetylacetonates or, better still, on rhodium(III) or iridium(III) chloride.[94]

$$MX_3 + C_5H_5MgBr \longrightarrow (C_5H_5)_2M^+ \qquad (27)$$
$$(M = Rh, Ir)$$

It is characteristic that, despite the excess of cyclopentadienylmagnesium bromide, the resulting metallocinium salts are not reduced to neutral metallocenes.

Cobalt, rhodium, and iridium metallocene cations, isoelectronic with ferrocene, are exceptionally stable toward oxidants and do not decompose when boiled with concentrated sulfuric or nitric acid or when treated with ozone in a mixture of ice and acetic acid. A colbalticinium molecule can only be destroyed by fusing with alkali or boiling in fuming perchloric acid. Fischer and Herberich[95] used this astonishing stability to oxidize a side chain in the salts of 1,1'-dimethylcobalticinium and bis(indenyl)cobalt(III) with potassium permanganate at 100°. They obtained the salts of 1,1-dicarboxycobalticinium and 1,2,1',2'-tetracarboxycobalticinium, respectively. The yields in both cases were about 70%.

Under the action of nucleophiles that are strong reducing agents (alkali metals, complex hydrides,[96] or organolithium or organosodium compounds[95,97]) the formal valency of the metals in bis(cyclopentadienyl) cobalt and rhodium cations is reduced. The nature of one metal–ring bond is

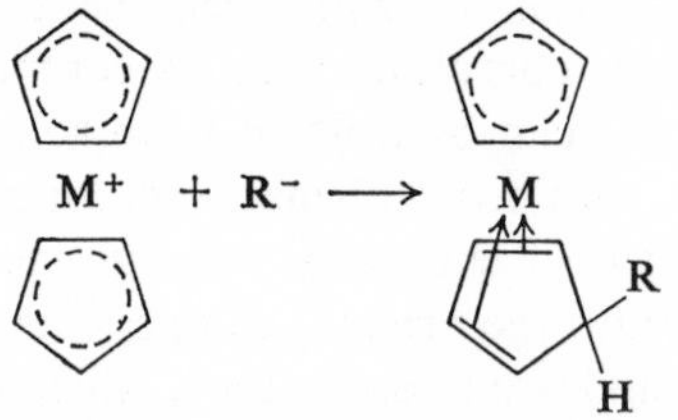

$$M^+ + R^- \longrightarrow M \qquad (28)$$

(8)

$$(M = Co; R = H, D, CH_3, C_6H_5, C_5H_5)$$
$$(M = Rh; R = H, C_6H_5, C_5H_5)$$

changed from a delocalized "arene"-type bond to the two olefinic-type bonds in compound (8).

The action of 2 N HCl or carbon tetrachloride on cyclopentadienylcyclopentadiene complexes of cobalt or rhodium [(8), R = H] leads to a reverse transformation, i.e., the formation of bis(cyclopentadienyl) metallocinium chloride and hydrogen or chloroform, respectively.[96]

When oxidants act on cyclopentadienylcyclopentadiene complexes of cobalt, the molecule is decomposed completely[95] or R is abstracted and the colbalticinium ion is formed.[98]

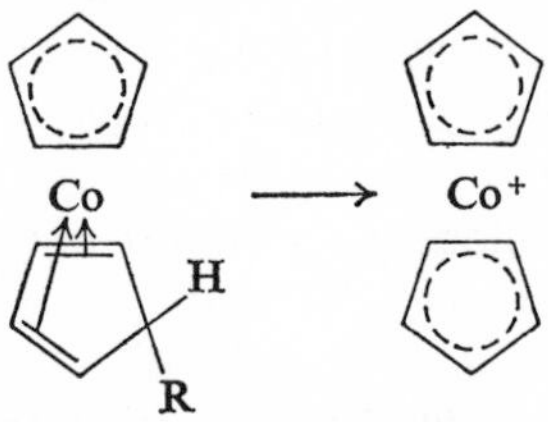

$$\text{Co} \longrightarrow \text{Co}^+ \tag{29}$$

(R = C_6H_5, CCl_3)

In contrast, cyclopentadienyl-1-phenylcyclopentadienerhodium, when acted on by hydrogen peroxide, gives an almost quantitative yield of a phenyl derivative of bis(cyclopentadienyl)rhodium.[97] In this case a proton is

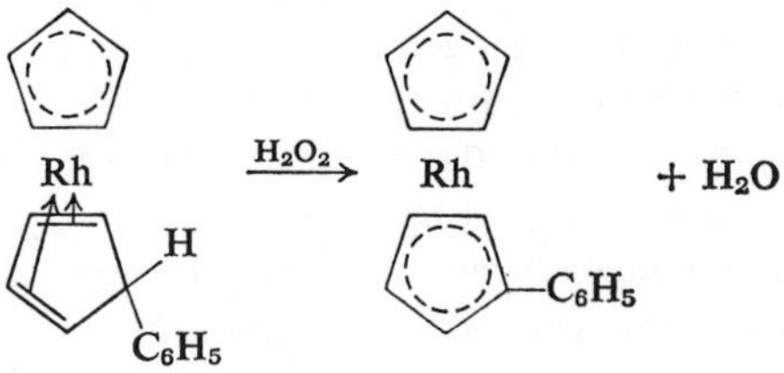

$$\text{Rh} \xrightarrow{\ H_2O_2\ } \text{Rh} \quad + H_2O \tag{30}$$

probably abstracted and a cyclopentadiene ligand is converted to a cyclopentadienyl ring.

Page and Wilkinson,[47] who studied the polarographic reduction of the cobalticinium ion on the dropping-mercury electrode in an aqueous solution of 0.1 N $HClO_4$, observed a one-electron reduction wave with the potential -1.16 V versus the normal calomel electrode, but the reduction product could not be isolated from the solution.

A detailed study of the mechanism and products of cobalticinium reduction on a dropping-mercury electrode conducted by Vlćek[99] showed that cobalticinium was reduced to cobaltocene with the loss of one electron, the process being reversible. The pH of the solution does not affect the reduction of cobalticinium. Therefore hydrogen ions cannot share in the electrode reaction, and cyclopentadienylcyclopentadiene complexes cannot form in the reduction process.[99]

A polarographic study[99] of the reaction products shows that the reduction of ethanolic cobalticinium ion by sodium borohydride proceeds in a similar manner. The polarographic reduction of cobalticinium itself in various solvents has also been studied.[56] The cobaltocene–cobalticinium oxidation–reduction system has been considered as a reference electrode since its potential is only slightly dependent on the nature of the solvent.

The reduction of the bis(cyclopentadienyl)rhodium cation, $(C_5H_5)_2Rh^+$, on a dropping-mercury electrode also occurs by a one-electron mechanism (the reduction potential is -1.53 V versus the normal calomel electrode). However, the bis(cyclopentadienyl)iridium cation, $(C_5H_5)_2Ir^+$, is not reduced under similar conditions. (Only a catalytic wave of hydrogen evolution was observed.[94])

The salts of all three metallocene cations are not further oxidized to higher states.

D. Nickelocene Oxidation–Reduction Transformations

Nickelocene oxidizes in the air very easily, especially in solution, to a singly-charged nickelocinium cation, $(C_5H_5)_2Ni^+$. However, the aqueous solution then decomposes spontaneously.[100] When air is passed through nickelocene dissolved in an ether solution of picric acid, a black precipitate of nickelocinium picrate forms.[100,101] Nickelocene is also oxidized by benzoquinone in the presence of hydrogen bromide or chloride,[101] dilute nitric acid,[2,101] silver nitrate,[101] or cerium sulfate.[101]

The cation $(C_5H_5)_2Ni^+$ is reduced to neutral nickelocene by titanium sulfate. (The action of $SnCl_2$ does not lead to reduction.[101])

Nickelocene could not be oxidized to a doubly-charged cation, isoelectronic with ferrocene, by such chemical reactants[102] as bromine or iodine, or by polarography.[101] However, Goan et al.,[81] in reacting p-chloranil with nickelocene, obtained a stable complex whose electron-spin-resonance spectrum is indicative of structure (9), including a doubly-charged nickelocinium cation.

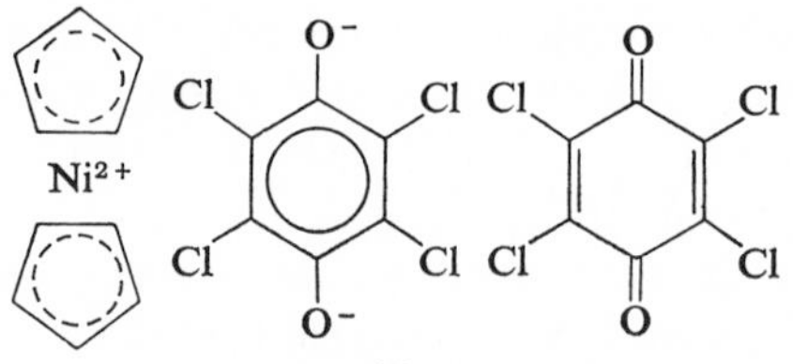

(9)

A polarographic study[100,101] of nickelocene oxidation in 90% ethanol (background 0.1 M solution of $NaClO_4$) has shown that this proceeds as a one-electron process ($E_{1/2} = -0.08$ V versus the normal calomel electrode). The cation $(C_5H_5)_2Ni^+$ is reduced at a potential ($E_{1/2} = -0.21$ V versus the normal calomel electrode) that differs from the nickelocene oxidation potential under the same conditions.[101]

According to Tirouflet and co-workers,[67] nickelocene oxidation in a 0.5 N solution of $HClO_4$ in 50% ethanol is reversible [$E_{1/2}$ (anode) = -0.18 V, $E_{1/2}$ (cathode) = -0.21 V].

References

1. F. J. Kealy and P. L. Pauson, *Nature*, **168**, 1039 (1951).
2. G. Wilkinson, F. A. Cotton, and J. M. Birmingham, *J. Inorg. Nucl. Chem.*, **2**, 95 (1956).
3. C. B. R. Ward, *Dissert. Abstr.*, **16**, 2327 (1956).
4. V. Weinmayr, *J. Amer. Chem. Soc.*, **77**, 3012 (1955).
5. G. Wilkinson, M. Rosenblum, M. C. Whiting, and R. B. Woodward, *J. Amer. Chem. Soc.*, **74**, 2125 (1952).
6. V. Weinmayr, *J. Amer. Chem. Soc.*, **77**, 3009 (1955).
7. P. L. Pauson, *Quart. Rev.*, **9**, 391 (1955).
8. S. A. Miller, J. A. Tebboth, and J. F. Tremain, *J. Chem. Soc.*, **1952**, 632.
9. D. R. Stranks, *Inorg. Syntheses*, **7**, 201 (1963).
10. A. N. Nesmeyanov, E. G. Perevalova, and L. P. Yur'eva, *Chem. Ber.*, **93**, 2729 (1960).
11. A. I. Titov, E. S. Lisytsyna, and M. F. Shemtova, *Dokl. Akad. Nauk SSSR*, **130**, 341 (1960).
12. M. Rosenblum, J. O. Santer, and W. G. Howells, *J. Amer. Chem. Soc.*, **85**, 1450 (1963).
13. H. Franz, *Z. Chem.*, **3**, 106 (1963).
14. H. P. Fritz and Z. Schäfter, *Z. Naturforsch.*, **19b**, 169 (1964).
15. R. A. Stukan and L. P. Yur'eva, *Dokl. Akad. Nauk SSSR*, **167**, 1311 (1966).
16. A. N. Nesmeyanov and E. G. Perevalova, *Usp. Khim.*, **27**, 11 (1958).
17. R. Riemschneider and D. Helm, *Chem. Ber.*, **89**, 155 (1956).
18. A. N. Nesmeyanov, E. G. Perevalova, R. V. Golovnya, T. V. Nikitina, and N. A. Simukova, *Izv. Akad. Nauk SSSR, Ser. Khim.*, **1956**, 739.
19. A. V. Savitskii and Ya. K. Syrkin, *Dokl. Akad. Nauk SSSR*, **120**, 119 (1958).
20. A. V. Savitskii, *Zh. Obshch. Khim.*, **30**, 3167 (1960).
21. A. V. Savitskii and Ya. K. Syrkin, *Trudy po Khim. i Khim. Tekhnol.*, **1**, 165 (1961).
22. A. V. Savitskii and Ya. K. Syrkin, *Mechanism and Thermodynamics of Ferrocene or Osmocene Oxidation with Iodine*, in abstracts of a symposium on homolytic, reactions in the liquid phase in Gor'ki, USSR, 1960, p. 27 (in Russian).
23. S. I. Zhdanov and A. A. Pozdeeva, *Zh. Obshch. Khim.*, **37**, 935 (1967).
24. C.-H. Wang, *J. Amer. Chem. Soc.*, **85**, 2339 (1963).
25. M. F. Hawthorne, *J. Org. Chem.*, **21**, 363 (1956).
26. A. L. J. Beckwith and R. J. Leydon, *J. Amer. Chem. Soc.*, **86**, 952 (1964).
27. J. H. Richards and E. A. Hill, *J. Amer. Chem. Soc.*, **81**, 3484 (1959).
28. K. L. Rinehart, Jr., C. J. Michejda, and P. A. Kittle, *J. Amer. Chem. Soc.*, **81**, 3162 (1959).
29. A. Berger, W. E. McEwen, and J. Kleinberg, *J. Amer. Chem. Soc.*, **83**, 2274 (1961).
30. C. Jutz, *Tetrahedron Letters*, **1959**,1.
31. M. Cais and A. Eisenstadt, *J. Org. Chem.*, **30**, 1148 (1965).
32. A. N. Nesmeyanov, D. N. Kursanov, V. N. Setkina, N. V. Kislyakova, and N. S. Kochetkova, *Tetrahedron Letters*, **1961**, 41.
33. A. N. Nesmeyanov, D. N. Kursanov, V. N. Setkina, N. V. Kislyakova, N. S. Kochetkova, and R. B. Materikova, *Dokl. Akad. Nauk SSSR*, **143**, 351 (1962).
34. K. H. Pausacker, *Australian J. Chem.*, **11**, 509 (1958).

35. L. M. Postnikov, E. M. Tochina, and V. Ya. Shlapintokh, *Dokl. Akad. Nauk SSSR*, **172**, 651 (1967).
36. P. L. Pauson, M. A. Sandhu, and W. E. Watts, *J. Chem. Soc.*, **1966C**, 251.
37. A. L. J. Beckwith and R. L. Leydon, *Tetrahedron Letters*, **1963**, 385.
38. E. Collinson, F. S. Dainton, and H. Gills, *J. Phys. Chem.*, **65**, 695 (1961).
39. R. A. Mitsch, *J. Amer. Chem. Soc.*, **87**, 328 (1965).
40. Z. Wolf, H. Franz, and H. Hennig, *Angew. Chem.*, **72**, 635 (1960).
41. B. Sansoni and O. Sigmund, *Angew. Chem.*, **73**, 299 (1961).
42. G. D. Broadhead and P. L. Pauson, *J. Chem. Soc.*, **1955**, 367.
43. E. O. Fischer and W. Pfab, *Z. Naturforsch.*, **7b**, 377 (1952).
44. A. A. Pendin, M. S. Zakhar'evskii, and P. K. Leont'evskaya, *Kinetika i Kataliz*, **7**, 1074 (1966).
45. A. A. Pendin, M. S. Zakhar'evskii, and P. K. Leont'evskaya, *Zh. Obshch. Khim.*, **36**, 397 (1966).
46. A. N. Nesmeyanov, E. G. Perevalova, and L. P. Yur'eva, *Izv. Akad. Nauk SSSR, Ser. Khim.*, **1967**, 694.
47. J. A. Page and G. Wilkinson, *J. Amer. Chem. Soc.*, **74**, 6149, (1952).
48. D. E. Bublitz, G. Hoh, and T. Kuwana, *Chem. Ind. (London)*, **1959**, 635.
49. M. W. Dietrich, *Dissert. Abstr.*, **23**, 455 (1962). M. W. Dietrich and A. C. Wahl, *J. Chem. Phys.*, **38**, 1591 (1963).
50. N. Sutin and R. W. Dodson, *J. Inorg. Nucl. Chem.*, **6**, 81 (1958).
51. D. R. Stranks, *Discussions Faraday Soc.*, **29**, 73 (1960).
52. F. S. Dainton, G. S. Laurence, W. Schneider, D. R. Stranks, and M. C. Vaidya, *Radioisotopes Sci. Res., Proc. Intern. Conf. Paris*, **2**, 305 (1957).
53. C. Wahl, *Z. Elektrochem.*, **64**, 90 (1960).
54. I. Pavlik and J. Klikorka, *Coll. Czech. Chem. Commun.*, **30**, 664 (1965).
55. B. P. Nikol'skii, A. A. Pendin, and M. S. Zakhar'evskii, *Dokl. Akad. Nauk SSSR*, **160**, 1131 (1965).
56. H. M. Koepp, H. Wendt, and H. Strehlow, *Z. Elektrochem.*, **64**, 483 (1960).
57. J. G. Mason and M. Rosenblum, *J. Amer. Chem. Soc.*, **82**, 4206 (1960).
58. K. Schlögl and M. Peterlik, *Monatsh.*, **93**, 1328 (1962).
59. S. P. Gubin and E. G. Perevalova, *Dokl. Akad. Nauk SSSR*, **143**, 135 (1962).
60. E. G. Perevalova, S. P. Gubin, S. A. Smirnova, and A. N. Nesmeyanov, *Dokl. Akad. Nauk SSSR*, **147**, 384 (1962).
61. T. Kuwana, D. E. Bublitz, and G. Hoh, *J. Amer. Chem. Soc.*, **82**, 5811 (1960).
62. G. L. K. Hoh, W. E. McEwen, and J. Kleinberg, *J. Amer. Chem. Soc.*, **83**, 3949 (1961).
63. W. F. Little, C. N. Reilley, J. D. Johnson, and H. P. Sanders, *J. Amer. Chem. Soc.*, **86**, 1382 (1964).
64. W. F. Little, C. N. Reilley, J. D. Johnson, and K. N. Lynn, A. P. Sanders, *J. Amer. Chem. Soc.*, **86**, 1376 (1964).
65. J. Boichard and J. Tirouflet, *Bull. Soc. Chim. France*, **1960**, 1032.
66. J. Komenda and J. Tirouflet, *Compt. Rend.*, **254**, 3093 (1962).
67. J. Tirouflet, E. Laviron, R. Dabard, and J. Komenda, *Bull. Soc. Chim. France*, **1963**, 857.
68. E. G. Perevalova, S. P. Gubin, S. A. Smirnova, and A. N. Nesmeyanov, *Dokl. Akad. Nauk SSSR*, **155**, 837 (1964).
69. E. G. Perevalova, S. P. Gubin, and A. N. Nesmeyanov, *Reakcionnaya Sposobnost' Organicheskikh Soyedin.*, **3**, No. 1(7), 68 (1966).
70. E. G. Perevalova, K. I. Grandberg, N. A. Zharikova, S. P. Gubin, and A. N. Nesmeyanov, *Izv. Akad. Nauk SSSR, Ser. Khim.*, **1966**, 832.

71. A. N. Nesmeyanov, E. G. Perevalova, S. P. Gubin, K. I. Grandberg, and A. G. Kozlovskii, *Tetrahedron Letters*, **1966**, 2381.
72. S. P. Gubin, *Izv. Akad. Nauk SSSR, Ser. Khim.*, **1966**, 1551.
73. O. W. Webster, W. Mahler, and R. E. Benson, *J. Amer. Chem. Soc.*, **84**, 3678 (1962).
74. M. Rosenblum, R. W. Fish, and C. Bennett, *J. Amer. Chem. Soc.*, **86**, 5166 (1964).
75. B. Hetnarski, *Dokl. Akad. Nauk SSSR*, **156**, 604 (1964).
76. B. Hetnarski, *Bull. Acad. Polon. Sci.*, **13**, 515 (1965).
77. B. Hetnarski, *Bull. Acad. Polon. Sci.*, **13**, 523 (1965).
78. B. Hetnarski, *Bull. Acad. Polon. Sci.*, **13**, 557 (1965).
79. B. Hetnarski, *Bull. Acad. Polon. Sci.*, **13**, 563 (1965).
80. A. N. Nesmeyanov, E. G. Perevalova, and O. A. Nesmeyanova, *Dokl. Akad. Nauk SSSR*, **100**, 1099 (1955).
81. G. C. Goan, E. Berg, and H. E. Podall, *J. Org. Chem.*, **29**, 975 (1964).
82. R. L. Brandon, I. N. Osiecki, and A. Ottenberg, *J. Org. Chem.*, **31**, 1214 (1966).
83. M. Aly, R. Bramley, J. Upadhyay, and A. Wassermann, P. Woolliams, *Chem. Commun.*, **1965**, 404.
84. R. L. Collins and R. Pettit, *J. Inorg. Nucl. Chem.*, **29**, 503 (1967).
85. E. Adman, M. Rosenblum, S. Sullivan, and T. N. Margulis, *J. Amer. Chem. Soc.*, **89**, 4540 (1967).
86. T. D. Smith, *J. Chem. Soc.*, **1961**, 473.
87. N. C. Peterson and F. R. Dune, *J. Phys. Chem.*, **67**, 531 (1963).
88. B. P. Nikol'skii, A. A. Pendin, and M. S. Zakhar'evskii, *Zh. Neorg. Khim.*, **12**, 1803 (1967).
89. E. O. Fischer and H. Grubert, *Chem. Ber.*, **92**, 2302 (1959).
90. G. Wilkinson, *J. Amer. Chem. Soc.*, **74**, 6146 (1952).
91. A. N. Nesmeyanov, A. A. Lubovich, L. P. Yur'eva, S. P. Gubin, and E. G. Perevalova, *Izv. Akad. Nauk SSSR, Ser. Khim.*, **1967**, 935.
92. E. O. Fischer, *Angew. Chem.*, **67**, 475 (1955).
93. J. M. Birmingham, *Adv. Organometal. Chem.*, **2**, 378 (1964).
94. F. A. Cotton, R. O. Whipple, and G. Wilkinson, *J. Amer. Chem. Soc.*, **75**, 3586 (1953).
95. E. O. Fischer and G. E. Herberich, *Chem. Ber.*, **94**, 1517 (1961).
96. M. L. H. Green, L. Pratt, and G. Wilkinson, *J. Chem. Soc.*, **1959**, 3753.
97. R. J. Angelici and E. O. Fischer, *J. Amer. Chem. Soc.*, **85**, 3733 (1963).
98. S. Katz, J. F. Weiher, and A. V. Voigt, *J. Amer. Chem. Soc.*, **80**, 6459 (1958).
99. A. A. Vlček, *Coll. Czech. Chem. Commun.*, **30**, 952 (1965).
100. G. Wilkinson, P. L. Pauson, J. M. Birmingham, and F. A. Cotton, *J. Amer. Chem. Soc.*, **75**, 1011 (1953).
101. G. Wilkinson, P. L. Pauson, and F. A. Cotton, *J. Amer. Chem. Soc.*, **76**, 1970 (1954).
102. E. O. Fischer and R. Jira, *Z. Naturforsch.*, **8b**, 217 (1953).

III. OXIDATION–REDUCTION REACTIONS OF GROUP VII METAL BIS(CYCLOPENTADIENYL) COMPOUNDS

In contrast to ionic bis(cyclopentadienyl)manganese,[1] bis(cyclopentadienyl) compounds of technetium[2] ad rhenium,[3,4] (C_5H_5)$_2$TcH and (C_5H_5)$_2$ReH, respectively, belong to the covalent class of metallocenes. Oxidation–reduction reactions have been carried out only for bis(cyclopentadienyl)rhenium hydride.[5,6]

The action of halogens (chlorine and bromine) on $(C_5H_5)_2ReH$ oxidizes rhenium(III) to rhenium(IV) and causes the replacement of a hydrogen atom by a halogen.[5,6] A reverse transformation of bis(cyclopentadienyl)rhenium

$$(C_5H_5)_2ReH \xrightarrow{X_2} [(C_5H_5)_2ReX_2]^+X^- \qquad (31)$$
$$(X = Cl, Br)$$

dihalide to the original hydride is easily performed with lithium aluminum hydride.[6] These reactions are similar to the oxidation–reduction transformations of bis(cyclopentadienyl) compounds of molybdenum and tungsten discussed in Section IV-B.

$$[(C_5H_5)_2ReX_2]^+ \xrightarrow{LiAlH_4} (C_5H_5)_2ReH \qquad (32)$$

References

1. G. Wilkinson, F. A. Cotton, and J. M. Birmingham, *J. Inorg. Nucl. Chem.*, **2**, 95 (1956).
2. D. K. Huggins and H. D. Kaesz, *J. Amer. Chem. Soc.*, **83**, 4474 (1961).
3. G. Wilkinson and J. M. Birmingham, *J. Amer. Chem. Soc.*, **77**, 3421 (1955).
4. M. L. H. Green, L. Pratt, and G. Wilkinson, *J. Chem. Soc.*, **1958**, 3916.
5. R. L. Cooper and M. L. H. Green, *Z. Naturforsch.*, **19b**, 652 (1964).
6. R. L. Cooper and M. L. H. Green, *J. Chem. Soc.*, **1967A**, 1155.

IV. OXIDATION–REDUCTION REACTIONS OF GROUP VI METAL BIS(CYCLOPENTADIENYL) COMPOUNDS

A. Oxidation–Reduction Transformations of Bis(cyclopentadienyl)chromium

Finely crushed chromocene, $(C_5H_5)_2Cr$, oxidizes extremely easily, even to the extent of spontaneous combustion in air.[1] The action of iodine on bis-(cyclopentadienyl)chromium solution in a nitrogen atmosphere causes the formation of the iodide,[2] $(C_5H_5)_2CrI$. Fischer and Ulm[3] found that this compound is best obtained by the action of allyl iodide on chromocene:

$$(C_5H_5)_2Cr + CH_2{=}CHCH_2I \longrightarrow (C_5H_5)_2CrI \qquad (33)$$

Heating at 180° in high vacuum with zinc or copper powder leads to the reduction of bis(cyclopentadienyl)chromium iodide and the formation of chromocene in high yield.[3]

Chromocene interaction with carbon tetrachloride in benzene or tetrahydrofuran gives a compound of the composition $C_{15}H_{15}Cr_2Cl_3$, which has been found to be the salt (10) of the bis(cyclopentadienyl)chromium cation.[4]

$$(C_5H_5)_2Cr \xrightarrow{CCl_4} [(C_5H_5)_2Cr]^+[C_5H_5CrCl_3]^- \qquad (34)$$
$$(10)$$

B. Oxidation–Reduction Transformations of Bis(cyclopentadienyl) Compounds of Molybdenum and Tungsten

No neutral bis(cyclopentadienyl) compounds of molybdenum and tungsten have been obtained. Only bis(pentaphenylcyclopentadienyl)molybdenum, $[(C_6H_5)_5C_5]_2Mo$, has been described.[5] It is paramagnetic and practically insoluble in organic solvents. Bromine in chloroform oxidizes it to the corresponding singly-charged cation, which can be reduced by magnesium in methanol to the original cyclopentadienyl compound.[5]

$$(Ph_5C_5)_2Mo \underset{Mg,CH_3OH}{\overset{Br_2}{\rightleftarrows}} [(Ph_5C_5)_2Mo]^+Br_3^- \qquad (35)$$

Neutral hydrides and halides of bis(cyclopentadienyl) compounds of molybdenum(IV) and tungsten(IV), $(C_5H_5)_2MH_2$ and $(C_5H_5)_2MX_2$, are also known. The halides are reduced by sodium borohydride or lithium aluminum hydride to the corresponding hydrides.[6,7]

$$(C_5H_5)_2MX_2 \underset{CHCl_3 \text{ (or } CHBr_3, CH_3I, \text{ or } I_2)}{\overset{NaBH_4 \text{ (or } LiAlH_4)}{\rightleftarrows}} (C_5H_5)_2MH_2 \qquad (36)$$
$$(M = Mo, W)$$

The reverse transformation of hydrides to halides is easily performed with halogenated methanes (chloroform, bromoform, or methyl iodide) or iodine.[8]

The action of chlorine or bromine on bis(cyclopentadienyl dihydrides of molybdenum and tungsten causes oxidation of the metal to the molybdenum (V) or tungsten(V) state and replacement of the hydride hydrogens by halogens.[8] A reverse transformation occurs[7] when lithium aluminum hydride

$$(C_5H_5)_2MH_2 \overset{X_2}{\longrightarrow} [(C_5H_5)_2MX_2]^+ HX_2^- \qquad (37)$$
$$(M = Mo, W; X = Cl, Br)$$

acts on the bis(cyclopentadienyl) halides of molybdenum and tungsten cations. The bis(cyclopentadienyl)tungsten dihydride obtained when lithium aluminum

$$[(C_5H_5)_2MCl_2]^+ \overset{LiAlH_4}{\longrightarrow} (C_5H_5)_2MH_2 \qquad (38)$$
$$(M = Mo, W)$$

deuteride reacts with $(C_5H_5)_2WCl_2$ or $(C_5H_5)_2WCl_4$ contains deuterium in a cyclopentadienyl ring. However, deuteration of the cyclopentadienyl ring does not take place when $(C_5H_5)_2WH_2$ is similarly reacted.[7]

In addition to the paramagnetic cation, bis(cyclopentadienyl)molybdenum(V) dichloride, the diamagnetic cation, bis(cyclopentadienyl)molybdenum(IV) monochloride, has been obtained. It has been found[9] that the latter is oxidized to the former:

$$[(C_5H_5)_2MoCl]^+ \longrightarrow [(C_5H_5)_2MoCl_2]^+ \qquad (39)$$

No electrochemical study of the oxidation–reduction reactions of chromium, molybdenum, and tungsten bis(cyclopentadienyl) compounds has been performed.

C. Example of Syntheses: Bis(cyclopentadienyl)chromium Iodide[3]

All operations are performed in an atmosphere of a thoroughly purified inert gas; the solvents are first distilled in an inert-gas atmosphere. Special attention should be devoted to the quality of ground joints and stopcocks. In a three-necked flask fitted with a stirrer and a dropping funnel 2.77 g (15.2 millimoles) of bis(cyclopentadienyl)chromium is dissolved in 50 ml of benzene. To this flask is added 1.38 ml (15.2 millimoles) of allyl iodide, dropwise and with constant stirring. A dark-yellow precipitate, which then turns brown, forms immediately. After all of the allyl iodide has been added, the reaction mixture is stirred for 1–2 hr more to complete precipitation. The precipitate is filtered, washed twice with 10-ml portions of benzene and then with pentane until the solution becomes colorless, and finally dried for 5 hr in high vacuum. Bis(cyclopentadienyl)chromium iodide is obtained in almost quantitative yield as a powder-like, pyrophoric, ochre-colored compound, m.p. 150° (decomposition), which should be stored in an inert-gas atmosphere.

References

1. E. O. Fischer, H. Hafner, and H. O. Stahl, *Z. Anorg. Allg. Chem.*, **282**, 47 (1955).
2. E. O. Fischer and H. P. Kögler, *Angew. Chem.*, **68**, 462 (1956).
3. E. O. Fischer and K. Ulm, *Chem. Ber.*, **95**, 692 (1962).
4. E. O. Fischer K. Ulm, and P. Kuzel, *Z. Anorg. Allg. Chem.*, **319**, 253 (1962).
5. W. Hübel, and R. Merenyi, *J. Organometal. Chem.*, **2**, 213 (1964).
6. M. L. H. Green, C. N. Street, and G. Wilkinson, *Z. Naturforsch.*, **14b**, 738 (1959).
7. R. L. Cooper and M. L. H. Green, *J. Chem. Soc.*, **1967A** 1155.
8. R. L. Cooper and M. L. H. Green, *Z. Naturforsch.*, **19b**, 652 (1964).
9. F. A. Cotton and G. Wilkinson, *Z. Naturforsch.*, **9b**, 417 (1954).

V. OXIDATION–REDUCTION REACTIONS OF GROUP V METAL BIS(CYCLOPENTADIENYL) COMPOUNDS

A. General Survey

Several bis(cyclopentadienyl) compounds of group V transition metals have been reported. They include vanadium(II), vanadium(III), and vanadium(IV) derivatives of the type $(C_5H_5)_2V$, $(C_5H_5)_2VX$, and $(C_5H_5)_2VX_2$ (where X is a halogen or a hydrocarbon radical); compounds of niobium(II), niobium(IV), and niobium(V), such as $(C_5H_5)_2Nb$, $(C_5H_5)_2NbCl_2$, and $(C_5H_5)_2NbX_3$; and the tantalum(V) compound $(C_5H_5)_2TaX_3$ (where X is a halide). However, oxidation–reduction transformations have been observed only for the vanadium compounds.

$$(C_5H_5)_2VX_2 \rightleftarrows (C_5H_5)_2V \longrightarrow (C_5H_5)_2VX \qquad (40)$$

Vanadocene, which contains three nonpaired electrons, rapidly oxidizes in air both as a solid (sometimes with self-ignition) and in solution.[1] In an inert atmosphere vanadocene is stable to water and perchloric acid, and is oxidized by nitric acid[2] to the dication $(C_5H_5)_2V^{2+}$. Iodine in ether solution smoothly oxidizes vanadocene to bis(cyclopentadienyl)vanadium iodide (yield 70%).[3]

$$(C_5H_5)_2V + I_2 \longrightarrow (C_5H_5)_2VI \tag{41}$$

When vanadocene interacts with certain alkyl halides, such as CH_3I, C_2H_5Br, and $C_6H_5CH_2Cl$ (taken in excess), oxidation occurs under mild conitions and such vanadium(III) derivatives as alkylbis(cyclopentadienyl)-vanadium and bis(cyclopentadienyl)vanadium halide are formed.[3]

$$2(C_5H_5)_2V + RX \longrightarrow (C_5H_5)_2VR + (C_5H_5)_2VX \tag{42}$$

When alkyl halide is taken in excess, only bis(cyclopentadienyl)vanadium halide forms. In the case of the reaction with benzyl chloride, dibenzyl is isolated as a by-product.

The following sequence of reactions is suggested:

$$(C_5H_5)_2V + RX \longrightarrow [(C_5H_5)_2VRX] \tag{43}$$

$$[(C_5H_5)_2VRX] + (C_5H_5)_2V \longrightarrow (C_5H_5)_2VR + (C_5H_5)_2VX \tag{44}$$

$$(C_5H_5)_2VR + RX \longrightarrow (C_5H_5)_2VX + R_2 \tag{45}$$

This scheme may be true for vanadocene reactions with allylmagnesium chloride;[4] an excess of vanadocene gives allylbis(cyclopentadienyl)vanadium (an unstable compound identified by ultraviolet spectra) and bis(cyclopentadienyl)vanadium chloride. If there is an excess of allylmagnesium-chloride, only bis(cyclopentadienyl)vanadium chloride is formed.

Bis(cyclopentadienyl)vanadium halide is most easily formed[3,5] when equimolar amounts of vanadocene and bis(cyclopentadienyl)vanadium dihalide are mixed in the absence of oxygen.

$$(C_5H_5)_2V + (C_5H_5)_2VX_2 \longrightarrow 2(C_5H_5)_2VX \tag{46}$$

The transformation of $(C_5H_5)_2VCl$ to $(C_5H_5)_2VCl_2$ by hydrogen chloride and oxygen has been described.[3,5]

Treatment of the halide $(C_5H_5)_2VCl$ with organolithium or organo-magnesium compounds gives $(C_5H_5)_2VR$.[3-5]

The derivatives of vanadium(IV), such as bis(cyclopentadienyl)vanadium dihalide, that contain one unpaired electron are highly sensitive to atmospheric oxygen. As Abakumov, Shilov, and Shulyndin[7] found, oxidation by oxygen in solvents is accompanied by the abstraction of cyclopentadienyl rings and the formation of $C_5H_5VOCl_2$ and $VOCl_2$.

The reduction of bis(cyclopentadienyl)vanadium dichloride to vanadocene by lithium aluminum hydride in 70% yield has been described.[7] Phenyllithium reduces bis(cyclopentadienyl)vanadium dichloride to a vanadium(III) derivative and, at the same time, replaces the halogen with a phenyl radical.[5]

$$(C_5H_5)_2VCl_2 + 2C_6H_5Li \longrightarrow (C_5H_5)_2VC_6H_5 \xrightarrow{\text{HCl}} (C_5H_5)_2VCl \qquad (47)$$

Phenyl bis(cyclopentadienyl)vanadium was not isolated from the solution but converted by hydrochloric acid, in the absence of oxygen, to the corresponding chloride.

An electrochemical study of oxidation–reduction transformations has been conducted[8]

$$(C_5H_5)_2V^{2+} + e^- \rightleftarrows (C_5H_5)_2V^+ \qquad (48)$$

and the reaction was found to be electrochemically reversible (the half-wave potential is 0.32 V versus the normal calomel electrode).

During electrochemical reduction on a dropping-mercury electrode bis(cyclopentadienyl)niobium tribromide gave two poorly determined cathode waves with potentials of -0.44 and 0.71 V versus the normal calomel electrode. When the reduction product is obtained in a Jones reductor, it decomposes rapidly.[8]

Under similar conditions bis(cyclopentadienyl)tantalum tribromide is not active polarographically.[8]

B. Examples of Syntheses

All operations should be conducted in an atmosphere of purified inert gas; solvents should be distilled in an inert-gas atmosphere.

1. Bis(cyclopentadienyl)vanadium Monochloride[3]

A solution of 12.9 g of $(C_5H_5)_2V$ in 30 ml of ether is added to 18 g of $(C_5H_5)_2VCl_2$ at room temperature. A quick oxidation–reduction reaction gives $(C_5H_5)_2VCl$. The solvent is removed, and the residue is sublimed *in vacuo* (0.2 mm, 165°) several times to give 22 g (71%) of bis(cyclopentadienyl)vanadium chloride, m.p. 206–207° (indigo-colored crystals).

2. Bis(cyclopentadienyl)vanadium Monobromide[3]

To a solution of 2 g of vanadocene in 50 ml of low-boiling petroleum ether an excess of ethyl bromide (2 ml) is added. In time long needles of bis(cyclopentadienyl)vanadium bromide appear. These are filtered and sublimed twice *in vacuo* (2 mm, 165°) to give 2.4 g (83%) of bis(cyclopentadienyl)vanadium bromide, m.p. 221–222° (dark-blue crystals).

3. Bis(cyclopentadienyl)vanadium Monoiodide[3]

A solution of 1.1 g of iodine in 25 ml of ether is added dropwise at room temperature to a solution of 1.6 g of vanadocene in 25 ml of ether. A quick reaction is observed; the solvent becomes green, and a green precipitate forms. The solvent is removed *in vacuo*, and the residue is washed with 20 ml of cold low-boiling petroleum ether. The product is sublimed twice *in vacuo* (0.2 mm, 165°) to give 1.9 g (70%) of bis(cyclopentadienyl)vanadium iodide, m.p. 214–215° (dark-green crystals).

Monohalogen bis(cyclopentadienyl)vanadium derivatives are relatively stable in the solid state and in solvents of low polarity. They are poorly soluble in nonpolar solvents, petroleum ether or cyclohexane, moderately soluble in diethyl ether, and fairly soluble in Dimethyl Cellosolve. All these compounds are sensitive to atmospheric oxygen.

References

1. E. O. Fischer and S. Vigoureux, *Chem. Ber.*, **91**, 2205 (1958).
2. G. Wilkinson, F. A. Cotton, and J. M. Birmingham, *J. Inorg. Nucl. Chem.*, **2**, 95 (1956).
3. H. J. de Liefde Meijer, M. J. Janssen, and G. J. M. van der Kerk, *Rec. Trav. Chim.*, **80**, 831 (1961).
4. H. A. Martin and F. Jellinek, *Angew. Chem.*, **76**, 274 (1964).
5. H. J. de Liefde Meijer, M. J. Janssen, G. J. M. van der Kerk, *Chem. Ind. (London)*, **1960**, 119.
6. G. A. Abakumov, A. K. Shilov, S. V. Shulyndin, *Kinetika i Kataliz*, **5**, 228 (1964).
7. J. M. Birmingham, A. K. Fischer, and G. Wilkinson, *Naturwissenschaften*, **42**, 96 (1955).
8. G. Wilkinson and J. M. Birmingham, *J. Amer. Chem. Soc.*, **76**, 4281 (1954).

VI. OXIDATION–REDUCTION REACTIONS OF GROUP IV METAL BIS(CYCLOPENTADIENYL) COMPOUNDS

A. General Survey

Three types of titanium bis(cyclopentadienyl) compound have been reported: $(C_5H_5)_2Ti$, $(C_5H_5)_2TiX$, and $(C_5H_5)_2TiX_2$. Bis(cyclopentadienyl)-titanium dihalides are among the easiest to synthesize; they are bright-red crystalline compounds, stable in air, and fairly soluble in most organic solvents. As a rule, other bis(cyclopentadienyl)titanium compounds are obtained by starting from the dihalides.

$$(C_5H_5)_2Ti \rightleftharpoons (C_5H_5)_2TiCl_2 \rightleftharpoons C_5H_5TiX \qquad (49)$$

Bis(cyclopentadienyl)titanium dihalides can be reduced to bis(cyclo-pentadienyl)titanium or bis(cyclopentadienyl) derivatives of titanium(III), depending on the conditions applied.

Bis(cyclopentadienyl)titanium dichloride, $(C_5H_5)_2TiCl_2$, is reduced to the monochloride $(C_5H_5)_2TiCl$ under mild conditions, i.e., with lithium aluminum hydride,[1]* zinc powder,[1] or dimethylaluminum chloride.[3] The yield of the monochloride can be as high as 85% with the last reductant.

Extensive investigations into the interaction of bis(cyclopentadienyl)-titanium dichloride with alkylated aluminum compounds have been carried out.[3-9] This interaction leads to the formation of complexes soluble in hydrocarbons:

$$(C_5H_5)_2TiCl_2Al(C_2H_5)_2,$$
$$(C_5H_5)_2TiCl_2Al(C_2H_5)Cl, \quad \text{and} \quad (C_5H_5)_2TiCl_2AlCl_2$$

The complexes catalyze the polymerization of olefins.[3,6,7,10,11]

An X-ray investigation[12] of the complex $(C_5H_5)_2TiCl_2Al(C_2H_5)_2$ suggests that it has structure (11):

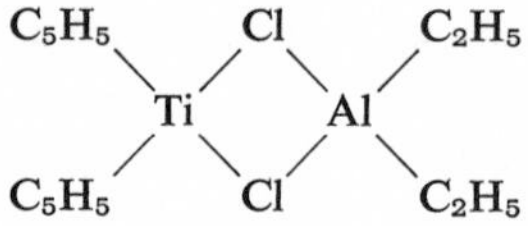

(11)

An X-ray investigation of the complex $[(C_5H_5)_2TiAl(C_2H_5)_2]_2$ was also carried out.[13]

Many papers report on the reaction of $(C_5H_5)_2TiCl$ with alkylated aluminum compounds as well as the mechanism of the olefin polymerization initiated by the above complexes.[14-17] Unlike lower alkylated aluminum compounds, bis(isobutyl)aluminum causes the abstraction of a cyclopentadienyl ring from bis(cyclopentadienyl)titanium dichloride.[18]

Organomagnesium or organolithium compounds, as well as alkoxide ions,[19-25] do not reduce bis(cyclopentadienyl)titanium dihalides but only induce a substitution of the halogen by a hydrocarbon or alkoxy radical. However, the reaction with allylmagnesium bromide is accompanied by reduction:[26,27]

$$(C_5H_5)_2TiCl_2 \xrightarrow{CH_2=CHCH_2MgBr} (C_5H_5)_2Ti(CH_2CH=CH_2) \qquad (50)$$

The reduction of $(C_5H_5)_2TiCl_2$ with cyclopentadienylsodium goes together with a substitution of the chlorine by a cyclopentadienyl group in which a monomeric tris(cyclopentadienyl)titanium derivative is formed, $(C_5H_5)_3Ti$.[28]

Reduction of $(C_5H_5)_2TiCl_2$ to $(C_5H_5)_2Ti$ occurs under the action of sodium amalgam[29,30] or naphthylsodium.[31] The yield of bis(cyclopentadienyl)-titanium is as high as 60% with the latter reductant.

The conversion of $(C_5H_5)_2TiCl_2$ to titanocene goes via two steps: σ-alky-

---

* Unlike $LiAlH_4$, lithium borohydride reacts with $(C_5H_5)_2TiCl_2$ to form the borohydride[2] $(C_5H_5)_2TiBH_4$.

lated or σ-arylated bis(cyclopentadienyl)titanium derivatives are obtained first and are then reduced by hydrogen to $(C_5H_5)_2Ti$.

$$(C_5H_5)_2TiCl_2 \xrightarrow{MR_n} (C_5H_5)_2TiR_2 + 2MR_{n-1}Cl \qquad (51)$$
$$(M = Li, Al, Mg)$$

$$(C_5H_5)_2TiR_2 + H_2 \longrightarrow (C_5H_5)_2Ti + 2RH \qquad (52)$$
$$(R = CH_3, C_6H_5)$$

Titanocene is also formed during the thermolysis of $(C_5H_5)_2Ti(C_6H_5)_2$ dissolved in benzene or alcohol.[32] Razuvaev and co-workers[32] think that this is an oxidation–reduction reaction:

$$(C_5H_5)_2TiR_2 \longrightarrow (C_5H_5)_2TiR + R\cdot \qquad (53)$$

$$(C_5H_5)_2TiR \longrightarrow (C_5H_5)_2Ti + R\cdot \qquad (54)$$

The reverse reaction, conversion of titanocene to bis(cyclopentadienyl)-titanium dichloride, readily occurs with mercury(II) chloride,[32] halogenated methane derivatives[32,33] (carbon tetrachloride, benzyl chloride, or triphenyl-

$$(C_5H_5)_2Ti + 2CCl_4 \longrightarrow (C_5H_5)_2TiCl_2 + C_2Cl_6 \qquad (55)$$

methyl chloride), or concentrated hydrochloric acid.[34] None of these reactions can be interrupted at bis(cyclopentadienyl)titanium monochloride.

Dilute hydrochloric or sulfuric acid oxidizes titanocene to a $[(C_5H_5)_2TiOH]^+$ cation.[34] Benzoyl peroxide also causes the formation of a titanium(IV) compound.[35] Only iron(III) chloride oxidizes titanocene to a titanium(III) derivative.[34]

$$(C_5H_5)_2Ti + (C_6H_5COO)_2 \longrightarrow (C_5H_5)_2Ti(OCOC_6H_5)_2 \qquad (56)$$

$$(C_5H_5)_2Ti \xrightarrow{FeCl_3} (C_5H_5)_2Ti^+ \qquad (57)$$

An oxidation–reduction reaction has been reported[36] in which an inter-action of titanocene with diphenylacetylene leads to the formation of an adduct, $(C_5H_5)_2Ti[C_2(C_6H_5)_2]_2$, which is thought to have structure (12).

$$
(C_5H_5)_2Ti + 2PhC{\equiv}CPh \longrightarrow
\begin{array}{c}
\text{Ph} \quad \text{Ph} \\
\text{C}_5\text{H}_5 \quad \text{C=C} \\
\diagdown \quad \diagup \quad | \\
\text{Ti} \quad | \\
\diagup \quad \diagdown \quad | \\
\text{C}_5\text{H}_5 \quad \text{C=C} \\
\text{Ph} \quad \text{Ph}
\end{array}
\qquad (58)
$$
$$\textbf{(12)}$$

Bis(cyclopentadienyl)titanium monochloride is readily oxidized by oxygen in the presence of hydrochloric acid, giving bis(cyclopentadienyl)titanium dichloride or (in an inert solvent) an oxide of the composition $[(C_5H_5)_2TiCl]_2O$.[37]

The polarography of $(C_5H_5)_2TiX_2$ (X = Cl, Br) has been studied[38-42] in water and other polar solvents (formamide or dimethylformamide). Bis(cyclopentadienyl)titanium dihalide, dissolved in water, has been shown[38,39,42] to be hydrolyzed to a singly-charged cation, $[(C_5H_5)_2TiOH]^+$, which is then further reduced to a $(C_5H_5)_2Ti^+$ cation. The reduction involves one electron and one proton.[42] In dimethylformamide $(C_5H_5)_2TiCl_2$ is reduced to a monochloride.[42] The process is reversible in both cases.

$$[(C_5H_5)_2TiOH]^+ + e^- + H^+ \rightleftarrows (C_5H_5)_2Ti^+ + H_2O \qquad (59)$$

Bis(cyclopentadienyl)zirconium dihalide cannot be reduced polarographically.[38,39]

B. Examples of Syntheses

All the operations, including crystallization and isolation of the products, must be carried out in an inert-gas atmosphere (dry argon or nitrogen containing no traces of oxygen). Absolute solvents must be used. These are first purified as usual and then distilled in an inert-gas atmosphere to remove dissolved oxygen. In filling the apparatus with an inert gas the system must be evacuated several times. In so doing one must make sure that the ground joints are airtight; this applies especially to the stirrer seal in operating a conventional stirrer.

1. Bis(π-cyclopentadienyl)titanium Monochloride[3]

A mixture of $(C_5H_5)_2TiCl_2$ (10 g, 40 millimoles) and dimethylaluminum chloride (7 ml, 70 millimoles) is heated with an air condenser in an oil bath at 100°. After a few minutes, a gas (methane) is evolved, and the solution becomes blue. The mixture is cooled to room temperature and diluted with 10 ml of benzene. Then 50 ml of ether is gradually added with cooling. At $-80°$ green crystals precipitate and are filtered, washed with ether and pentane, and dried in vacuo. The yield is 85%. The crude product is crystallized from a mixture of tetrahydrofuran and ether to give 5.8 g (68%) of the compound.

If diethylaluminum chloride or triethylaluminum is used, the yield is approximately 10% higher.

2. Bis(π-cyclopentadienyl)titanium[31]

All the operations are carried out in a dry box filled with a carefully purified inert gas. The $(C_6H_5)_2TiCl_2$ (9.46 g, 38 millimoles) is added to a mixture of sodium (1.75 g, 76 millimoles), naphthalene (11 g, about 10% molar excess), and tetrahydrofuran (100 ml) in a 250-ml flask. After 24 hr of stirring, the solution becomes dark green. The solvent is removed in vacuo, and the residue is extracted with benzene. The green benzene solution is evaporated *in vacuo*, and the naphthalene is sublimed off at room temperature and 10^{-2} torr pressure. The bis(cyclopentadienyl)titanium (6.1 g, 90%) is then sublimed at the same pressure and 100° as fine, dark-green, pyrophoric crystals that decompose above 200°. The compound is readily soluble in benzene, toluene, and tetrahydrofuran; it is somewhat less soluble in cyclohexane or *n*-hexane. It reacts with all other solvents.

3. *Bis(π-cyclopentadienyl)titanium Boronate*[2]

In this preparation 71 ml of a 0.282 M solution of $LiBH_4$ in ether is added to a stirred solution of $(C_5H_5)_2TiCl_2$ (2.49 g) in ether (20 ml). The diborane evolved during the reaction is trapped in an absorber filled with tetrahydrofuran. The reaction is completed in 2 hr when evolution of gas ceases and the whole mixture becomes violet. The residue is carefully filtered, and the diborane, dissolved in the ether filtrate, is removed *in vacuo*. After removal of the solvent, the compound crystallizes as dark-violet crystals. Sublimation *in vacuo* at 120–130° gives regular, dark-violet needles of $(C_5H_5)_2TiBH_4$ (1.6 g, 83%). The compound is readily soluble in ether, dioxane, and tetrahydrofuran. It is insoluble in petroleum ether and poorly soluble in aromatic compounds at room temperature but more soluble on heating. It is soluble in pyridine, dimethylformamide, amines, and halogenated hydrocarbons, and it partially interacts with these solvents. It is extremely sensitive to oxidation in solution as well as in the solid state.

References

1. J. M. Birmingham, A. K. Fischer, and G. Wilkinson, *Naturwissenschaften*, **42**, 96 (1955).
2. H. N. Noth and R. Hartwimmer, *Chem. Ber.*, **93**, 2238 (1960).
3. K. Clauss and U. Bestian, *Ann.*, **654**, 8 (1962).
4. D. S. Breslow, Belgian Patent 551,283 (1957); U.S. Patent 2,827,446 (1958).
5. D. S. Breslow and N. R. Newburg, *J. Amer. Chem. Soc.*, **79**, 5072 (1957).
6. D. S. Breslow and N. R. Newburg, *J. Amer. Chem. Soc.*, **81**, 81 (1959).
7. G. Natta and G. Mazzanti, *Tetrahedron*, **8**, 86 (1960).
8. A. H. Maki and E. W. Randall, *J. Amer. Chem. Soc.*, **82**, 4109 (1960).
9. P. E. M. Allen, J. K. Browen, and R. M. S. Obaid, *Trans. Faraday Soc.*, **59**, 1808 (1963).
10. W. P. Long, *J. Amer. Chem. Soc.*, **81**, 5312 (1959).
11. W. P. Long and D. S. Breslow, *J. Amer. Chem. Soc.*, **82**, 1953 (1960).
12. G. Natta, P. Corradini, and I. W. Bassi, *J. Amer. Chem. Soc.*, **80**, 755 (1958).
13. P. Corradini and A. Sirigu, *Inorg. Chem.*, **6**, 601 (1957).
14. I. C. W. Chien, *J. Amer. Chem. Soc.*, **81**, 86 (1959).
15. A. K. Zefirova, N. N. Tikhomirova, and A. E. Shilov, *Dokl. Akad. Nauk SSSR*, **132**, 1082 (1960).
16. A. K. Zefirova and A. E. Shilov, *Dokl. Akad. Nauk SSSR*, **136**, 599 (1961).
17. A. E. Shilov, A. K. Shilova, and B. N. Bobkov, *Vysokomol. Soyedin.*, **4**, 1688 (1962).
18. P. D. Bartlett and B. Seidel, *J. Amer. Chem. Soc.*, **83**, 581 (1961).

19. M. D. Rausch, *Inorg. Chem.*, **3** (2) 300 (1964).
20. P. M. Treichel, M. A. Chaudhari, and F. G. A. Stone, *J. Organometal Chem.*, **1**, (1), 98 (1963).
21. M. A. Chaudhari, P. M. Treichel, and F. G. A. Stone, *J, Organometal. Chem.*, **2**, 206 (1964).
22. L. Sammers and R. H. Uloth, *J. Amer. Chem. Soc.*, **76**, 2278 (1954).
23. L. Sammers, R. H. Uloth, and A. Holms, *J. Amer. Chem. Soc.*, **77**, 3604 (1955).
24. A. N. Nesmeyanov, O. V. Nogina, A. M. Berlin, A. S. Girshovich, and G. V. Shatalov, *Izv. Akad. Nauk SSSR, Ser. Khim.*, **1961**, 2146.
25. G. V. Drozdov, A. L. Kelbanskii, and V. A. Bartashev, *Zh. Obshch. Khim.*, **33**, 2422 (1963).
26. H. A. Martin and F. Jellinek, *Angew. Chem.*, **76**, 274 (1964).
27. H. A. Martin and F. Jellinek, *J. Organometal. Chem.*, **6**, 293 (1966).
28. E. O. Fischer and A. Zochner, *Z. Naturforsch.*, **15b**, 266 (1960).
29. K. Yokokawa and K. Azuma, *Bull. Chem. Soc. Japan*, **38**, 859 (1965).
30. K. Shikata, *J. Chem. Soc. Japan, Ind. Chem. Sect.*, **68**, 1248 (1965).
31. G. W. Watt, L. J. Baye, and F. O. Brummond, Jr., *J. Amer. Chem. Soc.*, **88**, 1138 (1966).
32. G. A. Razuvaev, V. N. Latyaeva, and L. I. Vyshinskaya, *Dokl. Akad. Nauk SSSR*, **134**, 612 (1960).
33. G. A. Razuvaev, V. N. Latyaeva, and L. I. Vyshinskaya, *Zh. Obshch. Khim.*, **35**, 169 (1965).
34. A. K. Fischer and G. Wilkinson, *J. Inorg. Nucl. Chem.*, **2**, 149 (1956).
35. G. A. Razuvaev, V. I. Latyaeva, and L. I. Vyshinskaya, *Dokl. Akad. Nauk SSSR*, **138**, 1126 (1961).
36. M. E. Vol'pin, V. A. Dubovitskii, O. V. Nogina, and D. N. Kursanov, *Dokl. Akad. Nauk SSSR*, **151**, 1100 (1963).
37. H. Noth and R. Hartwimmer, *Chem. Ber.*, **93**, 2246 (1960).
38. G. Wilkinson, P. L. Pauson, J. M. Birmingham, and F. A. Cotton, *J. Amer. Chem. Soc.*, **75**, 1011 (1953).
39. G. Wilkinson and J. M. Birmingham, *J. Amer. Chem. Soc.*, **76**, 4281 (1954).
40. L. A. Korshunov and N. I. Malygina, *Zh. Obshch. Khim.*, **34**, 734 (1964).
41. H. S. Hsiung and G. H. Brown, *J. Electrochem. Soc.*, **110**, 1085 (1963).
42. S. Valcher and M. Mastrogostino, *J. Electroanal. Chem.*, **14**, 219 (1967).

Appendix*

Chapter 1

II. HYDROGEN SUBSTITUTIONS OF C_5H_5-RINGS IN FERROCENE AND ITS DERIVATIVES

A. General

New reactions of hydrogen substitution have been described in ferrocene, such as the interaction with boron halides, tropylium salts, other stable carbonium ions, and cobalt carbonyl derivatives.

The scope of reaction types previously described is now expanded. Most papers are concerned with the acylation and metalation of substituted ferrocenes. These reactions were also intermediate stages in the synthesis of other ferrocene derivatives.

Ferrocene reacts with B_2Cl_4 to give ferrocenyldichloroborane,[1,2] a compound very sensitive to the air while its complex with trimethylamine is more stable.

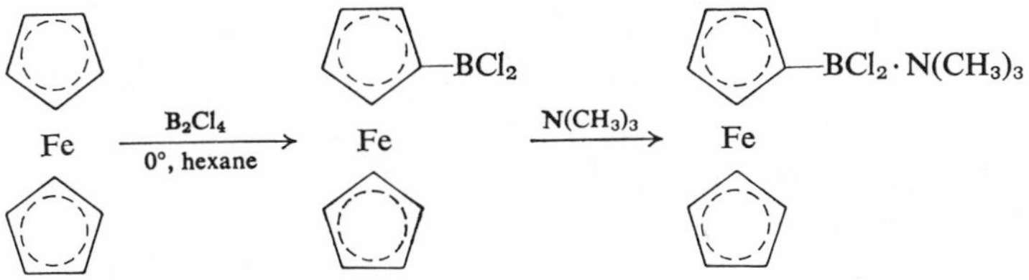

The action of $C_6H_5BCl_2$ on ferrocene in the presence of $ZnCl_2$ gives polymers in which boron and ferrocene are involved.[3]

The reaction of ferrocene with tropylium tetrafluoroborate and with its molybdenum-containing complex $[C_7H_7Mo(CO)_3]^+BF_4^-$ led to ferrocenyltropylium tetrafluoroborate and to its molybdenum-containing complex, respectively.[4]

Ferrocene reacts with 3,3-dichloro-1,2-diphenylcyclopropene in the presence of boron trifluoride etherate to produce the salt of 1,2-diphenyl-3-ferrocenylcyclopropenyl.[4]

Ferrocene interaction with $ClCCo_3(CO)_9$ has been described.[5] For the compound obtained the structure (1) was suggested:

* This appendix contains supplementary material added in proof to "Reactions of Bis(π-cyclopentadienyl) Transition-Metal Compounds," which begins on p. 163. Papers published in 1968–1970 have been reviewed. Headings here correspond to those in the chapters.

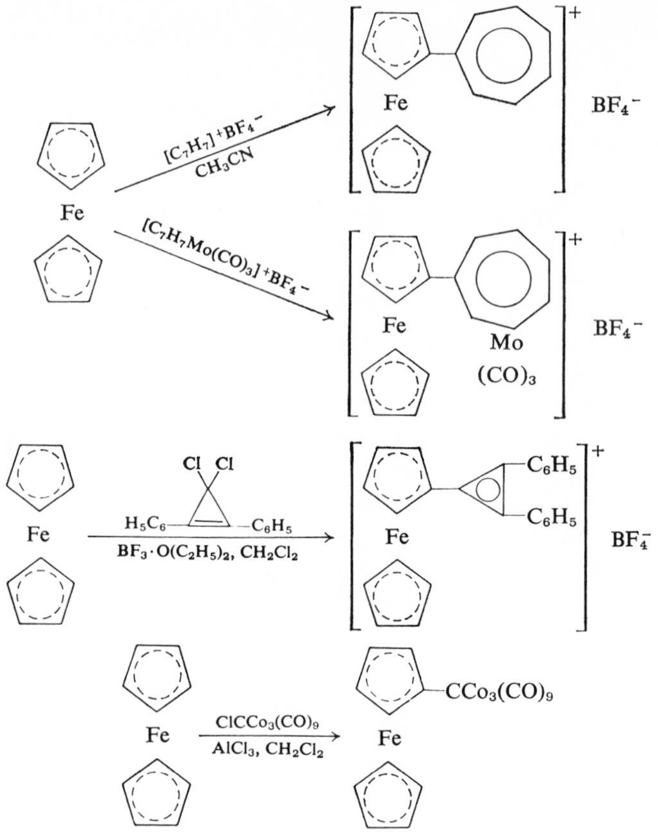

(1)

B. Deuteration

The kinetics of hydrogen isotopic exchange in alkylferrocenes was studied in a mixture of acetic and deuterotrifluoroacetic acids in CH_2Cl_2 at 25.0°. The relative deuteration rates of ferrocene, tert-butylferrocene, 1,1',3-tri-tert-butylferrocene, 1,1',3,3'-tetra-tert-butylferrocene, and ethylferrocene are 1, 6, 34, 80, and 8, respectively. The activating effect of tert-butyl group on the hydrogen exchange rate is somewhat less pronounced than that of ethyl.[6]

The rate constants of hydrogen exchange in methylthioferrocenes dissolved in deuterotrifluoroacetic acid have been measured. The SCH_3 group in electrophilic substitution in the ferrocene series has a weak electron-withdrawing effect. The relative deuteration rates of ferrocene, methylthio-, and 1,1'-dimethylthioferrocene are 1.0, 0.35, and 0.20, respectively.[7]

The exchange rates at the 1', 2, and 3 positions for methoxy-, chloro-, and 1,1'-dichloroferrocene do not differ much (less than one order).[7]

Monosubstituted ferrocenes $C_5H_5FeC_5H_2D_2R$, $R = CH_2N(CH_3)_2$, $CH_2N(CH_3)_3I$, $CH_2P(C_6H_5)_3$, $CH=C(C_6H_5)_2$, CH_3, CHO, $COCH_3$, $C(Cl)=CHCHO$, $CH=CH_2$, $C\equiv CH$, $C\equiv CC_6H_5$ dideuterated into the 2,5 position were synthesized by various methods ensuring that deuterium will reach positions adjacent to the substituent. Direct deuteration was not used. Collation of NMR spectra of deuterated and nondeuterated compounds sustained the assignments made earlier by analogy with the effects in the benzene ring.[8]

C. Acylation and Formylation

Ferrocene acetylation by acetic anhydride catalyzed by BF_3 was studied.[9] The main product was 1,1'-diacetylferrocene; also, 1,2-diacetylferrocene and acetylferrocene are obtained. Their ratio depends on the amount and quality of BF_3. Even in its low concentrations, HF inhibits the formation of diacetylferrocenes.

Ferrocene was acylated[10,11] in the presence of $AlCl_3$ by anhydrides and by the acyl halides of fluorinated carboxylic acids: $(F_3CCO)_2O$, $(F_5C_2CO)_2O$, $(F_7C_3CO)_2O$, F_7C_3COCl, $F_2HC(CF_2)_3COCl$, and F_5C_6COCl. Only monoacyl derivatives of ferrocene were obtained. The yields were low (3 to 15%),[10] except pentafluorobenzoylferrocene (48%).[11] Ferrocene is largely oxidized into ferricinium cation.

The conditions required to obtain 1,1'-diacryloylferrocene $Fe(C_5H_4COCH=CH_2)_2$ or 1,1-dicrotonoylferrocene $Fe(C_5H_4COCH=CHCH_3)_2$ from ferrocene and β-chloropropionyl chloride or β-chlorobutyryl chloride, respectively, have been described.[12,13]

Ferrocene reaction with crotonoyl chloride in the presence of $AlCl_3$ gave a mixture of bridged stereoisomeric diketones (2) and (3), and a small amount of monocrotonoylferrocene $C_5H_5FeC_5H_4COCH=CHCH_3$.[13]

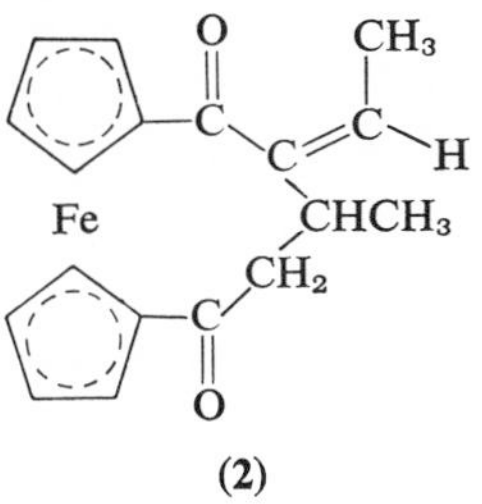

(2) 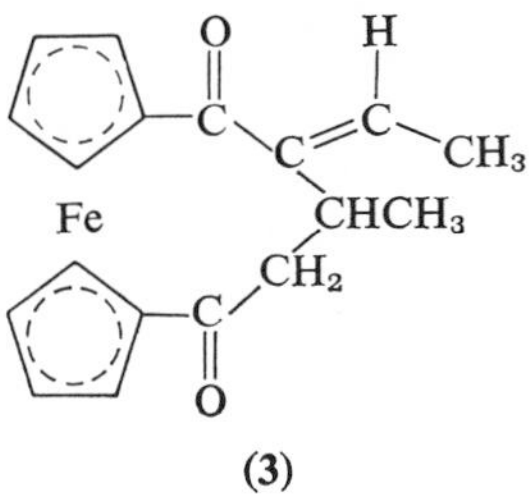   (3)

Acryloyl or methacryloyl chlorides react with ferrocene under the Friedel-Crafts conditions to form bridged ferrocenes (4) and (5).[14]

Ferrocene was benzoylated by p-, m-, or o-substituted benzoyl chlorides[15,16] (some substituted benzoyl ferrocenes were described earlier, see Table I). 1,1'-Di(p-fluorobenzoyl) and 1,1'-di(m-fluorobenzoyl) ferrocenes were

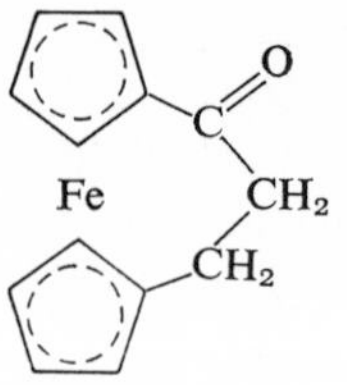

(4) 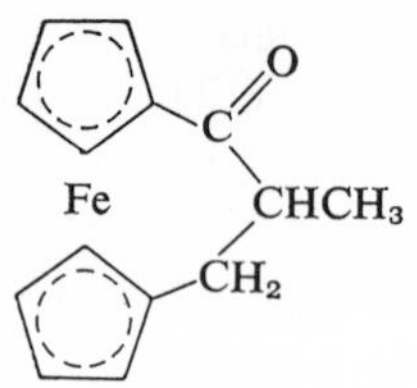   (5)

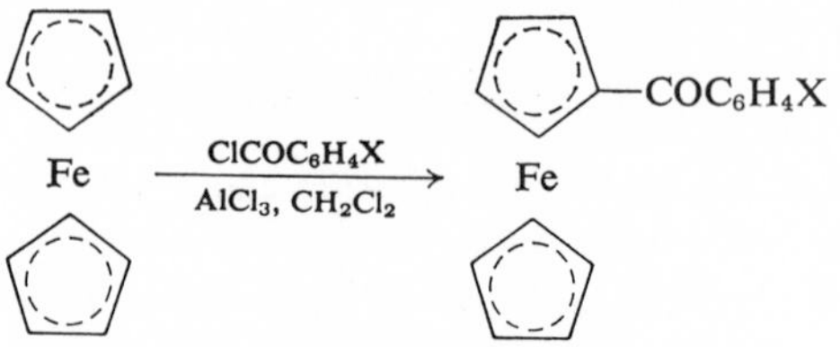

para, X = CH$_3$, OCH$_3$, Br, Cl, F.[15]
meta, X = CH$_3$, OCH$_3$, Br, Cl, F, NO$_2$.[15]
ortho, X = OCH$_3$.[16]

synthesized.[11] The action of p-NO$_2$C$_6$H$_4$COCl on ferrocene failed to give the ketone both at lowered temperatures and with AlCl$_3$ replaced by other catalysts (ZnCl$_2$, BF$_3$, SnCl$_4$, pyrophosphoric acid).[15] The reaction with α-naphthoyl chloride gave α-naphthoylferrocene.[15]

The ester of ketonoacid C$_5$H$_5$FeC$_5$H$_4$COCH$_2$COOC$_2$H$_5$ was obtained under the Friedel-Crafts conditions from ClCOCH$_2$COOC$_2$H$_5$ and ferrocene.[17]

The reaction of ferrocene with Fe(C$_5$H$_4$COCl)$_2$ enabled isolation of the ketones (**6**), (**7**), and (**8**).[18]

The diketone (**6**) was also obtained from carbomethoxyferrocenoyl chloride by the scheme below.[18]

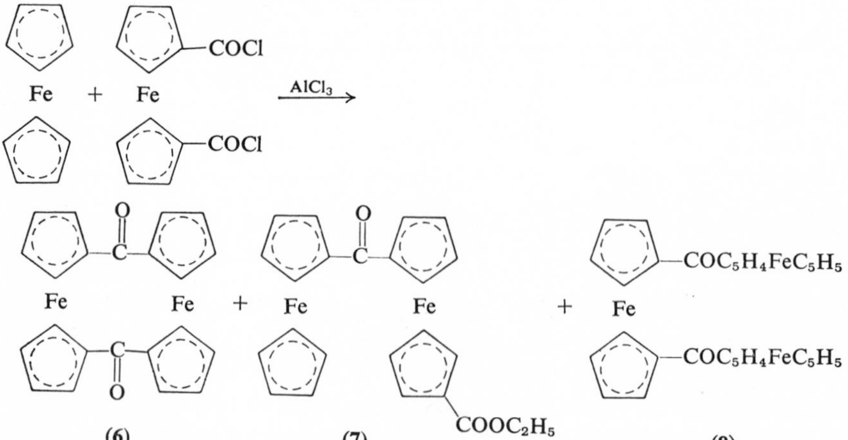

(6)   (7)   (8)

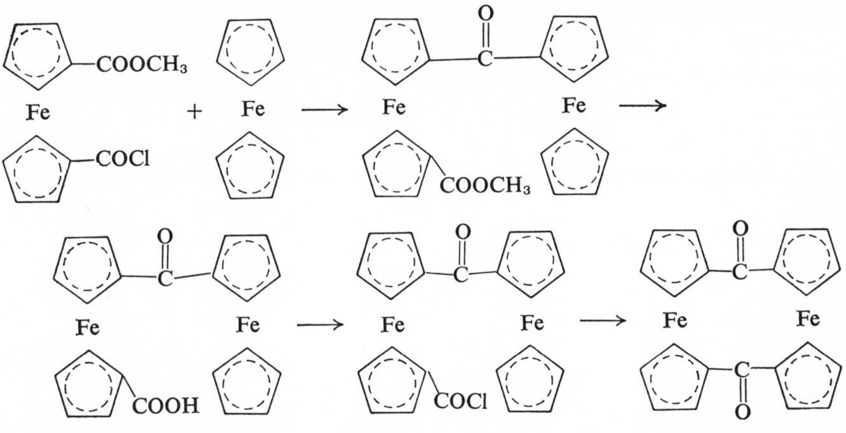

(6)

Methods of obtaining metalocene thiocarboxylate esters were patented.[19] For example, $i\text{-}C_3H_7SCOCl$ and ferrocene gave $C_5H_5FeC_5H_4COSC_3H_7\text{-}i$. This reaction was described earlier[20] in the open literature. The reaction of ferrocene with trivalent phosphorus amides with $AlCl_3$ as the catalyst was studied.[21] The following reactivity series was established: $PCl_3 \ll R_2NPCl_2 > (R_2N)_2PCl > (R_2N)_3P$. New phosphoramide derivatives of ferrocene $(C_5H_5FeC_5H_4)_2PNR_2$ and $(C_5H_5FeC_5H_4)_2P(O)NR_2$ were obtained.

For ferrocene arylation by arylhydrazines in the presence of $AlCl_3$ see under Section II-H.

In ferrocene formylation by the Vilsmeier technique the use of dimethyl-formamide instead of N-methylformanilide was suggested[22] (the yield of 71 to 74%). Vilsmeier complex perchlorate (9) was obtained.

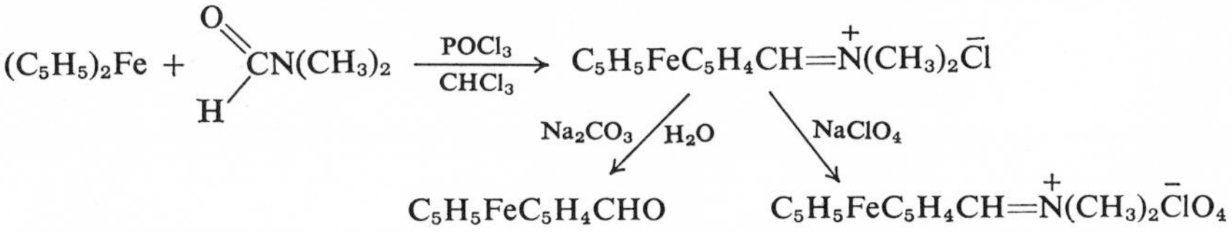

$$(C_5H_5)_2Fe + \underset{H}{\overset{O}{\underset{\diagdown}{\overset{\diagup}{C}}}}N(CH_3)_2 \xrightarrow[CHCl_3]{POCl_3} C_5H_5FeC_5H_4CH{=}\overset{+}{N}(CH_3)_2\overset{-}{Cl}$$

$$\xmapsto{Na_2CO_3/H_2O} C_5H_5FeC_5H_4CHO \qquad \xmapsto{NaClO_4} C_5H_5FeC_5H_4CH{=}\overset{+}{N}(CH_3)_2\overset{-}{Cl}O_4$$

(9)

The formylation of biferrocenyl by N-methylformanilide gave a mixture of formylated biferrocenyls. 1'-Formyl- and 1',1''-diformylbiferrocenyls were isolated.[23]

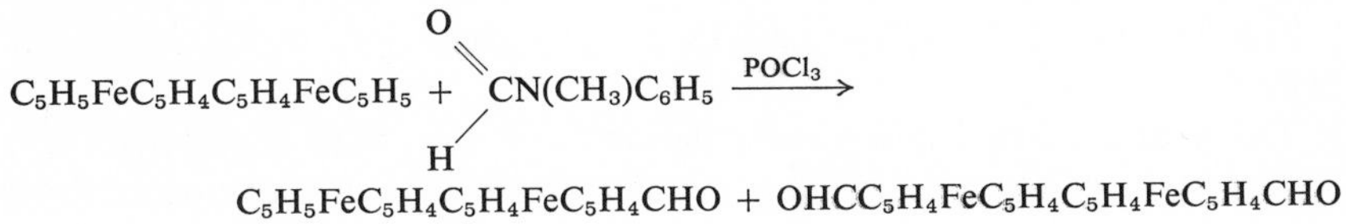

$$C_5H_5FeC_5H_4C_5H_4FeC_5H_5 + \underset{H}{\overset{O}{\underset{\diagdown}{\overset{\diagup}{C}}}}N(CH_3)C_6H_5 \xrightarrow{POCl_3}$$

$$C_5H_5FeC_5H_4C_5H_4FeC_5H_4CHO + OHCC_5H_4FeC_5H_4C_5H_4FeC_5H_4CHO$$

The acetylation of [m]ferrocenophanes (10)–(12), 3-phenyl[5]ferroceno-phane (13), 1,1'-dimethyl- and 1,1'-diethylferrocene in the same conditions was studied.[24]

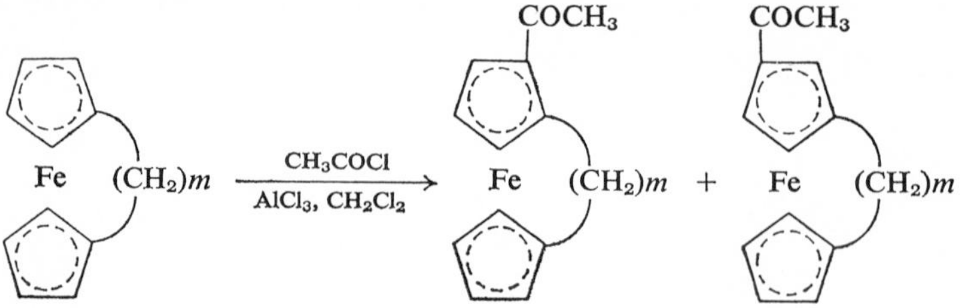

	Isomer Ratio	
(10), $m = 3$	1	1.57
(11), $m = 4$	1	1.65
(12), $m = 5$	1	2.19

Scheme 1

The isomer ratio for the [m]ferrocenophanes (10)–(12) is given in Scheme 1; for the phenyl derivative (13), for 1,1'-dimethyl and 1,1'-diethylferrocene this ratio is 2.62, 1.95, and 2.88, respectively.

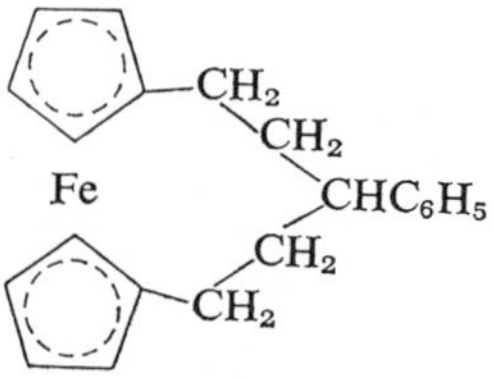

(13)

The reaction of [3]ferrocenophane (10) with N,N-diphenylcarbamyl chloride gave diphenylamides of the respective acids (14),(15).[25]

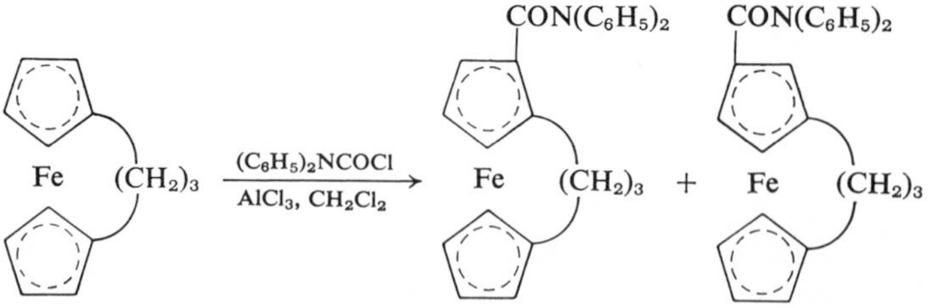

The amount of the 1,3-isomer (15) is three times that of the 1,2-isomer (14).

The benzoylation[14] and succinoylation[26] of the [3]ferrocenophane (10) were described. The chief product of the reaction of N,N-diphenylcarbamyl chloride with the [3][3]-(1,3)-ferrocenophane (16) is the monoacylated compound (17).[25]

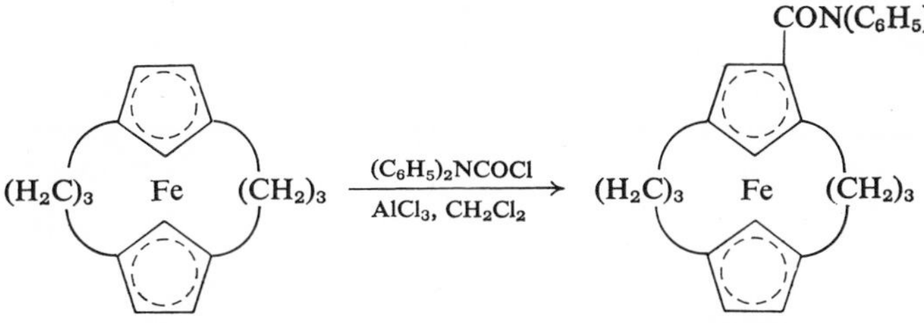

(16) $\xrightarrow[\text{AlCl}_3,\ \text{CH}_2\text{Cl}_2]{(\text{C}_6\text{H}_5)_2\text{NCOCl}}$ (17)

The monoacylation of methylferrocene under the Friedel-Crafts conditions with $ClCOCH_2CH_2COOCH_3$ was described.[27]

The reaction of acetylferrocene with $ClCOCH{=}CHC_6H_5$ in the presence of $AlCl_3$ gave 1-acetyl-1'-cinnamoylferrocene.[12]

The substituted ferrocenylbutyric[26-28] and ferrocenylvaleric[29] acids given below were homoannularly cyclized.

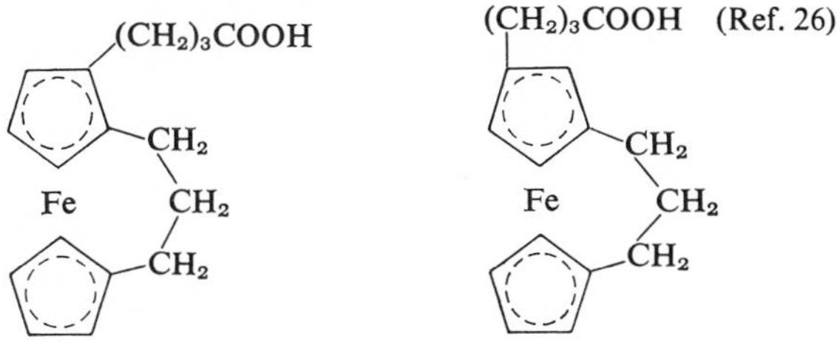

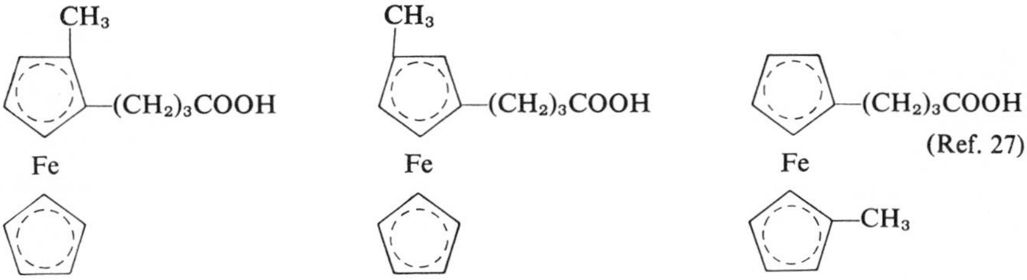

$C_5H_5FeC_5H_4CH_2CH_2CH(CH_3)COOH$; $C_5H_5FeC_5H_4CH_2CH(CH_3)CH_2COOH$

(Ref. 28)

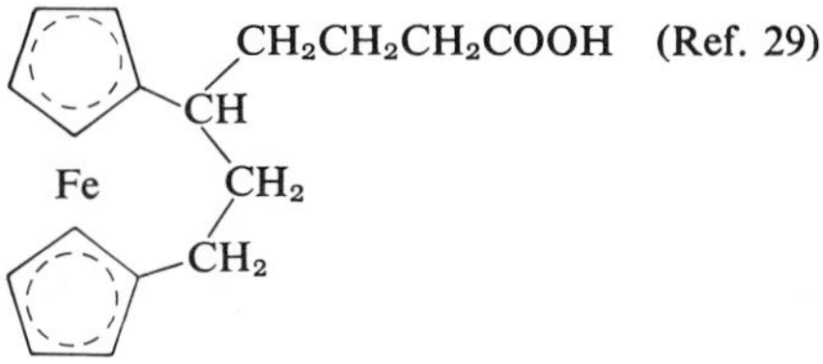

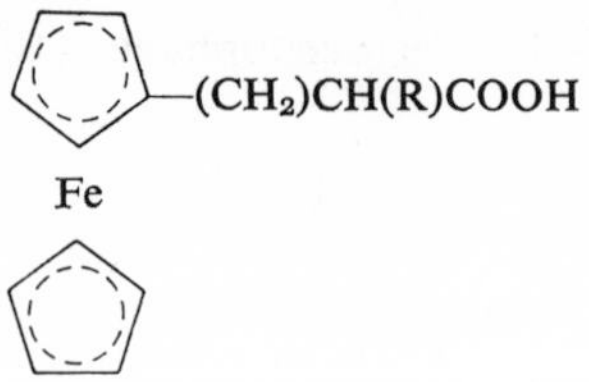

$R = CH(CH_3)_2$ (Ref. 30), C_6H_5 (Ref. 31), $(CH_2)_3COOH$ (Ref. 29)

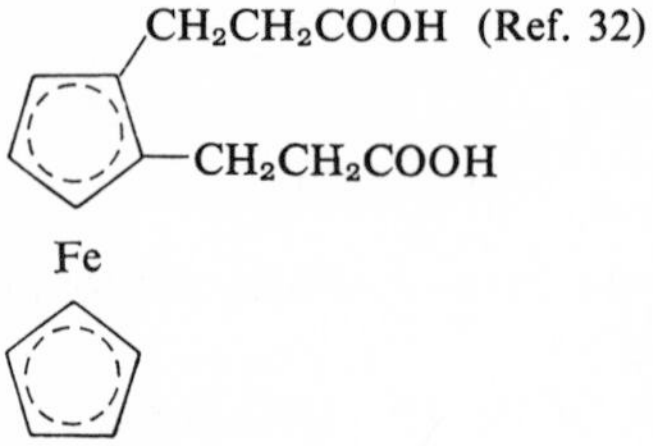

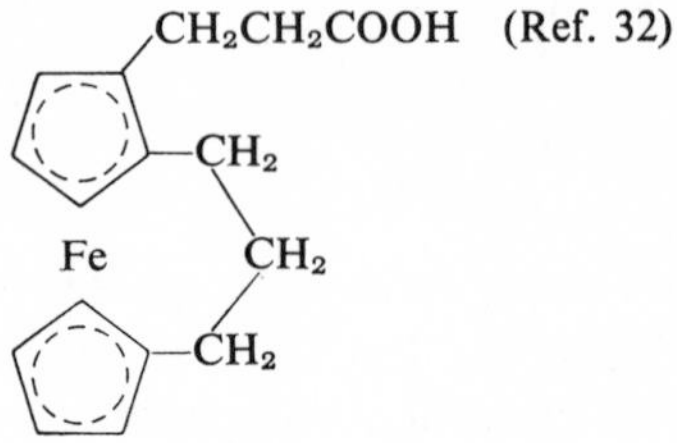

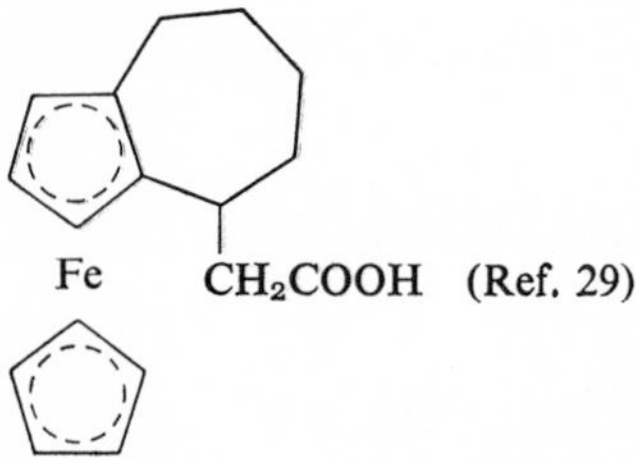

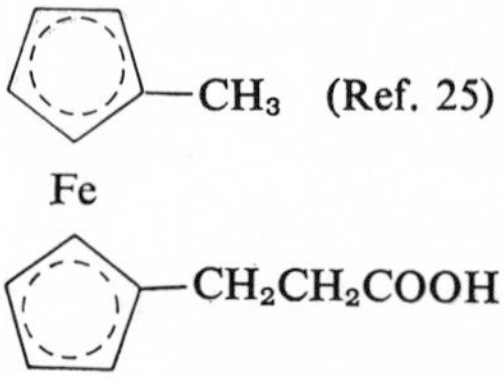

CH_2CH_2COOH (Ref. 32)

CH_2CH_2COOH (Ref. 32)

—CH_3 (Ref. 25)

$(C_5H_5FeC_5H_4CH_2)_3CCOOH$ (Ref. 17)

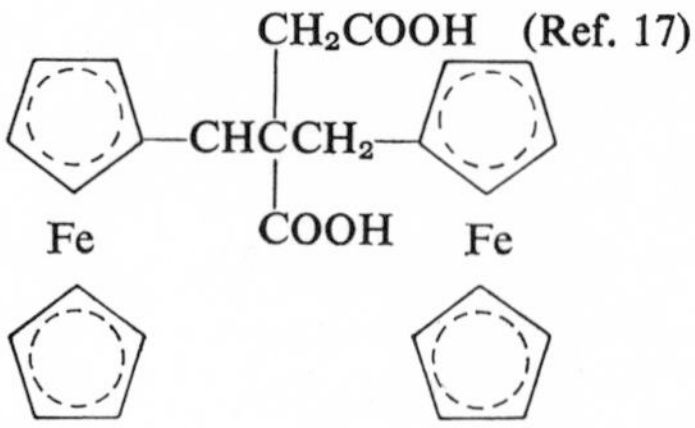

$(C_5H_5FeC_5H_4CH_2)_2CCH_2COOH$ (Ref. 17)

COOH

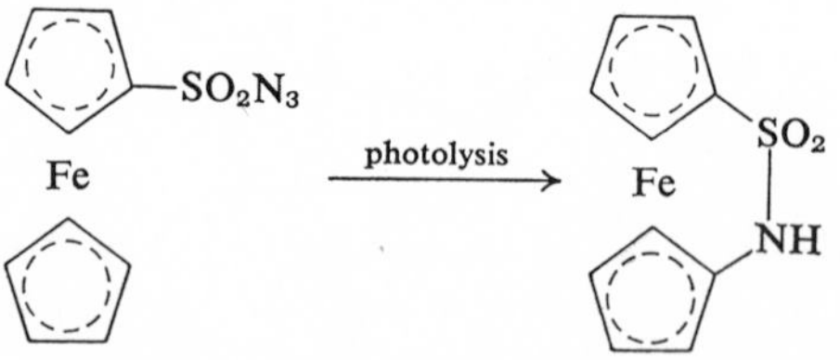

(18)

photolysis

(19)

A number of examples are given[17,25,29–32] where substituted ferrocenyl-propionic acids (whose formulae are given below) were cyclized. In this way [3]ferrocenophanes and their derivatives were synthesized.

The photolysis of ferrocenesulfonic acid azide (18) led to [2-ferroceno-

phanethiazine-1,1'-dioxide (19) which is a ferrocene derivative bridged with
—SO$_2$NH—.[33]

D. Alkylation

The studies of ferrocene decomposition and alkylation by aluminum
chloride in a dichloromethane medium were continued.[34] Ferrocene is
alkylated by dichloromethane to give diferrocenylmethane to a small extent
only. The prevalent processes are those involving the rupture of the metal-
ring bond followed by the interaction of the intermediate products with the
ferrocene ring. [1,1]Ferrocenophane (20), cyclopentadienyl derivatives (21),
(22), (23), (24) and polymers (molecular weight 600 to 2400) were isolated.

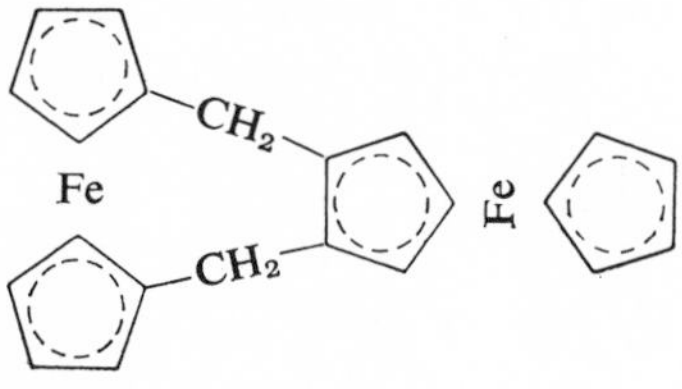

(20)

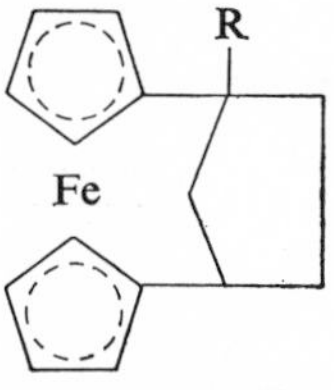

R = H, CH$_3$
(21), (22)

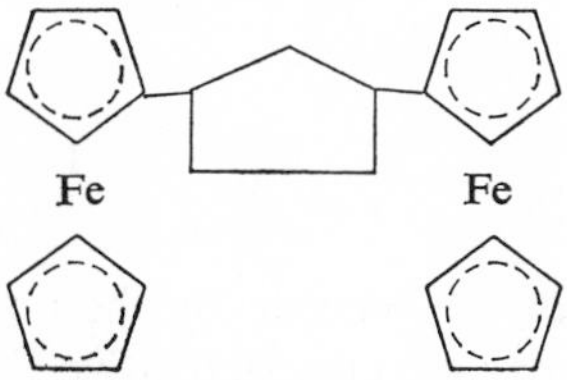

(23) 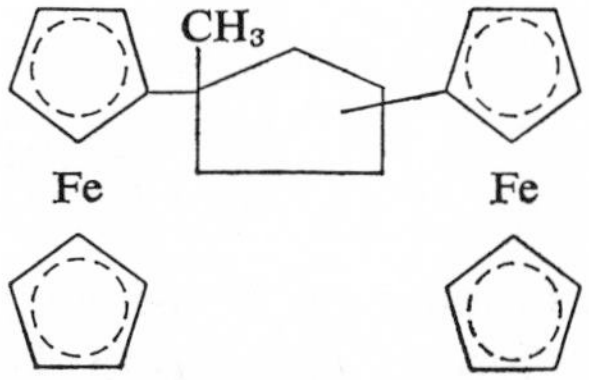   (24)

Tetraferrocenylmethane and diferrocenyldichloromethane were reportedly
obtained[34] alongside with other products in the reaction of ferrocene with
carbon tetrachloride in the presence of aluminum chloride.

Ferrocene alkylation by alkyl halides in an organic solvent in the presence
of a catalyst was patented.[35]

E. Sulfonation

Ferrocenesulfonic acid (18) azide and its transformation into the bridged
derivative (19) were described.[33]

F. Dimethylaminomethylation

Ferrocene dimethylaminomethylation by a complex of tetramethyldiaminomethane with aluminum chloride was suggested.[36] The yield of di-

methylaminomethylferrocene was 80%. In this way aminomethylated poly-methyleneferrocenylene was obtained containing two $CH_2N(CH_3)_2$ groups per each three ferrocene nuclei.[37]

The dimethylaminomethylation of methyl-, isopropyl-, 1,1′-dimethyl-, and 1,1′-di-isopropylferrocene was studied,[38,39] the structure of the resulting mono- and diaminomethylated alkylferrocenes was identified.[27] The structure of 1,2-halo-(dimethylaminomethyl)ferrocenes was studied.[40]

G. Metalation

The vinylferrocene derivative (**25**) was mercurated and iodine was substituted for the group HgCl.

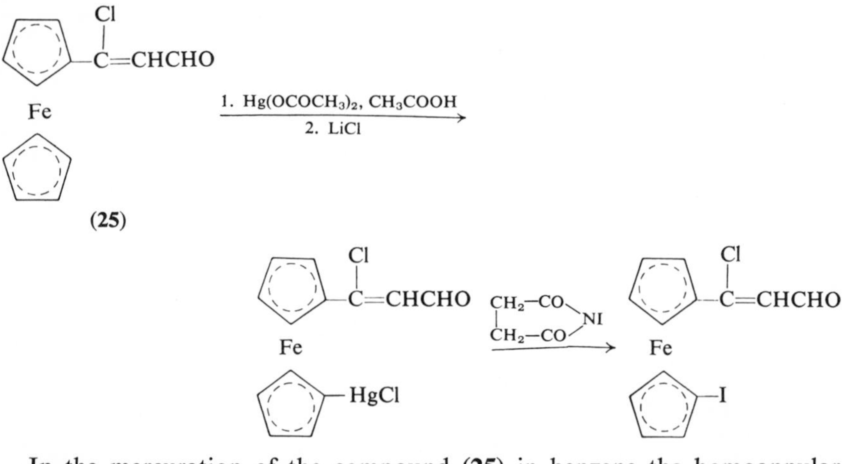

In the mercuration of the compound (**25**) in benzene the homoannular product is formed as well as the heteroannular mercury derivative.[41]

Mercury exchange in other mercurated derivatives of ferrocene is described in the Appendix to Chapter 2.

1,1′-Dilithiumferrocene is obtained in a high yield via metalation of ferrocene by n-butyllithium in the presence of N,N,N',N'-tetramethylethylene-diamine in hydrocarbon solvents.[42-44]* This approach was also used in the synthesis of monolithiumferrocene.[43,46] Ferrocene was polymetalated by n-butyllithium.[47] A mixture of polylithiated products was obtained containing 1 to 7 lithium atoms per each ferrocene molecule. The metalation of mono-, di- and trisubstituted ferrocenes containing a heteroatom (nitrogen, phosphorus or oxygen) in the substituent was studied. The metalation of α-pyridylferrocene (**26**) involves the addition of n-butyllithium to the pyridine ring and the mono- or dimetalation of the pyridine ring. The main direction is

---

* The papers on metalation are reviewed in Ref. 45. The synthesis of ferrocenyllithium from haloferrocenes and ferrocenylmercury chloride is described in the Appendix to Chapter 2, Sections III and IV.

metalation into position 2 to form the compound (27). The metalation products were hydrolyzed and made to react with benzophenone.[48]

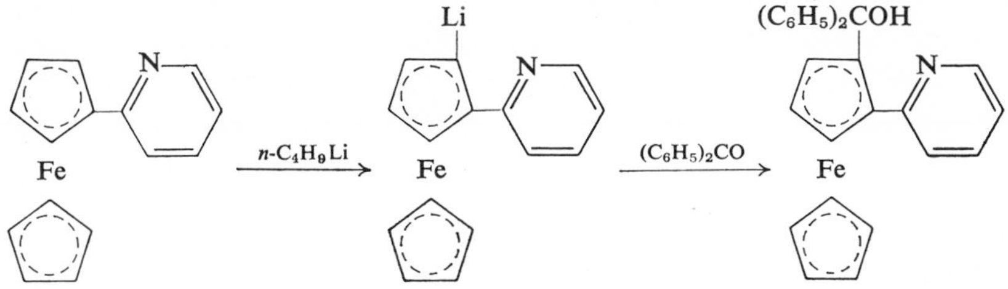

N,N-Dimethyl-β-ferrocenylethylamine (28) is chiefly metalated at position 2 as well.[49]

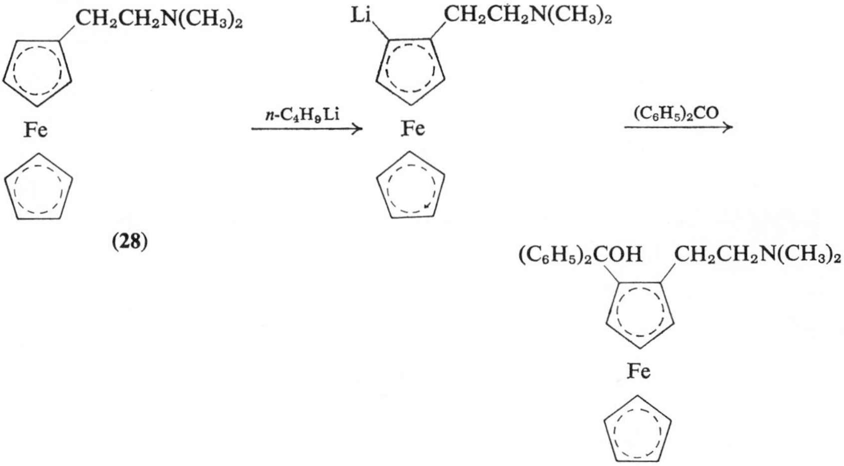

Methyl or ethyl ethers of ferrocenylcarbinol (29) are also metalated at position 2.[50]

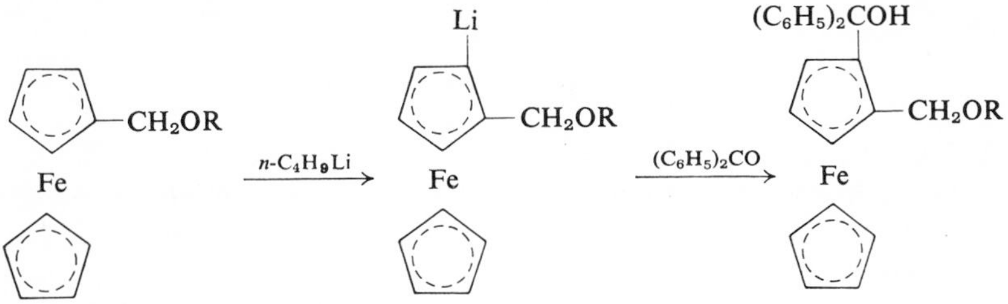

The metalation of 1,1′-bis(N,N-dimethylaminomethyl)ferrocene by *n*-butyllithium was studied.[51] The 1,2-disubstituted ferrocene (30) is metalated chiefly to a position next to the group $CH_2N(CH_3)_2$. The reactions

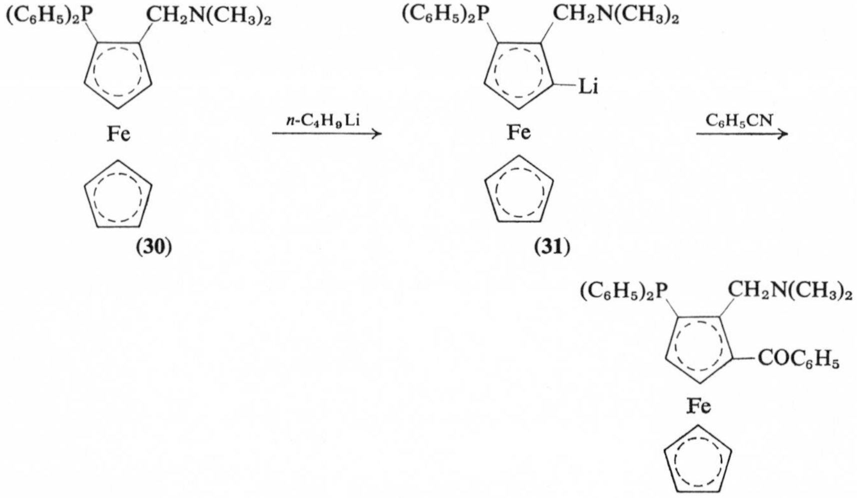

of the lithium derivative (31) with benzophenone, paraformaldehyde, and benzonitrile were described.[52] In the same paper[52] the synthesis of the phosphine compound (32) was described.

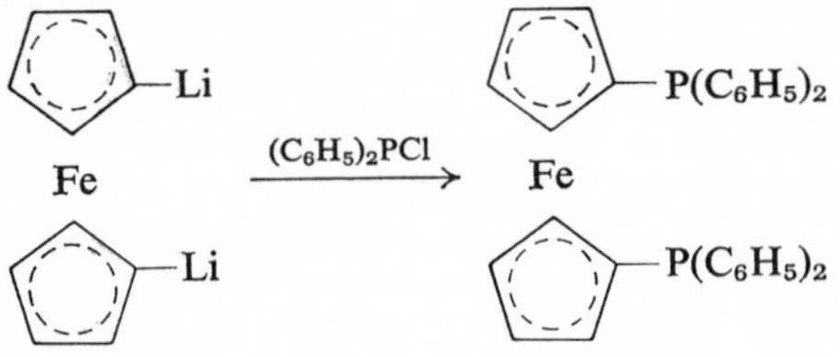

It should be noted that unlike other substituted ferrocenes, ferrocenylacetonitrile is metalated by *n*-butyllithium at the CH_2-group.[53]

The reactions of lithiated ferrocenes are also described in the Appendix to Chapter 2.

H. Reactions with Free Radicals

The groups $—COOC_2H_5$, $—CHO$, and $—CH_2OC_2H_5$ were substituted for the hydrogen in ferrocene under ultraviolet irradiation of ferrocene dissolved in a mixture of haloalkanes and ethanol. The reaction does not involve the formation of an intermediate ferricinium cation.[54]

The arylation of ferrocene by arylhydrazines in the presence of aluminum chloride was described.[55] The reaction mechanism is presumably ionic.

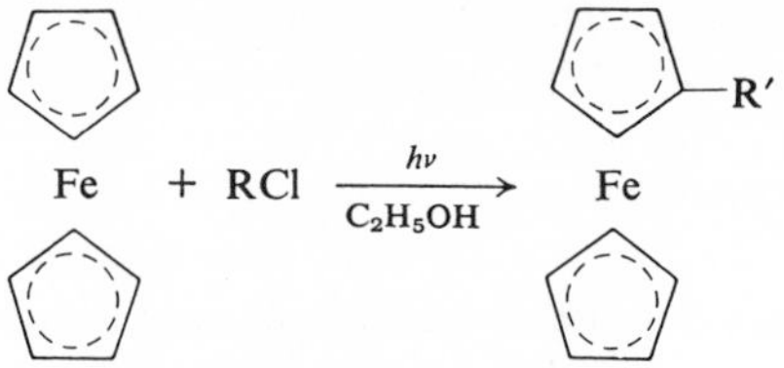

$R = CCl_3$; $R' = COOC_2H_5$
$R = CHCl_2$; $R' = CHO$
$R = CH_2Cl$; $R' = CH_2OC_2H_5$

Ferrocene attacks the benzene ring via a nucleophilic route, accompanied by the simultaneous removal of hydrazide ion under the action of aluminum chloride.

$$FeC_{10}H_{10} + \overset{\delta+}{Ar}NHNH_2\cdot\overset{\delta-}{Al}Cl_3 \longrightarrow [FeC_{10}H_9ArH]^+[H_2NNHAlCl_3]^- \longrightarrow FeC_{10}H_9Ar + H_2NNHAlCl_2 + HCl$$

This is the sole instance of ferrocene arylation where an ionic mechanism is assumed.

J. Condensation

The reaction of ferrocene with chloral in the presence of $AlCl_3$ gave the alcohol (**33**) and the unsaturated compound (**34**).[56]

$$(C_5H_5)_2Fe \xrightarrow{Cl_3CCHO,\ AlCl_3} C_5H_5FeC_5H_4CH(OH)CCl_3 \quad \textbf{(33)}$$

$$(C_5H_5)_2Fe \xrightarrow[AlCl_3\ excess]{Cl_3CCHO} C_5H_5FeC_5H_4CH{=}CCl_2 \quad \textbf{(34)}$$

The reaction of ferrocene with 1,1,3,3-tetramethoxypropane gave the vinyl ether (**35**).[57]

$$(C_5H_5)_2Fe + (CH_3O)_2CHCH_2CH(OCH_3)_2 \xrightarrow[CHCl_3]{BF_3\cdot O(C_2H_5)_2} C_5H_5FeC_5H_4CH{=}CHOCH_3 \quad \textbf{(35)}$$

Ferrocene polycondensation with various ketones and aldehydes was described (with acetone, methyl ethyl ketone, cyclohexanone, acetophenone, benzophenone,[58] paraformaldehyde,[59] terephthalic aldehyde, and 1,1′-ferrocenedicarboxaldehyde[60]).

Ferrocene-containing polymers were obtained[61] by the condensation of ferrocene with $C_6H_5PCl_2$, $C_6H_5P(O)Cl_2$, and $C_6H_5P(S)Cl_2$ in the presence of $ZnCl_2$.

III–IV. HYDROGEN-SUBSTITUTION REACTIONS OF
C_5H_5-RINGS OF METALLOCENES (EXCEPT FERROCENE)

The reaction of hydrogen substitution in ferrocene was the subject of extensive studies of the latest three years (see Section II of this chapter). The number of papers on other metallocenes is not large. Ruthenocene was reacted with *o*-methoxybenzoyl chloride in the presence of $AlCl_3$.

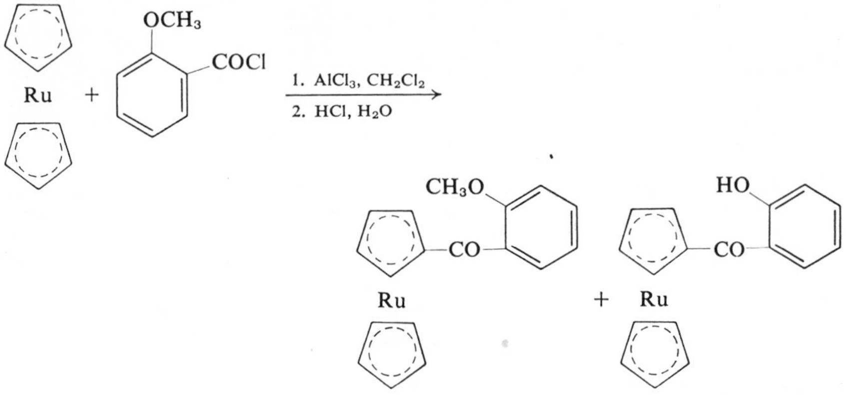

The acylation of ruthenocene by succinic anhydride and the subsequent transformation of the ketoacid (**36**) to the cyclic ketone (**37**) was described.[62]

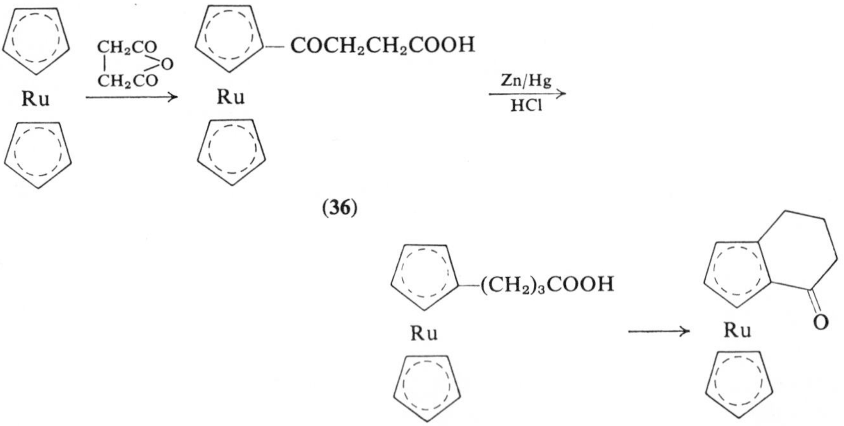

Ruthenocene was dimethylaminomethylated.[62] A number of substitution reactions were carried out[62] with methylruthenocene, such as the metalation by butyllithium and the subsequent carboxylation, the cyanation by hydrocyanic acid in the presence of $FeCl_3$, the formylation by *N*-methylformanilide, and the reaction with N,N-diphenylcarbamyl chloride in the presence of $AlCl_3$. Optically active ruthenocene derivatives were isolated.[63]

Vinyl derivatives of ruthenocene and osmocene, and polymers containing ruthenium and boron (in the interaction of ruthenocene with $C_6H_5BCl_2$ in the presence of $ZnCl_2$) were obtained.[3,64]

For cobalticinium the hydrogen isotopic exchange in an alkali medium was described.[65] The kinetics was studied. No exchange takes place in acid media.

A unique hydrogen exchange reaction was carried out for titanocene,[66] which, heated with triethylaluminum, gives ethane and forms a red diamagnetic compound for which the following structure (38) was suggested.

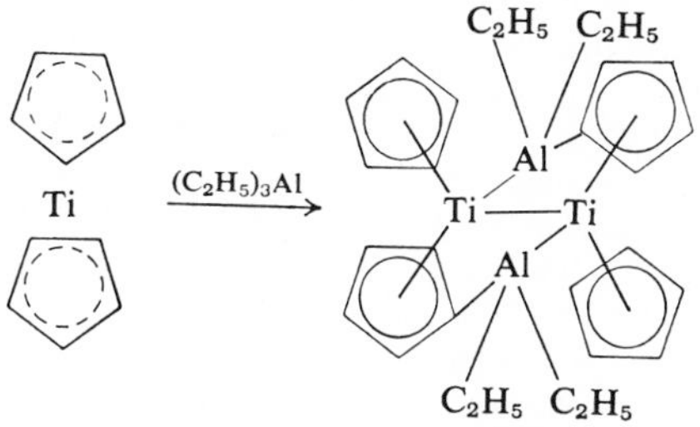

(38)

Trimethylaluminum reacts as triethylaluminum. The reaction of $(C_5H_5)_2Zr$ with $(C_2H_5)_3Al$ or with $(CH_3)_3Al$ also gives the alkane and a mixture of two compounds. One of these is trimeric.[66]

REFERENCES

1. J. C. Kofz and E. W. Post, *J. Amer. Chem. Soc.*, **90**, 4503 (1968).
2. J. C. Kofz and E. W. Post, *Inorg. Chem.*, **9**, 1661 (1970).
3. W. Neuse, *J. Macromol. Sci.*, **2**, 751 (1968).
4. M. Cais and A. Eisenstadt, *J. Amer. Chem. Soc.*, **89**, 5468 (1967).
5. R. Dolby and B. H. Robinson, *Chem. Commun.*, **1970**, 1058.
6. V. N. Setkina, N. V. Kisliakova, N. S. Kochetkova, A. N. Nesmeyanov, and D. N. Kursanov, *Doklady Akad. Nauk SSSR*, **178**, 119 (1968).
7. D. N. Kursanov, V. N. Setkina, E. I. Fedin, M. N. Nefedova, and A. I. Khotami, *Dokl. Akad. Nauk SSSR*, **192**, 339 (1970).
8. M. D. Rausch and A. Siegel, *J. Organomet. Chem.*, **17**, 117 (1969).
9. P. Carty and M. F. H. Dove, *J. Organomet. Chem.*, **21**, 195 (1970).
10. E. B. Sokolova, G. P. Chalykh and A. P. Suslov, *Zh. Obshch. Khim.*, **38**, 537 (1968).
11. Ye. I. Smyslova and E. G. Perevalova, unpublished results.
12. T. H. Barr and W. E. Watts, *Tetrahedron*, **24**, 3219 (1968).
13. T. H. Barr and W. E. Watts, *Tetrahedron*, **25**, 861 (1969).
14. A. Eisenstadt and M. Cais, *Israel J. Chem.*, **5**, 4a, 37 (1967).
15. V. D. Tyurin, N. S. Nametkin, S. P. Gubin, G. Otmanin, and M. V. Sokolovskaya, *Izv. Akad. Nauk SSSR, Ser. Khim.*, **1968**, 1866.
16. T. Kashima, R. Kobayashi, and N. Sugiyama, *J. Chem. Soc. Japan, Pure Chem. Sec.*, **90**, 1053, A57 (1969).

17. A. Dormond and J. Decombe, *Compt. Rend.*, **267C**, 693 (1968).
18. T. H. Barr, H. L. Lentzner, and W. E. Watts, *Tetrahedron*, **25**, 6001 (1969).
19. D. E. Bublitz and G. H. Harris, U.S. Pat. 3387009 (June 4, 1968); *Chem. Abstr.*, **69**, 87191 (1968).
20. D. E. Bublitz and G. H. Harris, *J. Organomet. Chem.*, **4**, 404 (1965).
21. G. P. Sollott and W. R. Peterson, Jr., *J. Organomet. Chem.*, **19**, 143 (1969).
22. M. Sato, H. Cono, M. Shiga, I. Motoyama, and K. Hata, *Bull. Chem. Soc., Japan*, **41**, 252 (1968).
23. M. D. Rausch and T. M. Gund, *J. Organomet. Chem.*, **24**, 463 (1970).
24. T. H. Barr, E. S. Bolton, H. L. Lentzner, and W. E. Watts, *Tetrahedron*, **25**, 5245 (1969).
25. H. Falk, O. Hofer, and K. Schlögl, *Monatsh. Chem.*, **100**, 624 (1969).
26. J. P. Monin and J. Tirouflet, *Compt. Rend.*, **265C**, 1127 (1967).
27. P. Dixneuf and P. Dabard, *Bull. Soc. Chim. France*, **1969**, 2164.
28. B. Gautheron and J. Tirouflet, *Compt. Rend.*, **265C**, 273 (1967).
29. A. Dormond, *Compt. Rend.*, **268C**, 2102 (1969).
30. B. Gautheron and J.-C. Leblanc, *Compt. Rend.*, **269C**, 431 (1969).
31. J.-P. Ravoux and J. Decombe, *Bull. Soc. Chim. France*, **1969**, 146.
32. C. Moise and J. Tirouflet, *Compt. Rend.*, **265C**, 457 (1967).
33. R. A. Abramovitch, C. I. Azogu, and R. G. Sutherland, *Chem. Commun.*, **1969**, 1439.
34. E. W. Neuse, *J. Org. Chem.*, **33**, 3312 (1968).
35. A. N. Nesmeyanov, N. P. Palitsyn, and N. S. Kochetkova, USSR Pat. 210160 (February 6, 1968). *Chem. Abstr.*, **69**, 44026 (1968).
36. Ye. A. Kalennikov, T. P. Vishniakova, and T. G. Makarov. *Zh. Organ. Khim.*, **5**, 1517 (1969).
37. Ye. A. Kalennikov and T. P. Vishniakova, *Vysokomolekul. Soyedin.*, *Ser. B*, **12**, 44 (1970).
38. P. Dixneuf and R. Dabard, *Compt. Rend.*, **266C**, 1244 (1968).
39. R. Dabard and P. Dixneuf, *Bull. Soc. Chim. France*, **1969**, 2158.
40. D. W. Slocum and T. R. Engelmann, *J. Org. Chem.*, **34**, 4101 (1969).
41. M. Rosenblum, N. M. Brown, D. J. Ciappenelli, and J. Tancrede, *J. Organomet. Chem.*, **24**, 469 (1970).
42. M. D. Rausch and D. J. Ciappenelli, *J. Organomet. Chem.*, **10**, 127 (1967).
43. A. W. Langer, Fr. Pat. 1499653 (October 27, 1967), *Chem. Abstr.*, **69**, 77449 (1968).
44. G. Marr and T. M. White, *J. Chem. Soc.*, **1970C**, 1789.
45. D. W. Slocum, T. R. Engelmann, C. Ernst, C. A. Jennings, W. Jones, B. Koonsvitsky, J. Lenrs, and P. Shenkin, *J. Chem. Educ.*, **46**, 144, (1969).
46. C. Elschenbroich and M. Cais, *J. Organomet. Chem.*, **18**, 135 (1969).
47. A. F. Halasa and D. P. Tate, *J. Organomet. Chem.*, **24**, 769 (1970).
48. D. J. Booth and B. W. Rockett, *J. Chem. Soc.*, **1968C**, 656.
49. T. R. Engelmann and C. A. Jennings, *Austral. J. Chem.*, **21**, 2319 (1968).
50. D. W. Slocum and B. P. Koonsvitsky, *Chem. Commun.*, **1969**, 846.
51. E. S. Bolton, P. L. Pauson, M. A. Sandu, and W. E. Watts. *J. Chem. Soc.*, **1969C**, 2260.
52. G. Marr and T. Hunt, *J. Chem. Soc.*, **1969C**, 1070.
53. G. Marr and J. Ronayne, *Chem. Commun.*, **1970D**, 350.
54. Y. Hoshi, T. Akiyama, and A. Sugimari, *Tetrahedron Lett.*, **1970**, 1485.
55. G. P. Sollot and W. R. Peterson, Jr., *J. Org. Chem.*, **34**, 1506 (1969).
56. W. Reeve and E. F. Group, *J. Org. Chem.*, **32**, 122 (1967).
57. P. Dudnik, J. M. Tancrede, and M. Rosenblum, *J. Organomet. Chem.*, **18**, 365 (1969).

58. T. A. Sokolinskaya, T. P. Vishniakova, Ya. M. Paushkin, and Ya. A. Popova, *Vysokomolekul. Soyedin.*, **9A**, 677 (1967).
59. H. Valot, *Bull. Soc. Chim. France*, **1969**, 564.
60. N. Bilow and H. Rosenberg *J. Polymer Sci.*, **7A–I**, 2689 (1969).
61. C. U. Pittman, *J. Polymer Sci.*, **5A–I**, 2927 (1967)
62. O. Hofer and K. Schlögl, *J. Organomet. Chem.*, **13**, 443 (1968).
63. O. Hofer and K. Schlögl, *J. Organomet. Chem.*, **13**, 457 (1968).
64. M. D. Rausch and A. Siegel, *J. Organomet. Chem.*, **11**, 317 (1968).
65. D. N. Kursanov, V. N. Setkina, N. K. Baranetskaya, G. G. Dvoriantseva, and R. B. Materikova, *Dokl. Akad. Nauk SSSR*, **161**, 847 (1965).
66. P. C. Wailes and H. Weigold, *J. Organomet. Chem.*, **24**, 713 (1970).

Chapter 2

II. LITHIUM AND SODIUM EXCHANGE

The synthetic application of mono- and dilithiumferrocenes has considerably expanded over the recent years, especially the use of lithium ferrocenes substituted in the position 2.* This is caused by the fact that the metalation of dimethylaminomethylferrocene and of similar compounds containing the

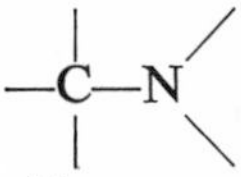

—C—N group attached to the ferrocene nucleus and the metalation of

chloro- and methoxyferrocenes, gives 2-lithiumferrocenes in good yields.

The reactions of 1-dimethylaminomethyl-2-lithiumferrocene with para-formaldehyde,[1] acetaldehyde, acetylferrocene,[2]† benzonitrile,[3] pyridine,[2] tri(n-butyl) borate,[4] and mercury(II) chloride[5] give the respective disubstituted ferrocenes shown below (for some compounds diastereomeric forms were isolated). The homolog of lithium(dimethylaminomethyl)ferrocene (1) was introduced into the reaction with trimethylchlorosilane, formaldehyde and benzophenone.[6] Lithiated (ferrocenylmethyl)pyrrolidine (2) and -piperidine (3) were reacted with benzophenone.[7]

The interaction of lithiated N-(ferrocenylmethyl)-α-methylpiperidine with trimethylchlorosilane and carbon dioxide was studied.[8–10] Substituted α-pyridylferrocenes (4), (5) were obtained in the reaction of the lithium derivative of α-pyridylferrocene with dimethylformamide, benzonitrile, tri(n-butyl) borate[2,11] and benzophenone.[12]

An improvement was introduced[13] into the technique developed earlier[14] to obtain 2-chloroferrocenylcarboxylic acid via 1-lithium-2-chloroferrocene.

From 1,1'-dichloroferrocene, perchloroferrocene[15] was synthetized via lithium derivatives. Dichloroferrocene was metalated by n-butyllithium; then chlorine was substituted for the lithium under the action of hexachloroethane and this sequence was iterated until perchloroferrocene was obtained.

---

* See also the Appendix to Chapter 1, Section II-G.
† For the reaction with norbornanone see at the end of this section.

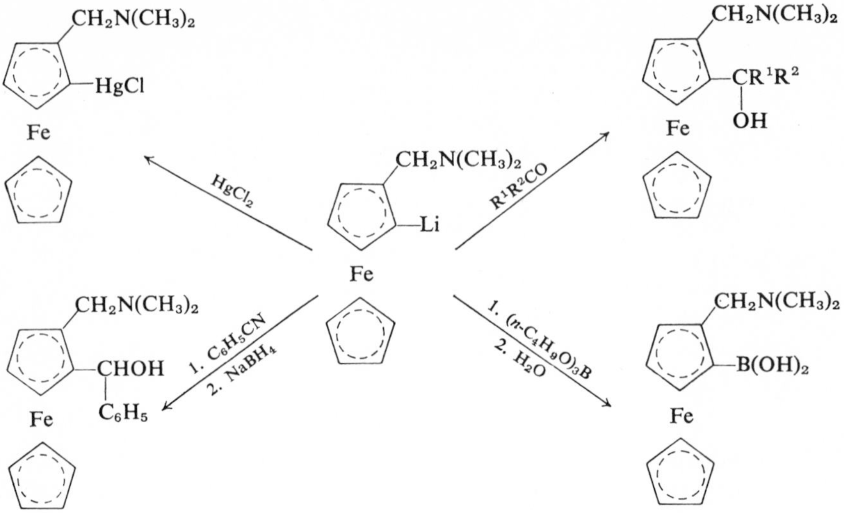

$$R^1 = R^2 = H$$
$$R^1 = H; \quad R^2 = CH_3$$
$$R^1 = CH_3; \quad R^2 = C_5H_4FeC_5H_5$$

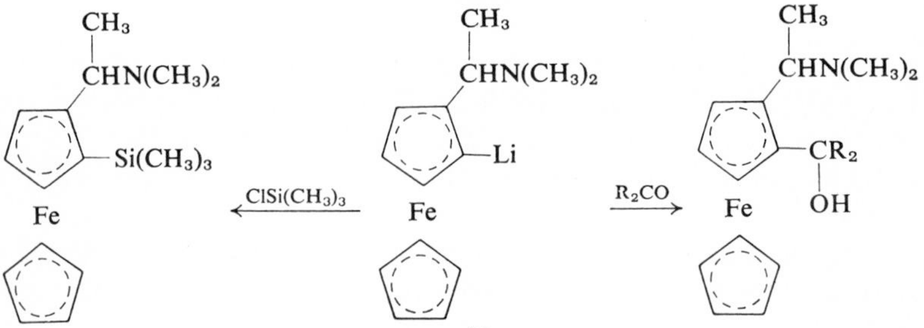

(1)

$$R = H, \, C_6H_5$$

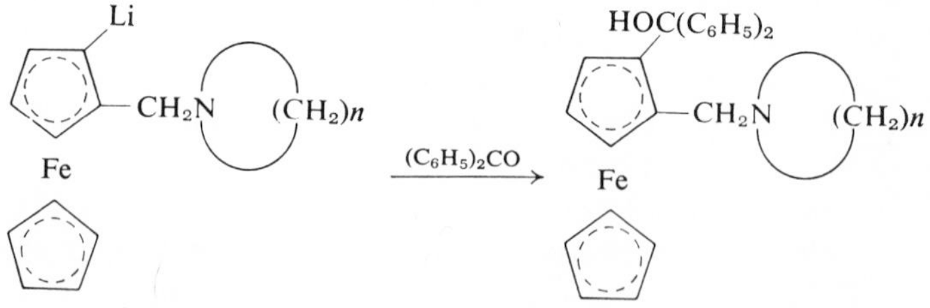

(2), $n = 4$
(3), $n = 5$

The reaction of perchloroferrocene with n-butyllithium gave the lithium compound (8) which was transformed into the diacid (9) and the diiodide (10).[15]

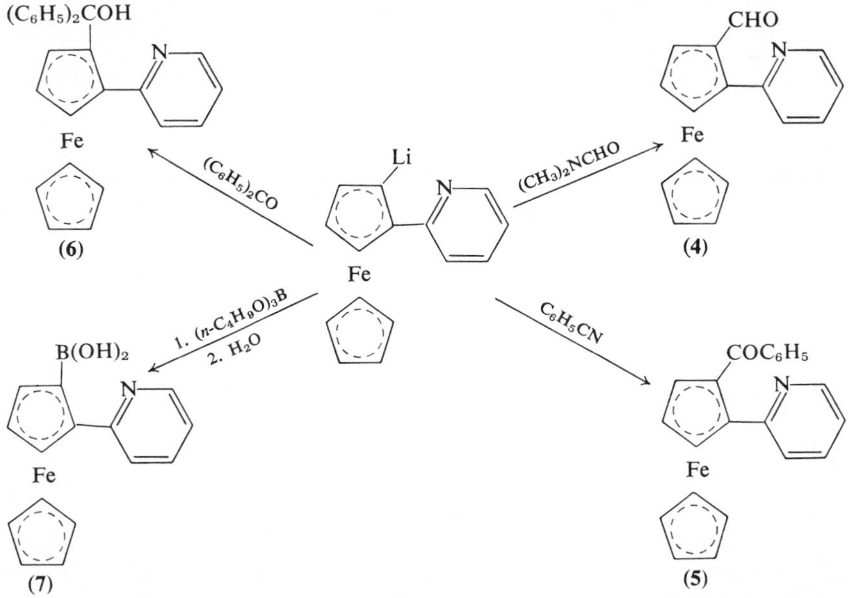

The metalation of isopropylferrocene by n-butyllithium in the presence of (−)sparteine gave a dilithium derivative which reacted with $ClSi(CH_3)_3$ and CO_2 (later CH_2N_2) to produce the optically active compounds (11) and (12).[8,9]

In recent years the scope of compounds reacting with mono and dilithiumferrocenes has expanded.

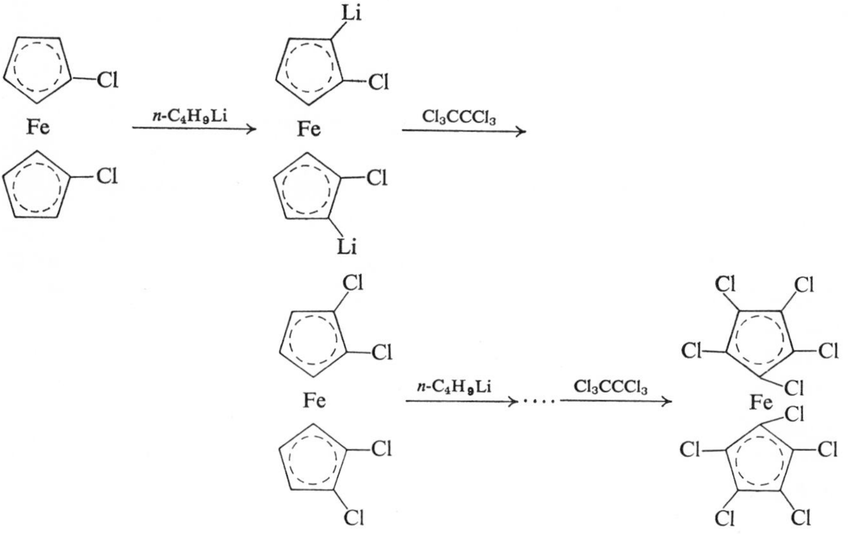

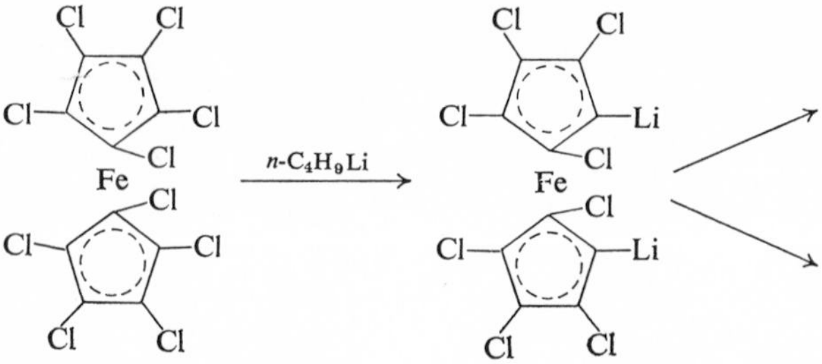

$$Fe(C_5Cl_4COOH)_2$$
(9)

$$Fe(C_5Cl_4I)_2$$
(10)

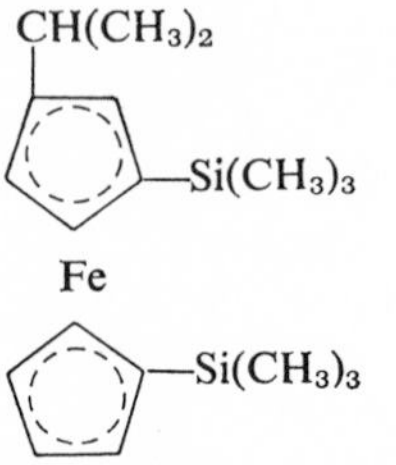

(11) 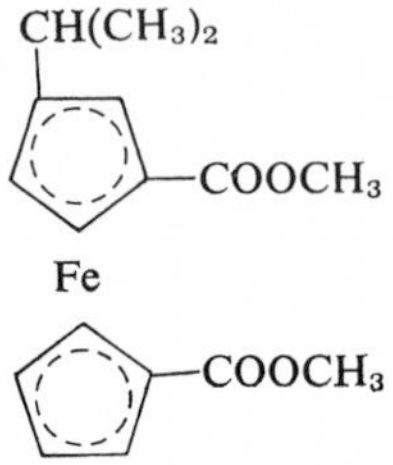   (12)

Other metals were made to substitute lithium. In this way there were obtained ferrocenyl derivatives of tin, $C_5H_5FeC_5H_4SnR_3$ and $Fe(C_5H_4SnR_3)_2$,[16,17] lead, $C_5H_5FeC_5H_4Pb(C_6H_5)_3$,[18] magnesium, $C_5H_5FeC_5H_4MgBr$,[19] univalent gold, $C_5H_5FeC_5H_4AuP(C_6H_5)_3$,[20] trivalent gold, $(C_5H_5FeC_5H_4)_2AuCl \cdot P(C_6H_5)_3$,[21] and mercury[5] (see pp. 397, 398). The reaction of dilithiumferrocene with sulfur gave 1,2,3trithia[3]ferroceno-phane (13).[22] It was shown[23] that the reaction of ferrocenyllithium with

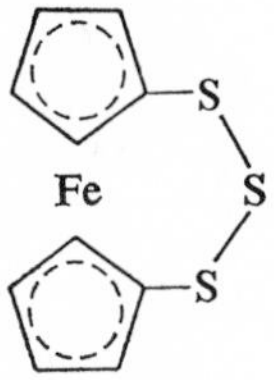

(13) 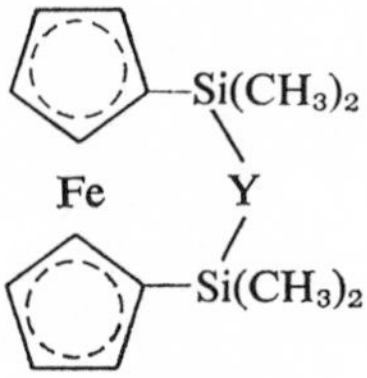   (14)

$$Y = CH_2, CHCH_3, CHC_2H_5, C(CH_3)_2$$

$BF_3 \cdot O(C_2H_5)_2$ gives diferrocenylboric acid, its anhydride, and triferrocenyl-boron. The methods of obtaining ferrocenylboric and 1,1'-ferrocenylene-diboric acids were improved.[24] Lithium derivatives of ferrocene were reacted with chlorosilanes and silicon-containing derivatives of ferrocene were obtained,[25–28] $C_5H_5FeC_5H_4Si(CH_3)_2Ar$; Ar = p- and m-$CH_3C_6H_4$; p- and m-$BrC_6H_4$; p- and m-$ClC_6H_4$; p- and m-$CH_3OC_6H_4$; α-$C_{10}H_7$,[25] $C_5H_5FeC_5H_4Si(CH_3)(CH=CH_2)R$; $Fe[C_5H_4Si(CH_3)(CH=CH_2)R]_2$; R = CH_3; C_2H_5, C_6H_5;[26] $Fe[C_5H_4Si(CH_3)_2Si(CH_3)_3]_2$;[27] and organosili-con-bridged ferrocenes (14).[28]

The reaction of lithiumferrocenes with perfluoropropylene led to the synthesis of $C_5H_5FeC_5H_4CF\!=\!CFCF_3$ and $Fe(C_5H_4CF\!=\!CFCF_3)_2$.[29] The technique for obtaining nitroferrocene was described.[30] Several alcohols of the ferrocene series were obtained in the reaction of ferrocenyllithium with the derivatives of ethylene epoxide[19] and with norbornan-2-one.[31] The latter compound was also reacted with 1-dimethylamino-2-lithiumferrocene.[31] The reaction of ferrocenyllithium with aromatic aldehydes was studied.[32]

III. MERCURY EXCHANGE

The BCl_2-group was substituted for mercury.[33] The synthesis of lithiated ferrocenes from mercury derivatives was described.[5,19] The technique of

$$C_5H_5FeC_5H_4HgCl \xrightarrow[\text{hexane}]{BCl_3} C_5H_5FeC_5H_4BCl_2$$

obtaining bromoferrocene from ferrocenylmercury chloride and N-bromosuccinimide was improved.[32] Various groups were substituted for mercury

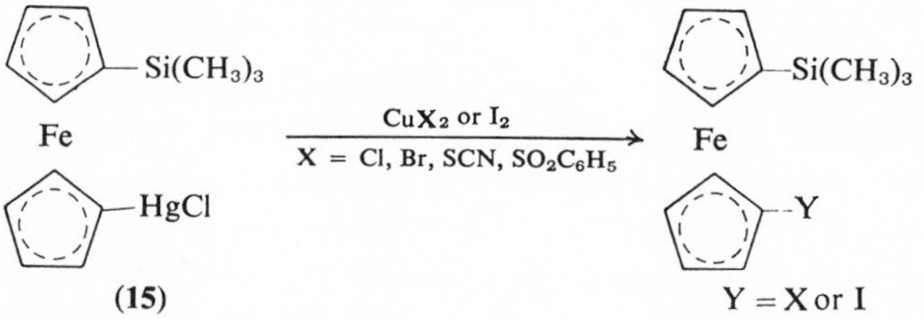

in (1′-trimethylsilylferrocenyl)mercury chloride (15).[34] 1,2-Dimethylaminomethyl(iodo)ferrocene (17) was obtained[5] from the mercury compound (16).

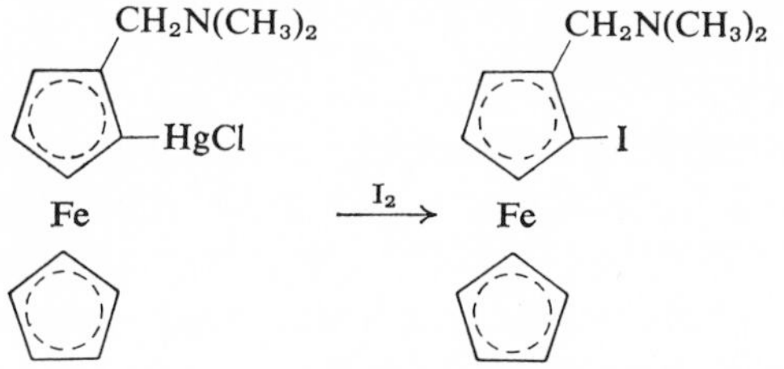

The organomercurial (18) was transformed into the iodide (19) under the action of N-iodosuccinimide.[35] The reaction of mercury derivatives of ferrocene with halogens at low temperatures was studied.[36] Ferrocenylmercury chloride with equimolar amounts of bromine or chlorine was found to form blue complexes stable in the air (20), (21). Iron in these complexes

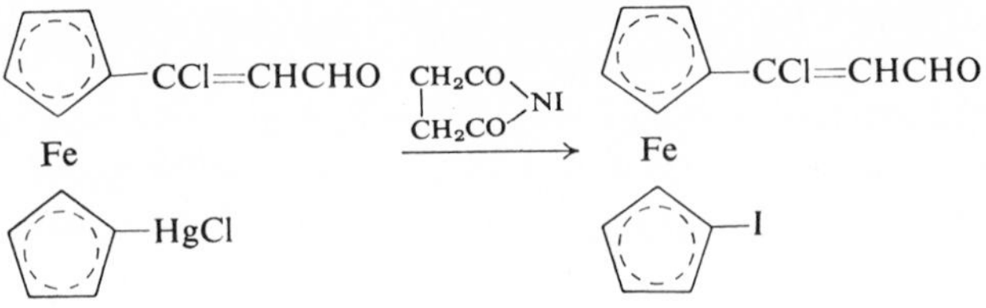

(18)   **(19)**

is in its ferricinium state as evidenced by Mössbauer spectra. The magnetic susceptibility of the complex **(20)** is 2.78 Bohr magnetons which signifies the presence of two nonpaired electrons. These complexes are believed[36] to be

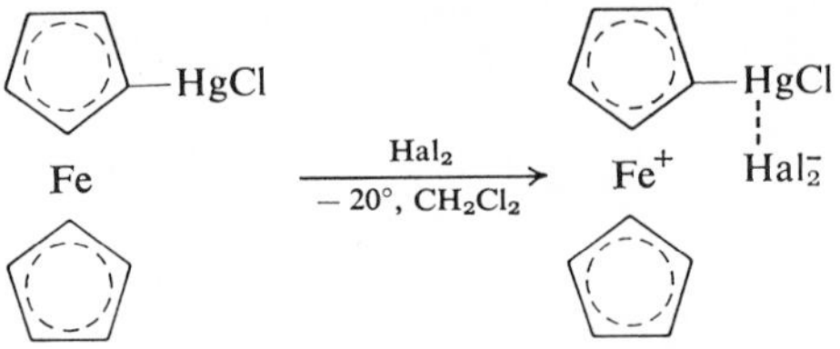

(20), Hal = Br
(21), Hal = Cl

ferricinium salts with the radical anion Hal_2^-, coordinated at the mercury atom **(20) (21)**. A similar complex of ferrocenylmercury chloride with iodine is unstable and decomposes quickly to give iodoferrocene in a high (over 70%) yield. This technique to obtain iodoferrocene is simpler than the one described earlier where excess iodine is used.

The reaction of diferrocenylmercury with bromine at low temperatures results in a blue solution of the complex **(22)** whose decomposition gives bromoferrocene, ferrocenylmercury bromide, the complex of ferrocenylmercury bromide with bromine **(23)**, and the initial diferrocenylmercury.[36]

$$(C_5H_5FeC_5H_4)_2Hg$$

$$\downarrow \begin{array}{l} Br_2 \\ -30°, CH_2Cl_2 \end{array}$$

$$[C_5H_5FeC_5H_4HgC_5H_4FeC_5H_5]^+ Br_2^- \longrightarrow C_5H_5FeC_5H_4Br + C_5H_5FeC_5H_4HgBr$$
$$\textbf{(22)}$$
$$\downarrow C_5H_5FeC_5H_4HgBr$$

$$C_5H_5Fe^+C_5H_4HgBr + (C_5H_5FeC_5H_4)_2Hg$$
$$\textbf{(23)} \quad Br_2^-$$

The rate of protodemercuration in the series of heteroannularly substituted mercurated ferrocenes (substituents Cl, Br, OCH_3, $OCOCH_3$, $COOCH_3$) was studied.[37,38]

The heating of polyferrocenylenemercury ($-HgC_5H_4FeC_5H_4-$)$_n$ in ferrocene medium forms polyferrocenylene $H(C_5H_4FeC_5H_4)_n-H$.[39] The pyrolysis of polyferrocenylenemercury gave 1,1'-biferrocenylene.[40] Ferrocene-containing polymers[41] were obtained by condensing 1,1'-di(halomercurated) ferrocenes with polyhalogenated compounds such as CCl_4, $Br_2CHCHBr_2$, dichlorodimethylsilane, dibromopropionitrile, and so on.

IV. HALOGEN EXCHANGE

Halogen was exchanged in substituted haloferrocenes subject to the action of copper salts. Thus 2-(chloro)-α-pyridylferrocene (**24**) gave the acetoxy-derivative (**25**)[42] while in 2-(bromo)-α-pyridylferrocene the bromine is

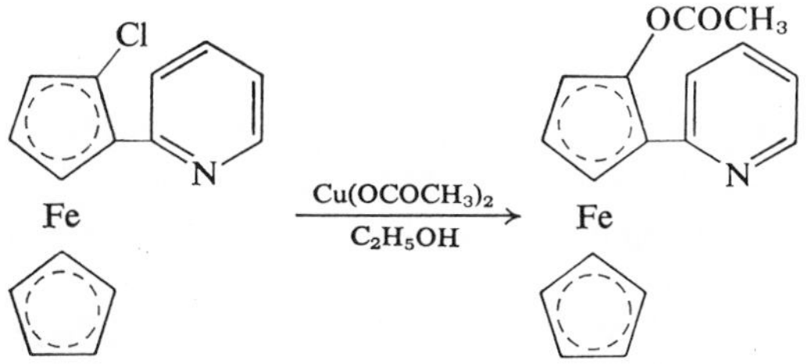

(**24**)   (**25**)

replaced by a CN-group under the action of CuCN. The ease of halogen exchange for the compounds (**26**) was shown[43] to decrease in the series $X = C_2H_5 > H > Cl > COCH_3$. It was also noted[34] that the bromine in

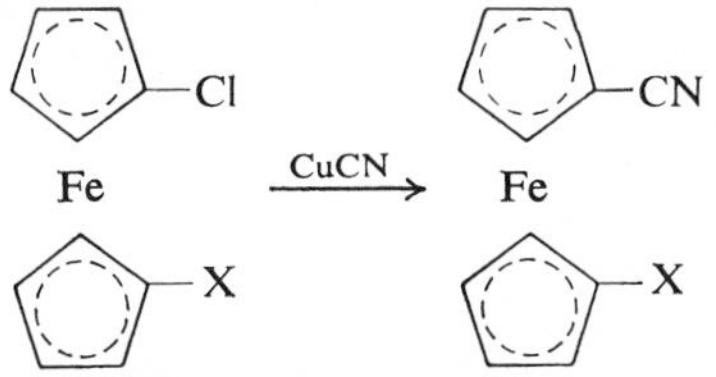

(**26**)
$X = C_2H_5, H, Cl, COCH_3$

1-trimethylsilyl-1'-bromoferrocene reacted with CuCN is harder to exchange than in bromoferrocene. The copper salt of 1-ethynyl-1'-iodoferrocene (**27**) gave [2,2]ferrocenophane-1,13-diyne (**28**).[35] From 1,1'-diiodoferrocene,

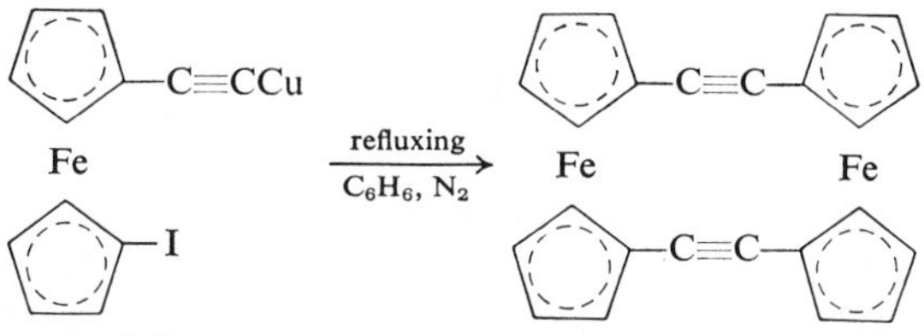

(**27**)   (**28**)

1,1'-biferrocenylene (29) was synthesized[44] by a modified Ullmann technique; haloferrocenes with 1,1'-diiodoferrocene gave ferrocene oligomers (30).[45]

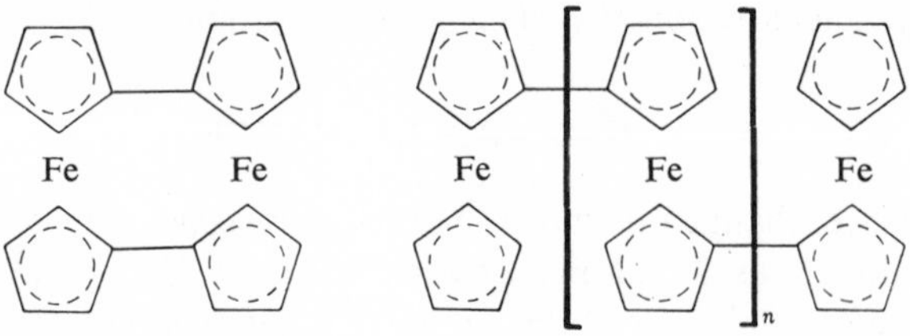

(29) $n = 0, 1, 2, 3, 4$
                                              (30)

The techniques to obtain lithiumferrocene from bromo- and iodoferrocene,[32,46] 1,1'-dilithiumferrocene from 1,1'-dibromo and -diiodoferrocene,[46] and 1,1'-dilithiumoctachloroferrocene from perchloroferrocene[15] were described.

The photolysis of iodoferrocene in cyclohexane or toluene leads to ferrocenyl free radicals which react with the solvent.[47]

V. B(OH)₂-GROUP EXCHANGE

Halogen was replaced for the $B(OH)_2$-group in the 2-substituted ferroceneboric acids (31)[2,11] and (32).[4] The action of cupric acetate on compounds (31) and (32) led to disubstituted biferrocenyls.[11,48] The substitution of

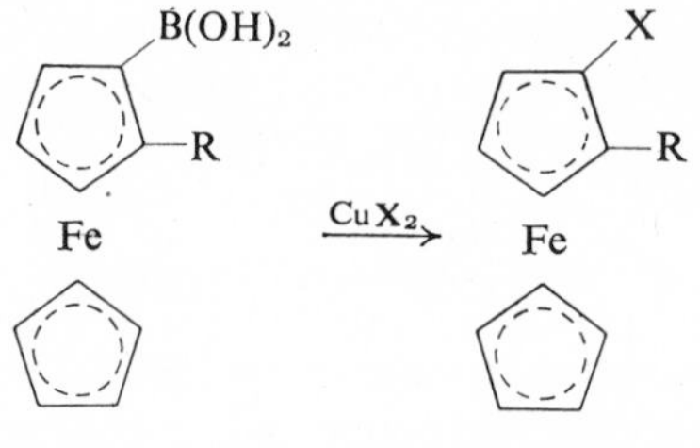

$X = Cl, Br, I$

(31) R =

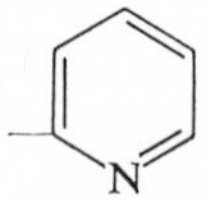

(32) R = $CH_2N(CH_3)_2$

HgCl for the $B(OH)_2$-group in the compound (32) and in heteroannular methoxy- and acetoxyferroceneboric acids was described.[49] Organosilver compounds (34) were obtained from haloferroceneboric acids (33).[50,51] Ferroceneboric acid irradiated in methanol gives ferrocene.[52]

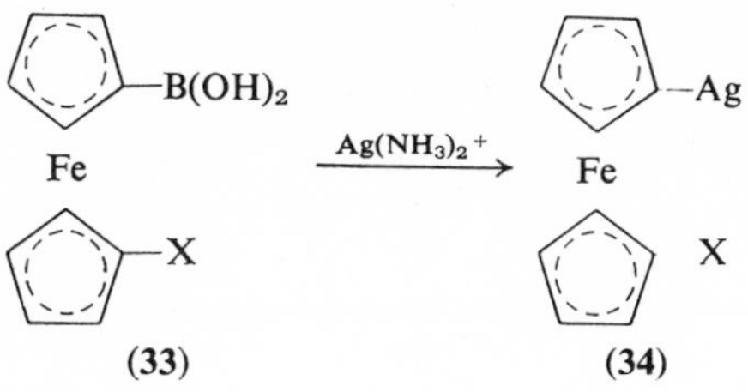

$$\text{(33)} \xrightarrow{\text{Ag(NH}_3)_2{}^+} \text{(34)}$$

VI. EXCHANGE OF OTHER GROUPS

In recent years a number of papers described the studies of the reactivity of the metal–carbon bond in ferrocenylderivatives of silver, gold, and bismuth.

The reaction of 1-(1'-bromoferrocenyl)silver (**35**) with Hg_2Br_2, $BiBr_3$ or H_2S gave 1-bromo-1'-chloromercuriferrocene (**36**), tris-[1-(1'-bromo-ferrocenyl)]bismuth (**37**), and bromoferrocene, respectively.[51]

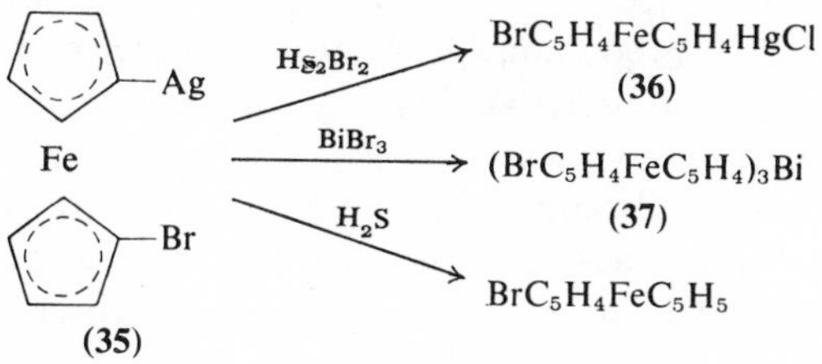

The thermal decomposition of the compound (**35**) gives bis[1-(1'-bromo-ferrocenyl)].[51] Similar reactions are also possible for 1-(1'-chloroferrocenyl)-silver[50] and 1-(2-chloroferrocenyl)silver.[50,53]

The Au–C bond in ferrocenylgold triphenylphosphine (**38**) is easily broken by acids and halogens.[20,54] An equimolar amount of bromine reacts with (**38**) in organic compounds below 0° to give an unstable addition product* (**39**) which further gives bromoferrocene, biferrocenyl, and $BrAuP(C_6H_5)_3$. The ratio of bromoferrocene and biferrocenyl in the reaction products varies with the order in which the reactants are mixed and with the rate of mixing. The complex (**39**) is believed[54] to produce bromoferrocene through an intramolecular reaction. Biferrocenyl is formed in the reaction of the complex (**39**) with the initial (**38**). Chlorine reacts with (**38**) analogously to bromine while iodine gives only iodoferrocene and $IAuP(C_6H_5)_3$; biferro-cenyl is not formed.[54]

The reaction of ferrocenylgoldtriphenylphosphine (**38**) with bromine and chlorine, which leads to the haloferrocenes, is probably related to the cyana-

---

* The addition product (**39**) is assumed to be structured analogously to the complexes of ferrocenylmercury halides with halogens (see the Appendix to Chapter 2, Section III).

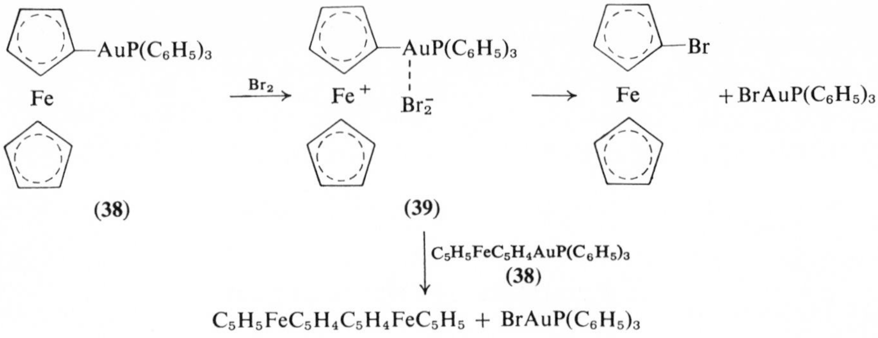

$$C_5H_5FeC_5H_4C_5H_4FeC_5H_5 \ + \ BrAuP(C_6H_5)_3$$

tion of ferricinium salts. Indeed, the halogen, like the CN-anion, first reacts with the iron and then the intramolecular transformation leads to the formation of a bond with the carbon of the five-membered ring.[54]

The decomposition of the Bi–C bond in $(BrC_5H_4FeC_5H_4)_3Bi$ in the presence of acids is described.[51] The study of protodesilylation of $C_5H_5FeC_5H_4Si(CH_3)_3$ is continued.[55] A strong similarity of kinetic characteristics for the protodesilylation of $C_5H_5FeC_5H_4Si(CH_3)_3$ and $p\text{-}CH_3OC_6H_4Si(CH_3)_3$ convinces that the mechanisms are in both cases similar and the protodesilylation of $C_5H_5FeC_5H_4Si(CH_3)_3$ proceeds without the initial electrophilic attack at the iron atom.[55] One $Si(CH_3)_3{}^-$ group was substituted[34] by HgCl in 1,1'-bis(trimethylsilyl)ferrocene reacted with $HgCl_2$.

A mercury compound, $ClHgC_5H_4FeC_5H_4COOCH_3$, was obtained in the reaction of the sulfinic acid $HO_2SC_5H_4FeC_5H_4COOCH_3$ with $HgCl_2$.[37]

REFERENCES

1. C. Moise and J. Tirouflet, *Bull. Soc. Chim. France*, **1969**, 1182.
2. D. J. Booth, G. Marr, B. W. Rockett, and A. Rushworth, *J. Chem. Soc.*, **1969C**, 2701.
3. C. Moise and J. Tirouflet, *Compt. Rend.*, **267C**, 414 (1968).
4. G. Marr, R. E. Moore, and B. W. Rockett, *J. Chem. Soc.*, **1968C**, 24.
5. D. W. Slocum and T. R. Engelmann, *J. Organomet. Chem.*, **24**, 753 (1970).
6. D. Marguarding, H. Klusacek, G. Gokel, P. Hoffmann, and I. Ugi, *J. Amer. Chem. Soc.*, **92**, 5389 (1970).
7. M. Hadlington, B. W. Rockett, and A. Nelhaus, *J. Chem. Soc.*, **1967C**, 1436.
8. T. Aratani, T. Gonda, and H. Nozaki, *Tetrahedron Lett.*, **1969**, 2265.
9. T. Aratani, T. Ganda, and H. Nozaki, *Tetrahedron*, **26**, 5453 (1970).
10. G. Gokel, P. Hoffmann, H. Kleimann, and H. Klusacek, *Tetrahedron Lett.*, **1970**, 1771.
11. A. N. Nesmeyanov, V. A. Sazonova, and V. Ye. Fedorov, *Izv. Akad. Nauk SSSR, Ser. Khim.*, **1970**, 2133.
12. D. J. Booth and B. W. Rockett, *J. Chem. Soc.*, **1968C**, 656.

13. A. N. Nesmeyanov, T. V. Baukova, K. I. Grandberg, Yu. A. Ustynyuk, S. P. Gubin, and E. G. Perevalova, *Izv. Akad. Nauk SSSR, Ser. Khim.*, **1969**, 721.
14. J. W. Huffman, L. H. Keith, and R. L. Asbury, *J. Org. Chem.*, **30**, 1600 (1965).
15. F. L. Hedberg and H. Rosenberg, *J. Amer. Chem. Soc.*, **92**, 3239 (1970).
16. T. Dado, H. Suzuki, and T. Takiguchi, *Bull. Chem. Soc. Japan*, **43**, 288 (1970).
17. J. P. Pellegrini and I. J. Spilners, U.S. Pat. 3390087 (January 25, 1968); *Chem. Abstr.*, **69**, 68784 (1968).
18. J. P. Pellegrini and I. J. Spilners, U.S. Pat. 3350434; *Chem. Abstr.*, **68**, 44789g (1968).
19. W. Reeve and E. F. Group, *J. Org. Chem.*, **32**, 122 (1967).
20. A. N. Nesmeyanov, E. G. Perevalova, D. A. Lemenovsky, A. N. Kosina, and K. I. Grandberg, *Izv. Akad. Nauk SSSR, Ser. Khim.*, **1969**, 2030.
21. E. G. Perevalova, K. I. Grandberg, D. A. Lemenovsky, and T. V. Baukova, *Izv. Akad. Nauk SSSR, Ser. Khim.*, in print.
22. A. Davison and J. C. Smart, *J. Organomet. Chem.*, **19**, P7 (1969).
23. E. W. Post, P. C. Cooks, and J. C. Kotz, *Inorg. Chem.*, **9**, 1670 (1970).
24. A. N. Nesmeyanov, V. A. Sazonova, and N. S. Sazonova, *Izv. Akad. Nauk SSSR, Ser. Khim.*, **1968**, 2371.
25. V. D. Tyurin, N. V. Ushakov, S. P. Gubin, and N. S. Nametkin, *Izv. Akad. Nauk SSSR, Ser. Khim.*, **1968**, 1407.
26. Ye. B. Sokolova, S. M. Massarskaya, and N. A. Varfolomeeva, *Zh. Obshch. Khim.*, **40**, 1762 (1970).
27. K. Hirotsu, T. Higuchi, and A. Shimada, *Bull. Chem. Soc. Japan*, **41**, 1557 (1968).
28. M. Kumada, M. Ogura, H. Tsumeni, and M. Ishikawa, *Chem. Commun.*, **1969**, 207.
29. G. P. Chalykh, Ye. B. Sokolova, and T. I. Chernyshova, *Zh. Obshch. Khim.*, **40**, 2337 (1970).
30. C. Elschenbroich and M. Cais, *J. Organomet. Chem.*, **18**, 135 (1969).
31. M. J. A. Habbib and W. E. Watts, *J. Chem. Soc.*, **1970C**, 2552; **1969C**, 1469.
32. F. D. Popp and E. B. Moynahan, *J. Org. Chem.*, **34**, 454 (1969).
33. J. C. Kotz and E. W. Post, *Inorg. Chem.*, **9**, 1661 (1970).
34. G. Marr and T. M. White, *J. Chem. Soc.*, **1970C**, 1789.
35. M. Rosenblum, N. M. Brown, D. Ciappenelli, and J. Tancrede, *J. Organomet. Chem.*, **24**, 469 (1970).
36. A. N. Nesmeyanov, E. G. Perevalova, D. A. Lemenovsky, V. P. Alexeev, and K. I. Grandberg, *Dokl. Akad. Nauk SSSR*, **198**, 1099 (1971).
37. A. N. Nesmeyanov, E. G. Perevalova, S. P. Gubin, and A. G. Kozlovsky, *Izv. Akad. Nauk SSSR, Ser. Khim.*, **1968**, 654.
38. A. N. Nesmeyanov, E. G. Perevalova, S. P. Gubin, and A. G. Kozlovsky, *Dokl. Akad. Nauk SSSR*, **178**, 616 (1968).
39. E. W. Neuse and R. K. Crossland, *J. Organomet. Chem.*, **7**, 344 (1967).
40. M. D. Rausch, R. F. Kovar, and C. S. Kraihanzel, *J. Amer. Chem. Soc.*, **91**, 1259 (1969).
41. T. P. Vishnyakova, I. A. Golubeva, N. D. Sapuntsova, and I. K. Suvorova, *Vysokomolek. Soyedin.*, **12B**, 442 (1970).
42. A. N. Nesmeyanov, V. A. Sazonova, and V. Ye. Fedorov, *Dokl. Akad. Nauk SSSR*, **194**, 1332 (1970).
43. M. Sato, T. Ito, I. Motoyama, K. Watanabe, and K. Hata, *Bull. Chem. Soc. Japan*, **42**, 1976 (1969).
44. F. L. Hedberg and H. Rosenberg, *J. Amer. Chem. Soc.*, **91**, 1258 (1969).
45. M. D. Rausch, P. V. Poling, and A. Siegel, *Chem. Commun.*, **1970D**, 502.
46. F. L. Hedberg and H. Rosenberg, *Tetrahedron Lett.*, **1969**, 4011.
47. T. Sato, S. Shimada, and K. Hata, *Bull. Chem. Soc. Japan*, **42**, 2731 (1969).

48. G. Marr, R. E. Moore, and B. W. Rockett, *Tetrahedron Lett.*, **1968**, 2517.
49. A. N. Nesmeyanov and A. G. Kozlovsky, *Izv. Akad. Nauk SSSR, Ser. Khim.*, **1967**, 2574.
50. A. N. Nesmeyanov, V. A. Sazonova, N. S. Sazonova, and V. N. Plyukhina, *Dokl. Akad. Nauk SSSR*, **177**, 1352 (1967).
51. A. N. Nesmeyanov, N. S. Sazonova, V. A. Sazonova, and L. M. Meskhi, *Izv. Akad. Nauk SSSR, Ser. Khim.*, **1969**, 1827.
52. H. C. H. A. van Riel, F. C. Fischer, J. Lugtenburg, and E. Havinga, *Tetrahedron Lett.*, **1969**, 3085.
53. A. N. Nesmeyanov, V. A. Sazonova, and N. S. Sazonova, *Dokl. Akad. Nauk SSSR*, **176**, 598 (1967).
54. E. G. Perevalova, D. A. Lemenovsky, K. I. Grandberg, and A. N. Nesmeyanov, *Dokl. Akad. Nauk SSSR*, **199**, 832 (1971).
55. G. Marr and D. E. Webster, *J. Chem. Soc.*, **1968B**, 202.

Chapter 3

I. EXCHANGE OF CYCLOPENTADIENYL RINGS

The replacement of the cyclopentadienyl ring in $(RC_5H_4)_2MCl_2$ (M = Zr, Hf; R = CH_3, *tert*-C_4H_9) under the action of acetylacetone, 8-oxyquinoline, or acetic acid was described.[1]

The methoiodides of 2-(chloro)-α-pyridylferrocene (**1**) and *N*-ferrocenylisoindoline (**2**) were photolyzed.[2,3]

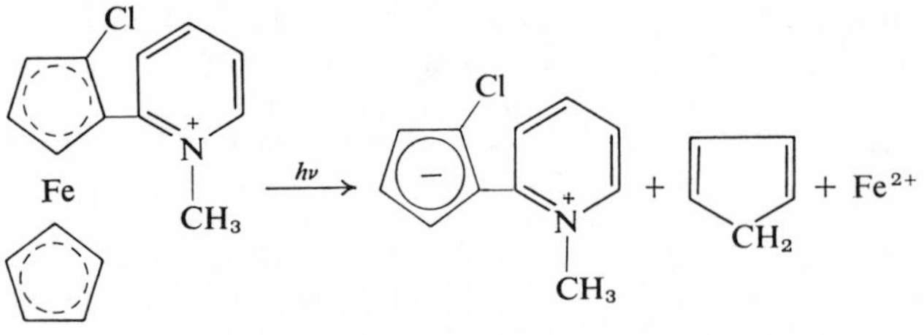

(1)

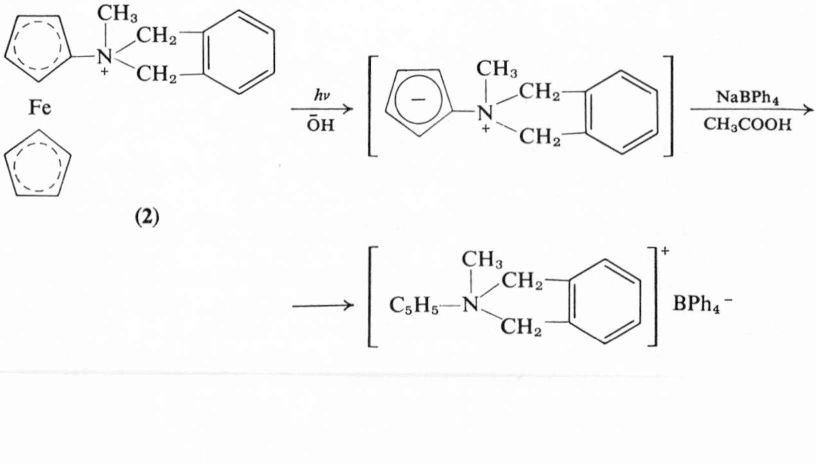

(2)

Ferrocene was found[4] to decompose in the reaction with *N*-bromo-succinimide in glacial acetic acid at 20° to form tribromocyclopentene and acetoxybromocyclopentene.

The exchange of cyclopentadienyl rings in polyalkylated ferrocenes in the presence of $AlCl_3$ was studied.[5]

A new ligand exchange in ferrocene was described.[6]

$$(C_5H_5)_2Fe + RuCl_3 \xrightarrow{250°} (C_5H_5)_2Ru \quad (50\%)$$

The ferrocene ligand exchange for arene in the presence of $AlCl_3$ and Al was extended. One cyclopentadienyl ring in ferrocene was exchanged for a number of polymethylsubstituted benzenes and for haloarenes.[7-9] In diethyl-ferrocene chlorobenzene may be substituted for one of the rings.[7]

Nickelocene with triphenylchloromethane forms[10] $NiCl_2$ and isomers of triphenylmethylcyclopentadiene

$$(C_5H_5)_2Ni \xrightarrow[CH_3NO_2]{ClC(C_6H_5)_3} NiCl_2 + C_5H_5C(C_6H_5)_3$$

while cobaltocene gives the complex salt (3) whose structure was verified by X-ray analysis.[11] Possible mechanisms of these reactions were discussed.

$$(C_5H_5)_2Co \xrightarrow{ClC(C_6H_5)_3} [(C_5H_5)_2Co^{III}]^+[Co^{II}Cl_4]^-$$
$$(3)$$

The reduction of ferrocene, 1,1'-dialkylferrocenes, and ferrocenophanes by lithium in propylamine was studied. [3]Ferrocenophane was shown to be harder to decompose than dialkylferrocenes while the two bridge groups in the ferrocene nucleus hamper the decomposition:[3][3]-(1,3)-ferroceno-phane is not affected at all.[12]

The reduction of alkylferrocenes by lithium in ethylamine with subsequent action by TlOH was suggested[13] as a method to synthesize alkylcyclopenta-dienyl derivatives of thallium (yields 65 to 75%).

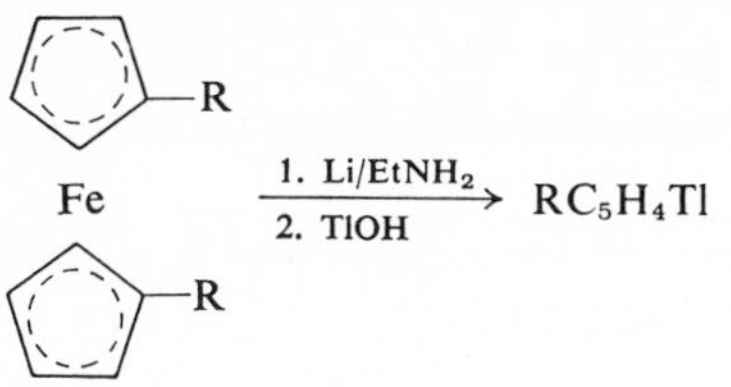

$$\text{Fe} \xrightarrow[\text{2. TlOH}]{\text{1. Li/EtNH}_2} RC_5H_4Tl$$

$$R = C_2H_5, \; t\text{-}C_4H_9$$

The decomposition of 1,1',3,3'-tetra-*tert*-butylferrocene by lithium in monoethylamine was used in the synthesis of homoannular homologs of ferrocene[14]:

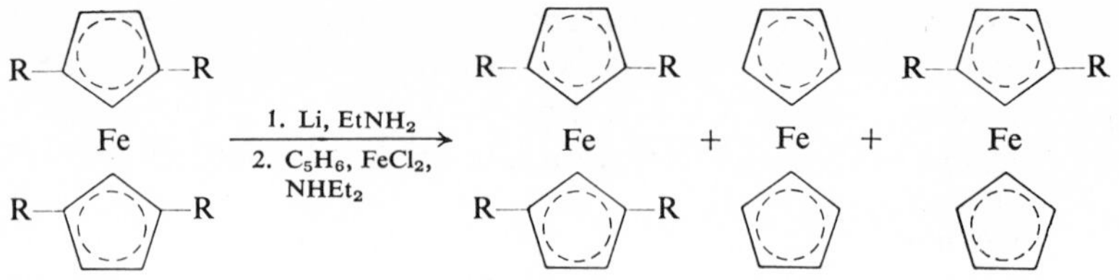

$$R = t\text{-}C_4H_9$$

Rupture of the C_5H_5–Ti bond by the action of organolithium compounds on biscyclopentadienyl derivatives of titanium was studied[15-17]:

$$(C_5H_5)_2TiR_2 + 3R'Li \longrightarrow [(C_5H_5)_2TiR_2R']^-Li^+ \longrightarrow$$
$$C_5H_5Li + Li + RH + 2R'H + RTiR'$$
$$R = Ph; \ R' = CH_3, \ CH_2Ph, \ Ph$$
$$R = CH_3; \ R' = Ph$$

The study of the reaction of acyl peroxides with biscyclopentadienyl compounds of vanadium and titanium was started.[18-20] Vanadium compounds reacted with acetyl, and benzoyl, peroxide or dicyclohexyl peroxydicarbonate readily lose one cyclopentadienyl ring to form monocyclopentadienyl compounds of vanadium

$$(C_5H_5)_2V(OCOR)_n + (RCOO)_2 \longrightarrow C_5H_5V(OCOR)_{n+1}$$
$$R = CH_3, \ C_6H_5 \qquad n = 1,2$$

In analogous derivatives of titanium the C_5H_5–Ti bond is more stable to peroxides: $(C_5H_5)_2Ti(OCOCH_3)_2$ and $(C_5H_5)_2Ti(OCOC_6H_5)_2$ do not react with acetyl or benzoyl peroxide. The reaction of biscyclopentadienyldiphenyltitanium, $(C_5H_5)_2Ti(C_6H_5)_2$, with benzoyl peroxide (1:1) proceeds through the intermediate complex $(C_5H_5)_2Ti(C_6H_5)_2 \cdot (C_6H_5COO)_2$ which decomposes to give $C_5H_5Ti(OCOC_6H_5)_2$, benzene, and a polyester. Biscyclopentadienylphenylvanadium, $(C_5H_5)_2V(C_6H_5)$, with benzoyl peroxide (1:1) gives $(C_5H_5)_2V(OCOC_6H_5)_2$, benzene, a polyester, and a small amount of $C_5H_5V(OCOC_6H_5)_3$. The yield of the latter increases with the amount of benzoyl peroxide.

The thermal decomposition of tri- and tetra-*tert*-butylferrocenes at 450–510° was studied[21]; the decomposition products were iron, carbon, methane, and hydrogen.

Cyclopentadienyl rings in nickelocene and in $(C_5H_5)_2TiCl_2$ were shown to exchange for 1,2-dithiolate ligands.[22,23]

$$(C_5H_5)_2Ni + Na_2[S_2C_2(CN)_2] \longrightarrow Na_2\left[Ni\left(\begin{array}{c} S-C-CN \\ \| \\ S-C-CN \end{array}\right)_2\right]$$

$$(C_5H_5)_2TiCl_2 \xrightarrow{[S_2C_6Cl_4]^{2-}} (C_5H_5)_2Ti(S_2C_6Cl_4) \xrightarrow{[S_2C_6Cl_4]^{2-}}$$
$$[C_5H_5Ti(S_2C_6Cl_4)_2] \xrightarrow{[S_2C_6Cl_4]^{2-}} [Ti(S_2C_6Cl_4)_3]^{2-}$$

II. REACTIONS OF METALLOCENES IN WHICH THE NATURE OF THE METAL-RING BOND IS TRANSFORMED

New additions to a cyclopentadienyl of nickelocene or cobaltocene were described.

Two adducts of tetrafluorobenzyne with nickelocene were obtained for which the structures (**4**) and (**5**) were suggested.[24]

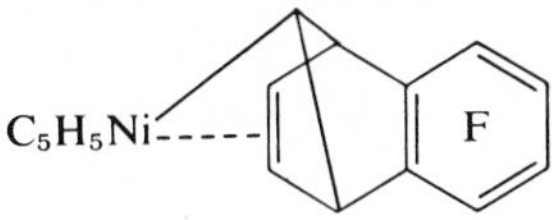

(**4**)

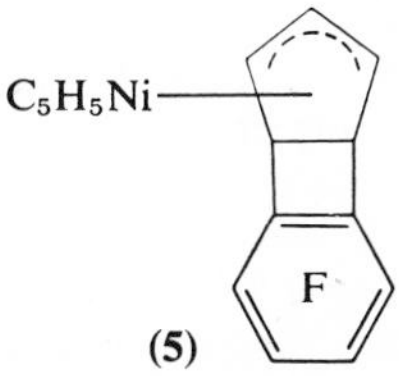

(**5**)

3,3,3-Trifluoropropyne was made to react with nickelocene and cobaltocene.[25]

$$(C_5H_5)_2Ni + CF_3C{\equiv}CH \longrightarrow [C_5H_5Ni]_2(CF_3C{\equiv}CH)$$

$$(C_5H_5)_2Co + CF_3C{\equiv}CH \longrightarrow$$

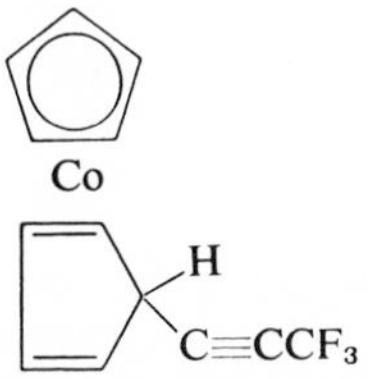

Cobaltocene captures free radicals that form in thermal decomposition of azoisobutyronitrile refluxed in toluene to give cyclopentadienyl-5-exo-(1-cyano-1-methylethyl)cyclopentadienecobalt (**6**).[26]

$$(C_5H_5)_2Co + \cdot C(CH_3)_2{-}CN \longrightarrow$$

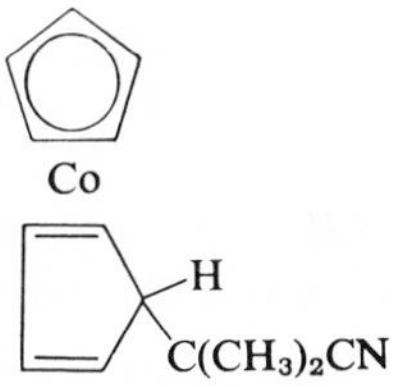

(**6**)

REFERENCES

1. M. Kh. Minacheva, E. M. Brainina, and L. A. Fyodorov, *Izv. Akad. Nauk SSSR, Ser. Khim.*, **1969**, 1104, 2492.
2. A. N. Nesmeyanov, V. A. Sazonova, and V. Ye. Fedorov, *Dokl. Akad. Nauk SSSR*, **194**, 1332 (1970).
3. A. N. Nesmeyanov, V. N. Postnov, V. A. Sazonova, and V. A. Dobriak, *Izv. Akad. Nauk SSSR, Ser. Khim.*, **1968**, 2372.
4. D. Dell, A. Modiano, and M. Cais, *Israel J. Chem.*, **7**, 779 (1969).

5. D. E. Bublitz, *J. Organometal. Chem.*, **16**, 149 (1969).
6. G. J. Gauthier, *Chem. Commun.*, **1969**, 690.
7. A. N. Nesmeyanov, N. A. Vol'kenau, Ye. I. Sirotkina, and V. V. Deriabin, *Dokl. Akad. Nauk SSSR*, **177**, 1110 (1967).
8. I. U. Khand, P. L. Pauson, and W. E. Watts, *J. Chem. Soc.*, **1968** C, 2257.
9. I. U. Khand, P. L. Pauson, and W. E. Watts, *J. Chem. Soc.*, **1968** C, 2261.
10. H. Werner, G. Mattmann, A. Salzer, and T. Winkler, *J. Organometal. Chem.*, **25**, 461 (1970).
11. H. Werner, G. Mattmann, and T. Winkler, *J. Organometal. Chem.*, **25**, 475 (1970).
12. A. D. Braun, Jr., and H. Reich, *J. Org. Chem.*, **35**, 1191 (1970).
13. A. N. Nesmeyanov, R. B. Materikova, E. I. Fedin, N. S. Kochetkova, P. V. Petrovsky, L. A. Fyodorov, and Ye. V. Leonova, *Dokl. Akad. Nauk SSSR*, **177**, 586 (1967).
14. A. N. Nesmeyanov, Ye. V. Leonova, N. S. Kochetkova, and L. Ya. Golovleva, *Dokl. Akad. Nauk SSSR*, **191**, 1070 (1970).
15. V. N. Latyaeva, L. I. Vyshinskaya, V. B. Shur, L. A. Fyodorov, and M. E. Vol'pin, *Dokl. Akad. Nauk SSSR*, **179**, 875 (1968).
16. V. N. Latyaeva, L. I. Vyshinskaya, V. B. Shur, L. A. Fyodorov, and M. E. Vol'pin, *J. Organometal. Chem.*, **16**, 103 (1969).
17. G. A. Razuvaev, V. N. Latyaeva, L. I. Vyshinskaya, and G. A. Vasil'eva, *Zh. Obshch. Khim.*, **40**, 2033 (1970).
18. G. A. Razuvaev, V. N. Latyaeva, and A. N. Lineva, *Dokl. Akad. Nauk SSSR*, **187**, 340 (1969).
19. G. A. Razuvaev, V. N. Latyaeva, and A. N. Lineva, *Zh. Obshch. Khim.*, **39**, 408 (1969).
20. G. A. Razuvaev, V. N. Latyaeva, and A. N. Lineva, *Zh. Obshch. Khim.*, **40**, 1804 (1970).
21. A. N. Nesmeyanov, G. I. Feklisov, B. Y. Andreev, L. M. Dyagileva, and B. G. Andreev, *Dokl. Akad. Nauk SSSR*, **177**, 859 (1967).
22. J. Loche and J. A. McCleverty, *Inorg. Chem.*, **5**, 1157 (1966).
23. T. A. James and J. A. McCleverty, *J. Chem. Soc.*, **1970** A, 3318.
24. D. M. Roe and A. G. Massey, *J. Organometal. Chem.*, **20**, P1 (1969).
25. D. A. Harborne and F. G. A. Stone, *J. Chem. Soc.*, **1968** A, 1765.
26. G. H. Herberich and J. Schwarzer, *Angew. Chem. Intern. Ed.*, **9**, 897 (1970).

Chapter 4

II. OXIDATION-REDUCTION REACTIONS OF GROUP VIII METAL BIS(CYCLOPENTADIENYL) COMPOUNDS

A. Oxidation-Reduction Transformations of Ferrocene and Its Derivatives

1,4. *Oxidation of Ferrocene and Its Derivatives*

The reaction of $FeCl_3$ or $FeBr_3$ with ferrocene gave new ferricinium salts:[1,2]

$$[C_{10}H_{10}Fe]^+FeCl_3^-, \ [C_{10}H_{10}Fe]^+FeBr_3^-, \ [C_{10}H_{10}Fe]^+Fe_2Cl_6^-$$

Ferrocene and its derivatives are oxidized by chloroauric acid to form ferricinium chloroaurates in a good yield.[3]

$$3C_5H_5FeC_5H_4R + 4HAuCl_4 \longrightarrow 3[C_5H_5FeC_5H_4R]^+AuCl_4^- + Au + 4HCl$$
$$R = H, \ Cl, \ Br, \ I, \ C_2H_5, \ C_6H_5, \ CN, \ NO_2, \ COCH_3, \ COC_6H_5, \ COOCH_3$$

The chloroaurates are isolated together with gold which was shown by X-ray analysis not to be bound chemically. In a number of cases (R = H, Cl, CN, COOCH$_3$) the gold can be washed out by aqua regia. Ferricinium tetrachloroferrate, $(C_{10}H_{10}Fe)^+FeCl_4^-$, is formed in the reaction of ferrocene with $(C_6H_5)_3CCl$,[2] with hexachlorocyclopentadiene, or with CCl_4.[4] In the latter two cases the reaction proceeds under irradiation. In a similar way tetrachloroferrates of substituted ferricinium cations (1) and (2) were obtained.[2]

$$\left(\begin{array}{c} \bigcirc\!\!-Si(CH_3)_3 \\ Fe \\ \bigcirc\!\!-Si(CH_3)_3 \end{array}\right)^+ FeCl_4^- \qquad \left(\begin{array}{c} \bigcirc\!\!-\!\!\bigcirc \\ Fe \quad Fe \\ \bigcirc \quad \bigcirc \end{array}\right)^+ FeCl_4^-$$

(1)   (2)

The reaction of ferrocene with $HgCl_2$ leads to the formation of a red solid compound (probably a charge transfer complex), which gives ferricinium spontaneously.[2]

The action of silver ions on ferrocenecarboxylic acid leads to decarboxylation and the formation of ferricinium cation.[5]

$$C_5H_5FeC_5H_4COOH + Ag^+ \longrightarrow (C_5H_5)_2Fe^+ + CO_2$$

The synthesis and physical properties were described for diferrocenyl picrates in whose molecules only one atom of iron is oxidized.[6,7] The electronic

$$\begin{array}{c} \bigcirc\!\!-\!\!\bigcirc \\ Fe \quad Fe \\ \bigcirc \quad \bigcirc \end{array} \xrightarrow[HOC_6H_2(NO_2)_3]{O\!\!=\!\!\bigcirc\!\!=\!\!O} \begin{array}{c} \bigcirc\!\!-\!\!\bigcirc \\ Fe \quad Fe^+ \text{ picrate}^- \\ \bigcirc \quad \bigcirc \end{array}$$

spectrum of this salt includes a 1900-mμ band (ϵ55) associated with an intramolecular electron transfer between the atoms of iron.[6]

The presence of ten substituents in a ferrocene molecule does not hamper the oxidation of the iron; decamethylferrocene is oxidized much easier than ferrocene.[8] Octachloroferrocene and decachloroferrocene, however, are not oxidized even in very drastic conditions (conc. HNO_3 or H_2SO_4, 100°).[9]

The reactions of ferrocene and its derivatives with inorganic acceptors AlX_3, TiX_4, SnX_4 (X = Cl,Br) were studied. Ferrocene and alkylferrocenes are oxidized by aluminum chloride or bromide in the presence of nitrobenzene into ferricinium cations, while with TiX_4 they form donatingwithdrawing complexes. The action of TiX_4 and SnX_4 on haloferrocenes results in the complexes $(C_5H_5)_2Fe \cdot 3TiX_4$, $(C_5H_5)Fe \cdot 2SnX_4$, respectively. Acetyl-, 1,1'-diacetyl-, cyano-, and 1,1'-dicyanoferrocene with $AlCl_3$, TiX_4, and SnX_4 form donating-withdrawing complexes.[10]

A method for amperometric titration of ferrocene by potassium ferricyanide was developed to determine the ferrocene content in complex products such as caoutchouc and polymers.[11]

Ferrocene was polarographically oxidized in a number of aprotic solvents such as dimethylformamide and methylcellosolve.[12]

The kinetics of oxidation and protonation of ferrocene, ethylferrocene, and 1,1'-diethylferrocene by concentrated sulfuric acid was studied. The reaction is of the first order. The oxidation rate increases with the basicity of the ferrocene nucleus. The protonation constants (pKa) are -6.60 (ferrocene), -5.69 (ethylferrocene), and -5.28 (1,1'-diethylferrocene).[13]

The polarographic oxidation of ferrocenylphenylchromium tricarbonylmethane (3) and ferrocenylphenylchromium tricarbonyl (4) on a platinum

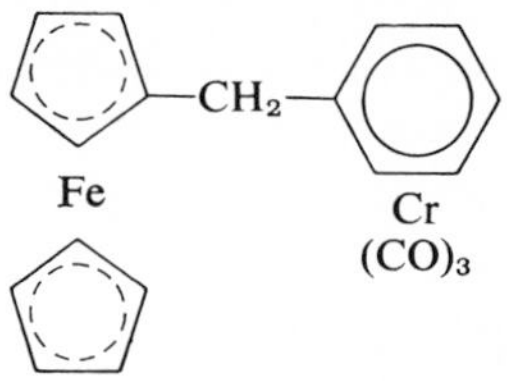

$$(3) \qquad\qquad (4)$$

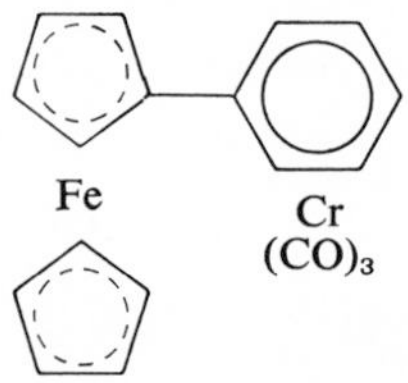

electrode in CH_3CN was investigated and E_{fo} of (3) was found by potentiometric titration. A set of σ-constants was calculated for the $(CO)_3CrC_6H_5$-group as a substituent.[13a]

Ferricinium cation was used in acetoin oxidation. The effect of acid and oxygen concentration on the rate of the reaction was studied.[14]

$$CH_3COCHOHCH_3 \xrightarrow[\text{EtOH/H}_2\text{O}]{C_{10}H_{10}Fe^+} CH_3COCOCH_3$$

The hydration heat of ferricinium ion was found (-46.8 ± 1 kcal/mole).[15]

3. Ferrocene ⇄ Ferricinium Cation System

Research was undertaken to find the values of formal redox potentials of a ferrocene nucleus in ferrocenylruthenocenylmethane,[16] cymantrenylferrocenylmethane,[17] ferrocenylcarborane,[18] (ferrocenylmethyl)alkylcarboranes,[18] α-vinylferrocenes containing in the β-position NO_2, CN, or $COCH_3$-groups,[19] p- or m-substituted phenyldimethylferrocenylsilanes and phenylferrocenylmethanes,[20] and in the series of heteroannular mercury derivatives of ferrocene $XC_5H_4FeC_5H_4HgCl$ and $(X—C_5H_4FeC_5H_4)_2Hg$

where $X = OCH_3$, H, $OCOCH_3$, Cl, Br, $COOCH_3$.[21] Correlational analysis of the values obtained was performed.

The relation of acid-basic and redox properties in the series of substituted ferrocenes was established and used in calculating the redox potential of disubstituted ferrocene from the values of ionization constants of the oxidized and reduced forms of this compound and from the oxidation potential of the protonated form.[22]

Electrodes reversible vis-a-vis ferricinium derivatives (*tert*-butylferricinium and benzylferricinium) were obtained. As exemplified by the *tert*-butyl-ferricinium electrode, these electrodes were shown to be applicable to the study of kinetics of hydrolytic decomposition of ferricinium derivatives.[23]

5,6. *The Formation of Ferrocene and Ferricinium Cation Complexes*

The formation and properties of mixed complexes containing both ferrocene and ferricinium were described.[24]

$$[(C_5H_5)_2Fe]^+Br^- \cdot (C_5H_5)_2Fe \cdot CH_3COC_2H_5$$
$$(C_5H_5)_2Fe \cdot [(C_5H_5)_2Fe^+FeBr_4^- \cdot H_2O]_3$$

The formation of semiconducting ferrocene complexes with benzoquinone derivatives was patented.[25]

The complex formation of the cations $(C_5H_5)_2Fe^+$ and $C_5H_4Fe^+C_5H_4CH_2N^+(CH_3)_3$ with the anions Cl^- and ClO_4^- in water was investigated.[26]

IR spectroscopy was used[27] to reveal the formation of hydrogen bonds of ferrocene with phenol, phenylacetylene, and deuterochloroform. There is evidence that the atom of iron does not contribute to the formation of the hydrogen bond.

C, D. Oxidation-Reduction Reactions of Cobaltocene and Nickelocene

Nickelocene was oxidized[28] to the di-charged cation $(C_5H_5)_2Ni^{2+}$, which unlike the isoelectronic $(C_5H_5)_2Fe$ and $(C_5H_5)_2Co^+$, is very unstable and decomposes quickly in the electrolyte at temperatures above $0°$. Its existence was proved[28] using cyclic voltammetry in acetonitryle solution at $-40°$.

The formation of the salt-like complex $[(C_5H_5)_2Co]^+[C_5H_5(CO)_3Cr]^-$ from cobaltocene and $[C_5H_5(CO)_3Cr]_2$ was described.[29]

The formation of semiconducting complexes from cobalticinium and benzoquinone or its derivatives was patented.[25,30]

IV–VI. REDOX REACTIONS OF BIS-CYCLOPENTADIENYL COMPOUNDS OF METALS OF GROUPS IV, V, AND VI

The reaction of chromocene, vanadocene, or titanocene with $(C_5H_5(CO)_3Cr)_2$ in benzene at room temperature gave binuclear crystalline colored complexes $(C_5H_5)_2M[C_5H_5(CO)_3Cr]$ where $M = Cr$, V, Ti, of which the first is salt-like and the latter two have a covalent M–Cr bond.[29]

In the reaction of $(C_5H_5)_2V$ with CS_2 *in vacuo* or in a nitrogen atmosphere, a carbon disulfide complex of biscyclopentadienylvanadium was trapped, the structure of which, as revealed by IR and NMR spectra, was assumed as (**5**).[31]

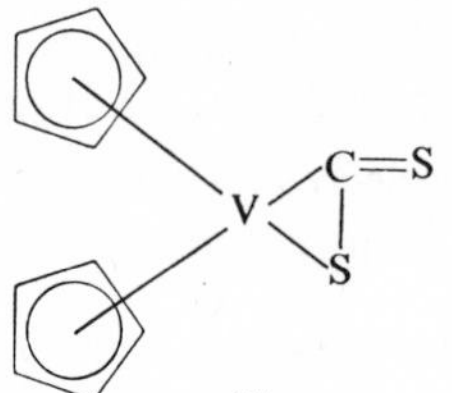

(5)

The polarographic behavior of biscyclopentadienyl compounds of titanium, $(C_5H_5)_2TiX_2$ (X = Cl, Br, I, F) and $(CH_3C_5H_4)(C_5H_5)TiCl_2$ was studied.[32]

The reduction of $(C_5H_5)_2HfCl_2$ by sodium in the presence of naphthalene gave biscyclopentadienylhafnium, $(C_5H_5)_2Hf$.[33]

The oxidation of $(C_5H_5)_2Ti$, $(C_5H_5)_2V$, and $(C_5H_5)_2VC_6H_5$ by acyl peroxides into biscyclopentadienyl compounds of quadrivalent titanium and vanadium, $(C_5H_5)_2M(OCOR)_2$ where $M = Ti$, V was studied.[34-36]

The reaction of $(C_5H_5)_2TiCl_2$ with C_2H_5MgBr gave[37] the π-crotylic complex Ti(III) (**6**). It is assumed that the crotyl group is formed from two ethylene molecules, generated in the course of the reaction.

$$(C_5H_5)_2TiCl_2 + C_2H_5MgBr \longrightarrow (C_5H_5)_2Ti\pi\text{-}C_4H_7$$
(6)

Studies of the thermal decomposition of $(C_5H_5)_2Ti(C_6H_5)_2$ in benzene[38] revealed that the formation of benzene from the abstracting phenyl group proceeds through the capture of hydrogen from the second phenyl group rather than through the solvent participation. The reaction is believed to proceed via the formation of the titanocene benzyne complex (**7**), which in the presence of tolan gives 1,1'-bis-π-cyclopentadienyl-2,3-diphenyl-1-titanoindene (**8**). Consequently, the free radical mechanism suggested earlier is incorrect.

A number of papers[39-45] were devoted to the study of the ability of low-valency titanium compounds (in particular, bis-cyclopentadienyl derivatives) to trap molecular nitrogen in mild conditions. Many papers are concerned with the systems based on Cp_2TiCl_2.

The first complex of a transition metal with a N_2 ligand, $((C_5H_5)_2TiN_2)_2$, was identified. Its reduction produces NH_3 quantitatively.[41]

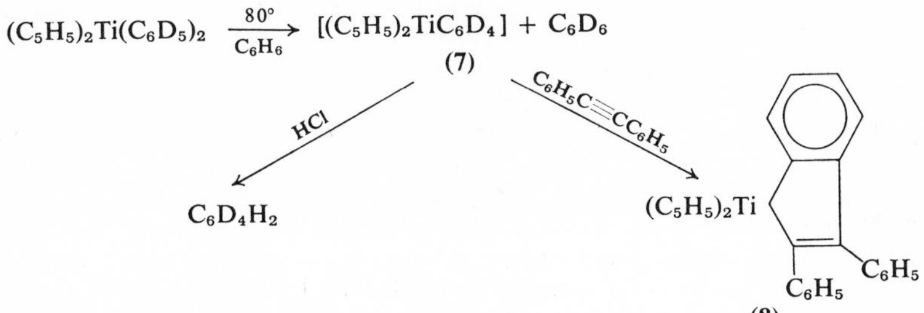

$$(C_5H_5)_2Ti(C_6D_5)_2 \xrightarrow[C_6H_6]{80°} [(C_5H_5)_2TiC_6D_4] + C_6D_6$$

(7)

$$C_6D_4H_2 \qquad\qquad (C_5H_5)_2Ti$$

(8)

There were obtained[46] donating-withdrawing complexes of biscyclopentadienyl compounds of tungsten, molybdenum, and rhenium with the electron-deficient compounds:

$$(C_5H_5)_2W \overset{H}{\underset{H}{\diagup}} \longrightarrow Al(CH_3)_3 \qquad (C_5H_5)_2M \overset{H}{\underset{H}{\diagup}} \longrightarrow BX_3$$

$$(C_5H_5)_2Re \overset{H}{\diagup} \longrightarrow Al(CH_3)_3$$

$$\binom{M = W, Mo}{X = F, Cl}$$

ESR spectroscopy was used[47,48] in the study of $(C_5H_5)_2TiMR_2$ and $/(C_5H_5)_2Ti(MR_2)/_2$ where M = N, P, As and R = CH_3, Ph.

Adduct (1:1) of bis-(cyclopentadienyl)vanadium bromide with tetracyanoethylene was obtained.[49]

REFERENCES

1. Sh. M. Aharoni and M. H. Litt, *J. Organometal. Chem.*, **22**, 179 (1970).
2. I. J. Spilners, *J. Organometal. Chem.*, **11**, 381 (1968).
3. A. N. Nesmeyanov, K. I. Grandberg, T. V. Baukova, A. N. Kosine, and E. G. Perevalova, *Izv. Akad. Nauk SSSR, Ser. Khim.*, **1969**, 1829.
4. Y. Hoshi, T. Akiyama, and A. Sugimori, *Tetrahedron Lett.*, **1970**, 1485.
5. M. A. Bernard and M. M. Borel, *Bull. Soc. Chim. France*, **1967**, 2918.
6. D. O. Cowan and F. Kaufman, *J. Amer. Chem. Soc.*, **92**, 219 (1970).
7. F. Kaufman and D. O. Cowan, *J. Amer. Chem. Soc.*, **92**, 6198 (1970).
8. G. Illuminati, G. Ortaggi, and S. Scurro, *Rend. Accad. Naz. Lincei*, **43**, 364 (1967).
9. F. L. Hedberg and H. Rosenberg, *J. Amer. Chem. Soc.*, **92**, 3239 (1970).
10. J. Klikorka, I. Pavlik, H. Windemannova, and K. Handlir, *Proc. 2nd Conf. Coordinat. Chem. Smolenice-Bratislava, S.A., 1969*. Bratislava, S.A., pp. 139–140.
11. V. T. Solomatin and A. A. Usvyatsov, *Zav. Lab.*, **35**, 778 (1969).
12. J. B. Headridge, M. Ashraf, and H. L. H. Dodds, *J. Electroanal. Chem. Interfacial. Chem.*, **16**, 114 (1968).

13. I. Pavlik and J. Doskočil, *Sb. Ved. Praci, Vysoka Škola Chem. Technol., Pardubice*, **15**, 5 (1967); *Chem. Abstr.*, **68**, 81722 (1968).

13a. S. P. Gubin and V. S. Khandkarova, *J. Organometal. Chem.*, **22**, 449 (1970).

14. J. Lubach and W. Drenth, *Recueil*, **89**, 144 (1970).

15. A. A. Pendin, P. K. Leont'evskaya, and B. P. Nikol'skii, *Zh. Obshch. Khim.*, **37**, 2359 (1967).

16. S. P. Gubin and A. A. Lubovich, *J. Organometal. Chem.*, **22**, 183 (1970).

17. A. N. Nesmeyanov, S. P. Gubin, I. B. Zlotina, and S. A. Smirnova, *Izv. Akad. Nauk. SSSR, Ser. Khim.*, **1969**, 1405.

18. L. I. Zakharkin, V. N. Kalinin, and A. P. Snyakin, *Zh. Obshch. Khim.*, **1970**, 2246.

19. A. A. Koridze and S. P. Gubin, *J. Organometal. Chem.*, **22**, 157 (1970).

20. N. S. Nametkin, V. D. Tyurin, S. P. Gubin, and S. A. Smirnova, *Dokl. Akad. Nauk SSSR*, **186**, 104 (1969).

21. A. N. Nesmeyanov, E. G. Perevalova, S. P. Gubin, and A. G. Kozlovsky, *Dokl. Akad. Nauk SSSR*, **178**, 616 (1968).

22. A. A. Pendin, P. K. Leont'evskaya, T. I. L'vova, and B. P. Nikol'skii, *Dokl. Akad. Nauk SSSR*, **189**, 115 (1969).

23. P. K. Leont'evskaya, T. A. Sokolinskaya, T. P. Vishnyakova, Ya. M. Paushkin, A. A. Pendin, and B. P. Nikol'sky, *Dokl. Akad. Nauk SSSR*, **188**, 1324 (1969).

24. Sh. M. Aharoni and M. H. Litt, *J. Organometal. Chem.*, **22**, 171 (1970).

25. Y. Matsunaga, U.S. Pat. 3352888; *Chem. Abstr.*, **68**, 54874 (1968).

26. T. I. L'vova, A. A. Pendin, and B. P. Nikol'skii, *Dokl. Akad. Nauk SSSR*, **176**, 586 (1967).

27. L. M. Epshtein, L. D. Ashkinadze, S. O. Rabicheva, and L. A. Kazitsyna, *Dokl. Akad. Nauk SSSR*, **190**, 128 (1970).

28. R. J. Wilson, L. F. Warren, Jr., and M. F. Hawthorne, *J. Amer. Chem. Soc.*, **91**, 758 (1969).

29. A. Miyake, H. Kondo, and M. Aoyama, *Angew. Chem.*, **81**, 498 (1969).

30. Y. Matsunaga, U.S. Pat. 3379740; *Chem. Abstr.*, **69**, 44025 (1968).

31. M. C. Baird, G. Hartwell, and G. Wilkinson, *J. Chem. Soc.*, **1967** *A*, 2037.

32. S. A. Smirnova and S. P. Gubin, *Izv. Akad. Nauk SSSR, Ser. Khim.*, **1969**, 1890.

33. G. W. Watt and F. O. Drummond, Jr., *J. Amer. Chem. Soc.*, **92**, 826 (1970).

34. G. A. Razuvaev, V. N. Latyaeva, and L. I. Vyshinskaya, *Dokl. Akad. Nauk SSSR*, **138**, 1126 (1961).

35. G. A. Razuvaev, V. N. Latyaeva, and A. N. Lineva, *Zh. Obshch. Khim.*, **39**, 408 (1969).

36. G. A. Razuvaev, V. N. Latyaeva, and A. H. Lineva, *Zh. Obshch. Khim.*, **40**, 1804 (1970).

37. Ye. F. Kvashina, Yu. G. Borod'ko, Ye. I. Plakhova, Sh. M. Pukhadze, and Y. Ye. Shilov, *Izv. Akad. Nauk SSSR, Ser. Khim.*, **1970**, 936.

38. J. Dvorak, R. J. O'Brien, and W. A. Santo, *Chem. Commun.*, **1970**, 411.

39. M. Ye. Vol'pin, A. A. Belyi, and V. B. Shur, *Izv. Akad. Nauk SSSR, Ser. Khim.*, **1965**, 2225.

40. R. Maskill and J. M. Pratt, *Chem. Commun.*, **1967**, 950.

41. E. E. van Tamelen, R. B. Fechter, S. W. Schneller, G. Boche, R. H. Greeley, and B. Akermark, *J. Amer. Chem. Soc.*, **91**, 1551 (1969).

42. G. Henrici-Olive, *Angew. Chem.*, **81**, 679 (1969).

43. E. E. van Tamelen, D. Seely, S. Schneller, H. Rudler, and W. Cretney, *J. Amer. Chem. Soc.*, **92**, 5251 (1970).

44. E. E. van Tamelen and H. Rudler, *J. Amer. Chem. Soc.*, **92**, 5253 (1970).

45. M. Ye. Vol'pin, A. A. Belyi, V. B. Shur, Yu. I. Lyakhovetsky, R. V. Kudravtsev, and N. N. Bubnov, *Dokl. Akad. Nauk SSSR*, **194**, 577 (1970).
46. H. Brunner, P. C. Wailes, and H. D. Kaesz, *Inorg. Nucl. Chem. Lett.*, **1**, 125 (1965).
47. J. G. Kenworthy, J. Myatt, and P. F. Todd, *Chem. Commun.*, **1969**, 263.
48. J. G. Kenworthy, J. Myatt, and P. F. Todd, *J. Chem. Soc.*, **1970** *B*, 791.
49. M. F. Rettig and R. M. Wing, *Inorg. Chem.*, **8**, 2685 (1969).

Subject Index